SUPER GREAT
LOGIC PROBLEMS

SUPER GREAT LOGIC PROBLEMS

Richard Manchester

BRISTOL
PARK
BOOKS

Visit www.pennydellpuzzles.com for more great puzzles

Originally published as *Colossal Grab A Pencil Book of
Logic Problems*

First Bristol Park Books edition published in 2015

Bristol Park Books
252 W. 38th Street
NYC, NY 10018

Bristol Park Books is a registered trademark of Bristol Park
Books, Inc.

Published by arrangement with Penny Publications LLC

ISBN: 978-0-88486-653-4

Printed in the United States of America

Contents

HOW TO SOLVE LOGIC PROBLEMS

Solving Logic Problems is entertaining and challenging. All the information you need to solve a Logic Problem is given in the introduction and clues, and in illustrations, when provided. If you've never solved a Logic Problem before, our sample should help you get started. Fill in the Sample Solving Chart as you follow our explanation. We use a "●" to signify "Yes" and an "X" to signify "No."

SAMPLE LOGIC PROBLEM

Five couples were married last week, each on a different weekday. From the information provided, determine the woman (one is Cathy) and man (one is Paul) who make up each couple, as well as the day on which each couple was married.

1. Anne was married on Monday, but not to Wally.
2. Stan's wedding was on Wednesday. Rob was married on Friday, but not to Ida.
3. Vern (who married Fran) was married the day after Eve.

SAMPLE SOLVING CHART:

	PAUL	ROB	STAN	VERN	WALLY	MONDAY	TUESDAY	WEDNESDAY	THURSDAY	FRIDAY
ANNE										
CATHY										
EVE										
FRAN										
IDA										
MONDAY										
TUESDAY										
WEDNESDAY										
THURSDAY										
FRIDAY										

EXPLANATION

Anne was married Mon. (1), so put a "●" at the intersection of Anne and Mon. Put "X"s in all the other days in Anne's row and all the other names in the Mon. column. (Whenever you establish a relationship, as we did here, be sure to place "X"s at the intersections of all relationships that become impossible as a result.) Anne wasn't married to Wally (1), so put an "X" at the intersection of Anne and Wally. Stan's wedding was Wed. (2), so put a "●" at the intersection of Stan and Wed. (don't forget the "X"s). Stan didn't marry Anne, who was married Mon., so put an "X" at the intersection of Anne and Stan. Rob was married Fri., but not to Ida (2), so put a "●" at the intersection of Rob and Fri., and "X"s at the intersections of Rob and Ida and Ida and Fri. Rob also didn't marry Anne, who was married Mon., so put an "X" at the intersection of Anne and Rob. Now your chart should look like chart 1.

1

	PAUL	ROB	STAN	VERN	WALLY	MONDAY	TUESDAY	WEDNESDAY	THURSDAY	FRIDAY
ANNE		X	X		X	●	X	X	X	X
CATHY						X				
EVE						X				
FRAN						X				
IDA		X				X				X
MONDAY		X	X							
TUESDAY		X	X							
WEDNESDAY	X	X	●	X	X					
THURSDAY		X	X							
FRIDAY	X	●	X	X	X					

Vern married Fran (3), so put a "●" at the intersection of Vern and Fran. This leaves Anne's only possible husband as Paul, so put a "●" at the intersection of Anne and Paul and Paul and Mon. Vern and Fran's wedding was the day after Eve's (3), which wasn't Mon. [Anne], so Vern's wasn't Tue. It must have been Thu. [see chart], so Eve's was Wed. (3). Put "●"s at the intersections of Vern and Thu., Fran and Thu., and Eve and Wed. Now your chart should look like chart 2.

2

	PAUL	ROB	STAN	VERN	WALLY	MONDAY	TUESDAY	WEDNESDAY	THURSDAY	FRIDAY
ANNE	●	X	X	X	X	●	X	X	X	X
CATHY	X			X		X		X	X	
EVE	X			X		X	X	●	X	X
FRAN	X	X	X	●	X	X	X	X	●	X
IDA	X	X		X		X		X	X	X
MONDAY	●	X	X	X	X					
TUESDAY	X	X	X	X						
WEDNESDAY	X	X	●	X	X					
THURSDAY	X	X	X	●	X					
FRIDAY	X	●	X	X	X					

The chart shows that Cathy was married Fri., Ida was married Tue., and Wally was married Tue. Ida married Wally, and Cathy's wedding was Fri., so she married Rob. After this information is filled in, Eve could only have married Stan. You've completed the puzzle, and your chart should now look like chart 3.

In summary: Anne and Paul, Mon.; Cathy and Rob, Fri.; Eve and Stan, Wed.; Fran and Vern, Thu.; Ida and Wally, Tue.

In some problems, it may be necessary to make a logical guess based on facts you've established. When you do, always look for clues or other facts that disprove it. If you find that your guess is incorrect, eliminate it as a possibility.

The solution for each problem is provided and contains an explanation of the puzzle, as well as a summary of the answer.

Welcome to the world of Logic Problems, where many hours of puzzle pleasure await you!

3

	PAUL	ROB	STAN	VERN	WALLY	MONDAY	TUESDAY	WEDNESDAY	THURSDAY	FRIDAY
ANNE	●	X	X	X	X	●	X	X	X	X
CATHY	X	●	X	X	X	X	X	X	X	●
EVE	X	X	●	X	X	X	X	●	X	X
FRAN	X	X	X	●	X	X	X	X	●	X
IDA	X	X	X	X	●	X	●	X	X	X
MONDAY	●	X	X	X	X					
TUESDAY	X	X	X	X	●					
WEDNESDAY	X	X	●	X	X					
THURSDAY	X	X	X	●	X					
FRIDAY	X	●	X	X	X					

THE PROBLEMS

LOGIC PROBLEM 1

Mrs. Ray likes to feed her children healthy snacks, while they much prefer junk food! As a compromise, she allows each child (including Ann) one soft drink a day. Today, each chose a different flavor of soft drink (one is cola). Except for the two children who had their soft drinks at 11:00 a.m., each of the children had his or her drink at a different time in the afternoon (12:00 p.m., 4:00 p.m., or 7:00 p.m.). From the information provided, determine the time each child had his or her soft drink.

1. Both Cal and the one who drank the black-cherry soda did so at 11:00 a.m. Eva and the one who had the orange soft drink consumed them at 4:00 p.m. and 7:00 p.m., in some order.

2. Dan had his drink at some point later in the day than at least one of his siblings but at some point earlier in the day than the one who drank the root beer.

3. One child drank the lemon-lime soda at 12:00 p.m. Bert saved his soft drink until 7:00 p.m.

		CHILD					SOFT DRINK				
		ANN	BERT	CAL	DAN	EVA	BLACK CHERRY	COLA	LEMON-LIME	ORANGE	ROOT BEER
TIME	11:00 a.m.										
	11:00 a.m.										
	12:00 p.m.										
	4:00 p.m.										
	7:00 p.m.										
SOFT DRINK	BLACK CHERRY										
	COLA										
	LEMON-LIME										
	ORANGE										
	ROOT BEER										

LOGIC PROBLEM 2

Five female employees of the UltraBig Co., Inc., went on business trips last month. Each was able to combine business with pleasure, taking her spouse along and enjoying a vacation after her business was completed. No two went to the same country. From the information provided, match each woman (Doris, Jane, Marj, Sally, or Tess) with her husband (Jim, John, Morris, Pete, or Sidney) and the country (one is Spain) to which they went.

1. Sidney accompanied his wife (who isn't Sally) to Sweden. Tess and her husband went to Turkey.
2. Jim accompanied his wife Jane. Marj and her husband, who isn't Morris, went to Malta.
3. Pete went with his wife to Poland.

		HUSBAND					COUNTRY				
		JIM	JOHN	MORRIS	PETE	SIDNEY	MALTA	POLAND	SPAIN	SWEDEN	TURKEY
WOMAN	DORIS										
	JANE										
	MARJ										
	SALLY										
	TESS										
COUNTRY	MALTA										
	POLAND										
	SPAIN										
	SWEDEN										
	TURKEY										

LOGIC PROBLEM 3

Five teachers at Southwest High School (two of whom—Ally and Brenda—are women, and three of whom—Clark, Larry, and Perry—are men) vacationed in the Caribbean over the holidays. Each went to a different island (one was Jamaica). From the information provided, determine the first and last names (one surname is Malone) of each teacher and the island each visited.

1. Mr. Godwin (who didn't go to Antigua) isn't Perry (who isn't the one who went to St. Lucia). Ms. Witt went to St. Thomas.
2. Neither Brenda Eckert nor Perry is the one who went to Barbados.
3. Larry (who isn't the one surnamed Shelton) went to Antigua.

		LAST NAME					ISLAND				
		ECKERT	GODWIN	MALONE	SHELTON	WITT	ANTIGUA	BARBADOS	JAMAICA	ST. LUCIA	ST. THOMAS
FIRST NAME	ALLY										
	BRENDA										
	CLARK										
	LARRY										
	PERRY										
ISLAND	ANTIGUA										
	BARBADOS										
	JAMAICA										
	ST. LUCIA										
	ST. THOMAS										

LOGIC PROBLEM 4   FRIENDS AT THE COFFEE SHOP

Rachel works at the local coffee shop and waited on five of her friends today, each of whom ordered a different type of coffee (one was Colombian) prepared a different way (one person had coffee with sugar only). From the information provided, can you determine the person who ordered each type of coffee and the way in which it was prepared?

1. Ross (who isn't the one who had his coffee with cream and one sugar) isn't the person who had the Kona coffee (who isn't Phoebe) or the one who had the Kenya AA coffee.

2. Chandler drank his coffee black. Joey had the house-blend coffee. Ross isn't the person who had his or her coffee with cream only.

3. Monica had the Arabica coffee with cream and two sugars. Phoebe didn't order coffee with cream and one sugar.

		ARABICA	COLOMBIAN	HOUSE BLEND	KENYA AA	KONA	BLACK	CREAM AND ONE SUGAR	CREAM AND TWO SUGARS	CREAM ONLY	SUGAR ONLY
PERSON	CHANDLER										
	JOEY										
	MONICA										
	PHOEBE										
	ROSS										
PREPARED	BLACK										
	CREAM AND ONE SUGAR										
	CREAM AND TWO SUGARS										
	CREAM ONLY										
	SUGAR ONLY										

LOGIC PROBLEM 5

Tim and four of his school friends have special plans for their summer vacations. Each of the five intends to spend a different number of weeks (4, 5, 6, 7, or 8) pursuing a different activity. From the information provided, can you determine the friend who intends to pursue each activity (one plans to take art classes) and the number of weeks he or she is planning to devote to it this summer?

1. The ones going to scout camp and music camp plan to spend odd numbers of weeks at their activities.

2. Val plans to spend exactly twice as long at his activity as does the one going on the Outward Bound trip (who isn't Wallis).

3. Sandy (who doesn't intend to spend five weeks at an activity) plans to spend more weeks at an activity than at least one other person but fewer weeks than Yale (who isn't going to scout camp), who intends to spend fewer weeks than the one going to science camp.

		ACTIVITY					WEEKS				
		ART CLASSES	MUSIC CAMP	OUTWARD BOUND	SCIENCE CAMP	SCOUT CAMP	4	5	6	7	8
FRIEND	SANDY										
	TIM										
	VAL										
	WALLIS										
	YALE										
WEEKS	4										
	5										
	6										
	7										
	8										

LOGIC PROBLEM 6

In exchange for the different household chore each of the five Wynott siblings performed, each received a nice dessert (one had cake). Match the chore each child performed with the dessert each had.

1. The one who washed the dishes isn't Chris or Wilt. The one who swept the porch isn't Wilt.

2. The two who had ice cream are either the one who washed dishes and the one who swept the porch or the one who bundled the newspapers and the one who took out the garbage. The two children who ate pie are either Babs and Pat or Wilt and Sam.

3. The one who walked the dog (who is neither Sam nor Wilt) had the same dessert as the one who took out the garbage (who isn't Pat).

		CHORE					DESSERT				
		DISHES	DOG	GARBAGE	NEWSPAPERS	PORCH	CAKE	ICE CREAM	ICE CREAM	PIE	PIE
CHILD	BABS										
	CHRIS										
	PAT										
	SAM										
	WILT										
DESSERT	CAKE										
	ICE CREAM										
	ICE CREAM										
	PIE										
	PIE										

LOGIC PROBLEM 7

It's taken her almost a month, but Mandy can finally remember which of her five children gets picked up by which driver for his or her ride to summer camp! Each child (including Justin) attends a different specialty camp, and each is picked up every morning by a counselor who drives a different make of car. Now if Mandy could only remember who prefers what for lunch! From the information provided, determine the type of camp (one is gymnastics) each child attends and the make of car (one is Saab) that takes him or her there.

1. Neither Allie nor Cole is the child who attends the camp devoted to arts and crafts. Neither Lauren nor Tricia is picked up by the Mazda driver.

2. Tricia attends drama camp. Cole is picked up by the Saturn driver. The driver of the Ford works at the horseback-riding camp.

3. Cole isn't the child who attends swimming camp (who is neither the child driven to camp in the Mazda nor the one driven in the Volvo). Lauren doesn't go to horseback-riding camp.

		CAMP					CAR				
		ARTS & CRAFTS	DRAMA	GYMNASTICS	HORSEBACK RIDING	SWIMMING	FORD	MAZDA	SAAB	SATURN	VOLVO
CHILD	ALLIE										
	COLE										
	JUSTIN										
	LAUREN										
	TRICIA										
CAR	FORD										
	MAZDA										
	SAAB										
	SATURN										
	VOLVO										

LOGIC PROBLEM 8   GET ME TO THE PERCH ON TIME

Even though the sign on Robin's Pet Shop states that the store opens at 10:00 every morning, Robin herself is not the most prompt of proprietors—which is why, each weekday last week, she arrived at a different time after 10:00 to find a customer already waiting! Each customer was there to buy a different accessory for his or her pet bird. This morning, Robin arrived to find that her sign no longer read 10:00—someone had changed it to 10:00ish! From the information provided, determine the time (10:05, 10:07, 10:10, 10:13, or 10:15) Robin arrived at her store on each weekday last week, as well as the item the person waiting that morning wished to purchase.

1. Robin sold a cuttlebone exactly two days before she let a customer in at 10:13. The Friday customer (who didn't wait past 10:10 for Robin) replaced his or her bird's food dish.

2. On Wednesday, Robin opened the shop exactly two minutes later than she did on the day she sold the swing (which wasn't Monday). The mirror wasn't purchased on Monday. The perch wasn't bought by the customer admitted at 10:07.

3. The customer whom Robin admitted at 10:05 (which wasn't on Tuesday) didn't buy the perch.

		TIME					ITEM				
		10:05	10:07	10:10	10:13	10:15	CUTTLEBONE	FOOD DISH	MIRROR	PERCH	SWING
WEEKDAY	MONDAY										
WEEKDAY	TUESDAY										
WEEKDAY	WEDNESDAY										
WEEKDAY	THURSDAY										
WEEKDAY	FRIDAY										
ITEM	CUTTLEBONE										
ITEM	FOOD DISH										
ITEM	MIRROR										
ITEM	PERCH										
ITEM	SWING										

"Waste not, want not" is the teacher's best motto, so when Ms. Cicolello found that she had a few stalks of celery left over after whipping up her latest batch of Waldorf salad, she brought them to school and had her second-graders conduct a little science experiment! She asked each of five children to immerse a stalk of celery in a glass of water tinted with a different food coloring and observe how it affected the vegetable's color. Now what to do with those extra walnuts? From the information provided, determine the first and last names (one first name is Mindy, and one surname is Mason) of each child, as well as the color of the water each child chose.

1. Reggie (who placed his stalk in a glass of yellow water) is neither the one surnamed Sorkin (who isn't the one who placed a stalk in red water) nor the one surnamed Hamilton.

2. Zach Acker chose his mother's favorite color—pink. Sol is neither the child who placed celery in blue water nor the one who placed celery in orange water.

3. Tabi (who isn't surnamed Sorkin) didn't immerse her stalk in the blue water. The one surnamed Vernon chose neither the yellow water nor the orange water.

		LAST NAME					COLOR				
		ACKER	HAMILTON	MASON	SORKIN	VERNON	BLUE	ORANGE	PINK	RED	YELLOW
FIRST NAME	MINDY										
	REGGIE										
	SOL										
	TABI										
	ZACH										
COLOR	BLUE										
	ORANGE										
	PINK										
	RED										
	YELLOW										

LOGIC PROBLEM 10

Five lucky ladies, including Beth, were surprised last night with beautiful diamond engagement rings—and were even more surprised to find that the rings fit their fingers perfectly! It seems that each man had surreptitiously raided his prospective fiancée's jewelry box for one of her old rings and taken it to Harvey Jewelers, where each ordered a ring with a diamond of a different cut in the correct size (no two women wear the same size ring). From the information provided, determine the size (5, 5½, 6, 6½, or 7) and cut of the ring each woman received.

1. One woman received an oval diamond in a size-7 setting. Suzanne wears a size-5½ ring.

2. Neither the size-5 ring nor the size-6 ring is the one set with the pear-cut diamond. Neither Gemma nor Karen (neither of whom wears a size-7 ring) is the one who received the marquise-cut diamond.

3. Margot (whose ring size isn't 5) received the two-carat emerald-cut diamond she had always dreamed of. Karen isn't the woman who was given the brilliant-cut diamond.

		SIZE					CUT				
		5	5½	6	6½	7	BRILLIANT	EMERALD	MARQUISE	OVAL	PEAR
WOMAN	BETH										
	GEMMA										
	KAREN										
	MARGOT										
	SUZANNE										
CUT	BRILLIANT										
	EMERALD										
	MARQUISE										
	OVAL										
	PEAR										

LOGIC PROBLEM 11

Last Thursday morning was a busy one at the Little Neck Post Office. When the windows opened, five people (including Simon) were already in a single-file line, each waiting to post a different class of mail. From the information provided, determine each person's place in line and the class of mail (one person was sending third-class mail) each was posting.

1. Celia (who was third in line) was using express mail to ensure her mother's birthday card would arrive on time.

2. Garrett (who isn't the person who was mailing a letter first class) was the fifth person in line. Sara was standing somewhere in front of the person who was mailing a package by parcel post (who wasn't the last person in line).

3. The person who was sending legal documents by priority mail (who isn't Matt) was fourth in line.

		PERSON					CLASS				
		CELIA	GARRETT	MATT	SARA	SIMON	EXPRESS	FIRST CLASS	PARCEL POST	PRIORITY	THIRD CLASS
PLACE	FIRST										
	SECOND										
	THIRD										
	FOURTH										
	FIFTH										
CLASS	EXPRESS										
	FIRST CLASS										
	PARCEL POST										
	PRIORITY										
	THIRD CLASS										

LOGIC PROBLEM 12   **LIGHTER THAN AIR**

Recently, Annie and four of her coworkers (two of whom—Ben and Cole—are men, and two of whom—Caitlin and Marie—are women) took advantage of the warm autumn weather by walking through the park on their lunch hour. Attracted by the colorful display, they stopped to buy balloons from a vendor, each person selecting a balloon of a different color (one person picked a blue balloon). From the information provided, can you determine the first and last names (one surname is Hasmond) of the person who chose the balloon of each color?

1. Cole Johnson isn't the man who chose the green balloon. Neither Annie nor Marie is the one surnamed Summers.

2. The one surnamed Beech chose the purple balloon. Neither Marie (who isn't surnamed Beech) nor Cole is the one who chose the red balloon.

3. The one who chose the yellow balloon (who isn't Cole) isn't the one surnamed Ward. Annie didn't select the purple balloon.

		LAST NAME					COLOR				
		BEECH	HASMOND	JOHNSON	SUMMERS	WARD	BLUE	GREEN	PURPLE	RED	YELLOW
FIRST NAME	ANNIE										
	BEN										
	CAITLIN										
	COLE										
	MARIE										
COLOR	BLUE										
	GREEN										
	PURPLE										
	RED										
	YELLOW										

When Will wanted to buy the new video game "Quest of the Intergalactic Gorillas from Planet Epsilon," five of his dad's friends, including Mr. Greer, hired Will to do odd jobs so he could earn the necessary money. Each gave Will a different chore to complete for a different amount of money ($5, $6, $7, $8, or $9). Can you determine, from the information given, the job each man assigned Will (one had Will clean his swimming pool) and the amount he earned for doing it?

1. The five men are Mr. Carlson, Mr. Stimson, the one who paid Will $6, the one who paid Will $9, and the one who hired Will to sweep his garage.

2. The five men are Mr. Babcock, Mr. Stimson, the one who paid Will $8, the one who paid Will $7, and the one who had Will mow his lawn.

3. Of the man who paid Will $7 and the one who paid him $5, one is Mr. Waverly and the other employed Will to paint some lawn furniture.

4. Will was hired to wax one man's car, but not for either $8 or $9.

		JOB					AMOUNT				
		CLEAN POOL	MOW LAWN	PAINT LAWN FURNITURE	SWEEP GARAGE	WAX CAR	$5	$6	$7	$8	$9
MAN	MR. BABCOCK										
	MR. CARLSON										
	MR. GREER										
	MR. STIMSON										
	MR. WAVERLY										
AMOUNT	$5										
	$6										
	$7										
	$8										
	$9										

LOGIC PROBLEM 14   MINIATURE GOLF

Last week, as a change from their usual Friday-night trip to the local cinema, Chase and four of his friends played miniature golf. Since none of them had played since grade school, each was thrilled when he or she shot a hole-in-one on a different hole. No two finished the game with the same score. From the information provided, determine the hole (one was the two-level hole) at which each person got a hole-in-one and each person's final score (43, 47, 52, 55, or 59).

1. Gretchen's final score was 52.
2. Irving got a hole-in-one at the hole with the goldfish pond.
3. The one who got a hole-in-one at the hole with the covered bridge had a final score of 43.
4. Alberta, who is not the one who got a hole-in-one at the hole with the windmill, had a final score of 55.
5. Deborah, who got a hole-in-one at the hole with the farmhouse, is not the one who had a final score of 59.

		HOLE					SCORE				
		COVERED BRIDGE	FARMHOUSE	GOLDFISH POND	TWO-LEVEL	WINDMILL	43	47	52	55	59
PERSON	ALBERTA										
	CHASE										
	DEBORAH										
	GRETCHEN										
	IRVING										
SCORE	43					
	47					
	52					
	55					
	59					

Queen Laxanna of Galactic Oasis Thesia holds a royal audience each week. During last week's audience, the Queen graciously received four of her loyal subjects, one after another. Mauli and the other three subjects each presented the Queen with a different valuable gift native to his planet. One gave Laxanna expensive Luxa Oil, which she is looking forward to using in her Royal Dust Bath. From the information provided, can you determine each subject's planet (one is Awavy) and the gift each gave, as well as the order (first through fourth) in which each was received by the Queen?

1. The subject from Distiania was received at some point after Quirko but at some point before the one who gave Queen Laxanna the bartolio fruit.

2. Asleo saw the Queen at some point before the one who brought her the priceless klink water.

3. The one who gave Laxanna the rare germaine seeds was received at some point after the one from Farlu.

4. Nodum was received at some point before the one who brought the bartolio fruit, who was received at some point before the subject from Nexdour.

		PLANET				GIFT				ORDER			
		AWAVY	DISTIANIA	FARLU	NEXDOUR	BARTOLIO FRUIT	GERMAINE SEEDS	KLINK WATER	LUXA OIL	FIRST	SECOND	THIRD	FOURTH
SUBJECT	ASLEO	✓	✗	✗	✗	✓	✗	✗	✗	✗	✗	✓	✗
	MAULI	✗	✗	✗	✓	✗	✗	✓	✗	✗	✗	✗	✓
	NODUM	✗	✓	✗	✗	✗	✓	✗	✗	✗	✓	✗	✗
	QUIRKO	✗	✗	✓	✗	✗	✗	✗	✓	✓	✗	✗	✗
ORDER	FIRST		✗			✗	✗						
	SECOND												
	THIRD												
	FOURTH		✗	✗		✗							
GIFT	BARTOLIO FRUIT		✗		✗								
	GERMAINE SEEDS			✗									
	KLINK WATER												
	LUXA OIL												

LOGIC PROBLEM 16   PINBALL WIZARDS

Last Saturday, Jason celebrated his tenth birthday at Nick's Pizza Parlor and Arcade with his four best friends. After pizza and soda, the five boys hit the arcade, where each boy was the high-scorer on a different pinball game. Each boy earned a different small prize for his efforts. From the information provided, determine each boy's first and last names (one surname is Collins), the pinball game on which he was the high-scorer, and the prize he received (one was baseball cards).

1. Duane, who is not the one who was the high-scorer on Xenon, received the jigsaw puzzle.

2. Harry and the boy surnamed Riley (neither of whom was the high-scorer on Mousetrap) are the high-scorer on Nip-It and the one who won ten free pinball games, in some order.

3. The boy surnamed Scott, who is not Wade, was the high-scorer on Black Knight; his score was higher than Brian's, and he did not receive the jigsaw puzzle as a prize.

4. The boy surnamed Burns had the highest score on Funhouse.

5. The model car was won by the high-scorer on Nip-It. The boy who was the high-scorer on Mousetrap, who is not Brian, won Martial Arts Mutant Alliance cartoon stickers.

6. The boy surnamed Mayer received the model car.

		LAST NAME					GAME					PRIZE				
		BURNS	COLLINS	MAYER	RILEY	SCOTT	BLACK NIGHT	FUNHOUSE	MOUSETRAP	NIP-IT	XENON	BASEBALL CARDS	FREE GAMES	JIGSAW PUZZLE	MODEL CAR	STICKERS
FIRST NAME	BRIAN	✓	X		✓		✓	✗	✗	X				X	X	✗
	DUANE	✓	✗	✗	✗	X	X	✓	✗	✗	X	X	X	✓	X	X
	HARRY	X	✓	X	X	X	X	✗	X	✓	X	✗	X	X	✓	X
	JASON	✗	X						✗		X			X	✗	
	WADE	✗	X			X	X	✗			X			X	X	
PRIZE	BASEBALL CARDS	✗		✗	X			X	✗	✗						
	FREE GAMES	✗	X	✗	✓	X		✗	✗	✗						
	JIGSAW PUZZLE	✓	✗	✗	✗	✗	✗	✓	✗	✗	✗					
	MODEL CAR	✗	✗	✓	✗	✗	✗	✗	✗	✓	✗					
	STICKERS	✗		✗	✓		X	✗	✓	✗	✗					
GAME	BLACK NIGHT	✗	X	✗	✗	✓										
	FUNHOUSE	✓	✗	✗	✗	X										
	MOUSETRAP	✗	✓	✗	X	✗										
	NIP-IT	✗	✗	✓	✗	✗										
	XENON	✗	✗	✗	✓	✗										

LOGIC PROBLEM 17

Pioneer women worked hard, performing different household activities with different implements, to create warm and happy homes in frontier America. These homes were created out of the materials at hand, often logs or even mud. Looking back to an afternoon in the lives of Carolyn and four other pioneer women, match each woman with the type of home (one is a log cabin) in which she lived, as well as the household implement (one is a spider) she used and the activity in which she engaged. (Note: The tool each used is not necessarily related to the activity in which she engaged.)

1. The five women are Evelyn, Mary Anne, the one who lived in the sod house, the one who lived in the dugout house, and the one who worked on a quilt.

2. Of Karen and Mary Anne, one made maple syrup and the other used the hearth crane, in some order.

3. The five women are Karen, Alice, the one who used the loom, the one who made soap, and the one who lived in the dugout house.

4. Neither the woman who lived in the bark hut nor the one who used the spinning wheel made maple syrup.

5. The woman who used the hominy block did not dip candles or make soap.

6. Alice did not dip candles or work on a quilt.

7. The five women are Evelyn, the one who lived in the cave, Mary Anne, the one who dipped candles, and the one who spun wool.

		HOME					IMPLEMENT					ACTIVITY				
		BARK HUT	CAVE	DUGOUT	LOG CABIN	SOD HOUSE	HEARTH CRANE	HOMINY BLOCK	LOOM	SPIDER	SPINNING WHEEL	CANDLE-DIPPING	QUILTING	SOAP-MAKING	SYRUP-MAKING	WOOL-SPINNING
WOMAN	ALICE	x	x	x	y	✓	x	✓	x	ء	٢	x	x	x	x	✓
	CAROLYN	٦	x	✓	x	٢	٧	٢	٧	٤	✓	✓	y	y	x	x
	EVELYN	✓	x	x	٢	x	٢	٢		٢	x	y	✓	٢	x	
	KAREN	٢	✓	x	٧	x	٢	x		٢	٢	٢	✓	x	٢	y
	MARY ANNE	٢	x	x	✓	x	٢	٢	✓	٢	٢	x	x	x	✓	y
ACTIVITY	CANDLE-DIPPING	٢	x	✓	x	x	٢	x	٢	٢	✓
	QUILTING			x		٧					٢
	SOAP-MAKING			x		x		x	٧		
	SYRUP-MAKING	y		x		٢	x	٢			x
	WOOL-SPINNING	x	x	x	y	✓	٢	✓	x	٢	٢
IMPLEMENT	HEARTH CRANE					
	HOMINY BLOCK					
	LOOM			x		x
	SPIDER					
	SPINNING WHEEL	x				

LOGIC PROBLEM 18   APPLE PICKING, PART 1*

It's apple-picking time at Cider Barrel Orchards, and five families each picked a different variety of apple. No two families picked the same number of pounds of apples. Each family was planning to make a different apple dessert when they got home. From the information provided, can you determine the variety of apple (one is Empire) each family picked, the number of pounds (20, 25, 30, 40, or 50) each picked, and the dessert each was planning to make?

1. The three families who picked red apples are the Gradys, the family who plans to bake an apple pie, and the family who took home 30 pounds of apples.

2. The family who picked the green Granny Smith apples picked exactly twice as many pounds of apples as the family who picked Yellow Delicious apples.

3. Between them, the Irvings and the family who plans to bake an apple coffeecake picked exactly 70 pounds of apples.

4. The family who plans to make the apple crisp picked more pounds of apples than the Judsons but fewer pounds than the family who picked McIntosh apples.

5. Between them, the family who picked Yellow Delicious and the one who picked Red Delicious apples picked exactly 45 pounds. One of these two families plans to make baked apples, and the other is the Franklins.

6. The family who plans to make applesauce picked more pounds of apples than the family who picked Red Delicious, who picked more pounds of apples than the Hancocks.

*This is the first part of a two-part puzzle. In order to solve part 2 on page 27, you will need the solution to part 1.

		VARIETY					POUNDS					DESSERT				
		EMPIRE	GRANNY SMITH	McINTOSH	RED DELICIOUS	YELLOW DELICIOUS	20	25	30	40	50	APPLE COFFEECAKE	APPLE CRISP	APPLE PIE	APPLESAUCE	BAKED APPLES
FAMILY	FRANKLIN															
	GRADY															
	HANCOCK															
	IRVING															
	JUDSON															
DESSERT	APPLE CAKE															
	APPLE CRISP															
	APPLE PIE															
	APPLESAUCE															
	BAKED APPLES															
POUNDS	20															
	25															
	30															
	40															
	50															

After picking their apples, each of the five families enjoyed hot cider and fresh doughnuts from the Cider Barrel Orchard store. Each family consumed a different number of doughnuts, then wandered through the store, where each bought a different kind of squash and a different decorative item. From the information provided, can you determine the number of doughnuts (6, 12, 18, 24, or 36) each family ate, as well as the kind of squash and decorative item (one was a large pot of mums) each bought?

1. The three families who picked red apples bought a total of 54 doughnuts. Of these three, the family who bought the grapevine basket bought exactly twice as many doughnuts as the family who bought the Hubbard squash.

2. The family who picked Granny Smith apples bought more doughnuts than the family who bought the butternut squash but fewer than the family who bought decorative gourds.

3. The family who bought the straw wreath bought exactly three times as many doughnuts as the family who is going to bake the apple pie.

4. The family who is going to make an apple crisp did not buy the zucchini.

5. The family who picked the most pounds of apples did not buy the most doughnuts.

6. The families who bought 12, 24, and 36 doughnuts are the one who bought the spaghetti squash, the one who bought the zucchini, and the one who picked the Empire apples, in some order.

7. The total number of doughnuts eaten by the two families who picked Delicious apples is exactly the same as the number of doughnuts eaten by the family who bought the Indian corn to hang on their door. None of these three families is the one who bought the acorn squash.

This is the second part in a two-part puzzle. In order to solve it, you need the solution to part 1 on page 26.

		DOUGHNUTS					SQUASH					DECORATIVE ITEM				
		6	12	18	24	36	ACORN	BUTTERNUT	HUBBARD	SPAGHETTI	ZUCCHINI	BASKET	GOURDS	INDIAN CORN	MUMS	STRAW WREATH
FAMILY	FRANKLIN															
	GRADY															
	HANCOCK															
	IRVING															
	JUDSON															
ITEM	BASKET															
	GOURDS															
	INDIAN CORN															
	MUMS															
	STRAW WREATH															
SQUASH	ACORN															
	BUTTERNUT															
	HUBBARD															
	SPAGHETTI															
	ZUCCHINI															

LOGIC PROBLEM 20 DEON'S INTERVIEWS

After precocious 11-year-old Deon Rodenborn was accepted to Western University as a physics major last week, four reporters (two of whom—Allison and Lori—are women, and two of whom—Bruno and Dexter—are men) interviewed her. Unfortunately, each of their news stories (each of which was for a different area of the news media) about Deon contained a different factual error (one said that Deon was accepted by West Point). From the information provided, can you determine the order in which the reporters interviewed Deon, the area of the news media in which each works (one works for a magazine), and the error each made?

1. Deon's first and last interviews were both with male reporters.
2. Lori is neither the reporter employed by a newspaper nor the one who works for a television station.
3. The reporter who mistakenly said that Deon was going to major in physical education interviewed her after both the newspaper reporter and the reporter who referred to Deon as "Leon" throughout the interview.
4. Both Allison and the reporter from the radio station interviewed Deon before both Dexter and the one who erroneously said that Deon was seven years old.

		REPORTER				NEWS MEDIUM				ERROR			
		ALLISON	BRUNO	DEXTER	LORI	MAGAZINE	NEWSPAPER	RADIO	TELEVISION	LEON	PHYSICAL EDUCATION	SEVEN YEARS OLD	WEST POINT
ORDER	FIRST												
	SECOND												
	THIRD												
	FOURTH												
ERROR	LEON												
	PHYS. ED.												
	SEVEN YEARS OLD												
	WEST POINT												
MEDIUM	MAGAZINE												
	NEWSPAPER												
	RADIO												
	TELEVISION												

Each of the five employees (including Roger) of "Partners in Grime," a cleaning service, is scheduled to perform a different cleaning service next week (one has been hired to clean a garage). Each job is for a different client and is scheduled for a different weekday next week. From the information provided, can you determine the employee hired by each client, his or her service, and the weekday on which the work is scheduled?

1. The employee slated to work for Mr. Nesbitt, who is not having his windows washed, is scheduled to work at some point later in the week than Gladys, who isn't the one scheduled to clean Ms. Heath's house.

2. Neither Ms. Heath nor the client who hired Ben is the one who needs his or her stove and refrigerator cleaned.

3. Mona, who isn't the one slated to wash windows, is scheduled to carry out her special cleaning service at some point later in the week than the person hired to wash the outdoor patios.

4. The project for Ms. Townsend is scheduled for some point earlier in the week than the one for which Zelda was hired but at some point later in the week than the stove and refrigerator cleaning.

5. Mr. Swartz's special service is scheduled for some point later in the week than the floor waxing.

6. Ben was hired for some point earlier in the week than the person hired by Ms. Curie, who will work at some point before the person washing the windows.

		CLIENT					SERVICE					WEEKDAY				
		MS. CURIE	MS. HEATH	MR. NESBITT	MR. SWARTZ	MS. TOWNSEND	CLEAN GARAGE	CLEAN STOVE & REFRIGERATOR	WASH PATIOS	WASH WINDOWS	WAX FLOORS	MONDAY	TUESDAY	WEDNESDAY	THURSDAY	FRIDAY
EMPLOYEE	BEN															
	GLADYS															
	MONA															
	ROGER															
	ZELDA															
WEEKDAY	MONDAY															
	TUESDAY															
	WEDNESDAY															
	THURSDAY															
	FRIDAY															
SERVICE	CLEAN GARAGE															
	CLEAN STOVE/REF															
	WASH PATIOS															
	WASH WINDOWS															
	WAX FLOORS															

LOGIC PROBLEM 22   A NEW LOOK

As an expert in decorating with a small budget, Moira's services as an interior decorator are in great demand in her hometown of Banksville. Last week, five friends asked for advice on redecorating their living rooms. After viewing each person's living room and noting that each contained a different, and quite dramatic, focal point, Moira helped each friend redecorate in a different style (including Southwestern) at a different, relatively low, cost ($420, $450, $480, $500, or $540). From the information provided, determine the style in which each friend redecorated his or her room, the focal point of each room, and the amount of money each spent.

1. The friend whose style of choice was Country French spent less than Rosalyn.

2. The living room featuring the fireplace as its focal point cost more to redecorate than the Victorian-style room but less than Sharon's living room (which isn't the one with the skylight as its focal point).

3. Bryan, who isn't the one who favored Art Deco, spent more money to redecorate than the friend whose room features a terrace as its focal point.

4. The Contemporary-style living room, which doesn't have a skylight, cost more to redecorate than the room whose focal point is a glorious picture window.

5. Warren spent less money to redecorate than the friend whose style was Art Deco but more than the one whose focal point was the cathedral ceiling (who isn't Glen).

		STYLE					FOCAL POINT					AMOUNT				
		ART DECO	CONTEMPORARY	COUNTRY FRENCH	SOUTHWESTERN	VICTORIAN	CATHEDRAL CEILING	FIREPLACE	PICTURE WINDOW	SKYLIGHT	TERRACE	$420	$450	$480	$500	$540
FRIEND	BRYAN															
FRIEND	GLEN															
FRIEND	ROSALYN															
FRIEND	SHARON															
FRIEND	WARREN															
AMOUNT	$420															
AMOUNT	$450															
AMOUNT	$480															
AMOUNT	$500															
AMOUNT	$540															
FOCAL POINT	CATHEDRAL															
FOCAL POINT	FIREPLACE															
FOCAL POINT	PICTURE WINDOW															
FOCAL POINT	SKYLIGHT															
FOCAL POINT	TERRACE															

Five housemates have developed a schedule guaranteed to increase efficiency in the kitchen—each night, one person will cook dinner while another will clean the kitchen. Last week was the first full week with the new schedule, and on each weeknight, a different housemate cooked a different delicious entrée (one made chili con carne) while another cleaned. Each person cleaned the kitchen exactly once last week. Now if only they can devise a schedule to increase bathroom efficiency! From the information provided, can you determine the person who cooked and the person who cleaned up each weeknight, as well as the entrée served each night?

1. Neither Lance nor Christopher either cooked or cleaned on Wednesday. Lance (who cleaned the kitchen the day someone made cheeseburgers) cleaned up the day before he cooked.

2. Calvin cleaned the kitchen the evening someone made chicken fajitas.

3. Vladimir cooked on Friday. On Tuesday, someone made fried chicken.

4. Calvin and Christopher cooked and cleaned on one night, in some order, and Calvin and Lance cooked and cleaned on another night, in some order.

5. Alonzo, who was not on the schedule two nights in a row, didn't clean the kitchen the same evening as one housemate prepared lasagna.

		COOKED					CLEANED UP					ENTREE				
		ALONZO	CALVIN	CHRISTOPHER	LANCE	VLADIMIR	ALONZO	CALVIN	CHRISTOPHER	LANCE	VLADIMIR	CHEESEBURGERS	CHICKEN FAJITAS	CHILI CON CARNE	FRIED CHICKEN	LASAGNA
WEEKNIGHT	MONDAY															
	TUESDAY															
	WEDNESDAY															
	THURSDAY															
	FRIDAY															
ENTREE	CHEESEBURGERS															
	CHICKEN FAJITAS															
	CHILI CON CARNE															
	FRIED CHICKEN															
	LASAGNA															
CLEANED UP	ALONZO															
	CALVIN															
	CHRISTOPHER															
	LANCE															
	VLADIMIR															

LOGIC PROBLEM 24   GAY NINETIES PICNICS

In the late 19th century, the residents of the town of Smithburg held a yearly picnic at a nearby lake, and the townsfolk would travel by various means to enjoy the activities and events. During the five-year period from 1891 to 1895, each of five families (including the Beans) volunteered during a different year to supervise a different activity at the picnic. Each of the five families arrived at the picnic by a different mode of transportation. From the information provided, can you determine the year each family volunteered, the activity they supervised, and the method of transportation they used to get to the picnic?

1. The family who rode the trolley volunteered the year after the family who traveled by carriage but the year before the Stoddards.

2. The family who volunteered to supervise the potato-sack race did not work in 1891 or 1895.

3. If the Kings volunteered at the 1891 picnic, they rode horseback to the picnic and supervised the dance. If not, the family who supervised the potato-sack race worked in 1892 and the family who volunteered in 1893 rode on horseback and supervised the horseshoe-throwing competition.

4. The family who walked to the picnic volunteered the year after the Finches worked and exactly three years after the family who volunteered to supervise the parade.

5. The Engels volunteered the year before the family who supervised the ball game but the year after the family who arrived by wagon.

		FAMILY					ACTIVITY					TRANSPORTATION				
		BEANS	ENGELS	FINCHES	KINGS	STODDARDS	BALL GAME	DANCE	HORSESHOE THROWING	PARADE	POTATO-SACK RACE	CARRIAGE	HORSEBACK	TROLLEY	WAGON	WALKED
YEAR	1891															
	1892															
	1893															
	1894															
	1895															
TRANSPORT.	CARRIAGE															
	HORSEBACK															
	TROLLEY															
	WAGON															
	WALKED															
ACTIVITY	BALL GAME															
	DANCE															
	HORSESHOE															
	PARADE															
	POTATO-SACK															

LOGIC PROBLEM 25

With its Victorian decor and excellent service, Bertram's Restaurant is a favorite meeting place for the maids, butlers, and chauffeurs of many of the area's wealthy families. Each Sunday, Cherie and four of her fellow maids meet at the same table. The five meet on Sunday because that is their only mutual full-day off (each one has a half-day off on a different weekday). Each has worked for a different wealthy family for a different number of years (5, 10, 15, 20, or 25). From the information provided, determine the maid who has a half-day off on each weekday, the family for whom she works, and the number of years she has held her current position.

1. Bridget's half-day off isn't Monday. The Bigwig family's maid doesn't have a half-day on Monday.

2. The maid whose half-day off is Thursday has held her position for 5 years.

3. The maid who works for the Banks family has held her position for exactly 10 years longer than Georgette (who works for the Worths). The half-day off of the Banks family's maid is the day before Georgette's half-day off.

4. The maid whose half-day off is Friday has worked for the Van Snoot family for 25 years.

5. Paulette's half-day off is Wednesday.

6. Fatima (who works for the Moneypenny family) is not the maid who has a half-day off on Monday.

		WEEKDAY					FAMILY					YEARS				
		MONDAY	TUESDAY	WEDNESDAY	THURSDAY	FRIDAY	BANKS	BIGWIG	MONEYPENNY	VAN SNOOT	WORTH	5	10	15	20	25
MAID	BRIDGET															
	CHERIE															
	FATIMA															
	GEORGETTE															
	PAULETTE															
YEARS	5															
	10															
	15															
	20															
	25															
FAMILY	BANKS															
	BIGWIG															
	MONEYPENNY															
	VAN SNOOT															
	WORTH															

LOGIC PROBLEM 26

OFF AND RUNNING

A very health conscious individual, Sally leaves for her morning jog at 5:00 a.m. every weekday morning. For a change of scenery, she jogged a different number of miles in a different area every weekday last week. Each day, while out jogging, she found a different interesting item during each of her morning jaunts. One day, for example, she found a piece of a robin's egg. With such an eclectic collection accumulated in one week, Sally plans on jogging in a different place every-day and adding to her collection of jogging treasure! From the information provided, can you determine the area (one was around the mall) in which Sally jogged each weekday, the number of miles (2, 3, 4, 5, or 6) she jogged, and the item she picked up to take home with her?

1. The item Sally picked up the day before she jogged four miles through the woods was not the feather.

2. On three consecutive days, in order from first to last, Sally jogged two miles, picked up a sparkling rock, and jogged around the high-school track.

3. Sally jogged for more miles on Monday than on the day she jogged along the beach but exactly one mile fewer than the day on which she picked up a uniquely shaped twig.

4. Sally picked a flower the day after she jogged through the park but the day before she jogged five miles.

		BEACH	MALL	PARK	TRACK	WOODS	2	3	4	5	6	FEATHER	FLOWER	ROBIN'S EGG	ROCK	TWIG
AREA							**MILES**					**ITEM**				
WEEKDAY	MONDAY															
	TUESDAY															
	WEDNESDAY															
	THURSDAY															
	FRIDAY															
ITEM	FEATHER															
	FLOWER															
	ROBIN'S EGG															
	ROCK															
	TWIG															
MILES	2															
	3															
	4															
	5															
	6															

. . . something new, something borrowed, something blue, and a lucky sixpence in her shoe. Ensuring a successful wedding day, five young brides (each of whom is getting married on a different Saturday) have combined the "something old" and "something borrowed" categories by borrowing treasured family heirlooms from their relatives. Each bride is borrowing a different heirloom. With such good luck secured, these brides will surely live a gloriously happy life with their grooms. From the information provided, determine the date in May (2nd, 9th, 16th, 23rd, or 30th) each bride (Annette, Cindy, Julie, Martha, and Paula) will marry her bridegroom (Brad, David, Greg, Jason, or Nathan), and the heirloom she will borrow (one is borrowing her grandmother's veil).

1. Julie and her fiancé, Nathan, are not the couple getting married the last Saturday in May.
2. Annette's wedding is the week after Brad's but the week before the wedding in which the bride will wear her great-aunt's brooch.
3. Jason is getting married the week before the bride who will carry her great-grandmother's linen handkerchief.
4. Cindy, who isn't marrying Brad, will wear her grandmother's pendant.
5. David is getting married the week after Martha, who is getting married the week after the bride who will wear her mother's earrings.

		BRIDE					BRIDEGROOM					HEIRLOOM				
		ANNETTE	CINDY	JULIE	MARTHA	PAULA	BRAD	DAVID	GREG	JASON	NATHAN	BROOCH	EARRINGS	HANDKERCHIEF	PENDANT	VEIL
DATE	2nd															
	9th															
	16th															
	23rd															
	30th															
HEIRLOOM	BROOCH															
	EARRINGS															
	HANDKERCHIEF															
	PENDANT															
	VEIL															
BRIDEGROOM	BRAD															
	DAVID															
	GREG															
	JASON															
	NATHAN															

LOGIC PROBLEM 28 UPS AND DOWNS

At closing time, the employees' elevator at Lacey's Department Store always experiences heavy traffic, and last night was no exception. On the way up to the 7th floor, five people entered the elevator, traveled one or more floors, and then exited. On the way down from the 7th floor, two other employees entered, traveled one or more floors, and then exited. On each floor, no more than one person got in and no more than one person got out. No person exited on the floor on which he or she had entered the elevator. From the information provided, determine the floor (1st through 7th) on which each employee (three of whom—Cathy, Judy, and Rose—are women, and four of whom—Fred, Leo, Paul, and Tony—are men) entered and exited the elevator.

1. Cathy, who went down exactly two floors, didn't enter on the 6th floor. The other person who traveled down got in on the 7th floor.
2. Tony, who went up exactly two floors, didn't exit on the 6th floor.
3. Leo entered the elevator on the 1st floor. Rosa exited on the 3rd floor.
4. A woman entered the elevator on the 2nd floor.
5. Fred left the elevator as Paul entered it, and Paul left the elevator as Judy entered it.

		ENTERED							EXITED						
		FIRST	SECOND	THIRD	FOURTH	FIFTH	SIXTH	SEVENTH	FIRST	SECOND	THIRD	FOURTH	FIFTH	SIXTH	SEVENTH
EMPLOYEE	CATHY														
	FRED														
	JUDY														
	LEO														
	PAUL														
	ROSA														
	TONY														
EXITED	FIRST														
	SECOND														
	THIRD														
	FOURTH														
	FIFTH														
	SIXTH														
	SEVENTH														

LOGIC PROBLEM 29

Some celebrate Valentine's Day in both small and big ways. On this special day, each of five husbands gave his wife a single candy heart, bearing a different heartfelt sentiment (including "Be Mine"), and a sealed envelope. Upon opening the envelope, each wife was delighted to discover tickets for a getaway to a different destination. From the information provided, match each husband (Alex, Brian, Clint, Doug, and Evan) with his wife (Angie, Barbara, Carla, Dana, or Eileen), the sentiment on the candy heart he gave her, and the getaway (one was a golf weekend at the Coronado Lakes Resort) he planned.

1. Three of the women—Alex's wife, the one whose heart read "S.W.A.K.," and Eileen— received their gifts in the morning.

2. Clint isn't the husband who gave his wife both tickets for an Alaskan Rail Excursion and a heart bearing the sentiment "Hug Me."

3. No husband and wife share the same first-name initial.

4. Clint presented his wife Angie with her gift in the evening, as did the husband who gave his wife the tickets for the Mississippi Steamboat Ride.

5. Barbara (who isn't the one whose candy heart read "Luv U") was delighted with the Colorado Whitewater Rafting weekend her husband had planned.

6. Brian surprised his wife with the special trip to the New Orleans Mardi Gras that she had always wanted.

7. Carla (who isn't married to Alex) received the heart bearing the "I'm Yours" sentiment.

8. Doug didn't give his wife the heart with the "I'm Yours" or the "S.W.A.K." sentiment.

		WIFE					SENTIMENT					GETAWAY				
		ANGIE	BARBARA	CARLA	DANA	EILEEN	BE MINE	HUG ME	I'M YOURS	LUV U	S.W.A.K.	ALASKAN RAIL EXCURSION	GOLF WEEKEND	NEW ORLEANS MARDI GRAS	STEAMBOAT RIDE	WHITEWATER RAFTING
HUSBAND	ALEX															
	BRIAN															
	CLINT															
	DOUG															
	EVAN															
GETAWAY	ALASKAN RAIL															
	GOLF WEEKEND															
	NEW ORLEANS															
	STEAMBOAT RIDE															
	WHITEWATER															
SENTIMENT	BE MINE															
	HUG ME															
	I'M YOURS															
	LUV U															
	S.W.A.K.															

LOGIC PROBLEM 30

The members of the DeCarr family (two of whom—Hubert and Lucas—are male, and three of whom—Isabel, Julie, and Kirsten—are female) love to hit the road in style. In the driveway, there are five different vehicles, each of which is a different type and is owned by a different DeCarr (either the mom or dad, or one of their three teenage offspring). Each vehicle, each of which is a different color, bears a bumper sticker with a different pithy message. From the information provided, match each person with his or her vehicle (one owns the station wagon), the vehicle's color (one is slate blue), and the message on the bumper sticker each sports.

1. One of the parents drives the delft-blue vehicle. Neither parent's vehicle is the one sporting the bumper sticker reading "TEAR ALONG THE DOTTED LINE!"

2. The three female DeCarrs are the driver of the plum-colored vehicle, the owner of the sports car, and the golf-lover whose bumper sticker proclaims that "IT'S TEE TIME!"

3. The two male family members are the driver of the truck and the one whose bumper sticker jests "DON'T LAUGH—IT'S PAID FOR!"

4. Neither the golf-lover nor the father is the owner of the compact car.

5. The three teenagers—Julie, Kirsten, and Lucas—are the music lover whose bumper sticker warns "RADIO ACTIVE," the owner of the truck, and the driver of the navy-blue vehicle.

6. The three blue vehicles are the one bearing the bumper sticker "I OWE, I OWE, SO IT'S OFF TO WORK I GO," Kirsten's, and the truck.

7. The Jeep isn't the cream-colored vehicle.

		VEHICLE					COLOR					BUMPER STICKER				
		COMPACT CAR	JEEP	SPORTS CAR	STATION WAGON	TRUCK	CREAM	DELFT BLUE	NAVY BLUE	PLUM	SLATE BLUE	DON'T LAUGH -- IT'S PAID FOR!	I OWE, I OWE	IT'S TEE TIME!	RADIO ACTIVE	TEAR ALONG THE DOTTED LINE
DECARR	HUBERT															
	ISABEL															
	JULIE															
	KIRSTEN															
	LUCAS															
STICKER	DON'T LAUGH															
	I OWE, I OWE															
	IT'S TEE TIME!															
	RADIO ACTIVE															
	TEAR ALONG															
COLOR	CREAM															
	DELFT BLUE															
	NAVY BLUE															
	PLUM															
	SLATE BLUE															

A rainbow of color burst across the sky as the 10th annual hot-air balloon race began at Mountainview Air Field yesterday. Of the five balloons that went the farthest, each was piloted by a team comprised of a different man (Alex, Chad, Gary, John, or Mark) and a different woman (Belinda, Darlene, Hilda, Kathy, or Polly) and traveled a different distance. No two of the top five balloons were the same combination of colors (one was aqua and coral). From the information provided, determine the combination of colors of the balloon piloted by each team (identified by man and woman) and the number of miles (20, 40, 60, 80, or 100) each team traveled.

1. John's balloon traveled farther than Hilda's, but not as far as the emerald-and-white balloon (which didn't travel 100 miles).

2. Belinda's balloon flew exactly twice as far as the lime-and-ruby balloon.

3. Gary's balloon traveled farther than the cobalt-and-lavender balloon, which traveled farther than Darlene's balloon (which isn't lime and ruby).

4. The ivory-and-sapphire balloon traveled exactly half as far as Alex's balloon.

5. Kathy's balloon traveled exactly 20 miles farther than Chad's (which didn't travel the shortest distance).

6. John's partner isn't Belinda.

		WOMAN					COLORS					MILES				
		BELINDA	DARLENE	HILDA	KATHY	POLLY	AQUA AND CORAL	COBALT AND LAVENDER	EMERALD AND WHITE	IVORY AND SAPPHIRE	LIME AND RUBY	20	40	60	80	100
MAN	ALEX															
	CHAD															
	GARY															
	JOHN															
	MARK															
MILES	20															
	40															
	60															
	80															
	100															
COLORS	AQUA AND CORAL															
	COBALT AND															
	EMERALD AND															
	IVORY AND															
	LIME AND RUBY															

LOGIC PROBLEM 32 OLYMPIC METALS

Six newly enrolled student-athletes (three of whom—Alex, Carl, and David—are men, and three of whom—Brenda, Elaine, and Faith—are women) at Madison University had competed at the last Summer Olympic Games, each in a different event. Two of the six athletes won gold medals, two won silver medals, and two won bronze medals. From the information provided, can you determine the first and last names (one surname is Johnson) of each athlete, the individual event in which each competed (one was 800-meter freestyle swimming), and the medal each won?

1. David and the gymnast (who isn't Brenda) won the same color medal. Brenda didn't win the same color medal as Carl (who didn't compete in the archery event).
2. The three female athletes are Elaine, the one who won the same color medal as Elaine, and Ms. Gibson.
3. Both Mr. Lawson (who had never met any of the other American athletes before the Atlantic Olympic Games) and the one who competed in the three-meter diving event won gold medals.
4. Neither the athlete who competed in fencing nor the one surnamed Ingles won a bronze medal.
5. Brenda (who didn't compete in the 400-meter hurdles event), the one surnamed Hayes, and the competitor in the archery event each won a different-colored medal.
6. The competitor in the 400-meter hurdles event (who didn't win a bronze medal) had met the one surnamed Kramer prior to the Atlantic Olympic Games, although she had never met either the competitor who won the same color medal as Kramer or a man who won a bronze medal.

		LAST NAME						EVENT						MEDAL					
		GIBSON	HAYES	INGLES	JOHNSON	KRAMER	LAWSON	ARCHERY	DIVING	FENCING	GYMNASTICS	HURDLES	SWIMMING	BRONZE	BRONZE	GOLD	GOLD	SILVER	SILVER
FIRST NAME	ALEX																		
	BRENDA																		
	CARL																		
	DAVID																		
	ELAINE																		
	FAITH																		
MEDAL	BRONZE																		
	BRONZE																		
	GOLD																		
	GOLD																		
	SILVER																		
	SILVER																		
EVENT	ARCHERY																		
	DIVING																		
	FENCING																		
	GYMNASTICS																		
	HURDLES																		
	SWIMMING																		

LOGIC PROBLEM 33

In the Tour de New York, cyclists race through each of the five boroughs of New York City. This year, the tour was dominated by five cyclists, each of whom belongs to a different cycling team. Each of the five cyclists pedaled the fastest through a different borough, and each finished among the top five at the end of the tour (there were no ties). From the information provided, can you determine the team each cyclist represents, the borough through which he rode the fastest (one was Staten Island), and his final position in the tour?

1. The five cyclists are Andy, Greg, the one who cycled the fastest through the Bronx, the fifth-place finisher, and the Wheel Deal representative.

2. The one who cycled fastest through Manhattan, who is not Andy, finished exactly one place higher than Raul but exactly one place lower than the Chain Lightning representative.

3. The Tires Afire representative finished exactly one place lower than Claudio, who finished exactly one place lower than the one who cycled fastest through Queens.

4. The one who cycled fastest through Brooklyn, who is not Raul, did not finish in the top three. The Holy Spokes representative did not finish in the bottom three.

5. The Pedal Pushers representative finished exactly one place higher than Pedro.

		TEAM					BOROUGH					POSITION				
		CHAIN LIGHTNING	HOLY SPOKES	PEDAL PUSHERS	TIRES AFIRE	WHEEL DEAL	BRONX	BROOKLYN	MANHATTAN	QUEENS	STATEN ISLAND	FIRST	SECOND	THIRD	FOURTH	FIFTH
CYCLIST	ANDY															
	CLAUDIO															
	GREG															
	PEDRO															
	RAUL															
POSITION	FIRST															
	SECOND															
	THIRD															
	FOURTH															
	FIFTH															
BOROUGH	BRONX															
	BROOKLYN															
	MANHATTAN															
	QUEENS															
	STATEN ISLAND															

LOGIC PROBLEM 34

Cherrystone Amusement Park spreads out over many acres, so the park provides five different methods of transportation to move people from one section of the park to another. Each method of transportation has a regular driver and a relief driver. The driver of each method wears a different hat, not necessarily in keeping with the type of transportation he or she operates. When the regular driver takes a break, he or she passes the hat to the relief driver. From the information provided, determine the regular driver (Brady, Crystal, Cyril, Georgette, or Nathan) and relief driver (Arthur, Rhonda, Roger, Suzy, or Violet) for each method of transportation, as well as the hat (one is a turban) worn by the drivers of each method of transportation.

1. Arthur is the relief driver on the mule train.
2. Neither Nathan nor his relief driver, Rhonda, are the ones who wear the helmet.
3. Neither Cyril and his relief driver nor the drivers of the riverboat are either the ones who wear the panama hat or the ones who wear the sombrero.
4. Georgette isn't the one who drives the stagecoach.
5. Neither Suzy nor Violet wears the sombrero.
6. Brady (who is the regular driver of the camel caravan) isn't the one relieved by Roger (who wears a panama hat when he relieves the regular driver of his method of transportation).
7. The driver of the minirail wears a derby. Violet is not the relief driver for the minirail.

		RELIEF					TRANSPORTATION					HAT				
		ARTHUR	RHONDA	ROGER	SUZY	VIOLET	CAMEL CARAVAN	MINIRAIL	MULE TRAIN	RIVERBOAT	STAGECOACH	DERBY	HELMET	PANAMA HAT	SOMBRERO	TURBAN
REGULAR	BRADY															
	CRYSTAL															
	CYRIL															
	GEORGETTE															
	NATHAN															
HAT	DERBY															
	HELMET															
	PANAMA HAT															
	SOMBRERO															
	TURBAN															
TRANSPORT.	CAMEL CARAVAN															
	MINIRAIL															
	MULE TRAIN															
	RIVERBOAT															
	STAGECOACH															

My boss, Mr. Murdoch, collects paperweights. In fact, in each of five months last year (August through December), he bought a new paperweight. Each of these paperweights is in the shape of a different animal and is made from a different material. Mr. Murdoch uses two of these paperweights to hold down incoming mail, two to hold down outgoing mail, and one to hold down papers that need to be filed. From the information provided, can you determine the animal shape (one is a unicorn) of the paperweight my boss purchased each month, the material from which each is made (one is a beautiful, clear crystal), and each one's current use?

1. The two paperweights on the incoming mail were not bought in consecutive months, nor were the two paperweights on the outgoing mail.

2. Three of the paperweights—the one made of lead, the one made of wood, and the one in the shape of a dove—are antiques.

3. The paperweight in the shape of a frog was purchased the month before the one that holds down the papers that need to be filed.

4. My boss purchased both the fish paperweight, which is not an antique, and the paperweight made from brass at some point after he bought the two that hold down the incoming mail.

5. The paperweight made of seashells was purchased at some point after the one made of wood (which is not on the incoming mail) but at some point before the one shaped like a Siamese cat.

		SHAPE					MATERIAL					USE				
		CAT	DOVE	FISH	FROG	UNICORN	BRASS	CRYSTAL	LEAD	SEASHELLS	WOOD	FILING	INCOMING MAIL	INCOMING MAIL	OUTGOING MAIL	OUTGOING MAIL
MONTH	AUGUST															
	SEPTEMBER															
	OCTOBER															
	NOVEMBER															
	DECEMBER															
USE	FILING															
	INCOMING MAIL															
	INCOMING MAIL															
	OUTGOING MAIL															
	OUTGOING MAIL															
MATERIAL	BRASS															
	CRYSTAL															
	LEAD															
	SEASHELLS															
	WOOD															

LOGIC PROBLEM 36   NEW TEACHER/COACHES

Richmond High School is expanding its athletic department and has hired five new teachers (three of whom—Otis, Quentin, and Simon—are men, and two of whom—Paula and Ruth—are women), each of whom will also be coaching a different sport. Each new teacher is transferring from a different state, and each has been assigned a different classroom along the west wall of wing B. From the information provided, determine each teacher's first and last names (one surname is Clinton), the sport each will be coaching, and the state (one is Colorado) from which each will be transferring.

1. Four of the new teachers are the golf coach, Otis (who is not the one surnamed Darcy), Ms. Bennett, and the one from Indiana.

2. Otis, who was given a classroom at the end of the hallway, has the classroom immediately next to that given to the one surnamed Farson (who is from Maine).

3. Quentin, who is not from Indiana, coaches basketball.

4. Ruth is from Alabama.

5. Simon, who does not coach golf, has a classroom immediately between the new track coach (who is from Florida) and Ruth, in some order.

6. Neither the one surnamed Darcy nor the coach from Indiana is the one hired to coach swimming.

7. The one surnamed Evans isn't the one who coaches volleyball.

		LAST NAME					SPORT					STATE				
		BENNETT	CLINTON	DARCY	EVANS	FARSON	BASKETBALL	GOLF	SWIMMING	TRACK	VOLLEYBALL	ALABAMA	COLORADO	FLORIDA	INDIANA	MAINE
FIRST NAME	OTIS															
	PAULA															
	QUENTIN															
	RUTH															
	SIMON															
STATE	ALABAMA															
	COLORADO															
	FLORIDA															
	INDIANA															
	MAINE															
SPORT	BASKETBALL															
	GOLF															
	SWIMMING															
	TRACK															
	VOLLEYBALL															

LOGIC PROBLEM 37

As a special treat for family get-togethers, five cousins took turns last year making fresh-baked bread. Each made a different kind of bread for a different occasion. From the information provided, can you determine each baker's first and last names, the kind of bread he or she baked, and the occasion for which it was baked?

1. Neither the banana-nut bread nor the sourdough bread was made by either Cristina or the one surnamed Eggers.
2. Johnny (who is neither the one surnamed Needham nor the one surnamed Eggers) is neither the one who baked bread for Easter (who isn't the one who made the rye bread) nor the one who baked for Grandma's birthday (who isn't the one who made the sourdough bread).
3. Neither the one surnamed Batterson nor the one surnamed Flournoy is either Herb (who isn't the one who made the zucchini bread) or the one who made bread for Christmas (who is not Ginger).
4. The sourdough bread, which was not the bread made for Thanksgiving, wasn't the bread made by the one surnamed Wheaton.
5. The zucchini bread (which was not made by Cristina) was not made by the person who baked for Grandma's birthday (who isn't Brad).
6. Neither the one surnamed Needham (who did not make the rye bread) nor Brad made bread for Easter. The cinnamon-raisin bread (which wasn't made by the one surnamed Needham) wasn't made for Easter (which isn't the occasion for which Ginger baked).
7. The one surnamed Batterson (who did not make the rye bread) isn't the one who made bread for Memorial Day (who is not Ginger).

		LAST NAME					BREAD					OCCASION				
		BATTERSON	EGGERS	FLOURNOY	NEEDHAM	WHEATON	BANANA NUT	CINNAMON RAISIN	RYE	SOURDOUGH	ZUCCHINI	CHRISTMAS	EASTER	GRANDMA'S BIRTHDAY	MEMORIAL DAY	THANKSGIVING
FIRST NAME	BRAD															
	CRISTINA															
	GINGER															
	HERB															
	JOHNNY															
OCCASION	CHRISTMAS															
	EASTER															
	GRANDMA'S B'DAY															
	MEMORIAL DAY															
	THANKSGIVING															
BREAD	BANANA NUT															
	CINNAMON RAISIN															
	RYE															
	SOURDOUGH															
	ZUCCHINI															

LOGIC PROBLEM 38

A new housing development on Lake Mohawk has just been completed, and five young couples have already begun moving in from their old houses. Each has bought a house on a different street in the development. From the information provided, can you determine the husband (Martin, Neil, Oliver, Philip, or Rex) and wife (Carolyn, Hope, Irene, Julia, or Laura) who make up each couple, as well as each couple's old address (2 Hill Street, 4 York Way, 6 Dale Road, 8 Sea Lane, or 10 Glen Avenue) and new address (1 Fern Road, 5 East Hill, 7 Oak Lane, 9 Byrd Street, or 13 West Way)?

1. Oliver and his wife moved from a lower-numbered house than Laura and her husband but moved to a higher-numbered house than Laura and her husband.
2. Neil and Carolyn moved to Fern Road.
3. Julia and her husband moved out of a house that had a number either exactly three higher or exactly three lower than the number of the house to which Rex and his wife moved.
4. One couple moved from Dale Road to Oak Lane.
5. The number of Irene's old house is exactly twice that of Hope's new one.
6. Martin and his wife moved from Hill Street to a house that has a number exactly four lower than that of Philip's new house.

		WIFE					OLD ADDRESS					NEW ADDRESS				
		CAROLYN	HOPE	IRENE	JULIA	LAURA	2 HILL STREET	4 YORK WAY	6 DALE ROAD	8 SEA LANE	10 GLEN AVENUE	1 FERN ROAD	5 EAST HILL	7 OAK LANE	9 BYRD STREET	13 WEST WAY
HUSBAND	MARTIN															
	NEIL															
	OLIVER															
	PHILIP															
	REX															
NEW	1 FERN ROAD															
	5 EAST HILL															
	7 OAK LANE															
	9 BYRD STREET															
	13 WEST WAY															
OLD	2 HILL STREET															
	4 YORK WAY															
	6 DALE ROAD															
	8 SEA LANE															
	10 GLEN AVENUE															

LOGIC PROBLEM 39

Last year, several of the players on the Palmetto High School baseball team had success playing two different positions. As the time for spring training nears, each of these five boys looks forward to another successful year of playing both his regular position (first base, left field, pitcher, shortstop, or third base) and his secondary position (catcher, first base, pitcher, right field, or second base). From the information provided, determine each player's first and last names, his regular position, and his secondary position.

1. Bob, who is not the one surnamed Collins, is neither the one who plays left field as a regular position nor the one who plays right field as a secondary position; however, Jack plays one of these positions, and Mr. Nelson plays the other.

2. The player whose regular position is pitcher is the only one with the same first and last initials.

3. Mr. Lewis's regular position is the same as Mickey's secondary position. Chet's secondary position is the same as Mr. Jordan's primary position.

4. Neither Mr. Miller nor Eric is the one who plays catcher as a secondary position.

5. Neither Mickey nor the boy surnamed Collins is the one who plays third base as a regular position.

		LAST NAME					REGULAR POSITION					SECONDARY POSITION				
		COLLINS	JORDAN	LEWIS	MILLER	NELSON	FIRST BASE	LEFT FIELD	PITCHER	SHORTSTOP	THIRD BASE	CATCHER	FIRST BASE	PITCHER	RIGHT FIELD	SECOND BASE
FIRST NAME	BOB															
	CHET															
	ERIC															
	JACK															
	MICKEY															
SECONDARY	CATCHER															
	FIRST BASE															
	PITCHER															
	RIGHT FIELD															
	SECOND BASE															
REGULAR	FIRST BASE															
	LEFT FIELD															
	PITCHER															
	SHORTSTOP															
	THIRD BASE															

LOGIC PROBLEM 40

UNDER THE BIG TOP

When the Rambling Brothers circus came to town, Nell and her five siblings couldn't wait to see the show. Each child remembered well what a thrill it had been to go to the circus last year, and each fondly remembered a different favorite attraction and a different favorite circus animal. Each child was also looking forward to a different, favorite treat from the food vendors. From the information provided, can you determine each child's favorite attraction, animal, and treat?

1. The six children are Billy, Louie, the child who loves popcorn, the one whose favorite act is the clowns (who does not like the horses), the one whose favorite act is the human cannonball, and the one who loves the elephants (who is not Joey).

2. Neither Emma nor Carrie is the child whose favorite act is the grand parade. The one whose favorite snack is peanuts is either Carrie or Nell.

3. Billy is neither the one who loves the tigers (whose favorite act is the trapeze artists) nor the one who loves the lions (whose favorite treat is peanuts).

4. The one who loves the tightrope walkers (who doesn't like snow cones or cotton candy) is neither the child who favors the bears (who isn't Joey) nor the one who prefers the horses.

5. Either Billy or the child whose favorite act is the clowns is the one who loves snow cones, and the other one loves candy apples.

6. Louie is either the one who favors cotton candy (which is not the favorite snack of the one who loves the acrobats) or the one who favors hot dogs. Neither the child who loves cotton candy nor the one who loves popcorn (who is not the one whose favorite animal is the monkeys) is the one who loves the trapeze artists.

		ATTRACTION						ANIMAL						TREAT					
		ACROBATS	CLOWNS	GRAND PARADE	HUMAN CANNONBALL	TIGHTROPE WALKERS	TRAPEZE ARTISTS	BEARS	ELEPHANTS	HORSES	LIONS	MONKEYS	TIGERS	CANDY APPLES	COTTON CANDY	HOT DOGS	PEANUTS	POPCORN	SNOW CONES
CHILD	BILLY																		
	CARRIE																		
	EMMA																		
	JOEY																		
	LOUIE																		
	NELL																		
TREAT	CANDY APPLES																		
	COTTON CANDY																		
	HOT DOGS																		
	PEANUTS																		
	POPCORN																		
	SNOW CONES																		
ANIMAL	BEARS																		
	ELEPHANTS																		
	HORSES																		
	LIONS																		
	MONKEYS																		
	TIGERS																		

Bunkerville is a small town, where most of the residents have lived their entire lives. Five Bunkerville women (Darcy, Ivy, Lily, Mary, and Vicky) who have been close friends since childhood each have one daughter and one son. Each woman's daughter (Brenda, Gina, Linda, Maura, or Sandra) is married to another woman's son; however, none of the five women has a son-in-law and a daughter-in-law from the same family. From the information provided, can you determine the first and last names of each woman (one surname is Hall), her daughter's name, and her daughter-in-law's name?

1. The five women are Mary, Maura's mother-in-law, Ms. Black, Brenda's mother-in-law, and Linda's mother.

2. Lily, who is not Linda's mother, is not Ms. Greer. Lily's son is married to Ms. Rand's daughter.

3. Neither Lily nor Darcy is Ms. Black. Neither Sandra nor Gina is Ms. Black's daughter.

4. Vicky, who is not Ms. Smith, is neither Brenda's mother nor Maura's mother.

5. Sandra did not marry Ms. Greer's son.

6. Darcy's daughter did not marry Ivy's son. Ivy is not Brenda's mother.

7. Vicky's daughter married Ms. Rand's son. Vicky is not Gina's mother-in-law.

		LAST NAME					DAUGHTER					DAUGHTER-IN-LAW				
		BLACK	GREER	HALL	RAND	SMITH	BRENDA	GINA	LINDA	MAURA	SANDRA	BRENDA	GINA	LINDA	MAURA	SANDRA
FIRST NAME	DARCY															
	IVY															
	LILY															
	MARY															
	VICKY															
IN-LAW	BRENDA															
	GINA															
	LINDA															
	MAURA															
	SANDRA															
DAUGHTER	BRENDA															
	GINA															
	LINDA															
	MAURA															
	SANDRA															

LOGIC PROBLEM 42

Loving mental math games, Judith challenged each of six friends to a simple, mental math test, and only one of them gave her the correct answer. After giving each friend (including Lewis) a different first number (21, 23, 26, 27, 31, or 33), she gave each a different second number, which was to be either added or subtracted to the first one. No two people gave the same answer. From the information provided, determine each friend's first number and second number and calculation (–7, +9, +13, –14, +16, or –17), as well as each person's answer (11, 17, 19, 22, 34, or 43). (Note: When considering whether a number is higher or lower than another, do not take the + or – calculation into account.)

1. The wrong answer Deb gave was the answer Alf should have given. Both Deb and Alf were asked to add their second number to the first.

2. Fred, whose first number wasn't 33, responded with a lower answer than Carol.

3. Gil's second number was higher than that of the person whose answer was 17 (whose first number was lower than that of the person whose answer was 11).

4. The second number of the person who gave the correct answer (whose first number was lower than that of the friend who was asked to subtract 14) was higher than that of the person whose first number was 23.

5. After being asked to add two numbers together, one person (whose first number was exactly 4 less than Carol's) answered 19.

6. Alf's second number was lower than Fred's second number.

		FIRST NUMBER						SECOND NUMBER						ANSWER					
		21	23	26	27	31	33	-7	+9	+13	-14	+16	-17	11	17	19	22	34	43
FRIEND	ALF																		
	CAROL																		
	DEB																		
	FRED																		
	GIL																		
	LEWIS																		
ANSWER	11																		
	17																		
	19																		
	22																		
	34																		
	43																		
SECOND NO.	-7																		
	+9																		
	+13																		
	-14																		
	+16																		
	-17																		

LOGIC PROBLEM 43

In his heyday, eccentric millionaire Howie Huge truly enjoyed surprising people. One time, years ago, Howie donated five different pieces to an auction house. Unbeknownst to the auctioneers, he cleverly concealed a different valuable item in each piece. Each auctioned piece was purchased by a different buyer for a different price ($650, $750, $800, $1,000, or $1,200), and recently, each purchaser was shocked to discover the valuable trinket hidden within each piece. Howie would have been pleased. From the information provided, determine the auctioned piece purchased by each buyer and the price of each, as well as the valuable item concealed within each piece.

1. Bridget spent less than the buyer who purchased the set of silk cushions.
2. The $1,000 piece (which isn't the one in which the miniature portrait was hidden) isn't the grandfather clock.
3. The piece in which the jeweled letter opener was concealed cost less than Cynthia's (which isn't the one in which the gold coins were hidden).
4. The piece that housed the emerald ring cost less than Ernest's piece, which cost less than the bookcase.
5. The piece that concealed the miniature portrait cost less than Rodney's.
6. Neither Rodney's piece nor the bookcase is the one that concealed the antique brooch.
7. Myrtle's piece (which cost less than the sofa) wasn't the set of silk cushions (which didn't house the gold coins).
8. The antique brooch wasn't hidden in Cynthia's piece.

		PIECE					PRICE					ITEM				
		BOOKCASE	CUSHIONS	GRANDFATHER CLOCK	SOFA	WARDROBE	$650	$750	$800	$1,000	$1,200	BROOCH	EMERALD RING	GOLD COINS	LETTER OPENER	MINIATURE PORTRAIT
BUYER	BRIDGET															
	CYNTHIA															
	ERNEST															
	MYRTLE															
	RODNEY															
ITEM	BROOCH															
	EMERALD RING															
	GOLD COINS															
	LETTER OPENER															
	MINIATURE															
PRICE	$650															
	$750															
	$800															
	$1,000															
	$1,200															

LOGIC PROBLEM 44

Cowboys from all over the country competed in this year's Ride 'Em 'n' Rope 'Em Rodeo held in San Antonio, but only one could be rodeo champion. The champion is determined by the total number of points accumulated in three different events—bronc riding, bull riding, and calf roping. The cowboy earning the highest total number of points is crowned Ride 'Em 'n' Rope 'Em Champion. At this year's rodeo, the competition for champion came down to five men from the Bar-B-Q Ranch. Each man earned a different number of points (25, 30, 40, 50, or 75) in bronc riding, a different number of points (40, 50, 60, 75, or 90) in bull riding, and a different number of points (25, 30, 45, 50, or 60) in calf roping. From the information provided, can you determine the number of points each cowboy earned in the bronc riding, bull riding, and calf roping competitions, as well as name this year's Ride 'Em 'n' Rope 'Em Champion?

1. Joe earned the same number of points in bronc riding as Tex did in bull riding.

2. The cowboy who earned 75 points in bull riding earned 30 points in calf roping.

3. Monty is the only cowboy who earned the same number of points in exactly two events, and he scored exactly 10 more points in the other event in which he competed.

4. The total number of points earned by Tex is exactly 30 more than that of Clyde, who earned exactly 10 more points in bull riding than he did in bronc riding.

5. Gabe earned exactly twice as many points in calf roping as he did in bronc riding.

6. The cowboy who earned 75 points in bronc riding earned 60 points in bull riding.

		BRONC RIDING					BULL RIDING					CALF ROPING				
		25	30	40	50	75	40	50	60	75	90	25	30	45	50	60
COWBOY	CLYDE															
	GABE															
	JOE															
	MONTY															
	TEX															
CALF ROPING	25															
	30															
	45															
	50															
	60															
BULL RIDING	40															
	50															
	60															
	75															
	90															

LOGIC PROBLEM 45

While home nursing a cold, Bernice took advantage of the marvelous bargains offered on the Shop At Home channel. Bernice received a discount of a different amount ($3, $4, $5, $6, $8, $9, or $10) off the original low price of each of the seven items (including a foot massager) she purchased! No two pieces have the same original price, and she paid a different amount ($34, $35, $36, $38, $39, $40, or $41) for each item. With such incredible bargains, Bernice plans to do all her shopping through Shop At Home! From the information provided, determine the number (1705, 2001, 2455, 2700, 4507, 6528, or 9823) of each item, the amount Bernice paid for each, and the discount she received off each item.

1. The item Bernice bought for $40, which was originally $45, isn't the Capodimonte figurine she purchased.

2. The reduced price of item 6528 is the same as the original price of the necklace. Bernice received $3 off the original price of the necklace.

3. Item 1705 cost Bernice $41. The discount off item 4507 was more than that of the clock radio, which isn't regularly $45.

4. Bernice paid an irresistible $36 for the knit jumpsuit. Item 2455's discount was $10.

5. Item 9823 (which is the NeverEver-dull knife set) exactly cost $2 less than item 2700, whose discount was exactly $2 more than that of the cookware set.

		NUMBER							PAID							DISCOUNT						
		1705	2001	2455	2700	4507	6528	9823	$34	$35	$36	$38	$39	$40	$41	$3	$4	$5	$6	$8	$9	$10
ITEM	CLOCK RADIO																					
	COOKWARE																					
	FIGURINE																					
	JUMPSUIT																					
	MASSAGER																					
	NECKLACE																					
	KNIFE																					
DISCOUNT	$3																					
	$4																					
	$5																					
	$6																					
	$8																					
	$9																					
	$10																					
PAID	$34																					
	$35																					
	$36																					
	$38																					
	$39																					
	$40																					
	$41																					

LOGIC PROBLEM 46   BONSOIR, BUONA SERA . . .

Friday night after work, Karen met four of her friends for dinner at a Japanese restaurant. Over the course of the evening, they discussed their various occupations (no two of which are the same) and the fact that each person's job requires him or her to be fluent in a different second language (one is French). An impromptu language lesson took place when each taught the others how to say "Good evening" in his or her second tongue. From the information provided, can you determine each person's first and last names (one surname is Blackburn), occupation, and second language?

1. Four of the friends are Karen (who doesn't speak Russian), the one surnamed Jones (who doesn't know Italian), the one fluent in Spanish, and the business manager.

2. Matt is the doctor. The one surnamed Hansen is the pilot.

3. The one who is fluent in Russian isn't the business manager. Sylvia isn't the one who is fluent in German.

4. Sean and the one surnamed Hadley are the banker and the doctor, in some order. Ron isn't the publisher.

5. Three of the friends are the business manager (who isn't the one surnamed Collins), the one who speaks Italian (who isn't Karen), and Ron.

		LAST NAME					OCCUPATION					SECOND LANGUAGE				
		BLACKBURN	COLLINS	HADLEY	HANSEN	JONES	BANKER	BUSINESS MANAGER	DOCTOR	PILOT	PUBLISHER	FRENCH	GERMAN	ITALIAN	RUSSIAN	SPANISH
FIRST NAME	KAREN															
	MATT															
	RON															
	SEAN															
	SYLVIA															
LANGUAGE	FRENCH															
	GERMAN															
	ITALIAN															
	RUSSIAN															
	SPANISH															
OCCUPATION	BANKER															
	BUSINESS MGR.															
	DOCTOR															
	PILOT															
	PUBLISHER															

LOGIC PROBLEM 47

In an effort to raise money for local charitable institutions, nuns from the five orders in the Springfield area pooled their efforts and sponsored a talent show. They were rewarded with a record number of pledges and donations. In addition to many other members of the community, one nun from each of the five sponsoring orders also participated in the event, dazzling the crowd, one after another, with a different talent. From the information provided, determine the order in which each nun performed, as well as the talent-show sponsor (one is the Sisters of Faith) each represents and the talent each displayed (one sang "Climb Ev'ry Mountain").

1. Sister Agnes (who isn't the nun who performed magic) performed at some point after the tap-dancing nun from the Sisters of Hope.

2. Sister Catherine (who played "Kumbaya" on the guitar) performed immediately before and immediately after Sister Beatrice (who isn't the nun from the Sisters of Charity) and the one who performed magic, in some order.

3. The nun from the Sisters of Fortitude didn't perform either immediately before or immediately after the one from the Sisters of Grace.

4. Sister Regina and at least one other nun performed at some point before Sister Catherine.

5. Sister Evangeline performed either immediately before or immediately after the one from the Sisters of Fortitude. The third nun to perform executed a ventriloquism act using a puppet named "Father Gilbert."

		NUN					SPONSOR					TALENT				
		AGNES	BEATRICE	CATHERINE	EVANGELINE	REGINA	SISTERS OF CHARITY	SISTERS OF FAITH	SISTERS OF FORTITUDE	SISTERS OF GRACE	SISTERS OF HOPE	PERFORMED MAGIC	PLAYED GUITAR	SANG	TAP-DANCED	VENTRILOQUISM
ORDER	FIRST															
	SECOND															
	THIRD															
	FOURTH															
	FIFTH															
TALENT	PERFORMED															
	PLAYED GUITAR															
	SANG															
	TAP-DANCED															
	VENTRILOQUISM															
SPONSOR	S. OF CHARITY															
	S. OF FAITH															
	S. OF FORTITUDE															
	S. OF GRACE															
	S. OF HOPE															

LOGIC PROBLEM 48   ELVIS IS EVERYWHERE

For many years, Brian Tessel has run the Elvis Sighting Hot Line, where people from all across the country call to report sightings of the King of Rock 'n' Roll. Last week, each of five callers (three of whom—Aaron, Hugh, and Roy—are men, and two of whom—Charlene and Mandy—are women) reported seeing Elvis in a different type of building in his or her home city (no two people live in the same city). Each caller was convinced that he or she had made a genuine sighting of the King because, in each case, the person in question was overheard humming a different famous Elvis tune. From the information provided, can you determine the city and type of building where each person spotted Elvis, as well as the song (one was "Hound Dog") Elvis was humming when sighted?

1. The man who overheard Elvis humming "Love Me Tender" isn't the person who spotted Elvis at a restaurant. The woman who overheard Elvis humming "Suspicious Minds" isn't the person from Hornell, New York.

2. The person from Bedford, Indiana, who spotted Elvis in a restaurant, isn't the one who overheard the King humming "Little Sister." The woman who saw Elvis at a stadium isn't the person from Randolph, Vermont.

3. Roy saw Elvis at a train depot. One person saw Elvis at a supermarket in Baker, Oregon.

4. Aaron overheard Elvis humming "Little Sister." Charlene (who is neither the person from Mandan, North Dakota, nor the one from Randolph) saw Elvis at a furniture store.

5. The one who overheard Elvis humming "Don't Be Cruel" doesn't live in Bedford.

		CITY					BUILDING					SONG				
		BAKER	BEDFORD	HORNELL	MANDAN	RANDOLPH	FURNITURE STORE	RESTAURANT	STADIUM	SUPERMARKET	TRAIN DEPOT	DON'T BE CRUEL	HOUND DOG	LITTLE SISTER	LOVE ME TENDER	SUSPICIOUS MINDS
PERSON	AARON															
	CHARLENE															
	HUGH															
	MANDY															
	ROY															
SONG	DON'T BE CRUEL															
	HOUND DOG															
	LITTLE SISTER															
	LOVE ME TENDER															
	SUSPICIOUS															
BUILDING	FURNITURE															
	RESTAURANT															
	STADIUM															
	SUPERMARKET															
	TRAIN DEPOT															

LOGIC PROBLEM 49

As last summer came to a close, five weekend warriors surveyed their lawns with a certain degree of pride. Early in the summer, a different type of weed had threatened to overrun his or her lawn, but each had the foresight to stop at a different garden store (one went to Let It Grow) for equipment to prevent the invasion. While there, each also bought a different decorative lawn item (including a birdbath). Their lawns secure, their jobs well done, the weekend warriors went inside for the winter and wondered what horticultural battles the next spring would bring. From the information provided, determine the type of weed that each person fought and the store from which each bought supplies to combat that weed, as well as the lawn item each purchased.

1. The person whose lawn was invaded by foxtail (who isn't Mr. Stansfield) isn't the one who bought the pink flamingo.

2. Ms. Esterhaus isn't the one who bought the bench at Green Thumb. Ms. Esterhaus, who isn't the person who bought the garden gnome, isn't the one who went to Bloomsday for supplies.

3. The woman who fought off an invasion of buckthorn isn't the person who went to Garden Variety.

4. Mr. Katemsky isn't the person whose lawn was attacked by thistle. The one who bought the pink flamingo at Bloomsday isn't the one whose lawn was attacked by chickweed.

5. When Ms. Ferguson bought supplies to protect her lawn from an invasion of plantain, she also purchased a statue.

6. The man who went to Planter's Punch is neither Mr. Katemsky nor Mr. Thomerdahl.

		WEED					STORE					ITEM				
		BUCKTHORN	CHICKWEED	FOXTAIL	PLANTAIN	THISTLE	BLOOMSDAY	GARDEN VARIETY	GREEN THUMB	LET IT GROW	PLANTER'S PUNCH	BENCH	BIRDBATH	GARDEN GNOME	PINK FLAMINGO	STATUE
PERSON	MS. ESTERHAUS															
	MS. FERGUSON															
	MR. KATEMSKY															
	MR. STANSFIELD															
	MR. THOMERDAHL															
ITEM	BENCH															
	BIRDBATH															
	GARDEN GNOME															
	PINK FLAMINGO															
	STATUE															
STORE	BLOOMSDAY															
	GARDEN VARIETY															
	GREEN THUMB															
	LET IT GROW															
	PLANTER'S PUNCH															

LOGIC PROBLEM 50　　　　　　　　　　　LAMPLIGHTERS

Recently, each of five travelers made a brief excursion to a different island to "get away from it all." While there, each found a rusty lamp that, when rubbed, produced an astonishing sight—a genie, who offered to grant him or her a single wish. After much thought, each person closed his or her eyes and made a different wish, which was magically granted by the freed genie (no two people were granted a wish by the same genie). From the information provided, determine the island (four are Falkner, Hispaniola, Patmos, and Rhodes) each person visited, the genie (two are Fabian and Waldemar) each one freed, and the wish (one was for happiness) each made.

1. The initial of each person's surname, the genie each freed, the wish each made, and the island each visited are four different letters.

2. The person who visited Wrangel Island didn't wish for preeminence. Ms. Porthouser isn't the one who wished for wisdom.

3. Hypatia (who granted one person riches) didn't grant Mr. Warren a wish. Ms. Hill wished for fame.

4. Mr. Fentress's wish (which wasn't for wisdom) was granted by the genie Ruella.

5. Mr. Robinson isn't the one who freed Phoenicia.

		ISLAND					GENIE					WISH				
		FALKNER	HISPANIOLA	PATMOS	RHODES	WRANGEL	FABIAN	HYPATIA	PHOENICIA	RUELLA	WALDEMAR	FAME	HAPPINESS	PREEMINENCE	RICHES	WISDOM
PERSON	MR. FENTRESS															
	MS. HILL															
	MS. PORTHOUSER															
	MR. ROBINSON															
	MR. WARREN															
WISH	FAME															
	HAPPINESS															
	PREEMINENCE															
	RICHES															
	WISDOM															
GENIE	FABIAN															
	HYPATIA															
	PHOENICIA															
	RUELLA															
	WALDEMAR															

LOGIC PROBLEM 51

The Riverdale Debate Club gives people from all walks of life the chance to meet and engage in vigorous conversation. Recently, five members of the Club (three of whom—Adam, Byron, and Wilbur—are men, and two of whom—Margia and Rosalind—are women) participated in a mock trial with debaters from other clubs in the region. Each Riverdale debater (no two of whom have the same occupation) played a different role in the trial (one was a juror). From the information provided, determine the first and last names (one surname is Foxx) of each Riverdale debater, the role each played in the mock trial, and each one's occupation (one is a research scientist).

1. Margia is an architect. Wilbur played the plaintiff.
2. Adam Knauss (who isn't an engineer) wasn't the defense attorney.
3. Ms. Maxwell (who isn't the one who played a witness) is a professor of English literature.
4. The debater surnamed Dewitt played the judge.
5. The one who played the defense attorney (who isn't the person surnamed Poff) is an editor.

		LAST NAME					ROLE					OCCUPATION				
		DEWITT	FOXX	KNAUSS	MAXWELL	POFF	DEFENSE ATTORNEY	JUDGE	JUROR	PLAINTIFF	WITNESS	ARCHITECT	EDITOR	ENGINEER	PROFESSOR	RESEARCH SCIENTIST
FIRST NAME	ADAM															
	BYRON															
	MARGIA															
	ROSALIND															
	WILBUR															
OCCUPATION	ARCHITECT															
	EDITOR															
	ENGINEER															
	PROFESSOR															
	RESEARCH															
ROLE	DEFENSE ATTY.															
	JUDGE															
	JUROR															
	PLAINTIFF															
	WITNESS															

LOGIC PROBLEM 52

IT MUST BE NICE

Many wealthy families spend only a few months of the year at their primary residences. The Banks family and four other families from the prestigious Palace Park area spend just six months a year at theirs. Over the course of the rest of the year, each family spends two months at their summer home (no two of which are in the same state), two months at their winter retreat (each of which is located in a different Florida city), and the remaining two months traveling abroad. Last year, each family visited a different Scandinavian country (one family visited Norway). From the information provided, can you determine the state in which each family's summer home is located, the Florida city in which each family's winter retreat is located, and the foreign country each family visited last year?

1. Neither the Worth family (whose winter retreat is located in Palm Beach) nor the Van Snoot family are the ones who spend their summers in New Hampshire.

2. The ones who summer in Vermont (who aren't the Worths) are neither the family whose winter retreat is located in Orlando nor the family whose winter retreat is located in Sarasota.

3. One family summers in Connecticut and winters in Tampa. The family whose winter retreat is located in Key West (who aren't the Van Snoots) traveled to Sweden last year.

4. The family whose summer home is in New Jersey traveled to Iceland last year.

5. The Bigwig family (who don't winter in Orlando) visited Finland last year.

6. The Moneypenny family (whose summer home is in Minnesota) aren't the ones who traveled to Denmark last year.

		STATE					CITY					COUNTRY				
		CONNECTICUT	MINNESOTA	NEW HAMPSHIRE	NEW JERSEY	VERMONT	KEY WEST	ORLANDO	PALM BEACH	SARASOTA	TAMPA	DENMARK	FINLAND	ICELAND	NORWAY	SWEDEN
FAMILY	BANKS															
	BIGWIG															
	MONEYPENNY															
	VAN SNOOT															
	WORTH															
COUNTRY	DENMARK															
	FINLAND															
	ICELAND															
	NORWAY															
	SWEDEN															
CITY	KEY WEST															
	ORLANDO															
	PALM BEACH															
	SARASOTA															
	TAMPA															

LOGIC PROBLEM 53

Fafnir the dragon and his four siblings recently hatched from their eggs. As is in their independent dragon nature, each immediately set about building his or her own nest. Since one little burp could turn normal nesting material into ash, each dragon chose a different precious stone (one used sapphires) as construction material. Each dragon (three of whom—Fafnir, Gargouille, and Smaug—are male, and two of whom—Jormungand and Vermithrax—are female) built a nest, one after another, in a different location. From the information provided, determine the material each dragon used, the location in which each built his or her nest (one was under a deep lake), and the order in which each finished his or her nest.

1. The five dragons are the female dragon who built her nest on top of a mountain (who isn't the one who used diamonds), the one who finished immediately after the female dragon who built her nest on top of a mountain, Smaug, the one who used rubies, and the one who finished his or her nest fourth.

2. Jormungand's nest was completed exactly two before the nest of emeralds, which was finished at some point before Gargouille's.

3. The male dragon who used topaz (which wasn't used for the nest built in the cave) finished his nest either second or third.

4. Vermithrax's nest was neither the one on the deserted island nor the one in the cave.

5. The nest built in the forest was completed first.

		MATERIAL					LOCATION					ORDER				
		DIAMONDS	EMERALDS	RUBIES	SAPPHIRES	TOPAZ	CAVE	FOREST	ISLAND	LAKE	MOUNTAIN	FIRST	SECOND	THIRD	FOURTH	FIFTH
DRAGON	FAFNIR															
	GARGOUILLE															
	JORMUNGAND															
	SMAUG															
	VERMITHRAX															
ORDER	FIRST															
	SECOND															
	THIRD															
	FOURTH															
	FIFTH															
LOCATION	CAVE															
	FOREST															
	ISLAND															
	LAKE															
	MOUNTAIN															

LOGIC PROBLEM 54

When Ventura Motors unveiled its latest line of automobiles at the big auto show, five onlookers were so impressed that each immediately bought one of the vehicles on display! Each person bought a different type and model of vehicle. After hanging a different item from the rearview mirror, each person drove off into the sunset. From the information provided, can you determine the model and type of car each person purchased, as well as the item (one is a pair of dice) that he or she hung from the rearview mirror?

1. Wylie didn't buy the Cygna, which isn't the minivan. The car with the air freshener hanging from the rearview mirror isn't the utility vehicle. Neither the Exotica nor the Suprema is the car with the Mardi Gras beads hanging from the rearview mirror.

2. Cornelia isn't the one who bought the sports car. June (who isn't the one who hung a graduation tassel from the rearview mirror) didn't buy the luxury sedan.

3. Three of the cars are Wylie's (which isn't the Omaha), the utility vehicle, and the one with the beads hanging from the rearview mirror (which is neither the station wagon nor the Omaha).

4. June isn't the one who bought the minivan. The Cygna isn't the luxury sedan. The Exotica doesn't have the air freshener hanging from the rearview mirror.

5. Adele is neither the one who hung the beads nor the one who hung the crystal from the rearview mirror. Cornelia's car (which isn't the utility vehicle) doesn't have beads hanging from the rearview mirror.

6. Rupert didn't buy the sports car (which isn't the Suprema). Neither the Cygna nor the Exotica has the tassel hanging from the rearview mirror. The Camelot isn't the minivan. June (who didn't buy the Cygna) didn't buy the utility vehicle or the sports car.

		MODEL					TYPE					ITEM				
		CAMELOT	CYGNA	EXOTICA	OMAHA	SUPREMA	LUXURY SEDAN	MINIVAN	SPORTS CAR	STATION WAGON	UTILITY VEHICLE	AIR FRESHENER	BEADS	CRYSTAL	DICE	TASSEL
PERSON	ADELE															
	CORNELIA															
	JUNE															
	RUPERT															
	WYLIE															
ITEM	AIR FRESHENER															
	BEADS															
	CRYSTAL															
	DICE															
	TASSEL															
TYPE	LUXURY SEDAN															
	MINIVAN															
	SPORTS CAR															
	STATION WAGON															
	UTILITY VEHICLE															

Calvin and four of his friends (two of whom—Drake and Eric—are boys, and two of whom—Michelle and Sophie—are girls) draw weekly comic strips for the Kids' Page of their local newspaper. Each child's comic strip follows the adventures of a different talking appliance, no two of whom have the same name. From the information provided, determine the first and last names (one surname is Brooks) of each cartoonist, as well as the type of appliance (one is a coffee maker) featured in each one's comic strip and each appliance's name.

1. The talking dishwasher isn't drawn by either Eric Miller or the boy surnamed Hanson. Young Mr. Hanson is neither the child who draws the strip about Blaine the talking blender nor the one who draws the strip about Antoine.

2. The one surnamed Hanson isn't the boy who draws the strip featuring Shep (who isn't the talking microwave oven).

3. Sophie named her character Ace.

4. The boy surnamed West features the microwave oven in his comic strip.

5. Michelle isn't the one surnamed Whitney. Drake isn't the child who named his or her character Birdy (who isn't the talking pressure cooker).

		LAST NAME					APPLIANCE					NAME				
		BROOKS	HANSON	MILLER	WEST	WHITNEY	BLENDER	COFFEE MAKER	DISHWASHER	MICROWAVE OVEN	PRESSURE COOKER	ACE	ANTOINE	BIRDY	BLAINE	SHEP
FIRST NAME	CALVIN															
	DRAKE															
	ERIC															
	MICHELLE															
	SOPHIE															
NAME	ACE															
	ANTOINE															
	BIRDY															
	BLAINE															
	SHEP															
APPLIANCE	BLENDER															
	COFFEE MAKER															
	DISHWASHER															
	MICROWAVE OVEN															
	PRESSURE															

LOGIC PROBLEM 56

INVENTING HONOR

Recently, Dr. Zarno and four other rather obscure inventors were featured in a special exhibit at the Museum of Science. Each is the originator of a different device or product (one inventor developed square fruit, so that it wouldn't roll out of a fruit basket), and each was funded by a different group or person (one was funded by the inventor's mother). Each device or product was created in a different year. From the information provided, determine the person responsible for each invention, the year (1845, 1895, 1900, 1945, or 1995) in which each was invented, and the source of each person's funding.

1. Dr. Quest (who invented the mechanical haberdasher) isn't the one whose invention was funded by the bridge club.

2. The aquanaut's lunchbox was invented exactly 50 years before the project funded by the university but exactly 50 years after Dr. Quest's work.

3. The sandwich dispenser (which was invented in 1900) wasn't Professor Brainard's invention.

4. The dentist funded the project invented exactly 100 years before Doc Brown's invention was created.

5. The petite piano (which wasn't built in 1845) was commissioned by the Duke to accommodate the Duchess' narrow hand width.

6. Dr. Moreau completed his project in 1945.

		INVENTION					YEAR					SOURCE				
		AQUANAUT'S LUNCHBOX	MECHANICAL HABERDASHER	PETITE PIANO	SANDWICH DISPENSER	SQUARE FRUIT	1845	1895	1900	1945	1995	BRIDGE CLUB	DENTIST	DUKE	MOTHER	UNIVERSITY
PERSON	PROF. BRAINARD															
	DR. BROWN															
	DR. MOREAU															
	DR. QUEST															
	DR. ZARNO															
SOURCE	BRIDGE CLUB															
	DENTIST															
	DUKE															
	MOTHER															
	UNIVERSITY															
YEAR	1845															
	1895															
	1900															
	1945															
	1995															

Ach! Groundskeeper Willie had his hands full last week. On each weekday, Willie performed a different job (one was scrubbing and repairing the fountains) at a different Highland castle. Donning kilt and work gloves, Willie went to work, only taking a well-deserved break at midday for lunch (he ate a different type of food for lunch each day—one day he ate kippers). From the information provided, determine the weekday on which Willie worked at each castle, the job he performed at each, and the lunch he ate.

1. Friday was neither the day Willie had salmon for lunch nor the day he worked at Castle MacDougall.
2. Willie had shepherd's pie for lunch the day before he worked at Castle MacGregor, which was the day before he worked at controlling some pesky gophers.
3. Friday was neither the day Willie worked on the herb garden nor the day he worked on the hedges.
4. Willie worked on the drainage gutters the day before he worked at Castle MacKenzie but the day after he had haggis for lunch.
5. Willie had oatmeal for lunch on either the day he worked at Castle MacAllister or the day he worked on the hedges. He worked at Castle MacAllister at some point before he worked on the hedges. Willie didn't work at Castle MacLean on Friday.

		CASTLE					JOB					LUNCH				
		MacALLISTER	MacDOUGALL	MacGREGOR	MacKENZIE	MacLEAN	FOUNTAINS	GOPHERS	GUTTERS	HEDGES	HERB GARDEN	HAGGIS	KIPPERS	OATMEAL	SALMON	SHEPHERD'S PIE
WEEKDAY	MONDAY															
	TUESDAY															
	WEDNESDAY															
	THURSDAY															
	FRIDAY															
LUNCH	HAGGIS															
	KIPPERS															
	OATMEAL															
	SALMON															
	SHEPHERD'S PIE															
JOB	FOUNTAINS															
	GOPHERS															
	GUTTERS															
	HEDGES															
	HERB GARDEN															

LOGIC PROBLEM 58 IT GROWS ON TREES!

For five lucky farmers in the land of Cornucopia (where all types of food—even dessert!—grow on trees), last year was a very profitable year. Each farmer (including Farmer Joe) had a bumper crop of a different food-producing tree (one was a hot-dog tree). Each farmer harvested his tree in a different month (March, June, July, August, or October) and stored his food until the annual Grand Tree Market, at which each farmer's crop earned a different profit ($10,000, $15,000, $20,000, $30,000, or $35,000). From the information provided, can you determine the type of tree with which each farmer had so much success, as well as the month each farmer harvested his tree and the profit he earned at the market?

1. The quiche tree was harvested the month before Farmer Cameron's.
2. Farmer Fred (who harvested his tree in October) earned exactly $15,000 more than Farmer Cameron.
3. Farmer Bill earned exactly half as much as the farmer who harvested his tree in July.
4. The lollipop tree, which wasn't the last to be harvested, didn't turn a profit of $15,000. The farmer who earned $15,000 (who isn't Farmer Dale) wasn't the first to harvest his tree.
5. Farmer Bill's tree was harvested the month before the ravioli tree.
6. The chocolate-chip-cookie tree wasn't harvested in October.

		TREE					MONTH					PROFIT				
		CHOCOLATE-CHIP COOKIE	HOT DOG	LOLLIPOP	QUICHE	RAVIOLI	MARCH	JUNE	JULY	AUGUST	OCTOBER	$10,000	$15,000	$20,000	$30,000	$35,000
FARMER	BILL															
	CAMERON															
	DALE															
	FRED															
	JOE															
PROFIT	$10,000															
	$15,000															
	$20,000															
	$30,000															
	$35,000															
MONTH	MARCH															
	JUNE															
	JULY															
	AUGUST															
	OCTOBER															

LOGIC PROBLEM 59

For George, who is a mail carrier, delivering to the houses on Westlawn Drive is always a challenge, since each of the five homeowners on that block (including the Jacobses) owns a rather rambunctious dog. Each of the five dogs is a different breed, and each has its own distinct way of making George's job a little more difficult (one tries to chew on his shoes whenever possible). From the information provided, can you determine the name (one is Alfie) and breed of each family's dog, as well as the special delivery problem each poses for George?

1. The five families on the block are the Porters, the Simpsons, the family who owns the bulldog, Baby's owners, and the family whose dog tries to block the front gate.
2. Neither the Billingses' dog nor the poodle (neither of whom is Dilly) is the dog who tries to chase George down the block.
3. Baby runs in circles around George whenever he approaches her house.
4. Curly, who isn't the collie, doesn't belong to the Porters.
5. The Doberman pinscher (who doesn't belong to the Simpsons) habitually tries to knock George down and lick his face.
6. Elvis (who isn't the Doberman pinscher) isn't the Lettmans' dog (who isn't the one who runs in circles).
7. Dilly (who doesn't belong to the Porters) is neither the collie nor the bulldog.
8. The family who owns the German shepherd lives next door to the Simpsons.
9. Curly, who isn't the dog who tries to chase George down the block, isn't the poodle.

		NAME					BREED					PROBLEM				
		ALFIE	BABY	CURLY	DILLY	ELVIS	BULLDOG	COLLIE	DOBERMAN PINSCHER	GERMAN SHEPHERD	POODLE	BLOCKS GATE	CHASES DOWN BLOCK	CHEWS ON SHOES	KNOCKS DOWN & LICKS FACE	RUNS IN CIRCLES
FAMILY	BILLINGS															
	JACOBS															
	LETTMAN															
	PORTER															
	SIMPSON															
PROBLEM	BLOCKS GATE															
	CHASES															
	CHEWS ON SHOES															
	KNOCKS DOWN															
	RUNS IN CIRCLES															
BREED	BULLDOG															
	COLLIE															
	DOBERMAN															
	GERMAN SHEP.															
	POODLE															

LOGIC PROBLEM 60

IN PLAIN ENGLISH

Each summer, the English department at Plainsville Community College sponsors a writing competition for young authors. Students between the ages of 13 and 19 are invited to submit entries in one of five different categories, one of which is biography. A winner is selected from each of the five categories, and this year, each winner (including Frank) is a different age (15 through 19 years). From the information provided, determine the age of each winner (identified by first and last names—one surname is Evans) and the category in which each won.

1. The winner surnamed Baxter (who is exactly 1 year older than Lindsay) submitted the winning fiction entry.

2. Jenny Garrison is exactly 2 years older than the author who won in the poetry category.

3. Amy (who isn't surnamed Baxter) is exactly 2 years older than the student who won in the history category.

4. The young author surnamed Robertson is exactly 1 year younger than Dwight, who submitted the winning entry in the news-reporting category.

5. The winner surnamed Martin is 18 years old.

		LAST NAME					AGE					CATEGORY				
		BAXTER	EVANS	GARRISON	MARTIN	ROBERTSON	15	16	17	18	19	BIOGRAPHY	FICTION	HISTORY	NEWS REPORTING	POETRY
FIRST NAME	AMY															
	DWIGHT															
	FRANK															
	JENNY															
	LINDSAY															
CATEGORY	BIOGRAPHY															
	FICTION															
	HISTORY															
	NEWS REPORTING															
	POETRY															
AGE	15															
	16															
	17															
	18															
	19															

LOGIC PROBLEM 61

Retired after years of working in the construction industry, Jim Hagan has replaced his hammer and tools with a new set of golf clubs, which he uses with more enthusiasm than skill. On each weekday last week, Jim played a round of golf on a different golf course with his friends. Although Jim played extremely well all week, he never succeeded in winning a match, attributing his defeat to a single, crucial mistake (once he hit the ball off the fairway and into the rough). During no two matches did he make the same mistake, and each mistake occurred on a different hole (6, 9, 12, 15, or 18). From the information provided, determine the weekday on which Jim played at each golf course (one is Willow Brook), as well as the mistake he made in each game and the hole on which each mistake occurred.

1. Jim's mistake on the 18th hole cost him the match at Butler's Golf Course.

2. The hole on which Jim hit a hole in one in the wrong hole was numbered exactly 6 lower than the hole on which he made a mistake at Schenley Park Golf Course. He played at Schenley Park the day after he hit the hole in one in the wrong hole.

3. The mistake at Riverview Golf Course occurred on a hole numbered exactly 6 lower than the hole on which he hit the ball into the water hazard.

4. Jim played at Linden Hall Golf Course the day before he had trouble getting out of the sand trap. His mistake at Linden Hall occurred on a hole numbered exactly 6 higher than the one on which his Friday mistake occurred.

5. Jim whiffed (swung at and missed) the ball the day after he made a mistake on the 12th hole but the day before he played at Butler's Golf Course.

		COURSE					MISTAKE					HOLE				
		BUTLER'S	LINDEN HALL	RIVERVIEW	SCHENLEY PARK	WILLOW BROOK	ROUGH	SAND TRAP	WATER HAZARD	WHIFFED BALL	WRONG HOLE	6	9	12	15	18
WEEKDAY	MONDAY															
	TUESDAY															
	WEDNESDAY															
	THURSDAY															
	FRIDAY															
HOLE	6															
	9															
	12															
	15															
	18															
MISTAKE	ROUGH															
	SAND TRAP															
	WATER HAZARD															
	WHIFFED BALL															
	WRONG HOLE															

LOGIC PROBLEM 62

In the spirit of George Washington Carver (who found over 300 uses for the common peanut), each of five scientists is hard at work experimenting on a different legume. Recently, each presented his or her research at a scientific conference. Each scientist is employed by a different lab (one is Alliance), and each is trying to manufacture a different substance (one is scouring powder) from the legume on which he or she is experimenting. Will their findings revolutionize the world? Only time will tell. In the interim, from the information provided, can you match each scientist with the lab for which he or she works, the legume (one is the navy bean) on which he or she is experimenting, and the substance he or she hopes to manufacture?

1. The scientist working on the chickpea (who isn't the one trying to manufacture a milk substitute) isn't employed by Productivity. Dr. Ambrose is neither the scientist employed by Datatron nor the one employed by Troubador.
2. Dr. Sawyer isn't the one working on the lentil. The one working for Productivity isn't the one who is trying to manufacture a moisturizer from the lima bean.
3. The scientist employed by Masterworks (who is trying to manufacture invisible ink) is neither the one working on the chickpea nor the one working on the tamarind. Neither Dr. Therrien nor the scientist employed by Datatron is working on the chickpea.
4. Dr. Martin isn't working on either the lima bean or the lentil. Dr. Therrien isn't trying to manufacture invisible ink.
5. Neither Dr. Dugdale nor Dr. Ambrose is either the one trying to manufacture lighter fluid or the one trying to manufacture invisible ink.
6. No scientist's surname initial is the same as the initial of the lab where he or she is employed.

		LAB					LEGUME					SUBSTANCE				
		ALLIANCE	DATATRON	MASTERWORKS	PRODUCTIVITY	TROUBADOR	CHICKPEA	LENTIL	LIMA BEAN	NAVY BEAN	TAMARIND	INVISIBLE INK	LIGHTER FLUID	MILK SUBSTITUTE	MOISTURIZER	SCOURING POWDER
SCIENTIST	DR. AMBROSE															
	DR. DUGDALE															
	DR. MARTIN															
	DR. SAWYER															
	DR. THERRIEN															
SUBSTANCE	INVISIBLE INK										
	LIGHTER FLUID										
	MILK SUBSTITUTE										
	MOISTURIZER										
	SCOURING										
LEGUME	CHICKPEA					
	LENTIL					
	LIMA BEAN					
	NAVY BEAN					
	TAMARIND					

LOGIC PROBLEM 63

To the five Jamieson children, the night before Halloween is "Fun Night," and this past October, the children (three of whom—Bela, Duke, and Tor—are boys, and two of whom—Joanna and Mona—are girls) spent the morning baking cookies with their mother. Each child was in charge of making a different type of cookie (one was oatmeal), and using icing, each painted a different design on his or her cookies. In the evening, their father took them to Red's Pumpkin Patch, where, with great anticipation, they waited for the Great Pumpkin to rise from the misty ground. Unfortunately, none of the children saw the Great Pumpkin, since each fell asleep after a different number of minutes (15, 30, 45, 60, or 75). From the information provided, determine the type of cookie each child baked, the design each painted on his or her cookies, and the number of minutes each child spent in the pumpkin patch before falling asleep.

1. Joanna isn't the one who painted the witch design on his or her cookies. Tor made the cookies with the cat design. Duke isn't the child who made the cookies with the ghost design. Bela and Duke made the chocolate-chip cookies and the pumpkinseed cookies, in some order.

2. Mona isn't the child who made the sugar cookies (which were neither the cookies bearing the ghost design nor the ones bearing the jack-o'-lantern design).

3. The cookies with the spider design weren't made by the child who fell asleep after waiting 30 minutes. The one who made the peanut-butter cookies fell asleep first. Neither Bela nor Duke is the one who made the cookies bearing the jack-o'-lantern design.

4. Neither girl fell asleep either first or last. The boy who fell asleep after waiting 45 minutes (who didn't make the chocolate-chip cookies) didn't paint a ghost design on his cookies.

		COOKIE					DESIGN					MINUTES				
		CHOCOLATE CHIP	OATMEAL	PEANUT BUTTER	PUMPKINSEED	SUGAR	CAT	GHOST	JACK-O'-LANTERN	SPIDER	WITCH	15	30	45	60	75
CHILD	BELA															
	DUKE															
	JOANNA															
	MONA															
	TOR															
MINUTES	15															
	30															
	45															
	60															
	75															
DESIGN	CAT															
	GHOST															
	JACK-O'-LANTERN															
	SPIDER															
	WITCH															

LOGIC PROBLEM 64

THE BLACK BIRD

It's been over 50 years since a sighting of the Maltese Falcon was reported in San Francisco, and, as everyone knows, that falcon was a fake. But rumor has it that the genuine statuette has appeared somewhere in Europe. Detective Babs Spade (daughter of Sam Spade) has picked up the case, and she and the five other detectives at her agency are trying to track down the falcon. No one is quite sure in which city it's located, so on a different day (Monday through Saturday) last week, each detective, including Babs, flew to a different European city. From the cryptic information recorded in Babs's diary, determine the city to which each detective flew and the day on which each traveled.

1. Troy (who traveled at some point earlier in the week than Yvonne) didn't go to Madrid.

2. Doreen (who didn't go to Moscow) traveled at some point later in the week than at least one other detective.

3. Neither Mike (who didn't go to Paris) nor the person who went to Madrid took either the Tuesday flight or the Wednesday flight.

4. The Tuesday flight was neither the flight that went to Paris nor the flight that went to London. The Wednesday flight didn't go to Paris.

5. Neither Yvonne nor Doreen sought the falcon in Madrid.

6. Saul took either the flight to Moscow (which left at some point earlier in the week than at least one other flight) or the flight to Brussels.

7. Babs (who didn't fly on Thursday) traveled at some point earlier in the week than Saul but the day after the detective who went to Rome.

		CITY						DAY					
		BRUSSELS	LONDON	MADRID	MOSCOW	PARIS	ROME	MONDAY	TUESDAY	WEDNESDAY	THURSDAY	FRIDAY	SATURDAY
DETECTIVE	BABS												
	DOREEN												
	MIKE												
	SAUL												
	TROY												
	YVONNE												
DAY	MONDAY												
	TUESDAY												
	WEDNESDAY												
	THURSDAY												
	FRIDAY												
	SATURDAY												

LOGIC PROBLEM 65

To encourage their budding interest in the Old West, Clark and Roxanne Randall took their children to a historical museum, where visitors could walk through reproductions of five fictional frontier towns. To show the differing evolutions of the towns, each was depicted as having been founded in a different year (1868, 1871, 1873, 1874, or 1876) to foster a different industry (one was cattle ranching). From the information provided, determine the order in which the Randalls walked through each town exhibit (one town is Fort Custer), the year each was founded, and each town's industry.

1. The farming community (which wasn't the second exhibit visited) was founded exactly three years after Medicine Bow.

2. The Randalls visited both Hadeyville and the community that sprang up due to the railroad before they visited both South Pass City and the town founded in 1868.

3. The family visited Alden's Grove immediately after they visited the town that formed around a trading post but immediately before the town founded in 1871.

4. Gold mining was the principal industry of the last town visited.

5. The second town the Randalls visited was founded immediately after South Pass City but immediately before the town that came into existence due to the railroad.

6. South Pass City was founded at some point before the farming community.

		TOWN					YEAR					INDUSTRY				
		ALDEN'S GROVE	FORT CUSTER	HADEYVILLE	MEDICINE BOW	SOUTH PASS CITY	1868	1871	1873	1874	1876	CATTLE RANCHING	FARMING	GOLD MINING	RAILROAD	TRADING POST
ORDER	FIRST															
	SECOND															
	THIRD															
	FOURTH															
	FIFTH															
INDUSTRY	CATTLE RANCHING															
	FARMING															
	GOLD MINING															
	RAILROAD															
	TRADING POST															
YEAR	1868															
	1871															
	1873															
	1874															
	1876															

LOGIC PROBLEM 66 SEE-SCAPE

Recently, each of five oceanographic explorers embarked on a quest to solve the mysteries of the watery deep. Each explorer, including Morgan, piloted a different submarine (one is *Deep Flight I*) into the murky depths, where, piercing the darkness of the abyss with his or her lights, each saw a different bizarre creature. Each sighting occurred at a different depth (1,600, 2,600, 4,600, 6,600, or 7,600 feet). From the information provided, determine the pilot of each submarine, the creature each saw, and the depth in feet at which each sighting occurred.

1. The pilot of *Deep Rover* sighted an anglerfish at a lower depth than the oceanographer who spied a cranchiid squid.
2. The gulper eel was sighted at a lower depth than the fangtooth (which was seen by Pratt).
3. The pilot of *Nautile*, who made the deepest sighting, didn't see the gulper eel. Baker isn't the one who saw the deep-sea shrimp.
4. The pilot of *Shinkai 6500* made a sighting at a lower depth than Abbott (who isn't the pilot of *Alvin*), who made a sighting at a lower depth than Dodd. *Shinkai 6500* isn't the submarine piloted by the oceanographer who made the sighting at 4,600 feet.
5. The *Deep Rover* didn't dive as low as the *Alvin*.

		ALVIN	DEEP FLIGHT I	DEEP ROVER	NAUTILE	SHINKAI 6500	ANGLERFISH	CRANCHIID SQUID	DEEP-SEA SHRIMP	FANGTOOTH	GULPER EEL	1,600	2,600	4,600	6,600	7,600
PILOT	ABBOTT															
	BAKER															
	DODD															
	MORGAN															
	PRATT															
FEET	1,600															
	2,600															
	4,600															
	6,600															
	7,600															
CREATURE	ANGLERFISH															
	CRANCHIID SQUID															
	DEEP-SEA SHRIMP															
	FANGTOOTH															
	GULPER EEL															

LOGIC PROBLEM 67

Last Sunday morning, all was well in the Donnelly household until—with a bang, a clang, a clatter, and a rattle—a soot-covered squirrel scurried down the chimney and into the Donnelly's fireplace! Trying to shoo their overexcited guest outside, the family members chased the squirrel through five different rooms before it escaped through an open window. In each room, the squirrel leaped onto a different household furnishing and knocked over a different item or decoration. From the information provided, can you determine the order in which the squirrel ran through each room (including the bathroom), as well as the furnishing on which it leaped and the item it knocked over in each room?

1. The living room (which isn't the room in which the squirrel jumped onto the bureau) isn't the room in which the squirrel knocked over the clock. The living room (which isn't the room in which the squirrel knocked over the pewter figurine) isn't the room in which it leaped onto the chair (which isn't the bedroom).

2. The squirrel went into the kitchen at some point before it knocked over the potted plant, which was at some point before it leaped onto the bureau (which isn't in the bedroom).

3. The dining room isn't the room in which the squirrel knocked over the vase (which wasn't the item knocked over on the table when the squirrel leaped onto it). The living room (which isn't the room in which the squirrel leaped onto the curtains) isn't the room in which the squirrel knocked over the framed picture.

4. In the first room, the squirrel knocked over the figurine. In the last room, the squirrel ricocheted off the chair and zipped out the window.

5. The squirrel knocked over the framed picture at some point before it jumped onto the shelf and knocked over the clock.

		ROOM					FURNISHING					ITEM				
		BATHROOM	BEDROOM	DINING ROOM	KITCHEN	LIVING ROOM	BUREAU	CHAIR	CURTAINS	SHELF	TABLE	CLOCK	FIGURINE	PICTURE	PLANT	VASE
ORDER	FIRST															
	SECOND															
	THIRD															
	FOURTH															
	FIFTH															
ITEM	CLOCK															
	FIGURINE															
	PICTURE															
	PLANT															
	VASE															
FURNISHING	BUREAU															
	CHAIR															
	CURTAINS															
	SHELF															
	TABLE															

LOGIC PROBLEM 68 THE BOOK CLUB

Sonya has started a book club with her friend Ann and three other women. Each woman will lead a discussion on a different book written by a different author (three of whom—Alma Kern, Karla Olivet, and Mae Morris—are women, and two of whom—Horace Brown and Tony Boot—are men). From the information provided, can you determine the first and last names (one surname is Young) of each woman, the book on which she will lead a discussion, and the author of each book?

1. Ms. Reed selected a book written by a female author. *Autumn Heat* was written by a man. Sonya isn't married.

2. The surname initial of the author of the book selected by Carly is B. Mae Morris is neither the author of *Quarter Moon* nor the author of *Winner's Circle*.

3. Joan will lead the discussion on *Lazy Dogs*. Ms. Wood's husband plans to read *Last Dance* (which wasn't written by Alma Kern) after his wife leads the discussion on it.

4. Adele Pogozowski chose Tony Boot's book (which isn't *Winner's Circle*). *Winner's Circle* was written by neither Karla Olivet nor Alma Kern.

5. Ms. Booker will discuss *Quarter Moon* (which wasn't written by Alma Kern).

		LAST NAME					BOOK					AUTHOR				
		BOOKER	POGOZOWSKI	REED	WOOD	YOUNG	AUTUMN HEAT	LAST DANCE	LAZY DOGS	QUARTER MOON	WINNER'S CIRCLE	ALMA KERN	HORACE BROWN	KARLA OLIVET	MAE MORRIS	TONY BOOT
FIRST NAME	ADELE															
	ANN															
	CARLY															
	JOAN															
	SONYA															
AUTHOR	ALMA KERN															
	HORACE BROWN															
	KARLA OLIVET															
	MAE MORRIS															
	TONY BOOT															
BOOK	AUTUMN HEAT															
	LAST DANCE															
	LAZY DOGS															
	QUARTER MOON															
	WINNER'S CIRCLE															

LOGIC PROBLEM 69

Madge has a hard time keeping track of the sheet music that belongs to her choir. In fact, on one particular evening last week, five people (three of whom—Ann, June, and Sheila—are women, and two of whom—George and Les—are men) asked Madge for extra copies of their music. Each person had a different reason for needing a copy, and no two members have the same part in the choir. From the information provided, determine the part each member plays in the choir, the composer (one was Mozart) of the musical score each had misplaced, and the reason each gave for needing a new copy.

1. The woman who left a score at home because she thought it wouldn't be needed isn't the alto (who isn't Ann).

2. The five choir members are the tenor, the person who needed the score by Hector Berlioz, June, the person who left a score at work, and Ann.

3. Les (who isn't the tenor) isn't the person who said the dog ate his or her Berlioz score. The member whose children had scribbled all over his or her score isn't the one who needed a score by Giuseppe Verdi.

4. Neither Ann (who isn't the pianist) nor the person who needed a copy of the Handel score is the member whose children scribbled on the score. The flutist is a man.

5. June (who doesn't play the piano) isn't the one who needed the score by Schubert (who isn't the soprano). The man who lost his score didn't need the Schubert piece.

		INSTRUMENT					COMPOSER					REASON				
		ALTO	FLUTIST	PIANIST	SOPRANO	TENOR	BERLIOZ	HANDEL	MOZART	SCHUBERT	VERDI	CHILDREN SCRIBBLED	DOG ATE	LEFT AT WORK	LOST	NOT NEEDED
MEMBER	ANN															
	GEORGE															
	JUNE															
	LES															
	SHEILA															
REASON	CHILDREN															
	DOG ATE															
	LEFT AT WORK															
	LOST															
	NOT NEEDED															
COMPOSER	BERLIOZ															
	HANDEL															
	MOZART															
	SCHUBERT															
	VERDI															

LOGIC PROBLEM 70   **MONSTERS OF RAP**

Last Saturday night, the national tour of the "Monsters of Rap" concert played at the local arena. Tanya and three of her friends (two of whom—Jeff and Will—are men, and one of whom—Pamela—is a woman) arranged to meet at the concert. When all four had arrived (no two arrived at the same time), they went inside, and each bought a T-shirt bearing the likeness of his or her favorite rap star (one is Ice Kream) performing in the concert. Each favors a different rap star, and no two paid the same amount for a T-shirt. From the information provided, determine each person's favorite rap star, the amount ($20, $21, $23, or $24) each paid for a T-shirt, and the order in which each friend arrived.

1. The women paid $20 and $24 for their T-shirts. Neither man was the first person to arrive.

2. Pamela's T-shirt cost either exactly $3 more or exactly $3 less than the Delicious D. T-shirt (which cost either exactly $1 more or exactly $1 less than the Buster Move T-shirt).

3. The amount Jeff spent on his T-shirt is evenly divisible, with no remainder, by the number representing the order in which he arrived. Pamela arrived last.

4. The woman whose favorite star is Slippery C. paid less for her T-shirt than at least one other person.

		RAP STAR				AMOUNT				ORDER			
		BUSTER MOVE	DELICIOUS D.	ICE KREAM	SLIPPERY C.	$20	$21	$23	$24	FIRST	SECOND	THIRD	FOURTH
PERSON	JEFF												
	PAMELA												
	TANYA												
	WILL												
ORDER	FIRST												
	SECOND												
	THIRD												
	FOURTH												
AMOUNT	$20												
	$21												
	$23												
	$24												

78

All Linda wanted to know was whether or not she should wear her slicker tomorrow, but when she monitored the five local newscasts, she found that no two meteorologists in the Twin Cities could agree on the next day's forecast! Each meteorologist (including Clint Isobar) appears on a different station, and each predicted a different type of weather for the next day. At the end of his or her segment, each also made a different announcement (one announced the opening of an agricultural fair). Linda gave up trying to plan ahead and decided to keep her slicker in her car! From the information provided, determine the person who predicts the weather for each station, his or her next-day forecast, and the special announcement each made at the end of his or her segment.

1. Wacky Waldo, who didn't announce the crafts show, isn't the forecaster on KNOW.
2. Of Dr. Swami and the meteorologist who predicted clear weather, one ended the segment by announcing that he or she was going on vacation, and the other wished a happy birthday to Ms. Mathilda Cosgrove (who turns 100 years young today).
3. Rita Sunshine predicted rain for tomorrow.
4. The one who closed with the announcement about the crafts show, who isn't the WHEW weather reporter, is neither the one whose forecast called for sleet nor the one whose forecast called for hail.
5. Neither the weather forecaster for WILL nor the one for WISH predicted rain. The meteorologists on KELP and KNOW are Dr. Swami and the one who announced he or she was going on vacation, in some order. The Prognosticator, who didn't predict sleet, ended his segment by welcoming new members of his fan club.
6. The weather forecaster for WILL isn't the one who predicted snow.

		STATION					FORECAST					ANNOUNCEMENT				
		KELP	KNOW	WHEW	WILL	WISH	CLEAR	HAIL	RAIN	SLEET	SNOW	AGRICULTURAL FAIR	BIRTHDAY	CRAFTS SHOW	FAN CLUB	VACATION
PERSON	CLINT ISOBAR															
	DR. SWAMI															
	PROGNOSTICATOR															
	RITA SUNSHINE															
	WACKY WALDO															
ANNOUNCE.	AGRICULTURAL															
	BIRTHDAY															
	CRAFTS SHOW															
	FAN CLUB															
	VACATION															
FORECAST	CLEAR															
	HAIL															
	RAIN															
	SLEET															
	SNOW															

LOGIC PROBLEM 72 ODE ON A GRECIAN URN

The pride of the Madison Art Museum's Classical Greek gallery is its small but perfectly preserved collection of painted urns and vases. Each of the six pieces in the collection is a different type of vessel, and each clearly depicts a different mythological scene. Altogether, the six urns represent four different painting styles—one is in the proto-Attic style, one is in the proto-Corinthian style, two are in the black-figure style, and two are in the red-figure style. In order to display these pieces to the best advantage, the urns have been placed side-by-side in a glass case, and each piece has been given a different exhibit number (from left to right, 101 through 106). From the information provided, can you determine the exhibit number of each type of urn, as well as the scene each depicts (one shows Hercules and Cerberus) and the style in which each is painted?

1. The kylix urn (which is decorated in the proto-Corinthian style) is somewhere to the left of the hydria urn.
2. Both the urn with exhibit number 102 (which depicts Perseus saving Andromeda) and the pithos urn are done in the black-figure style.
3. Of the urn with exhibit number 105 (which is not the one with the scene of Leda and the Swan) and the stamnos urn, one is painted in the proto-Attic style and the other is painted in the proto-Corinthian style.
4. The amphora urn is somewhere to the left of both of the urns painted in the red-figure style but somewhere to the right of the urn depicting the Abduction of Helen.
5. The piece depicting the Judgment of Paris isn't painted in the red-figure style. The deinos urn isn't the one with the scene of Odysseus and the Sirens. The scene on the urn with exhibit number 105 is neither the Judgment of Paris nor Odysseus and the Sirens.
6. No two urns done in the same style are immediately next to each other.

		EXHIBIT NUMBER						SCENE						STYLE					
		101	102	103	104	105	106	ABDUCTION OF HELEN	HERCULES AND CERBERUS	JUDGMENT OF PARIS	LEDA AND THE SWAN	ODYSSEUS AND THE SIRENS	PERSEUS SAVING ANDROMEDA	BLACK FIGURE	BLACK FIGURE	PROTO-ATTIC	PROTO-CORINTHIAN	RED FIGURE	RED FIGURE
URN	AMPHORA																		
	DEINOS																		
	HYDRIA																			
	KYLIX																			
	PITHOS																			
	STAMNOS																			
STYLE	BLACK FIGURE																			
	BLACK FIGURE																			
	PROTO-ATTIC																			
	PROTO-CORINTH.																			
	RED FIGURE																			
	RED FIGURE																			
SCENE	ABDUCTION																			
	HERCULES																			
	JUDGMENT/PARIS																			
	LEDA/SWAN																			
	ODYSSEUS																			
	PERSEUS																			

LOGIC PROBLEM 73

The roadie is called upon to perform all sorts of duties before the start of a rock 'n' roll tour. Last week, each of five roadies (each of whom works for a different band—one is Elbow Room) went to Clarence's Electronics Warehouse to buy a different number of rolls of cable in preparation for his or her band's upcoming tour. Because his or her band is about to embark on an extended nationwide tour of a different number of cities, each roadie (two of whom—Angela and Jesse—are women, and three of whom—Delbert, Skip, and Ty—are men) was sure to buy the correct type of cable. From the information provided, determine the band for which each roadie works, the number (7, 8, 9, 10, or 11) of rolls of cable each one purchased, and the number (25, 30, 35, 40, or 45) of cities on each band's tour.

1. The band whose roadie bought 10 rolls of cable (which isn't Starched Collars or Portentous Pilots) is touring more cities than Delbert's band but fewer cities than at least one other band. Portentous Pilots isn't touring 25 or 30 cities.

2. Angela (who isn't the roadie for Portentous Pilots) bought exactly 2 fewer rolls of cable than the man who is roadie for the band touring 25 cities.

3. The roadie for Iron Petticoats (who are embarking on a 35-city tour) bought exactly 2 fewer rolls of cable than Jesse.

4. The band whose roadie purchased 11 rolls of cable (which isn't Ty's band) is touring more cities than at least one other band.

5. The Watercoolers are touring exactly 10 more cities than the band whose roadie bought 8 rolls of cable.

		BAND					ROLLS					CITIES				
		ELBOW ROOM	IRON PETTICOATS	PORTENTOUS PILOTS	STARCHED COLLARS	WATERCOOLERS	7	8	9	10	11	25	30	35	40	45
ROADIE	ANGELA															
	DELBERT															
	JESSE															
	SKIP															
	TY															
CITIES	25															
	30															
	35															
	40															
	45															
ROLLS	7															
	8															
	9															
	10															
	11															

LOGIC PROBLEM 74

Last week, Prentice used five different social engagements to wear some of the more flamboyant socks in his extensive designer-sock collection. To each engagement (each of which was on a different weeknight), Prentice wore a pair of socks that bore a different design and was given by a different person. From the information provided, can you determine the design on the socks Prentice wore each weeknight, as well as the person (including his aunt) from whom he received those socks and the engagement (one was a fundraiser) to which he wore them?

1. Prentice went to the card game (which wasn't on Monday or Tuesday night) at some point before he went to the ball game. Neither Monday nor Tuesday night is either the night he wore the Escher socks or the night he wore the Spiderman socks.

2. Prentice wore the socks his mother gave him (which aren't the Spiderman socks) the night after he wore the ones from his wife (which aren't the ones he wore to the opera). His wife gave him neither the clown-face socks nor the Star Trek socks.

3. Prentice wore his Elvis socks (which weren't given to him by his mother) to the opera.

4. Prentice wore the socks from his coworker at some point after he wore the socks his wife gave him.

5. His Star Trek socks (which aren't the ones his son gave him) aren't the ones Prentice wore to the movie. He wore his Star Trek socks the night after he wore his clown-face socks.

		CLOWN FACE	ELVIS	ESCHER	SPIDERMAN	STAR TREK	AUNT	COWORKER	MOTHER	SON	WIFE	BALL GAME	CARD GAME	FUNDRAISER	MOVIE	OPERA
WEEKNIGHT	MONDAY															
	TUESDAY															
	WEDNESDAY															
	THURSDAY															
	FRIDAY															
ENGAGEMENT	BALL GAME															
	CARD GAME															
	FUNDRAISER															
	MOVIE															
	OPERA															
PERSON	AUNT															
	COWORKER															
	MOTHER															
	SON															
	WIFE															

Becca and four of her fifth-grade friends play on the Blazers soccer team. Last season was their best yet, since the five friends scored a combined total of 24 goals. Each girl scored a different number of goals, and each scored at least one goal. Each Blazer also has a different number on her uniform (6, 10, 12, 20, or 24). From the information provided, determine the first and last names of each Blazer, the uniform number each wears, and the total number of goals each scored last season.

1. Alice's total number of goals (which is the most of the five girls) is equal to the uniform number of one of the five girls. Ms. Ellis (who scored an odd number of goals) scored exactly half as many goals as Alice.
2. Mary's uniform number is lower than Ms. Holland's. Ms. Loving didn't score the most goals.
3. Audrey Jones scored exactly half as many goals as Ms. Smith.
4. Mary scored exactly four goals. The number on Mary's uniform is exactly twice that of Beth's. Ms. Ellis wears uniform number 12.

		LAST NAME					UNIFORM NUMBER					GOALS				
		ELLIS	HOLLAND	JONES	LOVING	SMITH	6	10	12	20	24					
FIRST NAME	ALICE															
	AUDREY															
	BECCA															
	BETH															
	MARY															
GOALS																
UNIFORM	6															
	10															
	12															
	20															
	24															

LOGIC PROBLEM 76

One night, after putting the paper to bed, the *Gazette*'s six editors (four of whom are women, and two of whom are men) discussed their early experiences in journalism. Each person (including Blair) is the editor of a different department (entertainment, local news, national news, op-ed, puzzles, or sports) at the *Gazette*, and each was the editor of one of these same departments for his or her college newspaper. From the information provided, determine the department each person headed for his or her college newspaper and the department he or she heads for the *Gazette*. (Note: All names can apply to either a man or a woman.)

1. Women headed their college newspapers' sports and op-ed departments, and women head the *Gazette*'s national-news and op-ed departments.

2. A man was entertainment editor for his college paper. A man heads the same department for the *Gazette* as Nicky did for his or her college paper. The one who headed the puzzle department in college is now the *Gazette*'s national-news editor.

3. Nicky heads the same department for the *Gazette* as Tyler did for his or her college newspaper.

4. Robin and Sydney are the *Gazette*'s local-news and sports editors, in some order. The college editors of the local-news and sports departments are Robin and Sydney, in some order.

5. Robin is a woman. Drew wasn't the editor of his or her college paper's op-ed department.

6. The op-ed editor for the *Gazette* wasn't the op-ed editor for his or her college newspaper. The local-news editor for the *Gazette* wasn't the local-news editor for his or her college newspaper. The entertainment editor for the *Gazette* wasn't the entertainment editor for his or her college newspaper.

		COLLEGE						GAZETTE					
		ENTERTAINMENT	LOCAL NEWS	NATIONAL NEWS	OP-ED	PUZZLES	SPORTS	ENTERTAINMENT	LOCAL NEWS	NATIONAL NEWS	OP-ED	PUZZLES	SPORTS
PERSON	BLAIR												
	DREW												
	NICKY												
	ROBIN												
	SYDNEY												
	TYLER												
GAZETTE	ENTERTAINMENT												
	LOCAL NEWS												
	NATIONAL NEWS												
	OP-ED												
	PUZZLES												
	SPORTS												

LOGIC PROBLEM 77

The first seven months of this year were busy ones, baby-wise, at Techniques, Inc., since each of five female employees (Amelia, Mary, Miranda, Steffi, or Tasha) gave birth to her first child. In each month (January, February, April, May, or July) that a baby was due, the employees held a baby pool. The winner of each pool was the one who correctly guessed the baby's birth date (each baby was born during the same month in which he or she was due). A different person won each pool, and no two winners chose the same day of the month. From the information provided, determine the month in which each mother was due, the winner (Abby, Brad, Ilse, Roger, or Suzanne) of each pool, and the date (3rd, 7th, 13th, 22nd, or 29th) that each winner chose.

1. The five babies are Miranda's, the one born on the 22nd, the one born in April, the one born on the date predicted by Suzanne, and the one born on the 3rd.

2. Brad, whose guess of the 29th made him a winner, isn't the person who won the pool for Tasha's baby. Brad didn't win the July pool.

3. Abby won the pool for the baby born three months after Amelia's baby.

4. Either Abby or Roger won the baby pool held for Steffi, whose baby was due the month before Suzanne won a pool, who won at some point earlier in the year than the person whose guess of the 7th made him or her a winner.

5. Mary's baby was born in May, but not on the 3rd.

		MOTHER					WINNER					DATE				
		AMELIA	MARY	MIRANDA	STEFFI	TASHA	ABBY	BRAD	ILSE	ROGER	SUZANNE	3rd	7th	13th	22nd	29th
MONTH	JANUARY															
	FEBRUARY															
	APRIL															
	MAY															
	JULY															
DATE	3rd															
	7th															
	13th															
	22nd															
	29th															
WINNER	ABBY															
	BRAD															
	ILSE															
	ROGER															
	SUZANNE															

LOGIC PROBLEM 78

Professional wild-mushroom gatherers are an adventurous bunch. Their job requires them to search out the deepest, darkest forests for gourmet fungi, and the pay they receive for their wild bounty more than compensates them for their efforts. Last weekend, Otto and four other fungus gatherers explored four thickly wooded areas, where each collected a different number of pounds (2, 4, 6, 8, or 10) of a different edible fungus. Each person explored only one area. From the information provided, can you determine the type of fungus collected by each gatherer, the number of pounds each collected, and the location where each harvested the fungus?

1. The one who collected field mushrooms didn't collect eight pounds of fungi. Theo didn't collect his fungus in Silent Woods.

2. Penelope (who isn't the one who collected in Oakwoods Forest) is neither the gatherer who collected in Silent Woods nor the one who picked the golden chanterelles.

3. The two people who collected in Tallpines Woods are Ralph and the gatherer (who isn't Penelope) who collected exactly two more pounds of fungi than the one who collected in Darkwood Forest (who harvested exactly two more pounds of fungi than the person who collected morels).

4. Theo (who picked oyster mushrooms) collected more pounds of fungi than Stacey, who collected more pounds of fungi than at least one other person.

5. The gatherer who collected the edible boletes (who isn't Penelope) didn't collect ten pounds of fungi. Edible boletes weren't collected in either Silent Woods or in Tallpines Woods.

		FUNGUS					POUNDS					LOCATION				
		EDIBLE BOLETES	FIELD MUSHROOMS	GOLDEN CHANTERELLES	MORELS	OYSTER MUSHROOMS	2	4	6	8	10	DARKWOOD FOREST	OAKWOODS FOREST	SILENT WOODS	TALLPINES WOODS	TALLPINES WOODS
GATHERER	OTTO															
	PENELOPE															
	RALPH															
	STACEY															
	THEO															
LOCATION	DARKWOOD															
	OAKWOODS															
	SILENT WOODS															
	TALLPINES															
	TALLPINES															
POUNDS	2															
	4															
	6															
	8															
	10															

Thanks to the movement to return Native American artifacts to their proper cultural context, the most recent exhibit at the Museum of Native Plains Peoples in Red Pines featured five new artifacts donated by Native American collectors. Each of the five collectors (three of whom—Dan Rainfeather, Joseph Red Crow, and Leroy Horsetamer—are men, and two of whom—Kim Two Clouds and Wilma Little Bear—are women) donated a different object that originated with a different tribe (one is the Osage). Each object dates from a different year (1820, 1835, 1850, 1865, or 1880). From the information provided, can you determine the object (one is a ceremonial pipe) each collector donated, as well as the tribe with which each object originated and the year from which each object dates?

1. The drum is exactly 30 years older than the bowl.

2. The pair of moccasins (which isn't the Kiowa object) was donated by a man. The shirt donated by Leroy Horsetamer is older than the moccasins.

3. The object donated by Wilma Little Bear is exactly 15 years older than the one donated by Kim Two Clouds, which is exactly 15 years older than the one donated by Dan Rainfeather.

4. The Arapaho object is exactly 30 years older than the Comanche object but younger than the Pawnee object (which isn't the shirt).

5. Joseph Red Crow didn't donate either the drum or the moccasins.

		COLLECTOR					TRIBE					YEAR				
		DAN RAINFEATHER	JOSEPH RED CROW	KIM TWO CLOUDS	LEROY HORSETAMER	WILMA LITTLE BEAR	ARAPAHO	COMANCHE	KIOWA	OSAGE	PAWNEE	1820	1835	1850	1865	1880
OBJECT	BOWL															
	DRUM															
	MOCCASINS															
	PIPE															
	SHIRT															
YEAR	1820															
	1835															
	1850															
	1865															
	1880															
TRIBE	ARAPAHO															
	COMANCHE															
	KIOWA															
	OSAGE															
	PAWNEE															

LOGIC PROBLEM 80

When Forrest retired from his job as a construction worker and moved to Florida, he wondered if he'd have anything in common with his new neighbors. Imagine his delight when he met four other retired construction workers at a neighborhood block party! As the five compared their careers as builders, they learned that at some point each had built one house for each of the same three construction companies—Ace, Champion, and Expert. Each worker had built a different style of house (Cape Cod, Colonial, Georgian, ranch, or Victorian) for each company, and no two built the same style of house for the same company. From the information provided, can you determine the style of house each man built for the Ace, Champion, and Expert construction companies?

1. Four of the men are the one who built the Georgian house for Expert (who isn't the one who built the Victorian house for Ace), the one who built the Cape Cod house for Champion, the one who built the ranch house for Champion, and the one who built the Colonial house for Expert.

2. Both Nelson and Quinn built Cape Cod houses. Rory has never built a Georgian house.

3. Abe (who has never built a ranch house) built a Colonial for Ace.

4. The man who built the Georgian house for Champion also built the ranch house for Expert.

5. Quinn isn't the one who built the Georgian house for Ace.

		ACE					CHAMPION					EXPERT				
		CAPE COD	COLONIAL	GEORGIAN	RANCH	VICTORIAN	CAPE COD	COLONIAL	GEORGIAN	RANCH	VICTORIAN	CAPE COD	COLONIAL	GEORGIAN	RANCH	VICTORIAN
MAN	ABE															
	FORREST															
	NELSON															
	QUINN															
	RORY															
EXPERT	CAPE COD										
	COLONIAL										
	GEORGIAN										
	RANCH										
	VICTORIAN										
CHAMPION	CAPE COD					
	COLONIAL					
	GEORGIAN					
	RANCH					
	VICTORIAN					

LOGIC PROBLEM 81

Leslie and four of her friends (three of whom—Brad, Kent, and Neil—are men, and one of whom—Tara—is a woman) were teammates in the 14th Annual Road Rally. Each person drove his or her own car along the course, earning points for traveling a certain distance within a given amount of time. Each racer took at least 2 hours, but fewer than 2 hours and 30 minutes, to get from the first checkpoint to the second checkpoint. No two friends drive the same model of car, and no two left the first checkpoint at the same time. From the information provided, determine the model of car (one is a Camaro) each friend drives, as well as the time (6:50, 6:55, 7:00, 7:05, or 7:10 a.m.) each left the first checkpoint and the time each arrived at the second checkpoint. (Note: All travel times are in multiples of five minutes.)

1. No one took exactly 2 hours and 25 minutes to get from the first checkpoint to the second checkpoint. The second-shortest travel time was exactly 10 minutes longer than the shortest travel time. The two female friends are the only two people who took exactly the same amount of time to get from the first checkpoint to the second checkpoint.

2. The woman who drives the Civic is a history major. Neil (who was the last one to leave the first checkpoint) took the shortest amount of time to reach the second checkpoint.

3. The friend who left the first checkpoint at 7:00 a.m. isn't the one who arrived at the second checkpoint at exactly 9:20 a.m. Brad left the first checkpoint at some point after Leslie but at some point before (but not immediately before) Kent.

4. Neil and Brad drive the Cherokee and the Explorer, in some order. Leslie (who is an art major) isn't the one who drives the Mustang. The friend who drives the Cherokee didn't take exactly 2 hours to reach the second checkpoint. Tara isn't the driver who arrived at the second checkpoint at exactly 9:15 a.m.

		MODEL OF CAR					TIME LEFT					TIME ARRIVED				
		CAMARO	CHEROKEE	CIVIC	EXPLORER	MUSTANG	6:50 a.m.	6:55 a.m.	7:00 a.m.	7:05 a.m.	7:10 a.m.					
FRIEND	BRAD															
	KENT															
	LESLIE															
	NEIL															
	TARA															
TIME ARRIVED																
TIME LEFT	6:50 a.m.															
	6:55 a.m.															
	7:00 a.m.															
	7:05 a.m.															
	7:10 a.m.															

LOGIC PROBLEM 82

BOXER REBELLION

Combination stores are all the rage these days—café/book stores, book/music stores, laundromats/tanning salons—so it's no wonder that the opening of Boxer Rebellion, a combination music and undergarment shop, has been such a fantastic success. Valerie and four of her friends recently paid a visit to the store for some one-stop shopping—each bought a pair of boxer shorts with a different design, a package of undershirts of a different style, and a different compact disc (one is *Ten Decibels*). From the information provided, determine the customer who bought each pair of boxers, each package of undershirts, and each compact disc.

1. The five pairs of boxers are the pair featuring the bananas (which were bought by the one who purchased white V-neck shirts), the pair Uriah purchased, the pair bought with the *Get to Work!* disc, the pair bought by the one who purchased white crew-neck undershirts, and the pair with the snowmen design.

2. The five customers are the person who bought *Frankentomato*, Theo (who bought a disc by Worm Farm), Xavier (who bought a disc by the group Crawdad), the friend who bought boxers featuring drumsticks (who bought a disc by the Beatnik Chicks), and the one who bought both a package of gray V-neck undershirts and a Worm Farm disc.

3. The person who bought *Superimplosion* didn't purchase the boxers with the snowmen. Winona isn't the friend who bought a package of tank-top undershirts.

4. The one who bought the boxers decorated with fleurs-de-lis also purchased a Beatnik Chicks disc. The person who bought a package of gray crew-neck undershirts purchased a Worm Farm disc. The friend who bought the boxers with the hearts design purchased the disc entitled *Cotton*.

		BOXERS					UNDERSHIRTS					COMPACT DISC				
		BANANAS	DRUMSTICKS	FLEURS-DE-LIS	HEARTS	SNOWMEN	GRAY CREW NECK	GRAY V NECK	TANK TOP	WHITE CREW NECK	WHITE V NECK	COTTON	FRANKEN-TOMATO	GET TO WORK!	SUPER-IMPLOSION	TEN DECIBELS
CUSTOMER	THEO															
	URIAH															
	VALERIE															
	WINONA															
	XAVIER															
DISC	COTTON															
	FRANKENTOMATO															
	GET TO WORK!															
	SUPERIMPLOSION															
	TEN DECIBELS															
UNDERSHIRTS	GRAY CREW															
	GRAY V NECK															
	TANK TOP															
	WHITE CREW															
	WHITE V NECK															

LOGIC PROBLEM 83

Each month, a schedule is posted in the Data Company office kitchen with coffee duty assignments. Last month, each of six employees (including Layla) was out of the office on his or her assigned day, so the schedule was rearranged so that each one's new date was the original date of a different one of the other five. No two people were scheduled to make coffee on the same date. From the information provided, determine the original date (23rd, 24th, 25th, 26th, 29th, or 31st) assigned to each person and the new date each was given.

1. Zack's original date was exactly two days before the new date given to the person whose original date was Zack's new date.
2. George's new date was earlier than Kat's new date.
3. Vinson's new date was originally assigned to the person whose new date was the 25th.
4. Diana's new date was Kat's original date.
5. Diana's new date was the day before her original date, which was the new date of the person whose original date was the 24th.

		ORIGINAL DATE						NEW DATE					
		23rd	24th	25th	26th	29th	31st	23rd	24th	25th	26th	29th	31st
PERSON	DIANA												
	GEORGE												
	KAT												
	LAYLA												
	VINSON												
	ZACK												
NEW DATE	23rd												
	24th												
	25th												
	26th												
	29th												
	31st												

LOGIC PROBLEM 84 HEAVY METAL

When young Jim Hawkins received a metal detector for his birthday, he was so excited that he immediately rushed down to the waterfront to try it out. During the course of his beachcombing expedition, he detected six items, each of which he imagined to be a different valuable object. However, when he uncovered each item, he found a different, quite ordinary object (in one case, a broken key chain). Jim unearthed each item at a different seaside location (one was found on the beach) at a different time. Each item was discovered either at a quarter past, half past, quarter to, or on the hour, and no item was found before 10:30 a.m. From the information provided, can you determine the time at which Jim found the item in each location, the item Jim imagined each discovery to be, and the actual identity of each item?

1. The penny was found exactly 3 hours after the object discovered under the boardwalk but exactly 15 minutes before the one thought to be a ring.

2. The item found near the rocks was discovered exactly 3 hours after the item Jim imagined to be a necklace (which wasn't found at 10:45 a.m.), which was unearthed at some point after the bent spoon.

3. The object found in the dunes at 12:15 p.m. was found at some point after the object discovered by the pier.

4. The last item Jim unearthed, which was a bottle cap he mistakenly thought was a silver dollar, was found at 2:00 p.m. The second item he discovered was a tin can.

5. A ball of aluminum foil was found either under the boardwalk or in the dunes. The penny wasn't the object unearthed at the playground.

6. Jim discovered the item he imagined to be a wristwatch at some point after the item he thought was a medallion but at some point before the item he imagined to be a gold doubloon.

		LOCATION						IMAGINED						ACTUAL					
		BEACH	BOARDWALK	DUNES	PIER	PLAYGROUND	ROCKS	GOLD DOUBLOON	MEDALLION	NECKLACE	RING	SILVER DOLLAR	WRISTWATCH	ALUMINUM FOIL	BOTTLE CAP	KEY CHAIN	PENNY	SPOON	TIN CAN
TIME																			
ACTUAL	ALUMINUM FOIL																		
	BOTTLE CAP																		
	KEY CHAIN																		
	PENNY																		
	SPOON																		
	TIN CAN																		
IMAGINED	GOLD DOUBLOON																		
	MEDALLION																		
	NECKLACE																		
	RING																		
	SILVER DOLLAR																		
	WRISTWATCH																		

LOGIC PROBLEM 85

Last week, contestants from all over the world met at the annual Kangaroo Klassic Boomerang Throwing Contest. Six contestants (including last year's champion, Kroc Durgens) took top honors in three events. In the speed segment, each contestant scored a different time in seconds (4, 5, 6, 7, 9, or 10) for throwing and catching a boomerang. In the target-throwing segment, each contestant hit a different number of bull's-eyes (3, 4, 6, 7, 8, or 9). Finally, in the juggling segment, each contestant juggled a different number of boomerangs (2, 3, 4, 6, 7, or 8). From the information provided, determine, for each contestant, the number of seconds required to retrieve his or her boomerang, the number of bull's-eyes each scored, and the number of boomerangs each juggled.

1. The one who threw and caught his or her boomerang in seven seconds threw exactly one bull's-eye fewer, but juggled more boomerangs, than Gillian.

2. Max was exactly one second quicker in the speed segment than the person who juggled exactly one more boomerang than the one who had eight bull's-eyes. Cameron was quicker in the speed segment than the one who scored eight bull's-eyes.

3. The one who juggled seven boomerangs had exactly one more bull's-eye than the one who scored nine seconds in the speed segment (who juggled more boomerangs than William).

4. The contestant who had seven bull's-eyes juggled exactly two more boomerangs than the one who had a throwing-and-catching time of six seconds (who had exactly two fewer bull's-eyes than the one who juggled two boomerangs).

5. The person who juggled two boomerangs took exactly one second longer to throw and catch a boomerang than the one who scored four bull's-eyes (who juggled fewer boomerangs than Robin).

		SECONDS						BULL'S-EYES						BOOMERANGS					
		4	5	6	7	9	10	3	4	6	7	8	9	2	3	4	6	7	8
CONTESTANT	CAMERON																		
	GILLIAN																		
	KROC																		
	MAX																		
	ROBIN																		
	WILLIAM																		
BOOMERANGS	2																		
	3																		
	4																		
	6																		
	7																		
	8																		
BULL'S-EYES	3																		
	4																		
	6																		
	7																		
	8																		
	9																		

LOGIC PROBLEM 86   SEPARATE VACATIONS

As five New Yorkers (including Thelma) recently discovered, the tiny island nation of Pokaponesia is also known as the Island of Lost Luggage. Upon arriving on Pokaponesia, each traveler (no two of whom are from the same New York borough) discovered that his or her luggage had been mistakenly sent to a different city! Fortunately, Iggy, the efficient luggage courier for Pokaponesia Airlines, swiftly located the missing bags and returned, one after another, each piece of luggage to its owner the next day. From the information provided, determine the order in which Iggy returned each person's luggage, the city (one is Cincinnati) to which his or her luggage had been sent, and the New York borough (one is Queens) in which each person lives.

1. Iggy returned luggage to Gwynne, who isn't from Brooklyn, at some point after returning the bags that were sent to Pittsburgh.

2. Neither the luggage that was accidentally sent to Chicago (which wasn't returned fifth) nor the luggage that was sent to Pittsburgh belongs to the traveler from Staten Island (whose bags weren't returned first).

3. Neither Isabel nor Rex is the person who lives in Manhattan. Iggy returned Vinnie's bags at some point after returning the luggage that was sent to Memphis.

4. One person had his or her luggage returned immediately after the traveler whose bags were sent to Houston but immediately before the Brooklyn resident (who received his or her luggage at some point before Rex).

5. Iggy returned the luggage that was sent to Pittsburgh at some point after returning luggage to the person from the Bronx (which was at some point after returning Isabel's luggage).

		PERSON					CITY					BOROUGH				
		GWYNNE	ISABEL	REX	THELMA	VINNIE	CHICAGO	CINCINNATI	HOUSTON	MEMPHIS	PITTSBURGH	BRONX	BROOKLYN	MANHATTAN	QUEENS	STATEN ISLAND
ORDER	FIRST															
	SECOND															
	THIRD															
	FOURTH															
	FIFTH															
BOROUGH	BRONX															
	BROOKLYN															
	MANHATTAN															
	QUEENS															
	STATEN ISLAND															
CITY	CHICAGO															
	CINCINNATI															
	HOUSTON															
	MEMPHIS															
	PITTSBURGH															

As dedicated bird-watchers know, not all birds fly south for the winter. Yesterday, Jean met with five of her fellow bird-watchers to discuss last week's sightings. Although each went bird-watching on only one day (each went on a different day), each sighted a different number of cardinals (5, 6, 7, 8, 10, or 11) and a different number of chickadees (6, 7, 8, 9, 11, or 12). From the information provided, determine the day (Sunday, Monday, Tuesday, Thursday, Friday, or Saturday) on which each person went bird-watching, as well as the number of cardinals and the number of chickadees each saw.

1. Tina went bird-watching at some point later in the week than the one who saw eight cardinals (who saw exactly 1 more chickadee than Tina). Henry went bird-watching at some point earlier in the week than the one who saw 11 chickadees (who spotted exactly one cardinal fewer than the one who went bird-watching on Saturday).

2. Carol spotted either exactly one cardinal more or exactly one cardinal fewer than the person who went bird-watching the day before the one who saw 7 chickadees (who saw more cardinals than Ryder).

3. Max went bird-watching at some point later in the week than the one who spotted ten cardinals (who saw exactly 1 more chickadee than the person who went bird-watching on Monday).

4. The one who went bird-watching on Saturday saw exactly 2 fewer chickadees than the person who spotted seven cardinals (who went bird-watching exactly two days after the one who spotted 8 chickadees).

		PERSON						CARDINALS						CHICKADEES					
		CAROL	HENRY	JEAN	MAX	RYDER	TINA	5	6	7	8	10	11	6	7	8	9	11	12
DAY	SUNDAY																		
	MONDAY																		
	TUESDAY																		
	THURSDAY																		
	FRIDAY																		
	SATURDAY																		
CHICKADEES	6																		
	7																		
	8																		
	9																		
	11																		
	12																		
CARDINALS	5																		
	6																		
	7																		
	8																		
	10																		
	11																		

LOGIC PROBLEM 88

NO PAIN, NO GAIN

Every Monday, Wednesday, and Friday after work, Rhoda and four of her friends stop at Ray's Gym for a brisk workout. Ray's Gym comes equipped with five types of exercise machines—Lifecycles, NordicTracks, rowing machines, StairMasters, and treadmills. Each day, each person warms up on a single different machine before beginning intensive work on abs, pecs, and delts. To make sure he or she gets a full-body workout, each person uses three different machines every week. From the information provided, can you determine the exercise machine each person uses Monday, Wednesday, and Friday?

1. One person uses the Lifecycle, treadmill, and rowing machine, in some order.
2. Phyllis, who uses the treadmill on Wednesdays, never uses the Lifecycle. Malcolm (who doesn't use the treadmill on Fridays) uses two of the same machines that Phyllis uses.
3. Zara uses the same machine on Wednesday that Woodrow uses on Friday.
4. Malcolm works out on the StairMaster every Monday.
5. The one who works out on the rowing machine on Mondays works out on the StairMaster on Fridays.
6. One person works out Wednesdays on the Lifecycle and Fridays on the NordicTrack.

		MONDAY					WEDNESDAY					FRIDAY				
		LIFECYCLE	NORDICTRACK	ROWING MACHINE	STAIRMASTER	TREADMILL	LIFECYCLE	NORDICTRACK	ROWING MACHINE	STAIRMASTER	TREADMILL	LIFECYCLE	NORDICTRACK	ROWING MACHINE	STAIRMASTER	TREADMILL
PERSON	MALCOLM															
	PHYLLIS															
	RHODA															
	WOODROW															
	ZARA															
FRIDAY	LIFECYCLE															
	NORDICTRACK															
	ROWING MACHINE															
	STAIRMASTER															
	TREADMILL															
WEDNESDAY	LIFECYCLE															
	NORDICTRACK															
	ROWING MACHINE															
	STAIRMASTER															
	TREADMILL															

96

LOGIC PROBLEM 89

Each summer, the town of Lawron sponsors outdoor concerts. This July, the Lawron Symphony performed five concerts, each of which featured the music of a different classical composer. Each concert took place in one of the town's four parks (including Seaside Park) and was conducted by one of the symphony's four conductors (two of whom—Dane and Peter—are men, and two of whom—Erica and Heather—are women). From the information provided, determine the conductor (identified by first and last names) of the concert featuring each composer and the park at which it was held.

1. Either the Bach concert and the Mozart concert both took place in the same park or both had the same conductor. Farmer's Park wasn't the setting for the Bach concert.

2. The four conductors are the one who conducted the Handel concert (who is neither Heather nor the one surnamed Waters), Dane, the one surnamed Tuchman, and the only one who conducted two concerts.

3. The Beethoven concert, the Haydn concert, and the only concert held in the Park in the Green featured three different conductors.

4. Erica is either the one surnamed Zucker or the conductor of a concert held in Veterans Park. Neither Heather nor the one surnamed Tuchman conducted the Mozart concert.

5. The four parks are the one in which the Beethoven concert was held, a park in which Peter conducted, a park in which Ms. Gresham conducted, and the only park in which two concerts were held.

		FIRST NAME				LAST NAME				PARK			
		DANE	ERICA	HEATHER	PETER	GRESHAM	TUCHMAN	WATERS	ZUCKER	FARMER'S PARK	PARK IN THE GREEN	SEASIDE PARK	VETERANS PARK
COMPOSER	BACH												
COMPOSER	BEETHOVEN												
COMPOSER	HANDEL												
COMPOSER	HAYDN												
COMPOSER	MOZART												
PARK	FARMER'S PARK												
PARK	PARK IN THE GR.												
PARK	SEASIDE PARK												
PARK	VETERANS PARK												
LAST NAME	GRESHAM												
LAST NAME	TUCHMAN												
LAST NAME	WATERS												
LAST NAME	ZUCKER												

LOGIC PROBLEM 90 THE CORY STORY

When Kim moved into her dormitory at the beginning of her first year of boarding school, she didn't know what to expect. She was assigned to share a suite with five other young women—two women in each room in the three-room suite—and, as no two suite mates were from the same state, Kim wondered if they would have anything in common. But the experience was easier than she expected, since the young women quickly discovered a common bond—all are devoted fans of famous teen heartthrob Cory! They spent their first night in the dorm talking about Cory and putting up their favorite posters of the celebrity (each hung up one poster showing Cory engaged in a different activity). From the information provided, determine each woman's roommate, her home state, and the Cory poster she hung up in the suite.

1. Kim and her roommate are the one from Delaware and the one who hung up the keen poster of Cory at the Oscars, in some order.
2. Rachel's roommate and Samantha's roommate are the one from Ohio and the one who hung up the rad poster of Cory playing the guitar, in some order. Rachel isn't Samantha's roommate.
3. Irene and her roommate (who isn't Samantha) are from Michigan and Virginia, in some order. Lizabeth and her roommate put up the cool posters of Cory surfing and Cory at the Eiffel Tower, in some order. Rachel is from Florida.
4. Jane and her roommate are the one from Washington and the one who hung up the dreamy poster of Cory in his convertible, in some order.
5. In an alphabetical list of suite mates, the name of the young woman who hung up the poster of Cory at the Eiffel Tower (who isn't from Virginia) comes immediately before the name of the young woman whose roommate's poster shows Cory lying in a field with a pensive expression on his face.

		ROOMMATE						STATE						POSTER					
		IRENE	JANE	KIM	LIZABETH	RACHEL	SAMANTHA	DELAWARE	FLORIDA	MICHIGAN	OHIO	VIRGINIA	WASHINGTON	CONVERTIBLE	EIFFEL TOWER	LYING IN A FIELD	OSCARS	PLAYING GUITAR	SURFING
YOUNG WOMAN	IRENE																		
	JANE																		
	KIM																		
	LIZABETH																		
	RACHEL																		
	SAMANTHA																		
POSTER	CONVERTIBLE																		
	EIFFEL TOWER																		
	LYING IN A FIELD																		
	OSCARS																		
	PLAYING GUITAR																		
	SURFING																		
STATE	DELAWARE																		
	FLORIDA																		
	MICHIGAN																		
	OHIO																		
	VIRGINIA																		
	WASHINGTON																		

LOGIC PROBLEM 91

After work on Tuesday, five coworkers from the Sacramento Arts & Crafts Center paid a visit to the Delightfully Delicious Dessert Depot—a shop specializing in unusual desserts. Each person ordered a different one of the shop's delectable menu choices, no two of which cost the same amount of money. From the information provided, determine the first and last names of each coworker, the dessert (one was a cherry torte) each chose, and the price of each dessert.

1. Jeanne spent exactly $1.00 more than the one surnamed Summers, who paid exactly twice as much as the person who ordered the chocolate soufflé.

2. Gage is neither the one surnamed Khalil nor the one surnamed Mooney.

3. Kay isn't the one who ordered the orange-chiffon cake.

4. The coworker who ordered the Bavarian cream spent exactly $2.00 more than the one surnamed Little, who spent exactly twice as much as Marcus.

5. Eleanor didn't spend the least amount of money.

6. The person surnamed Steging spent exactly twice as much as Kay, who spent exactly twice as much as the one who ordered the strawberries Romanoff.

7. The total bill for the desserts was over $12.00.

8. Neither Kay nor Marcus is surnamed Khalil.

9. The one surnamed Steging didn't order the chocolate soufflé.

		LAST NAME					DESSERT					PRICE				
		KHALIL	LITTLE	MOONEY	STEGING	SUMMERS	BAVARIAN CREAM	CHERRY TORTE	CHOCOLATE SOUFFLE	ORANGE-CHIFFON CAKE	STRAWBERRIES ROMANOFF					
FIRST NAME	ELEANOR															
	GAGE															
	JEANNE															
	KAY															
	MARCUS															
PRICE																
DESSERT	BAVARIAN CREAM															
	CHERRY TORTE															
	CHOC. SOUFFLE															
	ORANGE-CHIFFON															
	STRAWBERRIES															

LOGIC PROBLEM 92

When the one-of-a-kind Hoopla Diamond was discovered missing from the National Gallery, Headquarters knew only one man could retrieve it—Kirk Bonaventure. Quickly deducing that the diamond was in Vilnius or one of five other cities of the former U.S.S.R., the super secret agent visited each city in turn. Bonaventure was aided by a different Russian agent and spent a different amount of money in each city. As he searched with each agent, the ultra-dapper Bonaventure had to overcome a different obstacle (in one case, a clumsy waiter spilled coffee on his sleeve, staining the cuff). From the information provided, determine the agent who accompanied Bonaventure in each city, his total expenses ($30, $70, $120, $160, $210, or $250) while there, and the obstacle he had to overcome.

1. Agent Fyodor assisted Bonaventure in the city where his expenses totaled $70. In the city where he acquired the fake diamond made out of quartz (which wasn't acquired on Friday), Bonaventure encountered a setback when he attempted to check in to his hotel—he found it booked!

2. In Riga (where he acquired the fake diamond made of ice), Bonaventure's expenses were exactly $40 less than in the city where he was aided by Agent Vhorishkova. While with Vhorishkova, Bonaventure set his watch at a time that was exactly four hours before the setting he used in the city where his expenses totaled $250.

3. Bonaventure visited Odessa (where he was assisted by Agent Luvaduvsky) exactly two days after he visited the city where the Hoopla Diamond turned out to be a piece of rock candy.

4. In Moscow (where calamity struck when a waiter brought red wine instead of white to accompany Bonaventure's fish dinner), Bonaventure spent exactly $50 less than he did in Odessa. Moscow wasn't the city in which Bonaventure acquired the fake plastic diamond.

		CITY						EXPENSES						OBSTACLE					
		KIEV	MOSCOW	ODESSA	RIGA	ST. PETERSBURG	VILNIUS	$30	$70	$120	$160	$210	$250	FLAT TIRE	HOTEL BOOKED	MARTINI STIRRED	RED WINE	SILLY HAT	STAINED CUFF
AGENT	BULGAKOV																		
	FYODOR																		
	GOODNIK																		
	KINSKI																		
	LUVADUVSKY																		
	VHORISHKOVA																		
OBSTACLE	FLAT TIRE																		
	HOTEL BOOKED																		
	MARTINI STIRRED																		
	RED WINE																		
	SILLY HAT																		
	STAINED CUFF																		
EXPENSES	$30																		
	$70																		
	$120																		
	$160																		
	$210																		
	$250																		

*This is part 1 of a two-part puzzle. It is necessary to work back and forth between this part and part 2 on page 101 in order to solve the puzzle.

LOGIC PROBLEM 93

As secret agent Kirk Bonaventure combed Eastern Europe with the assistance of six Russian agents (each of whom helped him on a different day), he acquired a diamond in each city. While he did find the Hoopla Diamond, he also acquired five fake diamonds. Fortunately, the gemologist back at Headquarters was able to determine the real diamond from the different material from which each fake was made. While with each agent, Bonaventure escaped trouble by using a different feature on his gadget-packed wristwatch; he activated each feature by setting his watch to a different time. From the information provided, determine the agent who accompanied Bonaventure when he acquired each diamond, the watch setting (5:00, 6:00, 7:00, 9:00, 10:00, or 11:00) he used while with each agent, and the day (Monday through Saturday) on which he was aided by each agent.

1. In St. Petersburg, Bonaventure operated his watch at a setting that was exactly two hours before the setting he used while with Agent Kinski (who accompanied him in the city he visited the day after visiting St. Petersburg).

2. Agent Goodnik didn't accompany Bonaventure in the city where he acquired the fake diamond made out of rock candy (which wasn't in the city in which his expenses totaled $160).

3. Bonaventure was aided by Agent Bulgakov in the city he visited exactly two days after the one in which it was his misfortune to wear a silly hat as a disguise. When Bonaventure was with Bulgakov, he operated his watch at a setting that was exactly two hours after the setting he used while wearing the silly hat.

4. Bonaventure visited the city in which he was served a martini that was stirred (rather than shaken) the day before he visited the city in which his car had a flat tire. He used a later watch setting in the first of these two cities than he did in the second.

5. In Kiev (where he operated his watch at 10:00), Bonaventure's expenses were greater than in the city he visited on Monday but less than in the city where he was aided by Agent Kinski (with whom he acquired the fake glass diamond).

		DIAMOND						SETTING						DAY					
		GLASS	HOOPLA	ICE	PLASTIC	QUARTZ	ROCK CANDY	5:00 p.m.	6:00 p.m.	7:00 p.m.	9:00 p.m.	10:00 p.m.	11:00 p.m.	MONDAY	TUESDAY	WEDNESDAY	THURSDAY	FRIDAY	SATURDAY
AGENT	BULGAKOV																		
	FYODOR																		
	GOODNIK																		
	KINSKI																		
	LUVADUVSKY																		
	VHORISHKOVA																		
DAY	MONDAY																		
	TUESDAY																		
	WEDNESDAY																		
	THURSDAY																		
	FRIDAY																		
	SATURDAY																		
SETTING	5:00 p.m.																		
	6:00 p.m.																		
	7:00 p.m.																		
	9:00 p.m.																		
	10:00 p.m.																		
	11:00 p.m.																		

*This is part 2 of a two-part puzzle. It is necessary to work back and forth between this part and part 1 on page 100 in order to solve the puzzle.

LOGIC PROBLEM 94

It was an active Saturday for John and four of his friends (one of whom—Andrew—is a man, and three of whom—Diane, Katie, and Sally—are women), when each went hiking in the morning and swimming at the YMCA in the afternoon. No two hiked for the same period of time, and no two swam for the same period of time. After all this daytime activity, each passed the evening in a different quiet, solitary pursuit (one watched a movie on television). From the information provided, can you determine the period of time (8:45 a.m.-1:00 p.m., 9:00 a.m.-12:45 p.m., 9:15 a.m.-12:30 p.m., 9:30 a.m.-1:30 p.m., or 9:45 a.m.-12:30 p.m.) during which each person hiked, the period of time (2:15-4:15 p.m., 2:45-4:00 p.m., 2:45-4:30 p.m., 3:15-4:45 p.m., or 3:45-5:00 p.m.) during which each person swam, and the activity with which each passed the evening?

1. The person who went for an evening drive finished his or her hike exactly 15 minutes after Katie.

2. The one who put together a jigsaw puzzle in the evening (who spent the same amount of time in the pool as another person) completed his or her hike earlier than Andrew.

3. The person who passed the evening quietly with a good book spent exactly 90 more minutes hiking than swimming.

4. Diane, who came in from the pool before 4:30, finished her hike at 12:30, as did a person who swam for exactly 90 minutes.

5. The man who spent the evening solving crossword puzzles spent more time in the pool than the other man.

6. Katie felt cold and got out of the pool while Sally was still in it.

		HIKING					SWIMMING					ACTIVITY				
		8:45 a.m.-1:00 p.m.	9:00 a.m.-12:45 p.m.	9:15 a.m.-12:30 p.m.	9:30 a.m.-1:30 p.m.	9:45 a.m.-12:30 p.m.	2:15-4:15 p.m.	2:45-4:00 p.m.	2:45-4:30 p.m.	3:15-4:45 p.m.	3:45-5:00 p.m.	BOOK	CROSSWORD PUZZLES	DRIVE	JIGSAW PUZZLE	MOVIE
PERSON	ANDREW															
	DIANE															
	JOHN															
	KATIE															
	SALLY															
ACTIVITY	BOOK															
	CROSSWORD															
	DRIVE															
	JIGSAW PUZZLE															
	MOVIE															
SWIMMING	2:15-4:15 p.m.															
	2:45-4:00 p.m.															
	2:45-4:30 p.m.															
	3:15-4:45 p.m.															
	3:45-5:00 p.m.															

The Wiggins Foundation flew six high-school students, each of whom lives in a different state, to New York to compete for the Talented Teen Scholarship. Each student performed a different talent for the judges. The students were seen by the judges at 15-minute intervals. From the information provided, can you determine the time (1:00, 1:15, 1:30, 1:45, 2:00, or 2:15 p.m.) that each student (three of whom—Adam, Bill, and Marc—are men, and three of whom—Dina, Faye, and Jane—are women) performed, the talent (one was public speaking) that each demonstrated, and the state (one is Maine) from which each hails, and also determine the winner of the scholarship?

1. Faye, who isn't the pianist, didn't win the scholarship.
2. The young man who danced isn't the student from Iowa.
3. Marc and the magician (both of whom were among the final three students who performed before the judges) are the scholarship winner and the one from Hawaii, in some order.
4. Three students who performed consecutively from first to last are the young man who sang, the student from Utah, and Dina (who isn't the magician).
5. Two of the women performed consecutively, and neither of them won.
6. Adam was the first student to perform.
7. The young man from Texas performed at 1:15.
8. The young man who did stand-up comedy performed immediately before the student from Ohio.

		STUDENT						TALENT						STATE					
		ADAM	BILL	DINA	FAYE	JANE	MARC	COMEDY	DANCING	MAGIC	PIANO PLAYING	PUBLIC SPEAKING	SINGING	HAWAII	IOWA	MAINE	OHIO	TEXAS	UTAH
TIME	1:00 p.m.																		
	1:15 p.m.																		
	1:30 p.m.																		
	1:45 p.m.																		
	2:00 p.m.																		
	2:15 p.m.																		
STATE	HAWAII																		
	IOWA																		
	MAINE																		
	OHIO																		
	TEXAS																		
	UTAH																		
TALENT	COMEDY																		
	DANCING																		
	MAGIC																		
	PIANO PLAYING																		
	PUBLIC SPEAK.																		
	SINGING																		

LOGIC PROBLEM 96

Jason and Peg Wikowski, owners of Renovations, Plus, are organizing a portfolio showcasing their innovative ideas on various projects. For each of five kitchen renovations featured in the portfolio, a different type of cabinet material was used (one kitchen used whitewashed birch). The client for each of these jobs—very pleased with the Wikowskis' work—has agreed to act as a reference (the woman on Carver Way has gone further, recommending the Wikowskis to her friends). Each renovation, which is located on a different street and at a different number (11, 14, 17, 20, or 23), was completed in a different month (March, May, July, September, or November). From the information provided, determine the house number and street where each type of cabinet was used, as well as the month in which each renovation was completed.

1. The renovation completed in May is in a house numbered exactly three higher than the one with the new cherry cabinets, which is numbered exactly three higher than the house on Fir Street.

2. The Rover Street renovation was completed exactly two months before the one involving the stainless-steel cabinets, which was completed exactly two months before the one at number 20.

3. The installation of the knotty-pine cabinets was completed exactly two months before the renovation on Greenway Street.

4. The renovation of the Dayton Street house was completed exactly two months after the one at number 23 (which wasn't the one with the white Formica cabinets).

5. The house on Greenway Street is numbered exactly three higher than the house with the new knotty-pine cabinets.

		HOUSE NUMBER					STREET					MONTH				
		11	14	17	20	23	CARVER WAY	DAYTON STREET	FIR STREET	GREENWAY STREET	ROVER STREET	MARCH	MAY	JULY	SEPTEMBER	NOVEMBER
CABINET	BIRCH															
	CHERRY															
	FORMICA															
	PINE															
	STAINLESS STEEL															
MONTH	MARCH															
	MAY															
	JULY															
	SEPTEMBER															
	NOVEMBER															
STREET	CARVER WAY															
	DAYTON STREET															
	FIR STREET															
	GREENWAY ST.															
	ROVER STREET															

Slim well remembers the day six mysterious strangers rode up to his saloon, since each of these men rode a different unusual animal. Each stranger (two of whom are Bill and Mitch) came from a different town and asked Slim the way to a different establishment (one wanted to know the location of the dentist). After Slim gave his directions, each rode off, never to be seen by Slim again. From the information provided, determine the town (one is Dixon) from which each stranger came, the animal on which he rode, and the establishment to which he asked directions.

1. The six strangers are the only man whose first-name initial is the same as the initial of the town from which he came, a man whose first-name initial is the same as the initial of the animal he rode, the only man who rode the animal with the same initial as the town from which he came, the one who rode the mule, the one who rode the camel, and the one who asked for directions to the hotel.

2. Evan and the one who rode the elephant asked for directions to the judge and directions to the sheriff, in some order.

3. Drake and the one who rode the donkey are from Brockton and Chadwick, in some order.

4. Zeke and the one from Zalestown asked for directions to the bank and directions to the hotel, in some order.

5. The one from Edgehill and the one who asked for directions to the lawyer rode the camel and the buffalo, in some order.

6. Chet and the one who asked for directions to the judge are the one from Mortville and the one who rode the zebra, in some order.

		TOWN						ANIMAL						ESTABLISHMENT					
		BROCKTON	CHADWICK	DIXON	EDGEHILL	MORTVILLE	ZALESTOWN	BUFFALO	CAMEL	DONKEY	ELEPHANT	MULE	ZEBRA	BANK	DENTIST	HOTEL	JUDGE	LAWYER	SHERIFF
STRANGER	BILL																		
	CHET																		
	DRAKE																		
	EVAN																		
	MITCH																		
	ZEKE																		
ESTABLISHMENT	BANK																		
	DENTIST																		
	HOTEL																		
	JUDGE																		
	LAWYER																		
	SHERIFF																		
ANIMAL	BUFFALO																		
	CAMEL																		
	DONKEY																		
	ELEPHANT																		
	MULE																		
	ZEBRA																		

LOGIC PROBLEM 98 LOVE, SANTA

Every Christmas, Hayley and four of her friends pick up letters to Santa Claus from the dead-letter office and respond, as Santa, to the children who wrote them. This year, each friend sent a different number of responses, which he or she wrote on decorated holiday stationery. Each person used the same stationery for all of his or her letters, and no two people used stationery with the same design. From the information provided, determine the first and last names of each person, the stationery each used (one wrote on stationery decorated with snowmen), and the number of letters each person wrote.

1. Virgil, who isn't the one whose stationery is decorated with stockings hanging by a fireplace, wrote exactly 2 more letters than the one surnamed Stover. Becky is neither the one surnamed Flint nor the one surnamed Orndorff.

2. Exactly 5 fewer letters were written on the Christmas-tree stationery than on the reindeer stationery. Jack wrote exactly twice as many letters as Al. Virgil (whose stationery wasn't decorated with either Christmas trees or reindeer) isn't the one who wrote exactly 10 letters.

3. A total of 51 letters were written, and each person wrote at least 6 letters. Neither the friend surnamed Miller (who isn't Becky) nor the one surnamed Hupp wrote the most letters.

4. Al isn't the one who used stationery decorated with steaming cups of hot cocoa. The one surnamed Stover didn't write his or her letters on Christmas-tree stationery.

5. Al didn't write his letters on the stationery decorated with stockings.

6. Virgil isn't surnamed Miller. Flint didn't use reindeer stationery.

		LAST NAME					STATIONERY					LETTERS				
		FLINT	HUPP	MILLER	ORNDORFF	STOVER	CHRISTMAS TREES	HOT COCOA	REINDEER	SNOWMEN	STOCKINGS					
FIRST NAME	AL															
	BECKY															
	HAYLEY															
	JACK															
	VIRGIL															
LETTERS																
STATIONERY	CHRISTMAS TREE															
	HOT COCOA															
	REINDEER															
	SNOWMEN															
	STOCKINGS															

The Easter Bunny has reduced his workload this year by delegating some of his duties to five of his children. Each bunny will be responsible for delivering brightly colored Easter eggs to a different state (in one case, Virginia) and hiding them in a different type of location (one intends to conceal eggs in bushes). No two bunnies are delivering eggs of the same color (one is delivering purple eggs). From the information provided, determine the color of the eggs each bunny is delivering, as well as the state to which each is delivering and the type of hiding place each plans to use.

1. Flopsy isn't the bunny delivering eggs to Pennsylvania. Neither Flopsy (who isn't hiding eggs in trees) nor Hoppy is either the one hiding red eggs or the one hiding pink eggs.

2. The green eggs are neither the ones that will be hidden in trees nor the ones that will be hidden on house porches. Mopsy's eggs aren't red.

3. Neither Mopsy (who won't be delivering eggs to Alabama) nor Hoppy (who won't be visiting either Alabama or Pennsylvania) will hide eggs either in trees or on windowsills.

4. Porches aren't the chosen hiding spot of either the bunny delivering eggs to Maine (which isn't the state receiving the yellow eggs) or the one making deliveries to Pennsylvania. The eggs destined for Alabama won't be hidden on windowsills.

5. Fluffy will be delivering eggs to Texas. Cottontail's green eggs are neither the ones that will be concealed in mailboxes nor the ones that will be hidden on windowsills.

		COLOR					STATE					HIDING PLACE				
		GREEN	PINK	PURPLE	RED	YELLOW	ALABAMA	MAINE	PENNSYLVANIA	VIRGINIA	TEXAS	BUSHES	MAILBOXES	PORCHES	TREES	WINDOWSILLS
BUNNY	COTTONTAIL															
	FLOPSY															
	FLUFFY															
	HOPPY															
	MOPSY															
HIDING PLACE	BUSHES															
	MAILBOXES															
	PORCHES															
	TREES															
	WINDOWSILLS															
STATE	ALABAMA															
	MAINE															
	PENNSYLVANIA															
	VIRGINIA															
	TEXAS															

LOGIC PROBLEM 100   EVERY BLOOMING THING

When Karen had her baby, she was overwhelmed with flowers, till there was hardly enough space in her hospital room to put them all! In addition to the flowers sent by her husband and various relatives, each of five friends (including Carol) brought her a different, enormous floral arrangement (one was the New Addition arrangement), each of which featured a different type of rose (including Mascotte roses), which is Karen's favorite type of flower. Each floral arrangement also came with a different small gift (two were a basket and a mug). From the information provided, can you determine the arrangement each friend brought, as well as the type of rose featured in each arrangement and the gift that accompanied it?

1. Neither Nadine nor Norma brought the arrangement with the Charleston roses (which came with a stuffed animal).

2. The Mother's Joy arrangement brought by Maisie (which wasn't accompanied by a figurine) wasn't the one that featured the Charleston roses.

3. The Important Arrival arrangement featured Mermaid roses. Jelcanodir roses came in the same arrangement as the figurine (which wasn't in the Family Celebration arrangement). Norma brought the Family Celebration arrangement, which came with a gift that comes alphabetically after the gift attached to the It's a Girl! arrangement.

4. Agnes's arrangement was accompanied by a balloon. The arrangement with the Fragrant Cloud roses wasn't the Family Celebration arrangement.

		ARRANGEMENT					ROSE					GIFT				
		FAMILY CELEBRATION	IMPORTANT ARRIVAL	IT'S A GIRL!	MOTHER'S JOY	NEW ADDITION	CHARLESTON	FRAGRANT CLOUD	JELCANODIR	MASCOTTE	MERMAID	BALLOON	BASKET	FIGURINE	MUG	STUFFED ANIMAL
FRIEND	AGNES															
	CAROL															
	MAISIE															
	NADINE															
	NORMA															
GIFT	BALLOON															
	BASKET															
	FIGURINE															
	MUG															
	STUFFED ANIMAL															
ROSE	CHARLESTON															
	FRAGRANT CLOUD															
	JELCANODIR															
	MASCOTTE															
	MERMAID															

INTO THE WOODS

LOGIC PROBLEM 101

Every so often, members of the Great Outdoors Club meet to discuss travel experiences. At the last meeting, each of five members (including Frank) spoke about the trip he or she had taken to a different national forest (including Colville National Forest in Washington) within the past six months. Each person had visited the forest with a different relative (one brought his or her daughter). While there, each had enjoyed a different activity (one did a little fishing). From the information provided, determine the national forest each member visited, the activity in which each participated, and the relative by whom each was accompanied.

1. Nathan went to Bridger-Teton National Forest in Wyoming, but not with his sister.
2. Hannah had nothing but good things to report about her trip to Flathead National Forest in Montana. Rita (who spoke about her biking trip) isn't the person who journeyed to Idaho's Sawtooth National Forest (which is where one club member took his or her son).
3. One person went cross-country skiing with his or her sister. The one who visited Mount Hood National Forest in Oregon went hiking.
4. One person had a fantastic time snowshoeing with his or her spouse. Quinn traveled with his brother.

		NATIONAL FOREST					ACTIVITY					RELATIVE				
		BRIDGER-TETON	COLVILLE	FLATHEAD	MOUNT HOOD	SAWTOOTH	BIKING	CROSS-COUNTRY SKIING	FISHING	HIKING	SNOWSHOEING	BROTHER	DAUGHTER	SISTER	SON	SPOUSE
MEMBER	FRANK															
	HANNAH															
	NATHAN															
	QUINN															
	RITA															
RELATIVE	BROTHER															
	DAUGHTER															
	SISTER															
	SON															
	SPOUSE															
ACTIVITY	BIKING															
	CROSS-COUNTRY															
	FISHING															
	HIKING															
	SNOWSHOEING															

LOGIC PROBLEM 102

PUPPY MISCHIEF

The eyes of five of the children on Mulberry Street grew wide with delight on Christmas morning when each discovered a red-bowed puppy frolicking under his or her tree. Each puppy (no two of whom are the same breed) was immediately given a different knightly name (one is called Gawain) by his or her new master. Each puppy has a different peculiar trait which his or her owner quickly grew to love. From the information provided, determine the puppy that belongs to each child, as well as each puppy's breed and endearing trait (one chews on sticks).

1. Guenevere likes to bark at the doorbell. Percival is the collie. Todd's puppy likes to chase his or her tail. Sarah's dog is the Doberman.

2. Jennifer's dog is neither the Labrador (who likes to dig holes in the backyard) nor the dog who fetches (who isn't Sarah's dog).

3. Simon's puppy is named Arthur. Craig's dog is neither the Labrador nor the Scottish terrier (who isn't owned by Jennifer). Lancelot isn't the Chihuahua or the Scottish terrier.

		PUPPY					BREED					TRAIT				
		ARTHUR	GAWAIN	GUENEVERE	LANCELOT	PERCIVAL	CHIHUAHUA	COLLIE	DOBERMAN	LABRADOR	SCOTTISH TERRIER	BARKS AT DOORBELL	CHASES TAIL	CHEWS ON STICKS	DIGS HOLES	FETCHES
CHILD	CRAIG															
	JENNIFER															
	SARAH															
	SIMON															
	TODD															
TRAIT	BARKS															
	CHASES TAIL															
	CHEWS ON STICKS															
	DIGS HOLES															
	FETCHES															
BREED	CHIHUAHUA															
	COLLIE															
	DOBERMAN															
	LABRADOR															
	SCOTTISH TER.															

LOGIC PROBLEM 103

Although Beth and four of her friends have made several trips to Las Vegas in the intervening years, they all agreed that their first visit was the most enjoyable, since all of them came out ahead at the casinos! Each person played a different game (one played video poker), and each walked away with a different amount of winnings ($100, $125, $150, $175, or $200). To celebrate his or her good fortune, each person spent part of his or her winnings on tickets for a different celebrity show. From the information provided, can you determine the game each person played and the amount each won, as well as the show each enjoyed?

1. The roulette player won more money than the craps player but less than the person who won on the slot machines (who did not win the most money).

2. Veronica won more money than the one who saw Wayne Newton. The craps player's winnings did not total $100.

3. Nancy did not see David Copperfield. The person who went to see the Elvis Presley impersonator won more than the one who saw Tom Jones. The one who enjoyed the magic of Siegfried & Roy did not win the most money.

4. Eldon and the person who won $200 (who was not the blackjack player) are the ones who saw David Copperfield and Siegfried & Roy, in some order.

5. Steve and Veronica (neither of whom won at craps) are the ones who saw Tom Jones and Wayne Newton, in some order.

		GAME					AMOUNT					SHOW				
		BLACKJACK	CRAPS	ROULETTE	SLOT MACHINES	VIDEO POKER	$100	$125	$150	$175	$200	DAVID COPPERFIELD	ELVIS PRESLEY IMPERSONATOR	SIEGFRIED & ROY	TOM JONES	WAYNE NEWTON
PERSON	BETH															
	ELDON															
	NANCY															
	STEVE															
	VERONICA															
SHOW	D. COPPERFIELD															
	ELVIS PRESLEY															
	SIEGFRIED & ROY															
	TOM JONES															
	WAYNE NEWTON															
AMOUNT	$100															
	$125															
	$150															
	$175															
	$200															

LOGIC PROBLEM 104   A BIT SHORT-HANDED

When her secretary went for a week's vacation to Barbados, Ms. Jamison relied on the trusty men and women of the company's steno pool to take dictation for her. Each weekday, the pool sent a different stenographer to take dictation for Ms. Jamison. Although no two stenographers use the same method of shorthand (one uses Speedwriting), all were very efficient. In fact, each steno made only one tiny error—each omitted a different punctuation mark from a letter Ms. Jamison dictated that day. From the information provided, determine the weekday each steno took dictation from Ms. Jamison, the method of shorthand each uses, and the punctuation mark he or she omitted from a letter.

1. Clifford is neither the one who left out a comma (who uses the Pitman method) nor the one who omitted an apostrophe.

2. Dwight (who omitted a dash) is neither the one who took dictation on Monday nor the one who uses the Alphabet shorthand method. The one who took dictation on Friday omitted a question mark.

3. Eunice (who didn't omit an apostrophe or a semicolon) uses the Landmark method of shorthand. The one who took dictation on Tuesday is neither the one who omitted a dash nor the one who omitted a semicolon.

4. Pearl didn't omit an apostrophe. The steno who uses the Gregg method didn't take dictation on Wednesday. Mae took dictation on Thursday.

		WEEKDAY					METHOD					PUNCTUATION MARK				
		MONDAY	TUESDAY	WEDNESDAY	THURSDAY	FRIDAY	ALPHABET	GREGG	LANDMARK	PITMAN	SPEEDWRITING	APOSTROPHE	COMMA	DASH	QUESTION MARK	SEMICOLON
STENO	CLIFFORD															
	DWIGHT															
	EUNICE															
	MAE															
	PEARL															
PUNCTUATION	APOSTROPHE															
	COMMA															
	DASH															
	QUESTION MARK															
	SEMICOLON															
METHOD	ALPHABET															
	GREGG															
	LANDMARK															
	PITMAN															
	SPEEDWRITING															

Since the first-grade classes are starting a new unit on shapes and textures, each of the five first-grade teachers at Highview Elementary School (including Mr. Ingels) has decorated his or her bulletin board with a different geometric shape, each of which is a different texture (one is fuzzy). The students in each class (each of which is identified by a different figure on the class-room door) really enjoy touching the shapes. From the information provided, determine the geometric shape on each teacher's bulletin board, the texture of that shape, and the figure (one is a hand) on each teacher's door.

1. The man who teaches the apple class (who isn't the teacher with the sandy-textured shape on his or her bulletin board) isn't the one with the oval on his or her bulletin board. The shape on Ms. Jerrin's bulletin board is neither sandy-textured nor smooth-textured. The circle is on a woman's bulletin board.

2. Mr. Keyes has the spongy-textured shape on his bulletin board. The teacher of the leaf class (which has the most students) doesn't have the spongy-textured shape on his or her bulletin board.

3. Ms. Gentry's class (which doesn't have the most students) has recess at 11:00 a.m. The class of the male teacher who has the triangle on his bulletin board has recess at 11:00 a.m. The triangle isn't the wrinkly-textured shape.

4. Both Mr. Keyes's class and the book class have recess at 11:30 a.m. The class with the square on its bulletin board has recess at 11:45 a.m.

5. Mr. Keyes isn't the teacher of the pencil class.

6. The three female teachers are the one with the smooth-textured shape on her bulletin board, Ms. Hope, and the one whose bulletin board has the rectangle.

		SHAPE					TEXTURE					FIGURE				
		CIRCLE	OVAL	RECTANGLE	SQUARE	TRIANGLE	FUZZY	SANDY	SMOOTH	SPONGY	WRINKLY	APPLE	BOOK	HAND	LEAF	PENCIL
TEACHER	MS. GENTRY															
	MS. HOPE															
	MR. INGELS															
	MS. JERRIN															
	MR. KEYES															
FIGURE	APPLE															
	BOOK															
	HAND															
	LEAF															
	PENCIL															
TEXTURE	FUZZY															
	SANDY															
	SMOOTH															
	SPONGY															
	WRINKLY															

LOGIC PROBLEM 106 **CHARMED LIFE**

Ladies and gentlemen! The show is about to begin! Observe as the mysterious Ophelia Ophidian, sultana of serpents, regina of reptiles, arranges before her five baskets, each made of a different material. Bear witness as she produces from her silken robes five different woodwinds! Be dazzled as, with each instrument, the opulent Ophelia tantalizes and teases a different type of serpent from each basket! Behold as, at the sound of his name (each has a different name—one is Monty), each serpent hisses for Ophelia! See now, from the information provided, if you can determine the name of each type of snake as it arises from its basket, as well as the type of woodwind instrument by which each serpent is mesmerized!

1. The serpent charmed by the concert flute is not the taipan. Ouroboros arises from a nylon basket. The rattlesnake isn't charmed by Ophelia's clarinet.

2. Kaa isn't the snake in the acrylic basket (who isn't the cobra). The serpent hypnotized by the piccolo (who isn't the one in the acrylic basket) isn't Kaa. The serpent in the wool basket (who isn't the one mesmerized by the bass flute) is not the rattlesnake.

3. Yig (who isn't the taipan) rises from his basket only to the strains of the clarinet. The taipan is neither the serpent in the jute basket nor the one hypnotized by the recorder. Satha, the anaconda, isn't in the acrylic basket.

4. The black mamba is charmed by Ophelia's piccolo. The serpent in the cotton basket (who isn't the snake wooed by the rhythm of the recorder) isn't Kaa.

		SNAKE					BASKET					WOODWIND				
		ANACONDA	BLACK MAMBA	COBRA	RATTLESNAKE	TAIPAN	ACRYLIC	COTTON	JUTE	NYLON	WOOL	BASS FLUTE	CLARINET	CONCERT FLUTE	PICCOLO	RECORDER
NAME	KAA															
	MONTY															
	OUROBOROS															
	SATHA															
	YIG															
WOODWIND	BASS FLUTE															
	CLARINET															
	CONCERT FLUTE															
	PICCOLO															
	RECORDER															
BASKET	ACRYLIC															
	COTTON															
	JUTE															
	NYLON															
	WOOL															

LOGIC PROBLEM 107

After many long hours on the road last night, five long-haul truck drivers stopped at the Easy Exit Truck Stop for a cup of joe and a snack. Midway through their slices of apple pie, they fell into conversation, whereupon they discovered that each was carrying a different cargo. In addition, they found that each had started his trip in a different city (Denver, Des Moines, Duluth, Los Angeles, or Raleigh) and was bound for a different destination (Fresno, Houston, Phoenix, Portland, or Topeka). "Well, time for me to hit the road," one driver said. "That load of metal roofing isn't going to deliver itself." From the comments reported below, can you determine each driver's starting city, destination city, and the cargo each was hauling?

1. "When I left Des Moines, it had just starting snowing," reported Will. "Yeah," Luther responded, "it was snowing when I left Duluth, too. I may just stay an extra day when I get my load to sunny Phoenix."

2. "Are you hauling electronic equipment again?" Tullis asked the driver from Los Angeles. "No, it's aircraft parts," that driver answered. "I'm the one hauling electronic equipment this time," piped up Ramon, adding, "I'll be glad when I finally get it to Houston."

3. "I left Raleigh early yesterday with a load of kitchen cabinets," one driver told Luther. A third driver, who was listening, volunteered, "Well, I'm hauling a load of farm machinery this trip—I sure am glad I don't have to go all the way up to Portland."

4. "So long, fellows," said Mack, "I've got to get going if I'm going to get my load to Topeka by midnight."

		STARTING CITY					DESTINATION CITY					CARGO				
		DENVER	DES MOINES	DULUTH	LOS ANGELES	RALEIGH	FRESNO	HOUSTON	PHOENIX	PORTLAND	TOPEKA	AIRCRAFT PARTS	ELECTRONIC EQUIPMENT	FARM MACHINERY	KITCHEN CABINETS	METAL ROOFING
DRIVER	LUTHER															
	MACK															
	RAMON															
	TULLIS															
	WILL															
CARGO	AIRCRAFT PARTS															
	ELECTRONIC															
	FARM MACHINERY															
	KITCHEN															
	METAL ROOFING															
DESTINATION	FRESNO															
	HOUSTON															
	PHOENIX															
	PORTLAND															
	TOPEKA															

LOGIC PROBLEM 108

When five born-and-bred South Philadelphia friends returned to the old neighborhood for a mini-reunion, each also brought a surprise—his or her new significant other! Each of the friends (three of whom—Anthony, Louis, and Vincenzo—are men, and two of whom—Marissa and Roberta—are women) was raised on a different corner (8th, 9th, 10th, 12th, or 13th Street) of Passyunk Avenue in the heart of South Philly, and each took great delight in showing his girlfriend or her boyfriend a different Philadelphia landmark. Each also took his or her date to a different locally famous restaurant (including Bookbinder's) for lunch or dinner. From the information provided, determine the person who took his or her date to see each Philadelphia landmark and to dine at each renowned restaurant, as well as the corner of Passyunk Avenue on which each was raised.

1. The one who took his or her date to the Dock Street Brewery for dinner lived on a corner numbered exactly 3 lower than the street on which Louis was raised.

2. One of the men took his date to the Philadelphia Museum of Art, while a woman (who didn't live on either 12th or 13th Street) took her boyfriend to Pat's Steaks for lunch.

3. Neither Anthony nor the one who took his or her date to Dave & Buster's for dinner was raised on the corner of 13th and Passyunk. Marissa isn't the one who took his or her date to South Street.

4. Roberta (who treated her boyfriend to dinner at Le Bec-Fin) didn't live on either 12th or 13th Street. Anthony isn't the man who took his girlfriend to see the sights of Chinatown.

5. Vincenzo lived on a street numbered exactly 1 higher than that of the one who went to the Reading Terminal Market. The one who took his or her significant other to see Independence Hall wasn't raised on the corner of 10th and Passyunk.

		LANDMARK					RESTAURANT					CORNER				
		CHINATOWN	INDEPENDENCE HALL	MUSEUM OF ART	READING TERMINAL	SOUTH STREET	BOOKBINDER'S	DAVE & BUSTER'S	DOCK STREET BREWERY	LE BEC-FIN	PAT'S STEAKS	8th STREET	9th STREET	10th STREET	12th STREET	13th STREET
PERSON	ANTHONY															
	LOUIS															
	MARISSA															
	ROBERTA															
	VINCENZO															
CORNER	8th STREET															
	9th STREET															
	10th STREET															
	12th STREET															
	13th STREET															
RESTAURANT	BOOKBINDER'S															
	DAVE & BUSTER'S															
	DOCK STREET															
	LE BEC-FIN															
	PAT'S STEAKS															

LOGIC PROBLEM 109

When Leora Smith and Tandy Baxter were preparing the chapter entitled Place Names for their book on baby names, they not only conducted extensive research, but also interviewed five couples, each of whom had chosen to name their child after a place that had special meaning to them. Each couple chose a different name—Carlyle, Dallas, Hyatt, Madison, or Montana. From the information provided, determine the order in which the husband (Arley, Brady, Dylan, Pierce, or Slate) and wife (Greta, Julia, Quinn, Randy, or Tabitha) in each couple were interviewed, as well as the name they gave their baby.

1. Pierce is married to Julia's best friend, who isn't Greta (who spent all of her college years at the University of Virginia). Arley and his wife (who became engaged while strolling along the boardwalk in Atlantic City, New Jersey) weren't the first couple to be interviewed.

2. Madison's parents (who named their baby after the New York City street where they became engaged) were interviewed at some point after Quinn and her husband but at some point before Dylan and his wife.

3. Randy and her husband weren't interviewed second. Slate isn't married to Greta. The first couple interviewed (who didn't name their baby Hyatt) aren't Brady and his wife.

4. Brady and his wife aren't the couple who named their baby Dallas after their honeymoon location, who were interviewed immediately after Slate and his wife. Slate and his wife (who isn't Julia) aren't the ones who named their baby Montana after the state where they met while attending college.

5. Quinn and her husband (who aren't Dallas's parents) aren't the couple who were interviewed first. Neither Dylan nor Arley honeymooned in Dallas. Quinn isn't Montana's mother.

		HUSBAND					WIFE					BABY				
		ARLEY	BRADY	DYLAN	PIERCE	SLATE	GRETA	JULIA	QUINN	RANDY	TABITHA	CARLYLE	DALLAS	HYATT	MADISON	MONTANA
ORDER	FIRST															
	SECOND															
	THIRD															
	FOURTH															
	FIFTH															
BABY	CARLYLE															
	DALLAS															
	HYATT															
	MADISON															
	MONTANA															
WIFE	GRETA															
	JULIA															
	QUINN															
	RANDY															
	TABITHA															

LOGIC PROBLEM 110 THE BABY-SITTERS' GUILD

Gina and four of her friends (two of whom—Carl and Lenny—are boys, and two of whom—Lainie and Martha—are girls) have recently completed a baby-sitting course, so they pooled their resources to advertise their newly honed child-care skills. Together, they had fliers printed up with all of their phone numbers, and each also included a different testimonial blurb, including "wonderful," from a previous client describing his or her skills as a sitter. Each distributed the fliers to houses on a different street in their neighborhood, and, within hours, each received a call from a different family who requested his or her services for the coming weekend. From the information provided, determine the blurb each baby-sitter used on the flier, the street (one is Platte Drive) on which each distributed the fliers, and the family who hired each sitter.

1. Carl is either the one who distributed fliers on Oak Drive (who was described as "first rate") or the one who was hired by the Kings (who isn't the one who passed out fliers on Sunleaf Court).

2. The baby-sitter who handed out fliers on Highland Drive (who isn't the one described as "dependable") was hired by the Sellers.

3. Neither the girl who was hired by the Parkers nor the girl described as "terrific" (who isn't Lainie) is the baby-sitter who distributed fliers on Sunleaf Court (who wasn't hired by the Florentines).

4. Of Martha and the one who passed out fliers on Lowell Lane, one was described as being "very mature," and the other was hired by the Benedicts.

5. The baby-sitter described as "terrific" (who isn't the one hired by the Florentines) didn't distribute fliers on Highland Drive.

		BLURB					STREET					FAMILY				
		DEPENDABLE	FIRST RATE	TERRIFIC	VERY MATURE	WONDERFUL	HIGHLAND DRIVE	LOWELL LANE	OAK DRIVE	PLATTE DRIVE	SUNLEAF COURT	BENEDICTS	FLORENTINES	KINGS	PARKERS	SELLERS
BABY-SITTER	CARL															
	GINA															
	LAINIE																
	LENNY																
	MARTHA																
FAMILY	BENEDICTS																
	FLORENTINES																
	KINGS																
	PARKERS																
	SELLERS																
STREET	HIGHLAND DRIVE																
	LOWELL LANE																
	OAK DRIVE																
	PLATTE DRIVE																
	SUNLEAF COURT																

LOGIC PROBLEM 111

After years of urban apartment living, Ty and Lindsay Green were thrilled to finally move into a beautiful little house in the suburbs, complete with a patio and picket fence. Naturally, as soon as the house was ready, they invited five couples from their old building down for a barbecue. Each couple (including the Stollers) complimented their friends on their choice of home and also brought them a different housewarming gift appropriate to their new suburban lifestyle. From the information provided, can you match the husband (Adam, Barry, Jerry, Kurt, or Wayne) and wife (Gail, Judy, Olivia, Sonia, or Yvette) in each couple with their shared surname, as well as with the housewarming gift each couple brought for the Greens?

1. Four of the men are Mr. Tschida, Judy's husband (who isn't Adam), Yvette's husband, and the one who brought the wicker basket.

2. The five women are Ms. Fernandez, Ms. Janello (who isn't married to Kurt), Barry's wife, Jerry's wife, and the one who brought the wicker basket.

3. Olivia (who isn't Ms. Locklear) isn't married to Kurt. Gail and her husband (who isn't Adam) brought the houseplant.

4. The couples who brought the gardening tools and the wind chimes are Jerry and his wife and Sonia and her husband, in some order.

5. Yvette is neither the woman who brought the magazine rack nor the one who brought the gardening tools. Adam and his wife didn't bring the wicker basket.

		WIFE					SURNAME					GIFT				
		GAIL	JUDY	OLIVIA	SONIA	YVETTE	FERNANDEZ	JANELLO	LOCKLEAR	STOLLER	TSCHIDA	GARDENING TOOLS	HOUSEPLANT	MAGAZINE RACK	WICKER BASKET	WIND CHIMES
HUSBAND	ADAM															
	BARRY															
	JERRY															
	KURT															
	WAYNE															
GIFT	GARDENING															
	HOUSEPLANT															
	MAGAZINE RACK															
	WICKER BASKET															
	WIND CHIMES															
SURNAME	FERNANDEZ															
	JANELLO															
	LOCKLEAR															
	STOLLER															
	TSCHIDA															

LOGIC PROBLEM 112　　　CHOPPER POWER

It was a typically busy day for Skip Tracer, test pilot, as he ran test flights for five different helicopters (including the Typhon) produced by Falcon Industries. Each helicopter was designed for a different use (one was designed to deliver cargo to offshore oil drills), and Skip flew each helicopter for a different number of minutes (10, 20, 25, 40, or 50). From the information provided, determine the order in which Skip flew each helicopter, the use for which each helicopter was designed, and the number of minutes each flight lasted.

1. Skip flew the Xanthus at some point before flying the helicopter designed for crop-dusting and at some point after taking the 50-minute test flight.
2. His test flight for the Zephyrus was exactly twice as long as his test flight for the helicopter designed to observe volcanoes.
3. The Aeolus is designed for aiding workers at construction sites.
4. He flew the traffic helicopter, which isn't the Leto, for exactly half as long as he flew the fifth one and longer than he flew the crop-dusting one.
5. He flew the Zephyrus at some point after taking the 20-minute test flight.

		HELICOPTER					USE					MINUTES				
		AEOLUS	LETO	TYPHON	XANTHUS	ZEPHYRUS	CONSTRUCTION SITE	CROP-DUSTING	DELIVER CARGO	TRAFFIC	VOLCANOES	10	20	25	40	50
ORDER	FIRST															
	SECOND															
	THIRD															
	FOURTH															
	FIFTH															
MINUTES	10															
	20															
	25															
	40															
	50															
USE	CONSTRUCTION															
	CROP-DUSTING															
	DELIVER CARGO															
	TRAFFIC															
	VOLCANOES															

LOGIC PROBLEM 113

"Congratulations, Mr. Quintero," said the maternity-ward nurse, "you have a new baby girl . . . and a new baby boy, and a new baby girl, and a new baby boy, and a new baby girl!" "Well," thought the slightly dazed father, "looks like I'm going to need more cigars!" In the end, Mr. Quintero bought five boxes of cigars—one box to celebrate the birth of each child. Each box contained a different brand of cigars (one held Jirafa cigars), and each cost a different amount ($14, $16, $18, $20, or $22). From the information provided, can you determine the order in which each of the quintuplets (including Jan) was born, as well as the brand of cigar Mr. Quintero bought to celebrate each one's birth and the price per box of each brand? (Note: Babies were not necessarily born in the order in which they were announced.)

1. The Pasillo cigars (which were not the ones Mr. Quintero bought to celebrate the birth of his second child) cost less per box than the ones bought to celebrate Dan's birth.

2. The cigars Mr. Quintero bought to celebrate Fran's birth cost more per box than the Alianza cigars.

3. The cigars Mr. Quintero bought to celebrate the birth of his fourth child, Anne, cost more than the Olimpico cigars but less than at least two other brands.

4. The cigars Mr. Quintero bought to celebrate the birth of his first child cost exactly $4 more per box than those he bought to celebrate the birth of his third child (who isn't Stan).

5. The five brands of cigars are the Salvados, the ones Mr. Quintero bought to celebrate Stan's birth, the ones he bought to celebrate the birth of the second quintuplet, the box that cost $14, and the ones that cost $22.

		QUINTUPLET					CIGAR					PRICE				
		ANNE	DAN	FRAN	JAN	STAN	ALIANZA	JIRAFA	OLIMPICO	PASILLO	SALVADO	$14	$16	$18	$20	$22
ORDER	FIRST															
	SECOND																
	THIRD																
	FOURTH																
	FIFTH																
PRICE	$14																
	$16																
	$18																
	$20																
	$22																
CIGAR	ALIANZA																
	JIRAFA																
	OLIMPICO																
	PASILLO																
	SALVADO																

LOGIC PROBLEM 114 CRAZY CAPERS

Shooting is right on schedule for Pinnacle Studio's latest slapstick comedy, *Crazy Capers*. In the fast-paced scene being filmed today, the five main characters (including the kooky bank robber) are running in and out of rooms in a hotel hallway. One by one, each character enters the hallway through a different door (3 through 7) and immediately exits through one of those same five doors. No two characters exit through the same door. From the information provided, determine the order in which each character appears in the hallway, as well as the door through which each enters and the door through which each exits.

1. The scientist exits through door seven. The one who enters through door three exits through door four.

2. The one who enters through door four appears immediately after the sea captain and immediately before the character who exits through door five.

3. The policeman is the third character to appear. The one who enters through door five is the second character to appear.

4. The cook makes an appearance at some point after the character who enters through door seven (who appears immediately after the one who exits through door six).

		CHARACTER					ENTERS					EXITS				
		BANK ROBBER	COOK	POLICEMAN	SCIENTIST	SEA CAPTAIN	3	4	5	6	7	3	4	5	6	7
ORDER	FIRST															
	SECOND															
	THIRD															
	FOURTH															
	FIFTH															
EXITS	3															
	4															
	5															
	6															
	7															
ENTERS	3															
	4															
	5															
	6															
	7															

LOGIC PROBLEM 115

Remember the Hula-Hoop? For a brief period in the 1950s, that little gizmo was seemingly everywhere, and, at $1.99 a pop, it made its creators very rich indeed. Of course, for every success story, there are a thousand also-rans, and my family sure has had its share of them. In the 1950s, for instance, each of five of my relatives (including my Uncle Simon) patented a different gizmo, each in a different year. Each gave his or her gizmo a suitably faddish name (one was called the Silly Siphon), and, even though each had the chance to demonstrate it on a different television show that same year (one made an appearance on *Funny People*), none of the gizmos ever quite caught fire like the Hula-Hoop. From the information provided, determine the year (1954, 1955, 1957, 1958, or 1959) in which each relative patented his or her gizmo, as well as the television show on which he or she demonstrated it.

1. Uncle Theo patented his Wacky Whangee the year before another relative appeared on *Talk of the Town*. Neither Aunt Bertha nor Uncle Fred invented the Funky Funnel.

2. The first name of the relative who invented the Kooky Klaxon is exactly one letter longer than that of the one who appeared on *Talent Scouts* (who did so exactly four years before one relative patented the Funky Funnel).

3. Aunt Agnes's gizmo was patented exactly three years before the one that was demonstrated on *Art Linkley's Talent Time*.

4. Aunt Bertha's gizmo, which isn't the one that was demonstrated on *Amateur Hour*, was patented the year after the Zany Zither (which wasn't Uncle Fred's invention).

		AGNES	BERTHA	FRED	SIMON	THEO	FUNKY FUNNEL	KOOKY KLAXON	SILLY SIPHON	WACKY WHANGEE	ZANY ZITHER	AMATEUR HOUR	ART LINKLEY'S TALENT TIME	FUNNY PEOPLE	TALENT SCOUTS	TALK OF THE TOWN
YEAR	1954															
	1955															
	1957															
	1958															
	1959															
SHOW	AMATEUR HOUR															
	ART LINKLEY'S															
	FUNNY PEOPLE															
	TALENT SCOUTS															
	TALK OF TOWN															
GIZMO	FUNKY FUNNEL															
	KOOKY KLAXON															
	SILLY SIPHON															
	WACKY WHANGEE															
	ZANY ZITHER															

LOGIC PROBLEM 116   MANY HAPPY RETURNS

Last Tuesday, the Sav-U-Tax Service was able to make five new clients very happy. Each of the five couples came in at a different time (9:00 a.m., 10:00 a.m., 1:00 p.m., 2:00 p.m., or 4:00 p.m.). While there, each was advised to take advantage of a different tax adjustment (in one case, IRA deductions), and, as a result, each is expecting a different refund ($66, $135, $792, $810, or $1,555) from the Internal Revenue Service. From the information provided, determine the time of each client's appointment, the adjustment for which each is eligible, and the refund each is expecting.

1. The couple who had the 9:00 a.m. appointment (who aren't Mr. and Ms. Jussim) are expecting the smallest refund. The couple who came in at 10:00 a.m. are not receiving the largest refund. The Shearers came in at 4:00 p.m.

2. Mr. and Ms. Mohr (who came in at 2:00 p.m.) learned they were eligible for the Moving Expense deduction.

3. The couple eligible for the Child Care Credit are expecting exactly six times the refund amount of the recipients of the Moving Expense deduction.

4. Mr. and Ms. Jussim were able to increase their refund with a Mortgage Interest deduction. The Jussims came in at some point earlier in the day than the Burkes.

5. The Burkes are not eligible for the Child Care Credit. The Tafts aren't the ones eligible for the Charitable Contributions deduction.

		CLIENT					ADJUSTMENT					REFUND				
		BURKES	JUSSIMS	MOHRS	SHEARERS	TAFTS	CHARITABLE CONTRIBUTIONS	CHILD CARE CREDIT	IRA	MORTGAGE INTEREST	MOVING EXPENSE	$66	$135	$792	$810	$1,555
TIME	9:00 a.m.															
	10:00 a.m.															
	1:00 p.m.															
	2:00 p.m.															
	4:00 p.m.															
REFUND	$66															
	$135															
	$792															
	$810															
	$1,555															
ADJUSTMENT	CHARITABLE															
	CHILD CARE															
	IRA															
	MORTGAGE															
	MOVING EXPENSE															

LOGIC PROBLEM 117

After a typical day of driving his yellow cab around the city, New York taxi driver Abu Babawayh usually has to stop at the dispatcher's office to drop off shopping bags, umbrellas, and other items left in his cab by inattentive passengers. Today, however, each of five of his fares forgot a different, rather more unusual item (one left a sextant). Each person had been picked up in a different downtown neighborhood and subsequently dropped off at the intersection of a different midtown avenue (from east to west, 5th, 6th, 7th, 8th, or 9th Avenue) and a different cross street (from south to north, 42nd, 43rd, 44th, 45th, or 46th Street). From the information provided, can you match the neighborhood where each person was picked up with the intersection (identified by avenue and street) where each was dropped off, as well as determine the item that each person left in Abu's cab?

1. Three people dropped off at consecutive streets are, in order from south to north, the one who wanted to go to 6th Avenue, the one Abu picked up in Greenwich Village, and the one who left a boomerang in the cab.
2. Neither the person from Little Italy nor the one from Chinatown was dropped off on 46th Street.
3. The avenue where Abu dropped off the person from Tribeca is somewhere east of the avenue where the person from SoHo was dropped off and exactly two avenues to the west of the avenue where he dropped off the person from Little Italy.
4. The person from SoHo didn't leave either a pair of lederhosen or a boomerang in the cab. Neither the person who left a pair of lederhosen nor the one who left a boomerang was dropped off at 46th Street.
5. Four people dropped off at consecutive streets, from south to north, were the one who left a tea cozy in the cab, the one who wanted to go to 5th Avenue, the one Abu picked up in SoHo, and the one who left a duck decoy in the cab (who wasn't dropped off at 7th Avenue).

		AVENUE					STREET					ITEM				
		5th	6th	7th	8th	9th	42nd	43rd	44th	45th	46th	BOOMERANG	DUCK DECOY	LEDERHOSEN	SEXTANT	TEA COZY
NEIGHBOR.	CHINATOWN															
	GREENWICH															
	LITTLE ITALY															
	SOHO															
	TRIBECA															
ITEM	BOOMERANG															
	DUCK DECOY															
	LEDERHOSEN															
	SEXTANT															
	TEA COZY															
STREET	42nd															
	43rd															
	44th															
	45th															
	46th															

LOGIC PROBLEM 118 THE KATZMOBILE

For the past few years, Irwin and May Katz have been volunteer drivers for Help on Wheels, a community service that helps transport people about town. As May often says, "We have this great big van, the Katzmobile, so we might as well put it to good use!" Last night, the Chamber of Commerce held a ceremony honoring the program, and Irwin and May took the Katzmobile out to pick up their regular passengers and bring them to the hall. In all, the Katzmobile picked up five groups of people (at times with Irwin driving and at times with May driving), each on a different street (one was Beatty Avenue). Each group had a little surprise for the Katzes—a certificate for a different type of auto-maintenance work (including a tire rotation) to make sure the Katzmobile would be running far into the future! From the information provided, determine the order in which Irwin and May stopped on each street and the number of people picked up there, as well as the type of certificate Irwin and May received from that group.

1. Irwin and May picked up a total of 12 people last night. No group consisted of more than 3 people.

2. Irwin was driving the Katzmobile when they made the King Street stop (which was neither the first nor the last pickup of the night).

3. May drove the Katzmobile when they picked up both the third group and the group who presented them with the certificate for an oil change (who were picked up at some point after the Boyne Street group).

4. Three groups picked up by the Katzmobile, in consecutive order from first to last, were one consisting of a single person, the one on Victoria Street, and the one who gave Irwin and May a certificate for free winterization.

5. Irwin drove the Katzmobile when it picked up the group on Hancey Court (who didn't give a certificate for a transmission overhaul). Neither the group who gave a certificate for a new muffler nor the one who presented the transmission-overhaul certificate was the first group picked up.

6. The Hancey Court group was picked up at some point after a group of 2 people and at some point before the group who gave the winterization certificate.

		STREET					PEOPLE				CERTIFICATE				
		BEATTY AVENUE	BOYNE STREET	HANCEY COURT	KING STREET	VICTORIA STREET					NEW MUFFLER	OIL CHANGE	TIRE ROTATION	TRANSMISSION OVERHAUL	WINTERIZATION
ORDER	FIRST														
	SECOND														
	THIRD														
	FOURTH														
	FIFTH														
CERTIFICATE	NEW MUFFLER														
	OIL CHANGE														
	TIRE ROTATION														
	TRANSMISSION														
	WINTERIZATION														
PEOPLE															

126

In 1972, a few residents of Port Callister formed the Marathon Club, an informal group for runners planning to compete in the granddaddy of all long-distance events. These days, the club has five regular members (three of whom—Alvin, Chip, and Donald—are men, and two of whom—Dale and Minnie—are women), who this week are hard at work. Yesterday, each member, each of whom lives on a different street in Port Callister, started the day by running a different distance (14, 16, 18, 22, or 24 miles). For each, it was an increase over his or her previous personal best (each had a different previous personal best—10, 12, 14, 16, or 18 miles). At this rate, it won't be long before they're breaking the tape at the finish line of the New York City Marathon! From the information provided, determine the member who lives on each street (one is Rogers Street), as well as the number of miles he or she ran yesterday and his or her previous personal best.

1. The two women in the club are the one who lives on Salazar Street and the one who had a larger increase over her previous personal best than any other club member.

2. Yesterday, the one who lives on Waitz Street ran fewer miles than Dale but more miles than the man whose previous best was 16 miles (who isn't Donald).

3. The three members who improved their previous personal bests by the same number of miles are the one who lives on Salazar Street, Alvin (who is not the one who lives on Fleming Street), and the one whose previous best was 12 miles.

4. Yesterday, the person who lives on Kuscsik Street ran exactly 2 more miles than Chip.

		STREET					YESTERDAY					PREVIOUS BEST				
		FLEMING	KUSCSIK	ROGERS	SALAZAR	WAITZ	14	16	18	22	24	10	12	14	16	18
MEMBER	ALVIN															
	CHIP															
	DALE															
	DONALD															
	MINNIE															
PREVIOUS	10															
	12															
	14															
	16															
	18															
YESTERDAY	14															
	16															
	18															
	22															
	24															

LOGIC PROBLEM 120

When the grind of daily life gets to Mona and four of her friends, they sit back, relax, and have a bite of their favorite snack. The calming influence of this comfort food was especially needed today, since each had encountered a different, particularly trying situation (in one case, a bad haircut). After a quick sampling of his or her favorite food (no two people have the same type of comfort food), each person was lifted out of the doldrums. From the information provided, determine the food each person (identified by first and last names) used to elevate his or her spirits, as well as the situation from which each was trying to recover.

1. Sadie, who isn't the one who got stuck in a traffic jam, found solace in either ice cream or pizza. The popcorn eater isn't the one who had an unproductive day at work.

2. Neither Diane (whose last name is either Bacall or Wilde) nor Joey is the proponent of the curative powers of oatmeal.

3. Neither Joey (who isn't the one surnamed Janssen) nor the one surnamed Wilde had an unproductive day at work.

4. Neither Bill nor the one surnamed Bacall (who isn't Mona) turned to ice cream for therapy. The one surnamed Geary didn't get stuck in traffic.

5. The one surnamed Bacall didn't eat either pizza (which isn't the comfort food of either the one who had an unproductive workday or the one whose softball team lost) or chocolate. The one surnamed Geary (who isn't the one whose softball team lost) didn't resort to either oatmeal or chocolate.

6. Neither the one surnamed Janssen nor the one who had to deal with a broken washing machine is the one who finds ice cream to be therapeutic. Mona (who isn't the one surnamed Summerville) ate neither chocolate nor ice cream for relief.

7. The one surnamed Janssen (who isn't Bill) didn't eat oatmeal. A lost softball game wasn't the reason one person ate chocolate. Sadie didn't have an unproductive day at work.

		LAST NAME					FOOD					SITUATION				
		BACALL	GEARY	JANSSEN	SUMMERVILLE	WILDE	CHOCOLATE	ICE CREAM	OATMEAL	PIZZA	POPCORN	BAD HAIRCUT	LOST SOFTBALL GAME	TRAFFIC JAM	UNPRODUCTIVE DAY	WASHING MACHINE
FIRST NAME	BILL															
	DIANE															
	JOEY															
	MONA															
	SADIE															
SITUATION	BAD HAIRCUT															
	LOST GAME															
	TRAFFIC JAM															
	UNPRODUCTIVE															
	WASHING															
FOOD	CHOCOLATE															
	ICE CREAM															
	OATMEAL															
	PIZZA															
	POPCORN															

Dr. Marcus Klineman is quite pleased with the fleet of domestic robots he has acquired for his new home. Each robot is a different model (one is a brand-new Handibyte robot), and each has a different series number (300, 450, 600, 750, or 900). Each robot is programmed to efficiently perform a different function in Dr. Klineman's home, and, for ease of use, he has given each robot a different, affectionate nickname (Artie Deco, Robbie, Rusty, Sprockets, or Tintype). Things in Dr. Klineman's home are really running like clockwork now! From the information provided, determine the nickname the doctor gave each robot (identified by model and series number), as well as the job (one is a chef) each robot performs.

1. Tintype's series number is exactly 150 higher than that of the chauffeur (who isn't Artie Deco).

2. Neither the Domesticron nor the Radicon robot (neither of whom is from the 900 series) is either the maid or the valet.

3. Artie Deco's series number is exactly twice that of the gardener robot. Artie Deco is either the Domesticron or the Radicon robot.

4. Sprockets's series number is lower than that of the Domesticron robot but higher than Robbie's. Tintype, who is from the Lectroman line of robots, isn't the valet.

5. The Radicon robot (who doesn't have the lowest series number) isn't nicknamed Rusty. The Technotron robot isn't the valet.

		DOMESTICRON	HANDIBYTE	LECTROMAN	RADICON	TECHNOTRON	300	450	600	750	900	CHAUFFEUR	CHEF	GARDENER	MAID	VALET
		MODEL					SERIES NUMBER					JOB				
NICKNAME	ARTIE DECO															
	ROBBIE															
	RUSTY															
	SPROCKETS															
	TINTYPE															
JOB	CHAUFFEUR															
	CHEF															
	GARDENER															
	MAID															
	VALET															
SERIES NO.	300															
	450															
	600															
	750															
	900															

LOGIC PROBLEM 122 CARD COLLECTION

Karen McGee and four of her friends are avid card players who, not content with the popular card games, have researched and resurrected older games. One weekend each month, they play a different card game, and the winner of that game then treats the others to dinner. In the last five months, in fact, each woman has taken a turn hosting a card party for the other four. Each month they played a different game (including napoleon), which was won by a different one of the five. From the information provided, determine the month (August, September, October, November, or December) each woman hosted a card party and the game they played at that party, as well as the month each woman won at cards.

1. Virginia (who isn't the one who hosted the game of spoilfive) won at cards the month after the one who hosted the game of catch the ten and the month before the one who hosted the November party.

2. Peggy (who didn't host the game of red dog) didn't host the August party.

3. The one who hosted the August party won at cards the month after the one who hosted the game of red dog and the month before Mona (who did not host the September party).

4. The one who hosted the game of Michigan won the card game hosted by Faith.

5. Faith neither hosted nor won the August card game. Neither Mona nor Virginia won the same game she hosted.

		MONTH HOSTED					GAME					MONTH WON				
		AUGUST	SEPTEMBER	OCTOBER	NOVEMBER	DECEMBER	CATCH THE TEN	MICHIGAN	NAPOLEON	RED DOG	SPOILFIVE	AUGUST	SEPTEMBER	OCTOBER	NOVEMBER	DECEMBER
WOMAN	FAITH															
	KAREN															
	MONA															
	PEGGY															
	VIRGINIA															
MONTH WON	AUGUST															
	SEPTEMBER															
	OCTOBER															
	NOVEMBER															
	DECEMBER															
GAME	CATCH THE TEN															
	MICHIGAN															
	NAPOLEON															
	RED DOG															
	SPOILFIVE															

LOGIC PROBLEM 123

Critics are raving about the five new cinematic releases that opened over the weekend, including the horror-thriller, *Ophidiophobia*. Each movie was reviewed in a different newspaper by a different film critic, each of whom wrote a different quotable comment about the film in his or her review. Some of the critics have weekly television shows in which a critic is paired with one of the other four to jointly discuss new releases. Each critic hosts at most one show. No more than two critics are featured on any single television show. From the information provided, determine each film critic's quotable comment, the newspaper (one is the *Times*) for which each critic writes, and the movie each reviewed.

1. Michael (who isn't the film critic for the *Inquirer*) is not the one who reviewed *Open 24 Hours* (which isn't the movie about which a critic wrote, "I laughed! I cried!").

2. Leeza (who works for the *Chronicle*) isn't the one who reviewed *Extreme Measures*. Leeza's television show appears on Saturday nights.

3. Neither Roger (who isn't the one who wrote that *Piece of the Action 3: Blown to Pieces* was "Nonstop action!") nor the person with whom he co-hosts a television show is the one who wrote that *No Quarter* was "Riveting!"

4. Eugene and the person with whom he co-hosts a television show are the one who reviewed *Extreme Measures* and the one who works for the *Sun*, in some order. The critic who wrote, "Thumbs up!" about a movie does not have a television show.

5. The writer for the *Globe* referred to one film as "A tour de force!" The person with whom Leonard co-hosts a television show isn't the one who reviewed *Extreme Measures*. Roger does not write for the *Inquirer*.

		COMMENT					NEWSPAPER					MOVIE				
		A TOUR DE FORCE!	I LAUGHED, I CRIED!	NONSTOP ACTION!	RIVETING!	THUMBS UP!	CHRONICLE	GLOBE	INQUIRER	SUN	TIMES	EXTREME MEASURES	NO QUARTER	OPEN 24 HOURS	OPHIDIOPHOBIA	PIECE OF THE ACTION 3
CRITIC	EUGENE															
	LEEZA															
	LEONARD															
	MICHAEL															
	ROGER															
MOVIE	EXTREME															
	NO QUARTER															
	OPEN 24 HOURS															
	OPHIDIOPHOBIA															
	PIECE/ACTION 3															
NEWSPAPER	CHRONICLE															
	GLOBE															
	INQUIRER															
	SUN															
	TIMES															

LOGIC PROBLEM 124 VISITING SCHOLARS

Music teacher Ms. Johanssen couldn't have been more delighted last year when she received a visit from each of six former students (including Carla, Margarite, and Paul) whom she had instructed in her senior seminar. Even though each had gone off to attend college in a different state (including California, Indiana, and Ohio), each had made time to see Ms. Johanssen on a trip home during a different month (March, May, June, August, September, or December). Each student told Ms. Johanssen about college, where each has a different major (including theater arts). From the information provided, determine the month each student paid Ms. Johanssen a visit, as well as his or her major and the state in which each attends college.

1. The mathematics major has more letters in his or her name than the student who attends college in Maine (who visited in a month with a name that is exactly one letter shorter than that of the month in which Amy visited).

2. The name of the state in which Benjamin attends college is exactly one letter longer than that of the state in which the September visitor (who has more letters in his or her name than the physics major) attends college.

3. The name of the state in which the June visitor attends college is exactly two letters longer than that of the state in which the student who visited in March attends college. The name of the student who attends college in Kentucky (who isn't Quentin) is exactly two letters longer than that of the March visitor.

4. The history major attends college in a state with fewer letters in its name than the state in which the computer-science major attends college. The computer-science major visited in a month with fewer letters in its name than the month in which the one who attends college in Tennessee (who isn't the physics major) paid a visit.

5. The name of the political-science major has fewer letters than that of the August visitor. The name of the state in which the August visitor attends college has fewer letters than that of the state in which the political-science major attends college.

		MONTH						MAJOR						STATE					
		MARCH	MAY	JUNE	AUGUST	SEPTEMBER	DECEMBER	COMPUTER SCIENCE	HISTORY	MATHEMATICS	PHYSICS	POLITICAL SCIENCE	THEATER ARTS	CALIFORNIA	INDIANA	KENTUCKY	MAINE	OHIO	TENNESSEE
STUDENT	AMY																		
	BENJAMIN																		
	CARLA																		
	MARGARITE																		
	PAUL																		
	QUENTIN																		
STATE	CALIFORNIA																		
	INDIANA																		
	KENTUCKY																		
	MAINE																		
	OHIO																		
	TENNESSEE																		
MAJOR	COMPUTER																		
	HISTORY																		
	MATHEMATICS																		
	PHYSICS																		
	POLITICAL																		
	THEATER ARTS																		

In December, the Greenoak Company held a holiday party for its employees. Each employee brought a gift for the grab bag, and, at the end of the evening, each employee chose a gift at random from the bag. As it happened, each of the six members of the art department (including Albert) went home with a different gift (a compact disc, gift certificate, sand sculpture, scarf, teddy bear, or woodcarving) that another member of the art department had brought to the party. From the information provided, can you determine the gift each of these employees brought to the party and the gift each took home?

1. Philip (who brought the woodcarving) took home the gift that Jeremy brought. Jeremy took the gift that Elise brought to the party.
2. The employee who brought the scarf took the woodcarving (which was brought by the employee who took the compact disc).
3. Tessa brought the sand sculpture.
4. The employee who took home the scarf isn't the one who brought the gift certificate.
5. Elise took the gift that was brought to the party by Kim (who isn't the one who went home with the sand sculpture).

		BROUGHT						TOOK HOME					
		COMPACT DISC	GIFT CERTIFICATE	SAND SCULPTURE	SCARF	TEDDY BEAR	WOODCARVING	COMPACT DISC	GIFT CERTIFICATE	SAND SCULPTURE	SCARF	TEDDY BEAR	WOODCARVING
EMPLOYEE	ALBERT												
	ELISE												
	JEREMY												
	KIM												
	PHILIP												
	TESSA												
TOOK HOME	COMPACT DISC												
	GIFT CERTIFICATE												
	SAND SCULPTURE												
	SCARF												
	TEDDY BEAR												
	WOODCARVING												

LOGIC PROBLEM 126 UNDER WRAPS

When a recent sandstorm uncovered Hashenputphat's fabled Valley of Important Personages, the archaeology department at Tuscarora University immediately dispatched a team to the site. There, amidst the splendor and opulence of ancient tombs, the team discovered the mummies of five pharaohs, each of whom ruled during a different period (from earliest to latest, Early Dynastic, Old, Middle, New, or Late) in Hashenputphat history, and each of whom is credited with the construction of a different monument. In addition, a different number of mastabas—tombs for the pharaoh's family and courtiers—surrounded each mausoleum. From the information provided, determine the period during which each Hashenputphat pharaoh ruled, the monument he ordered constructed during his reign, and the number of mastabas (10, 13, 15, 20, or 25) built around each pharaoh's tomb.

1. Opprobrias ruled as pharaoh earlier than Porphorpot did. Cleophatra (who was not the pharaoh who constructed 15 mastabas) did not rule in the period immediately following the one during which Absinthes reigned.

2. The pharaoh who created the colossus (who did not reign during the Late Period) ruled at some point after Pharaoh Ramalamaten.

3. Exactly 10 more mastabas were erected in the tomb of the ruler who commanded the building of the obelisk than in that of the ruler who achieved immortality through the raising of a mighty pyramid. Absinthes ordered the construction of neither the obelisk nor the sphinx. The colossus was not built in the period immediately preceding that in which the temple was constructed.

4. The pharaoh whose tomb contained 20 mastabas reigned at some point before the one who built the sphinx (who isn't Porphorpot), who reigned at some point before the one who constructed the temple.

5. Exactly 5 more mastabas were built in the tomb of the New Period pharaoh than were built in the tomb of Absinthes (who did not erect the colossus). The Middle-Period ruler built fewer mastabas than the Late-Period pharaoh but more than at least one other pharaoh.

		PHARAOH					MONUMENT					MASTABAS				
		ABSINTHES	CLEOPHATRA	OPPROBRIAS	PORPHORPOT	RAMALAMATEN	COLOSSUS	OBELISK	PYRAMID	SPHINX	TEMPLE	10	13	15	20	25
PERIOD	EARLY DYNASTIC															
	OLD															
	MIDDLE															
	NEW															
	LATE															
MASTABAS	10															
	13															
	15															
	20															
	25															
MONUMENT	COLOSSUS															
	OBELISK															
	PYRAMID															
	SPHINX															
	TEMPLE															

Every December, the editors of the magazine *Tasselequa Monthly* publish a year-in-review issue, recapping some of the top local events of the previous year. They're already hard at work preparing six such stories for this year's issue, and they have sent their assistants to the library to cull articles from the three local papers. Each story requires a different number of articles (1, 2, 3, 4, 5, or 6) from the *Bugle*, a different number (1, 2, 3, 4, 5, or 6) from the *Gazette*, and a different number (1, 2, 3, 5, 6, or 7) from the *Tribune*. From the information provided, determine the number of *Bugle*, *Gazette*, and *Tribune* articles required for each story.

1. The story that requires one *Bugle* article (which isn't about this year's mayoral election) needs exactly one *Gazette* article fewer than the one that requires one *Tribune* article. The story that requires one *Bugle* article needs exactly three more *Tribune* articles than the one that requires one *Gazette* article (which needs more *Bugle* articles than the story on the celebration of the town's centennial).

2. The story on the town's centennial requires more *Bugle* articles, and exactly one *Gazette* article fewer, than the story that needs exactly one *Bugle* article fewer, and exactly three *Tribune* articles fewer, than the one on the high-school football championship (which requires more than one *Gazette* article).

3. The story on the construction of the new freeway requires more *Bugle* articles, and exactly two fewer *Tribune* articles, than the one that needs exactly one *Gazette* article fewer than the story about the controversial new poll tax. The poll-tax story requires fewer *Tribune* articles, and exactly one *Bugle* article fewer, than the story on the dedication of the new park. The story about the park requires exactly one more *Gazette* article than the one that uses three *Bugle* articles.

4. The story on the election for mayor requires exactly one more *Gazette* article than the one that needs exactly one *Tribune* article fewer than the story that requires five *Gazette* articles.

	BUGLE						GAZETTE						TRIBUNE					
	1	2	3	4	5	6	1	2	3	4	5	6	1	2	3	5	6	7
STORY CENTENNIAL																		
ELECTION																		
FOOTBALL																		
FREEWAY																		
PARK																		
POLL TAX																		
TRIBUNE 1																		
2																		
3																		
5																		
6																		
7																		
GAZETTE 1																		
2																		
3																		
4																		
5																		
6																		

LOGIC PROBLEM 128   JUST CLOWNING AROUND

The circus has arrived in town, and a huge crowd has gathered to watch it parade down Main Street. The parade was led by five clowns (including Chuckles), each of whom was wearing a rubber nose decorated with a different design. The onlookers cheered the antics of the clowns, each of whom was carrying a different prop. Each clown's costume had two designs on it, and no two clowns wore the same combination of designs. From the information provided, determine the design on each clown's nose and the pair of designs (hearts and rainbows, hearts and stars, lightning bolts and spirals, lightning bolts and stars, or rainbows and spirals) on each clown's costume, as well as the prop each carried.

1. The clown who wore the heart nose had no hearts on his or her costume. The clown who wore the lightning-bolt nose didn't wear the lightning-bolts-and-stars costume. The clown who wore the rainbow nose didn't wear the rainbows-and-spirals costume. The clown who wore the star nose had no stars on his or her costume. Of the two clowns with spirals on their costumes, one carried a seltzer bottle as a prop, and the other wore the rainbow nose.

2. The clown who wore the hearts-and-stars costume is neither the one who wore the big shoes as a prop nor the one who carried the cream pie as a prop.

3. Buster says spirals clash with the colors in his wig, so he never wears anything with spirals.

4. Cappy is either the one who wore the rainbow nose or the one who wore the spiral nose. If she wore the spiral nose, then she's the one who had a poodle as a prop.

5. Both Giggles and the one who used the cream pie as a prop share a design on their costumes.

6. Neither Zippy (who didn't wear the heart nose) nor the one whose prop was the horn wore either the hearts-and-rainbows costume or the lightning-bolts-and-stars costume. The clown who wore the heart nose isn't the one who wore the lightning-bolts-and-stars costume (who didn't have a poodle as a prop).

		NOSE					COSTUME					PROP				
		HEART	LIGHTNING BOLT	RAINBOW	SPIRAL	STAR	HEARTS/ RAINBOWS	HEARTS/STARS	LIGHTNING BOLTS/SPIRALS	LIGHTNING BOLTS/STARS	RAINBOWS/ SPIRALS	BIG SHOES	CREAM PIE	HORN	POODLE	SELTZER BOTTLE
CLOWN	BUSTER															
	CAPPY															
	CHUCKLES															
	GIGGLES															
	ZIPPY															
PROP	BIG SHOES															
	CREAM PIE															
	HORN															
	POODLE															
	SELTZER BOTTLE															
COSTUME	HEARTS/RAINBOW															
	HEARTS/STARS															
	LIGHTNING/SPIRAL															
	LIGHTNING/STARS															
	RAINBOWS/SPIRAL															

LOGIC PROBLEM 129

The highlight of Karen's bridal shower was "The Karen Quiz," a questionnaire compiled by Karen's mother, consisting of 20 questions about her daughter. Each of the six women at the shower answered a different number of questions correctly (Karen and her mother were disqualified from participating). Each woman gave Karen a different shower gift (one gave her a toaster), and, since Karen and her fiancé, Doug, were planning to go to Bermuda for their honeymoon, each also gave her a different beach item (a beach hat, beach towels, bikini, blanket, sandals, or suntan lotions). From the information provided, determine the number of correct answers (7, 8, 9, 10, 11, or 12) given by each woman, as well as the gift and beach item she gave Karen.

1. The one who gave Karen a blanket gave either 7 or 8 correct answers. Neither Maggie nor Shannon gave either 7 or 8 correct answers.

2. The woman who presented Karen with both the glassware and the beach hat gave exactly 1 more correct answer than Stephanie.

3. Maggie didn't give Karen the pasta-bowl set. Brianna isn't the one who gave her the five-quart skillet.

4. The one who presented Karen with the cappuccino maker gave exactly 1 correct answer fewer than the one who gave the bikini (who correctly answered an even number of questions).

5. The woman who gave Karen a china place setting (who isn't the one who gave the assortment of suntan lotions) correctly answered 11 questions.

6. Tia answered exactly 2 more questions correctly than the one who gave the pasta-bowl set, who answered exactly 2 more questions correctly than the one who gave Karen the beach towels (who isn't Raleigh).

		CORRECT ANSWERS						GIFT						BEACH ITEM					
		7	8	9	10	11	12	CAPPUCCINO MAKER	CHINA PLACE SETTING	GLASSWARE	PASTA-BOWL SET	SKILLET	TOASTER	BEACH HAT	BEACH TOWELS	BIKINI	BLANKET	SANDALS	SUNTAN LOTIONS
WOMAN	BRIANNA																		
	MAGGIE																		
	RALEIGH																		
	SHANNON																		
	STEPHANIE																		
	TIA																		
BEACH ITEM	BEACH HAT																		
	BEACH TOWELS																		
	BIKINI																		
	BLANKET																		
	SANDALS																		
	SUNTAN LOTIONS																		
GIFT	CAPPUCCINO																		
	CHINA PLACE																		
	GLASSWARE																		
	PASTA-BOWL SET																		
	SKILLET																		
	TOASTER																		

LOGIC PROBLEM 130

While waiting in the Madrid Airport for his flight back to the United States, Sylvester went to the restaurant for one last taste of Spanish cuisine. While there he met five other Americans who were also on their way home, so the six dined together (each ordered a different dish). Each had been staying at a different hotel in Madrid (one stayed at the Moderno). Since the past week in Madrid had been quite rainy, each traveler had visited the Museo del Prado to see some art. Each had been particularly excited to see a painting by his or her favorite artist (no two of whom are the same—one is Titian) at the Prado. From the information provided, determine the hotel where each person stayed, his or her favorite artist, and the dish he or she ordered at the airport restaurant.

1. Nora (who isn't the one who stayed at the Internacional) didn't buy 17 postcards. Nora, who ordered the gazpacho, bought exactly two fewer T-shirts than the one staying at the Victoria (who visited the Prado either the day before or the day after Nora).

2. Leon (who stayed at the Regente) visited the Prado exactly two days after the one who ordered paella. Leon, who isn't the one who bought three T-shirts, bought exactly 3 fewer postcards than the one who stayed at the Plaza. Velásquez is the favorite artist of the one who stayed at the Plaza (who isn't the one who had huevos alla flamenco).

3. The one who stayed at the Carlos V (who ordered ensalada valenciana) bought exactly 2 more postcards than Hugo, who bought exactly four more T-shirts than the person who purchased 5 postcards.

This is part 1 of a two-part puzzle. It is necessary to work back and forth between this part and part 2 on page 139 in order to solve the puzzle.

		HOTEL						ARTIST						DISH					
		CARLOS V	INTERNACIONAL	MODERNO	PLAZA	REGENTE	VICTORIA	EL GRECO	GOYA	MURILLO	RIBERA	TITIAN	VELÁSQUEZ	ARROZ CON POLLO	EMPANADAS	ENSALADA VALENCIANA	GAZPACHO	HUEVOS ALLA FLAMENCO	PAELLA
PERSON	HUGO																		
	LEON																		
	NORA																		
	ROBIN																		
	SYLVESTER																		
	TATUM																		
DISH	ARROZ CON																		
	EMPANADAS																		
	ENSALADA																		
	GAZPACHO																		
	HUEVOS ALLA																		
	PAELLA																		
ARTIST	EL GRECO																		
	GOYA																		
	MURILLO																		
	RIBERA																		
	TITIAN																		
	VELÁSQUEZ																		

LOGIC PROBLEM 131

As the six travelers boarded the plane, they were still discussing their visits to the Museo del Prado. As it turned out, each had visited the Prado on a different day of the week (Monday through Saturday), and each had purchased a different number of postcards (5, 7, 10, 12, 15, or 17) while there. The travelers had also spent much time locating souvenirs in Madrid, and, in fact, each had purchased a different number of T-shirts (2, 3, 4, 6, 7, or 8) for friends and family back home. All agreed that their Spanish holidays had provided wonderful experiences. From the information provided, determine the day each person visited the Prado, as well as the number of postcards and the number of T-shirts he or she bought.

1. The one who ordered the arroz con pollo (whose favorite artist is El Greco) bought either exactly two more or exactly two fewer T-shirts than the one who visited the Prado the day after the one who ordered huevos alla flamenco.

2. Tatum bought 15 postcards. The one who ordered paella (who isn't Sylvester) isn't the one who purchased 10 postcards.

3. The one who visited the Prado on Monday purchased either exactly two more or exactly two fewer T-shirts than the one who ordered empanadas.

4. The one whose favorite artist is Murillo visited the Prado the day before the one whose favorite artist is Goya (who isn't the one who bought two T-shirts).

5. Robin bought exactly two fewer T-shirts than the one whose favorite artist is Ribera, who visited the Prado either exactly two days before or exactly two days after Robin.

*This is part 2 of a two-part puzzle. It is necessary to work back and forth between this part and part 1 on page 138 in order to solve the puzzle.

		DAY						POSTCARDS						T-SHIRTS					
		MONDAY	TUESDAY	WEDNESDAY	THURSDAY	FRIDAY	SATURDAY	5	7	10	12	15	17	2	3	4	6	7	8
PERSON	HUGO																		
	LEON																		
	NORA																		
	ROBIN																		
	SYLVESTER																		
	TATUM																		
T-SHIRTS	2																		
	3																		
	4																		
	6																		
	7																		
	8																		
POSTCARDS	5																		
	7																		
	10																		
	12																		
	15																		
	17																		

LOGIC PROBLEM 132

Lodge Masonry has a fine reputation in Cahoga for fast, quality work. Today, Sam and the other four masons in the company were hard at work, each on a different type of project at a different address. By the time they all met for lunch at Pollitt's, each mason (three of whom are men and two of whom are women) had already laid a different number of bricks for his or her project. After a hearty lunch, they were ready to wield their trowels again. From the information provided, can you determine the mason working at each address (100 Patterway, 200 Patterway, 300 Fultonview, 400 Fultonview, or 500 Tresser), as well as the type of project on which he or she is working and the number of bricks (100, 200, 300, 400, or 500) he or she had laid by lunchtime? (Note: All names can refer to either men or women.)

1. At least two masons are working at addresses where the house number is at least 300 higher than the number of bricks laid there. The outdoor grill isn't being built at 300 Fultonview.

2. Both Lane (who is building a new furnace chimney) and the mason who is constructing the new patio are working on the same street. Lane didn't lay exactly 400 bricks.

3. Val (who is not at the address with the highest house number) laid exactly 100 bricks more than, but is not the same gender as, the mason working on the outdoor grill (which is not at the address with the lowest house number).

4. Jordan laid more bricks than the woman working at 100 Patterway. The one working on the front walk laid exactly 100 fewer bricks than the one working at 300 Fultonview.

5. Dana is a woman. The mason laying bricks for the fireplace is a man. The three men are not working at three consecutively numbered addresses.

		ADDRESS					PROJECT					BRICKS				
		100 PATTERWAY	200 PATTERWAY	300 FULTONVIEW	400 FULTONVIEW	500 TRESSER	CHIMNEY	FIREPLACE	FRONT WALK	GRILL	PATIO	100	200	300	400	500
MASON	DANA															
	JORDAN															
	LANE															
	SAM															
	VAL															
BRICKS	100															
	200															
	300															
	400															
	500															
PROJECT	CHIMNEY															
	FIREPLACE															
	FRONT WALK															
	GRILL															
	PATIO															

Rube Goldberg, Jr., in the tradition of his father, is a ceaseless inventor, constantly searching for ways to simplify the annoying little chores of daily life by creating labor-saving (though sometimes rather elaborate) devices. This year, he has come up with plans for five new devices (including a coffee grinder), each to serve a different purpose, that he intends to submit to the patent office as soon as possible. Each device uses a different number (2, 3, 4, 5, or 6) of battering rams, a different number (2, 4, 5, 6, or 7) of guillotines, and a different number (2, 3, 4, 5, or 7) of octopi. From the information provided, determine the number of battering rams, guillotines, and octopi used in each device.

1. The one that uses 4 octopi uses a combined total of exactly 7 battering rams and guillotines.

2. The dishwasher uses fewer guillotines than the automatic dog walker.

3. The rug cleaner (which uses a total of exactly 13 items) doesn't use 6 guillotines.

4. The device that uses 6 battering rams doesn't use 5 octopi.

5. The five devices are the dog walker (which doesn't use 3 battering rams), the can opener (which uses a total of exactly 12 items), the one that uses 6 guillotines and 5 battering rams, the one that uses a total of exactly 15 items, and the one that uses 2 octopi.

		BATTERING RAMS					GUILLOTINES					OCTOPI				
		2	3	4	5	6	2	4	5	6	7	2	3	4	5	7
DEVICE	CAN OPENER															
	COFFEE GRINDER															
	DISHWASHER															
	DOG WALKER															
	RUG CLEANER															
OCTOPI	2															
	3															
	4															
	5															
	7															
GUILLOTINES	2															
	4															
	5															
	6															
	7															

LOGIC PROBLEM 134 THE STUNT MAN

Thanks to his remarkable ability to turn virtual unknowns into international pop stars, Colonel Tom Perkins has become one of the most successful managers in the music business. At a recent roast honoring the Colonel, five of his most famous clients (three of whom—Arletty, Vandalay, and Zuleika—are women, and two of whom—Orestes and Stedman—are men) reminisced about the early stages of their careers. After having discovered each performing at a different location (one was crooning at a state fair), the Colonel devised a different publicity stunt for each (he had one perform a rooftop concert downtown at lunchtime) that caught people's attention and led to the breakthrough sales of his or her debut album. From the information provided, determine the location at which each singer was discovered, the name of his or her debut album (one was *Frequent Flier*), and the publicity stunt that made each famous.

1. The two women who debuted with two-word album titles are the one the Colonel discovered at a high-school talent show and the one whose publicity stunt involved singing while bungee jumping off a bridge.

2. *Bad Hair Day* was the debut album of the woman discovered at an open-mike night (who isn't Vandalay). Stedman isn't the singer whose debut album was *Arabesque*.

3. To publicize the singer who debuted with *Mondegreen*, the Colonel erected a large billboard downtown with that singer's name followed by a question mark. To generate publicity for Arletty, the Colonel circulated rumors of a romance with a famous athlete.

4. The singer discovered at a karaoke bar, who isn't Vandalay, debuted with a two-word album title. The one who debuted with *Chattering Class* (who isn't Zuleika) isn't the one who, for publicity's sake, claimed to be a descendant of Queen Liliuokalani of Hawaii.

5. The pop star discovered singing at the Colonel's nephew's birthday party didn't claim to be a descendant of Queen Liliuokalani.

		LOCATION					ALBUM					STUNT				
		BIRTHDAY PARTY	KARAOKE BAR	OPEN-MIKE NIGHT	STATE FAIR	TALENT SHOW	ARABESQUE	BAD HAIR DAY	CHATTERING CLASS	FREQUENT FLIER	MONDEGREEN	BILLBOARD	BUNGEE JUMP	DESCENDANT OF QUEEN	ROMANCE WITH ATHLETE	ROOFTOP CONCERT
SINGER	ARLETTY															
	ORESTES															
	STEDMAN															
	VANDALAY															
	ZULEIKA															
STUNT	BILLBOARD															
	BUNGEE JUMP															
	DESCENDANT															
	ROMANCE															
	ROOFTOP															
ALBUM	ARABESQUE															
	BAD HAIR DAY															
	CHATTERING															
	FREQUENT FLIER															
	MONDEGREEN															

LOGIC PROBLEM 135

The travel shelf at the Clarendon Bookstore is overflowing with new titles this week. Of particular interest are five new tour books, each of which describes a different island or set of islands. Each of these books is filled with the latest information on restaurants, accommodations, and areas of interest, and includes a different number of detailed maps (7, 8, 9, 10, or 11) and a different number of color photographs (11, 12, 14, 15, or 16). In a separate chapter about the history of the region, each book also contains a different number of sketches (9, 10, 12, 13, or 14) that reconstruct the possible appearance of a particular place in days long past. From the information provided, determine the number of maps, the number of photographs, and the number of sketches in each book.

1. The Bahamas book has fewer maps than the book that contains 15 photos and fewer sketches than at least one other book. The book that contains 15 photos does not contain 9 sketches. The Cayman Islands book has either exactly one map more or exactly one map fewer than the book that has exactly 1 more sketch than the Cayman Islands book.

2. The Jamaica book (which has fewer maps than the book with 12 photographs) has exactly 1 sketch fewer than the book with eight maps.

3. The Trinidad and Tobago book has exactly 1 photograph fewer than the book with nine maps.

4. The book on the Virgin Islands has exactly 1 more photograph and exactly one more map than the book with 14 sketches.

5. The book with 14 photographs has fewer sketches than at least two other books but more sketches than at least one other book.

		MAPS					PHOTOGRAPHS					SKETCHES				
		7	8	9	10	11	11	12	14	15	16	9	10	12	13	14
BOOK	BAHAMAS															
	CAYMAN ISLANDS															
	JAMAICA															
	TRINIDAD/TOBAGO															
	VIRGIN ISLANDS															
SKETCHES	9															
	10															
	12															
	13															
	14															
PHOTOS	11															
	12															
	14															
	15															
	16															

LOGIC PROBLEM 136

ON THE COUCH

Late Friday afternoon, psychiatrist Dr. Lapine spent some time compiling his notes from the past week. On each weekday he had seen a new patient (two of whom—Clifford and Rufus—are men, and three of whom—Faith, Hedda, and Priscilla—are women). Dr. Lapine noted that when shown the same inkblot, each patient had said it looked like something different (one said it looked like a teacup perched atop Mount Everest). Dr. Lapine also conducted a session of free association with each patient, where he was intrigued with the different response each gave to the word "mother." From the doctor's notes, reproduced below, can you determine the weekday each patient visited Dr. Lapine, as well as each patient's responses to the inkblot and the free-association session?

1. I saw the patient who said the inkblot looked like a dinosaur with binoculars the day before the one who responded "Nature" in free association, whom I saw the day before the one who said the inkblot looked like the President climbing a maple tree.

2. Priscilla came to my office the day after the one who told me that the inkblot looked like Napoleon flying a plane and the day before the one who responded "Wit" in free association.

3. In free association, Faith and the woman who said the inkblot looked like a marshmallow sandwich responded "Goose" and "Nature," in some order.

4. Hedda's free-association response was either "Wit" or "Superior." Clifford isn't the one who responded "Superior" in free association. The one who thought that the inkblot looked like Napoleon flying a plane (who isn't the one who replied "Hubbard" in free association) isn't Hedda.

		PATIENT					INKBLOT					FREE ASSOCIATION				
		CLIFFORD	FAITH	HEDDA	PRISCILLA	RUFUS	DINOSAUR WITH BINOCULARS	MARSHMALLOW SANDWICH	NAPOLEON FLYING PLANE	PRESIDENT CLIMBING MAPLE	TEACUP ON MOUNT EVEREST	GOOSE	HUBBARD	NATURE	SUPERIOR	WIT
WEEKDAY	MONDAY															
	TUESDAY															
	WEDNESDAY															
	THURSDAY															
	FRIDAY															
FREE ASSOC.	GOOSE															
	HUBBARD															
	NATURE															
	SUPERIOR															
	WIT															
INKBLOT	DINOSAUR															
	MARSHMALLOW															
	NAPOLEON FLYING															
	PRESIDENT															
	TEACUP/EVEREST															

Although only an afterthought in the original design, the lap pool at Memorial Town Pool seems at times to be more popular than both the kiddie pool and the free-swim area combined! This morning, for instance, only five minutes after opening, each of the five lanes of the lap pool was already occupied by a swimmer doing his or her best to keep fit. Each person worked out with a different swimming stroke, and each swam a different number of laps (10, 20, 30, 40, or 50). From the information provided, can you determine the swimmer in each lane (1 through 5), as well as each one's stroke and the number of laps each swam?

1. The lane number of the person who did the sidestroke (who isn't Greg) is either exactly one higher or exactly one lower than that of the person who did the butterfly.

2. The person who did the backstroke (who isn't Janet) is neither the one who swam in lane three nor the one who swam 30 laps.

3. Neither Audrey nor the one who did the butterfly swam in the lane numbered exactly one lower than that of the person who did the front crawl.

4. Esther swam either exactly 10 laps more or exactly 10 laps fewer than Burt (whose lane number is either exactly one higher or exactly one lower than Janet's).

5. The lane number of the person who did the front crawl is either exactly one higher or exactly one lower than that of the person who did the breaststroke, who did either exactly 10 laps more or exactly 10 laps fewer than the person who did the sidestroke.

6. Esther's lane number is either exactly one higher or exactly one lower than that used by Audrey, who swam either exactly 10 laps more or 10 laps fewer than Janet.

7. Greg swam exactly 10 laps fewer than the person in lane one but more laps than at least one other person. The one who did the butterfly (who isn't Greg) swam fewer laps than at least one other person.

		SWIMMER					STROKE					LAPS				
		AUDREY	BURT	ESTHER	GREG	JANET	BACKSTROKE	BREASTSTROKE	BUTTERFLY	FRONT CRAWL	SIDESTROKE	10	20	30	40	50
LANE	1															
	2															
	3															
	4															
	5															
LAPS	10											
	20											
	30											
	40											
	50											
STROKE	BACKSTROKE						
	BREASTSTROKE						
	BUTTERFLY						
	FRONT CRAWL						
	SIDESTROKE						

LOGIC PROBLEM 138 · KUNG-FU CALISTHENICS

Each morning, I set my alarm clock to ring early so that I can rise and shine and exercise with cable television's Noxema Jackson and her Kung-Fu Workout. In each of the five episodes I caught this week—each of which was filmed in a different sunny location—Noxema was helped by a different one of her regular assistants (in one, she was helped by Shaniqua). Each episode also featured a promotion for a different commercial product (including sneakers). After finishing her workout, Noxema ended each episode by breaking a different number of wooden boards with her head. From the information provided, determine the product placement in the episode filmed in each sunny locale, the assistant who appeared in that episode, and the number of boards Noxema broke in each.

1. Noxema was assisted by neither Cliff nor Alexis in the episode filmed in San Juan. Alexis did not assist Noxema in the episode filmed in Kaanapali. Neither Russ nor Alexis assisted in the episode in which Noxema broke exactly seven boards (which wasn't filmed in San Juan).

2. In the episode in which she was assisted by Russ, Noxema broke exactly one board more than she did in the episode filmed in Sedona and exactly one board fewer than in the episode in which a bottle of mineral water was conspicuously displayed.

3. Noxema broke exactly four fewer boards in the Miami episode than she did in the one that showed her eating an energy bar. Noxema broke exactly four fewer boards in the episode in which Alexis assisted than in the one where she wore a leotard prominently displaying the manufacturer's logo.

4. Noxema was assisted by Tricia in the episode filmed in Santa Barbara and by Cliff in the episode in which she broke exactly four wooden boards. The episode featuring barbells isn't the one in which Noxema broke the fewest boards.

		PRODUCT					ASSISTANT					BOARDS				
		BARBELLS	ENERGY BAR	LEOTARD	MINERAL WATER	SNEAKERS	ALEXIS	CLIFF	RUSS	SHANIQUA	TRICIA					
LOCALE	KAANAPALI															
	MIAMI															
	SAN JUAN															
	SANTA BARBARA															
	SEDONA															
BOARDS																
ASSISTANT	ALEXIS															
	CLIFF															
	RUSS															
	SHANIQUA															
	TRICIA															

LOGIC PROBLEM 139

One fine day, the six members of the Foreston Nature Club (four of whom—Etta, Gloria, Rochelle, and Theresa—are women, and two of whom—Kurt and Nate—are men) went out foraging for leaves. Each was looking for a different type of leaf (one was looking for orbicular leaves), and no two collected the same total number of leaves. When it grew dark, the group headed home to press the leaves they had found. After arranging his or her leaves between pieces of newspaper, each person placed a different weight (one used a typewriter) on top to preserve them forever. From the information provided, determine the type of leaf for which each person was searching, the number of leaves he or she found, and the weight he or she used to press the leaves.

1. Everyone found at least 15 and at most 50 leaves.
2. The woman who found exactly 35 leaves (who isn't Gloria) wasn't looking for cordate leaves.
3. Neither the one who used a dictionary (who found fewer leaves than at least one other person) nor the one who used clay bricks to press his or her leaves is either the one who was looking for spatulate leaves or the one who was looking for cordate leaves.
4. Nate found fewer leaves than Kurt but more leaves than Etta. The one who found the fewest leaves wasn't looking for spatulate leaves.
5. The man looking for reniform leaves found exactly 15 more leaves than the person who used a bag of flour as a weight and exactly 10 fewer leaves than Theresa.
6. The one in quest of peltate leaves (who isn't Theresa) found exactly twice as many leaves as the man who used the cinder block to press his leaves.
7. The man looking for deltoid leaves found exactly 15 fewer leaves than the person looking for cordate leaves (who isn't the one who used a collected edition of Shakespeare's plays to press leaves).

				LEAF						NUMBER						WEIGHT			
		CORDATE	DELTOID	ORBICULAR	PELTATE	RENIFORM	SPATULATE						BAG OF FLOUR	CINDER BLOCK	CLAY BRICKS	DICTIONARY	SHAKESPEARE	TYPEWRITER
PERSON	ETTA																	
	GLORIA																	
	KURT																	
	NATE																	
	ROCHELLE																	
	THERESA																	
WEIGHT	BAG OF FLOUR																	
	CINDER BLOCK																	
	CLAY BRICKS																	
	DICTIONARY																	
	SHAKESPEARE																	
	TYPEWRITER																	
NUMBER																		

LOGIC PROBLEM 140

NAMESAKES

At this year's Professional Women of the Year Awards, held at the Hotel Excelsior, all six honorees (Ali, Carly, Dee, Estelle, Fern, and Shelley) and their husbands (Allen, Franklin, Owen, Thomas, Trent, and Wilbur) were seated together in front of the podium. Each couple was staying in a different room (121, 123, 124, 126, 129, or 130) at the hotel. Before the speeches got underway, the 12 people were able to chat a little, and they discovered that each woman's surname was the same as the first name of the husband of a different one of the other five women! This coincidence made introductions a tad confusing, but all was cleared up in time for the awards ceremony. From the information provided, can you determine the wife and husband in each couple and their shared surname, as well as their room number at the hotel?

1. Both Dee and Ms. Wilbur had room numbers that were exactly three higher than those of other women.
2. Ms. Trent (who isn't Dee) isn't Owen's wife (who isn't Ms. Wilbur). Ms. Owen had a higher room number than Ms. Franklin.
3. Each of three women—Wilbur's wife, Shelley, and Allen's wife—had a room number that was exactly three lower than that of another woman.
4. Carly and her husband (who isn't Wilbur) had a lower room number than at least two other couples.
5. Franklin's wife isn't Carly (who isn't married to Allen), Ali, or Shelley.
6. In the case of one couple, the wife's first-name initial, surname initial, and husband's first-name initial (all of which are different) are the same as another wife's first-name initial, surname initial, and husband's first-name initial, in some order. Neither of these wives' surnames is the same as either of their husbands' first names. The first or last name of the husband of one of these couples, whose room number was lower than that of Owen and his wife, is the same as Owen's first or last name.

		HUSBAND						SURNAME						ROOM NUMBER					
		ALLEN	FRANKLIN	OWEN	THOMAS	TRENT	WILBUR	ALLEN	FRANKLIN	OWEN	THOMAS	TRENT	WILBUR	121	123	124	126	129	130
WIFE	ALI																		
	CARLY																		
	DEE																		
	ESTELLE																		
	FERN																		
	SHELLEY																		
ROOM NUMBER	121																		
	123																		
	124																		
	126																		
	129																		
	130																		
SURNAME	ALLEN																		
	FRANKLIN																		
	OWEN																		
	THOMAS																		
	TRENT																		
	WILBUR																		

LOGIC PROBLEM 141

While dining together recently, Ms. Chalmers, Mr. Pankhurst, and three other mathematicians challenged each other to come up with a proof of Ferret's Last Theorem, a notoriously unprovable theorem dating from the 18th century. Each person specializes in a different branch of mathematics (including algebra), and each used one of three mathematical principles in his or her proof (two used the principle of absorption, two used the principle of contraposition, and one used the principle of constructive dilemma). While attempting to prove the theorem, two mathematicians used pencils, two used chalk, and one used a fountain pen as a writing implement. From the information provided, determine the branch of mathematics in which each person specializes, the mathematical principle each used, and the writing implement with which each worked.

1. Ms. Sawyer isn't the one who specializes in probability. Neither of the two women used the principle of absorption, and neither wrote with a fountain pen.

2. Mr. Sternhagen (who doesn't specialize in probability) used a pencil. The woman who specializes in calculus did not use chalk. The man who studies statistics (who didn't use the principle of absorption) wrote his proof in chalk.

3. If the man who specializes in geometry (who isn't Mr. Wentworth) wrote with a pencil, then he didn't use the principle of absorption.

4. The two people who used the principle of contraposition, who aren't the same gender, did not use the same writing implement.

		BRANCH					PRINCIPLE					WRITING IMPLEMENT				
		ALGEBRA	CALCULUS	GEOMETRY	PROBABILITY	STATISTICS	ABSORPTION	ABSORPTION	CONSTRUCTIVE DILEMMA	CONTRAPOSITION	CONTRAPOSITION	CHALK	CHALK	FOUNTAIN PEN	PENCIL	PENCIL
PERSON	MS. CHALMERS															
PERSON	MR. PANKHURST															
PERSON	MS. SAWYER															
PERSON	MR. STERNHAGEN															
PERSON	MR. WENTWORTH															
IMPLEMENT	CHALK															
IMPLEMENT	CHALK															
IMPLEMENT	FOUNTAIN PEN															
IMPLEMENT	PENCIL															
IMPLEMENT	PENCIL															
PRINCIPLE	ABSORPTION															
PRINCIPLE	ABSORPTION															
PRINCIPLE	CONSTRUCTIVE															
PRINCIPLE	CONTRAPOSITION															
PRINCIPLE	CONTRAPOSITION															

LOGIC PROBLEM 142 — DOUBLE OR NOTHING

Last Friday, Felix brought a pair of dice, one black and one red, into the office. "I will wager," he declared to his coworkers at Microtech, "that on a single roll of the dice none of you can roll doubles." So, during lunch, six of his coworkers (three of whom—Carola, Emma, and Kathryn—are women, and three of whom—Jeffrey, Leopold, and Tyson—are men) attempted to prove him wrong. Each bet Felix a different number of pretzel rods (1 through 6) that he or she would roll doubles on a single roll of the dice. As it turned out, Felix went back to his desk with a great many pretzel rods, for in no case did both dice turn up the same number. Each of the six coworkers rolled a different number (1 through 6) on the red die and a different number (1 through 6) on the black die. From the information provided, determine the number of pretzel rods each coworker bet, as well as the numbers that turned up on each one's red die and black die.

1. Carola bet exactly one more rod than the man who rolled a five on the red die. Jeffrey's roll on the black die was exactly two higher than that of the woman who bet four rods.

2. Emma's roll on the red die was exactly three lower than that of the man who rolled a four on the black die. Kathryn bet exactly two fewer rods than the man who rolled a five on the black die.

3. Tyson's roll on the red die was exactly one lower than that of the woman who bet three rods. Leopold's roll on the black die was exactly two lower than that of the woman who rolled a two on the red die.

4. The sum of the numbers turned up by each coworker's roll was different. No one's roll on the black die resulted in a number equal to the number of rods he or she bet. The one who bet six rods did not roll a six on the red die.

		PRETZEL RODS						RED DIE						BLACK DIE					
		1	2	3	4	5	6	1	2	3	4	5	6	1	2	3	4	5	6
COWORKER	CAROLA																		
	EMMA																		
	JEFFREY																		
	KATHRYN																		
	LEOPOLD																		
	TYSON																		
BLACK DIE	1																		
	2																		
	3																		
	4																		
	5																		
	6																		
RED DIE	1																		
	2																		
	3																		
	4																		
	5																		
	6																		

When the calendar turned to March, Sima still had all of the flowers that she received for Valentine's Day! Each of her five arrangements was sent by a different person (one of whom is Dennis), and each is composed entirely of a different type of flower. She placed each arrangement in a different type of container, and although she never thought her thumb was particularly green, she isn't questioning the longevity of these flowers! From the information provided, determine the type of flower in the arrangement sent by each person, as well as the container in which Sima placed each arrangement.

1. Virginia sent the lilies, which are either the flowers in the basket or the ones in the glass vase.
2. The flowers from Norma, which aren't daisies, aren't the ones in the candy jar. The daisies are in either the flowerpot or the glass vase.
3. Carl (who isn't the person who sent gardenias) is neither the one who sent the arrangement in the coffee mug nor the one who sent the arrangement in the flowerpot.
4. The flowers in the coffee mug (which weren't sent by Norma) aren't gardenias. Neither the candy-jar arrangement nor the coffee-mug arrangement is the one containing tulips. Alan's arrangement isn't the one that contains carnations.

		CARNATIONS	DAISIES	GARDENIAS	LILIES	TULIPS	BASKET	CANDY JAR	COFFEE MUG	FLOWERPOT	GLASS VASE
PERSON	ALAN										
	CARL										
	DENNIS										
	NORMA										
	VIRGINIA										
CONTAINER	BASKET										
	CANDY JAR										
	COFFEE MUG										
	FLOWERPOT										
	GLASS VASE										

LOGIC PROBLEM 144

Mark your calendars, ladies and gentlemen, for August 1 is National Mustard Day! As usual, the festivities will be held in Mount Horeb, Wisconsin—where the hot dogs are free, and ketchup is nowhere to be found. At last year's event, each of five friends (three of whom—Carl, Mario, and Tom—are men, and two of whom—Kathryn and Rita—are women) tried a different, exciting flavor of mustard (one was orange-honey mustard) on a different food (one had bratwurst). Before heading home, each mustard-lover bought a different piece of Mustard Day memorabilia (one bought a T-shirt). Can you cut the mustard and determine, from the information provided, the type of food on which each person sampled his or her chosen mustard and the souvenir each purchased?

1. Neither Carl (who didn't order a hot dog to go with his mustard) nor Tom is the one who put mustard on ice cream (certainly, an acquired taste). The one who ate a hot dog bought the "I love mustard" mug.

2. Mario, who ate a hamburger, isn't the man who bought the wristwatch. The jalapeño mustard was sampled by the person who bought the poster.

3. Neither Tom (who isn't the one who sampled the rosemary-garlic mustard) nor the one who ate a pretzel is the man who tried the raspberry mustard.

4. Carl didn't buy the wristwatch. Neither Carl nor Mario is the one who bought the baseball cap.

5. Neither the rosemary-garlic mustard (which wasn't Rita's choice) nor the red-pepper mustard was slathered onto a bowl of ice cream.

		FOOD					MUSTARD					SOUVENIR				
		BRATWURST	HAMBURGER	HOT DOG	ICE CREAM	PRETZEL	JALAPENO	ORANGE HONEY	RASPBERRY	RED PEPPER	ROSEMARY GARLIC	BASEBALL CAP	MUG	POSTER	T-SHIRT	WRISTWATCH
PERSON	CARL															
	KATHRYN															
	MARIO															
	RITA															
	TOM															
SOUVENIR	BASEBALL CAP															
	MUG															
	POSTER															
	T-SHIRT															
	WRISTWATCH															
MUSTARD	JALAPENO															
	ORANGE HONEY															
	RASPBERRY															
	RED PEPPER															
	ROSEMARY GAR.															

Give Karla a needle and thread and she transforms ordinary articles of clothing into astonishing works of art! Just last month, she created five such masterpieces for her wardrobe: after sewing each of five different articles of clothing using a different type of fabric, she embroidered each with a different sign of the zodiac. Just to keep things interesting, each design also highlights a different embroidery stitch from Karla's repertoire. From the information provided, determine the type of fabric Karla used for each article of clothing and the zodiacal sign she embroidered on each, as well as the embroidery stitch highlighted by each design.

1. The design highlighting the Gobelin stitch isn't embroidered on the article made from crepe fabric (which doesn't have the Aries design). Karla didn't use the feather stitch for the Capricorn design (which isn't on the vest).

2. The jersey skirt isn't the article with the Aries design (which isn't the one embroidered with the feather stitch). The design spotlighting the diamond stitch isn't on the rayon item (which isn't the one with the Scorpio design).

3. Neither the Gemini design nor the one highlighting the Gobelin stitch is featured on the rayon item. The initial of the stitch highlighted on the trousers comes at some point alphabetically after the initial of the stitch used in the Virgo design.

4. The initial of the stitch featured on the dress comes at some point alphabetically after the initial of the stitch spotlighted in the Aries design. The twill piece (which isn't the jacket) isn't embroidered with the Aries design (which isn't the one that employs the eyelethole stitch).

5. The cross-stitched design isn't the one adorning the vest (which isn't made from velvet). The initial of the stitch highlighted on the jacket (which doesn't have the Capricorn design) comes at some point alphabetically after that of at least one other stitch. The jacket isn't the item made from velvet.

		ARTICLE OF CLOTHING					SIGN					STITCH				
		DRESS	JACKET	SKIRT	TROUSERS	VEST	ARIES	CAPRICORN	GEMINI	SCORPIO	VIRGO	CROSS	DIAMOND	EYELETHOLE	FEATHER	GOBELIN
FABRIC	CREPE															
	JERSEY															
	RAYON															
	TWILL															
	VELVET															
STITCH	CROSS															
	DIAMOND															
	EYELETHOLE															
	FEATHER															
	GOBELIN															
SIGN	ARIES															
	CAPRICORN															
	GEMINI															
	SCORPIO															
	VIRGO															

LOGIC PROBLEM 146

Jai alai is often called the fastest sport in the world, and with good reason—the ball, or pelota, can travel at speeds of up to 175 miles per hour! A jai alai player uses a cesta—a long, curved wicker basket attached to the wrist—to hurl the pelota against the wall of the court, after which an opposing player attempts to catch and return the pelota. At a recent practice session, each of five jai alai players (including Luis), each of whom has a different uniform number, achieved a different impressive speed (125, 130, 135, 140, or 150 miles per hour) with the pelota. From the information provided, determine the top speed each player (identified by first and last names—one surname is Zabala) achieved, as well as the number (7, 19, 23, 42, or 84) each wears on his uniform.

1. Alberto, who doesn't wear number 84, achieved a faster speed than the one surnamed Lopez, who attained a faster speed than the player who wears number 7.

2. Jorge's top speed was slower than that of the player wearing number 23, whose speed was slower than that of the one surnamed Iriondo.

3. The player surnamed Garcia (who isn't Raul) is neither the one who wears number 7 nor the one whose top speed was 125 miles per hour.

4. Miguel, who achieved a speed in excess of 130 miles per hour, isn't surnamed Lopez or Badiola.

5. The one surnamed Badiola attained a faster speed than at least two other players. At least two players achieved faster speeds than the player who wears number 19.

		ALBERTO	JORGE	LUIS	MIGUEL	RAUL	BADIOLA	GARCIA	IRIONDO	LOPEZ	ZABALA	7	19	23	42	84
SPEED	125 mph															
	130 mph															
	135 mph															
	140 mph															
	150 mph															
UNIFORM NO.	7															
	19															
	23															
	42															
	84															
LAST NAME	BADIOLA															
	GARCIA															
	IRIONDO															
	LOPEZ															
	ZABALA															

LOGIC PROBLEM 147

All is not well for the producers of the new Broadway musical adaptation of *12 Angry Men*, due to open tomorrow. Last night, five of the principal actors, each of whom plays a different juror, threatened to leave the show! Each actor (including Dexter) had a different grievance (one was distressed by the unflattering photo of himself in the playbill). As evidence of his worth and stature, each reminded the producers of the glowing reviews he had received in a different, previous role (one had played Willy Loman in *Death of a Salesman*). Fortunately, tempers cooled quickly, and with all of the actors now agreeing to perform, it looks as if the production will open as scheduled. From the information provided, determine the grievance of the actor playing each juror (#3, #4, #6, #9, or #11), as well as the previous role that had earned him his rave reviews.

1. Bernard is neither the actor who complained of a broken lock on his dressing room door nor the one playing Juror #4. Reginald, who has never essayed the role of Tartuffe, isn't playing Juror #3 in the current production.

2. The actor who received raves for his portrayal of Cyrano de Bergerac, who wasn't the one who wanted top billing, isn't assaying the role of Juror #9.

3. Both the actor who has played Richard III (whose costume isn't too tight) and the one who has portrayed Cyrano are making their professional debuts, while Terence (who isn't playing Juror #9) is a veteran of London's West End making his first Broadway appearance.

4. The actor enraged because his most powerful and moving lines had been cut, who isn't making his professional debut, is neither the one playing Juror #6 (who isn't Morris) nor the one who previously appeared as Tartuffe.

5. Both Reginald (who isn't appearing as either Juror #4 or Juror #9) and the actor portraying Juror #6 (who doesn't want top billing) are veterans of many Broadway shows.

6. The actor whose costume is too tight isn't the one who played Cyrano (who isn't portraying Juror #3 in the current production). The one playing Juror #6 (who isn't the actor acclaimed for his portrayal of Oedipus) doesn't have the tight costume.

		GRIEVANCE					JUROR					ROLE				
		BROKEN LOCK	COSTUME TOO TIGHT	LINES CUT	UNFLATTERING PHOTO	WANTED TOP BILLING	#3	#4	#6	#9	#11	CYRANO de BERGERAC	OEDIPUS	RICHARD III	TARTUFFE	WILLY LOMAN
ACTOR	BERNARD															
	DEXTER															
	MORRIS															
	REGINALD															
	TERENCE															
ROLE	CYRANO															
	OEDIPUS															
	RICHARD III															
	TARTUFFE															
	WILLY LOMAN															
JUROR	#3															
	#4															
	#6															
	#9															
	#11															

LOGIC PROBLEM 148 GLASS ACT

When Donald received the August issue of *Artful Glass*, he was thrilled to see that the feature article focused on the prestigious MasterGlass Design competition for the premier designers in glass art. This was hardly surprising, as Donald and four of his colleagues (two of whom—Ian and Toby—are men, and two of whom—Rebecca and Vanessa—are women) had been the recipients of the competition's top five prizes (in order from highest to lowest, gold medal, silver medal, bronze medal, trophy, and honorable mention—there were no ties). The author discussed each artist's masterpiece, noting that each carved a different design (including an elaborate water fountain) into a globe of glass using a different decorative technique (one used etching). To Donald's delight, the author concluded his article by praising these five artists as "the new masters in glass art"! From the information provided, determine the prize each artist won, as well as the decorative technique each used to carve his or her design.

1. The three men are the artist who received the honorable mention, the one who carved a hearts design, and the man who used the fired-decorating technique.

2. Rebecca (who is neither the one who used the cutting technique nor the one who used the sandblasting technique) placed higher than at least two other people. Toby, who didn't create the hearts design, didn't receive the honorable mention. The garden design wasn't carved using the fired-decorating technique.

3. The artist who received the honorable mention (who didn't create the garden design) isn't the man who used the copper-wheel-engraving technique (who isn't Ian).

4. Vanessa (who didn't use the cutting technique) didn't receive the bronze medal, and she isn't the artist who carved intricate musical notes on his or her masterpiece.

5. The artist who sandblasted his or her design (which was neither the garden nor the geese) placed lower than the one who used the copper-wheel-engraving technique but higher than at least two other people. Ian isn't the person who designed a flock of geese on his or her globe.

		PRIZE					TECHNIQUE					DESIGN				
		GOLD	SILVER	BRONZE	TROPHY	HONORABLE MENTION	COPPER-WHEEL ENGRAVING	CUTTING	ETCHING	FIRED DECORATING	SANDBLASTING	FOUNTAIN	GARDEN	GEESE	HEARTS	MUSICAL NOTES
ARTIST	DONALD															
	IAN															
	REBECCA															
	TOBY															
	VANESSA															
DESIGN	FOUNTAIN															
	GARDEN															
	GEESE															
	HEARTS															
	MUSICAL NOTES															
TECHNIQUE	COPPER-WHEEL															
	CUTTING															
	ETCHING															
	FIRED															
	SANDBLASTING															

LOGIC PROBLEM 149

The stellar results of Paperco's fourth quarter were announced at this morning's executive meeting, in which the market head of each of the company's five divisions (including the napkins division) reported a different gain (2%, 4%, 6%, 8%, or 10%) for the quarter. To the further delight of the CEO, each market head also announced that his or her division had achieved record sales in a different city (including Montpelier, Vermont). Raises for everyone! From the information provided, determine the head (one is Mr. Cadieux) of each division, the city in which that division had record sales, and the fourth-quarter gain for each division.

1. The paper-plates division's gain was exactly 4 percentage points higher than that of Ms. Allen's division.

2. The divisions that experienced the 2% and 4% gains are the cups department and the one that had record sales in Olympia, Washington, in some order.

3. Ms. Hurley and Mr. Watson are the market head of the tissues division and the one who reported the 2% gain (who didn't announce record sales in Pierre, South Dakota), in some order.

4. The gain experienced by the paper-towels department was exactly 2 percentage points higher than that of the division that achieved record sales in Lansing, Michigan, which was exactly 2 percentage points higher than that reported by Ms. Hurley.

5. Mr. Kennon, who isn't the one who spoke about sales in Jackson, Mississippi, reported a higher gain than the head of the plates division.

6. The division that achieved record sales in Pierre (which isn't the tissues department) experienced a lower gain than at least one other division.

		HEAD					CITY					GAIN				
		MS. ALLEN	MR. CADIEUX	MS. HURLEY	MR. KENNON	MR. WATSON	JACKSON	LANSING	MONTPELIER	OLYMPIA	PIERRE	2%	4%	6%	8%	10%
DIVISION	CUPS															
	NAPKINS															
	PLATES															
	TISSUES															
	TOWELS															
GAIN	2%															
	4%															
	6%															
	8%															
	10%															
CITY	JACKSON															
	LANSING															
	MONTPELIER															
	OLYMPIA															
	PIERRE															

LOGIC PROBLEM 150   LONDON CALLING

After a whirlwind week of sightseeing in London, the Grants and the four other couples with whom they were traveling realized they would not be able to see everything on their "to-do" list. So, on the last day, they split up, with each couple going to see a different London landmark (and taking plenty of pictures to share with the others). Afterward, each couple dined at a different historic pub (one was The Lamb, a former haunt of Charles Dickens) before meeting the others back at the hotel, to which each traveled via a different form of transportation. From the information provided, determine the landmark (Buckingham Palace, the Globe Theatre, the National Gallery, the Tower of London, or Westminster Abbey) each couple visited, the pub where they dined, and the type of transport they took back to the hotel.

1. The couple who saw Buckingham Palace are neither the ones who dined at the Freemason's Arms nor the ones who took one of the city's famous double-decker buses back to the hotel (who aren't the Moores).

2. The Atkinsons, the pair who took a taxi, and the couple (who are neither the Cooks nor the Moores) who ate at the Sherlock Holmes pub visited the Globe Theatre, the National Gallery, and the Tower of London, in some order. The Palins didn't visit Westminster Abbey.

3. The couple who went to Westminster Abbey, who aren't the Cooks, aren't the couple who dined at the Freemason's Arms (who aren't the ones who rode London's subway system, known as the "tube").

4. The couple who crossed the Thames on a Riverbus to get back to the hotel, who didn't visit Buckingham Palace or Westminster Abbey, aren't the Atkinsons. The Moores are neither the couple who dined at the Black Friar nor the couple who took the tube.

5. The couple who rode to the hotel in a taxi, who are neither the ones who dined at the Freemason's Arms nor the ones who dined at the Rose and Crown, didn't visit either the Tower of London or the National Gallery.

6. The couple who splurged on a horse-drawn carriage ride didn't see the Tower of London.

		LANDMARK					PUB					TRANSPORT				
		BUCKINGHAM PALACE	GLOBE THEATRE	NATIONAL GALLERY	TOWER OF LONDON	WESTMINSTER ABBEY	BLACK FRIAR	FREEMASON'S ARMS	THE LAMB	ROSE AND CROWN	SHERLOCK HOLMES	CARRIAGE	DOUBLE-DECKER BUS	RIVERBUS	TAXI	TUBE
COUPLE	ATKINSON															
	COOK															
	GRANT															
	MOORE															
	PALIN															
TRANSPORT	CARRIAGE															
	DOUBLE-DECKER															
	RIVERBUS															
	TAXI															
	TUBE															
PUB	BLACK FRIAR															
	FREEMASON'S															
	THE LAMB															
	ROSE AND CROWN															
	SHERLOCK															

DON'T TRY THIS AT HOME   LOGIC PROBLEM 151

At last Saturday's 23rd-annual Jacksonville Juggling Jamboree, the air was full of excitement—and flying objects!—as jugglers from around the country came to show their stuff. Of particular note were five performers (three of whom—Amy, Kristin, and Nicole—are women, and two of whom—Geoff and Robert—are men), each of whom wowed the crowd by juggling a different, impressive item. Then, as the audience watched in astonishment, each juggler threw caution to the wind; he or she juggled the same items a second time, but with a different, self-imposed handicap intended to increase the degree of difficulty (for example, one person juggled while standing on his or her head). It seems as if Jacksonville has caught juggling fever! From the information provided, can you determine the items juggled by each person (identified by first and last names—one surname is Riley) and the handicap each gave him- or herself?

1. Kristin isn't the juggler surnamed Byron (who isn't the one who juggled chairs). The one surnamed Calloway juggled using only one hand.

2. The three women are the one who juggled swords, the one who juggled while blindfolded, and the one who juggled with one hand. The two men are the one who juggled chain saws and the one surnamed Nugent.

3. Kristin (who isn't surnamed Calloway) didn't juggle while blindfolded. Byron isn't the one who juggled the fish bowls full of water—and fish! Amy is either the person who juggled bowling balls or the chair-juggler.

4. The person who juggled while skateboarding didn't use chain saws. Calloway didn't juggle the chairs (which weren't kept aloft by the skateboarder).

5. If Geoff is the one surnamed Nugent, then he's the performer who juggled with one hand; otherwise, he's the one surnamed Woodhall (who isn't the person who juggled items behind his or her back).

		LAST NAME					ITEMS					HANDICAP				
		BYRON	CALLOWAY	NUGENT	RILEY	WOODHALL	BOWLING BALLS	CHAIN SAWS	CHAIRS	FISH BOWLS	SWORDS	BEHIND BACK	BLINDFOLDED	ONE-HANDED	SKATEBOARDING	STANDING ON HEAD
FIRST NAME	AMY															
	GEOFF															
	KRISTIN															
	NICOLE															
	ROBERT															
HANDICAP	BEHIND BACK															
	BLINDFOLDED															
	ONE-HANDED															
	SKATEBOARDING															
	STANDING ON															
ITEMS	BOWLING BALLS															
	CHAIN SAWS															
	CHAIRS															
	FISH BOWLS															
	SWORDS															

LOGIC PROBLEM 152

Chloe is an avid collector of the works of Max Ernst, the surrealist artist well-known for his use of frottage—the technique of creating textures by drawing on paper laid over a relief-like surface. In fact, she has managed to track down five of Ernst's lost charcoal drawings, each of which she discovered in a different unexpected location (she found one in an old farmhouse). Each of the five works is a different size (from smallest to largest, 5″ × 7″, 8″ × 10″, 9″ × 12″, 16″ × 20″, or 24″ × 36″), and each has a different subject. However, what really appeals to Chloe's artistic side is the fact Ernst used a different frottage material (in one case, straw) to create each drawing. From the information provided, determine the frottage material used to draw each subject, as well as the size of each drawing and the location where Chloe found it.

1. Neither the 5″ × 7″ drawing (which wasn't done with coins) nor the one Chloe found in the garage (which isn't the one that depicts an English cottage) is the one Ernst drew using broken glass.

2. Neither the drawing of a covered bridge nor the one done with coins (which wasn't found at a tag sale) measures 24″ × 36″. The one Chloe found at a tag sale is neither the 5″ × 7″ nor the 24″ × 36″ drawing.

3. The drawing Chloe found in an attic (which measures 9″ × 12″) doesn't depict a rocking horse. The drawing done with wood chips is smaller than the one done with dried flowers.

4. The drawing that Chloe scooped up at an antique shop is smaller than the one Ernst drew using coins but larger than the one depicting a picnic. The drawing done with broken glass doesn't measure 8″ × 10″.

5. The drawing done with dried flowers (which isn't the one depicting a litter of romping kittens) isn't the one that features the rocking horse (which wasn't found in a garage).

		MATERIAL					SIZE					LOCATION				
		BROKEN GLASS	COINS	DRIED FLOWERS	STRAW	WOOD CHIPS	5″ X 7″	8″ X 10″	9″ X 12″	16″ X 20″	24″ X 36″	ANTIQUE SHOP	ATTIC	FARMHOUSE	GARAGE	TAG SALE
SUBJECT	COVERED BRIDGE															
	ENGLISH COTTAGE															
	KITTENS															
	PICNIC															
	ROCKING HORSE															
LOCATION	ANTIQUE SHOP															
	ATTIC															
	FARMHOUSE															
	GARAGE															
	TAG SALE															
SIZE	5″ X 7″															
	8″ X 10″															
	9″ X 12″															
	16″ X 20″															
	24″ X 36″															

LOGIC PROBLEM 153

Winston Grimm, the legendary Hollywood monster-movie veteran, was well-known in his time as "the man of many faces," perpetually changing his appearance from film to film. During one feverish year, in fact, Winston worked on five different movies (including the classic *Nothing to Fear*) at the same time! Each film featured Winston as a different creature chasing helpless humans through a different setting (in one movie, he cornered his victims in a subway tunnel). In addition to the hours he spent before the cameras, he had to endure marathon stints in the makeup chair to prepare for a day's work, since the creation of each monster required a different number of hours (2, 3, 4, 5, or 6) in makeup. From the information provided, can you determine the creature (one was a zombie) Winston played in each movie, the setting of each film, and the number of hours Winston spent in makeup to prepare for each role?

1. Winston's makeup for *Terror by Moonlight* took longer to apply than his mummy disguise (which wasn't the makeup he wore in *It's Alive*). His mummy role kept him in the makeup chair longer than his role in the film set in a remote farmhouse (which wasn't the movie in which Winston played the goblin).

2. The makeup Winston wore to creep through the corridors of a deserted train station took less than six hours to apply.

3. The sea monster makeup (which wasn't needed for the monster portrayed in *The Visitor*) took exactly two fewer hours to apply than the makeup for his role in *Don't Open the Door!*

4. The five monsters Winston played are the one that stalked the residents of a stately Victorian mansion, the werewolf, the one in *The Visitor*, the one that terrorized the family in the farmhouse, and the one Winston's makeup artist took just two hours to create.

5. It took exactly three hours to transform Winston into the creature that lived in an abandoned building (which wasn't the werewolf).

		MOVIE					SETTING					HOURS				
		DON'T OPEN THE DOOR!	IT'S ALIVE	NOTHING TO FEAR	TERROR BY MOONLIGHT	THE VISITOR	ABANDONED BUILDING	FARMHOUSE	SUBWAY TUNNEL	TRAIN STATION	VICTORIAN MANSION	2	3	4	5	6
CREATURE	GOBLIN															
	MUMMY															
	SEA MONSTER															
	WEREWOLF															
	ZOMBIE															
HOURS	2															
	3															
	4															
	5															
	6															
SETTING	ABANDONED BLDG.															
	FARMHOUSE															
	SUBWAY TUNNEL															
	TRAIN STATION															
	VICTORIAN															

LOGIC PROBLEM 154

THE HEAT IS ON

With the cold weather fast approaching, the Greens and four other families recently replaced their old gas water heaters with brand new electric ones. Realizing that the job was too big for their amateur plumbing skills, each family (each of whom lives on a different street in Maple Valley) secured the services of Gus the plumber to handle the installation. Each heater is a different capacity (30, 40, 60, 70, or 100 gallons) and required a different amount of time to install. From the information provided, can you determine the street on which each family resides and the capacity in gallons of each one's water heater, as well as the number of hours (3, 4, 5, 6, or 7) Gus spent installing each?

1. The water heater belonging to the family residing on Mason Avenue required exactly one more hour to install than the Hathaways' heater. The 30-gallon heater, which did not require seven hours to install, is not the one owned by the Mitchells.

2. The heater that required four hours to install holds exactly 30 more gallons of water than the one owned by the family residing on Hickory Hill Road (which required exactly two fewer hours to install than the Fontaines' water heater). The Fontaines aren't the Baldwin Street residents.

3. The 40-gallon heater required exactly one more hour to install than the heater for the Walnut Street family.

4. The 30-gallon heater and the Yeardons' water heater required the shortest and the longest installation times, in some order. The heater on Sunny Lane required more time to install than the 40-gallon heater but less time to install than the 70-gallon heater.

		STREET					GALLONS					HOURS				
		BALDWIN STREET	HICKORY HILL ROAD	MASON AVENUE	SUNNY LANE	WALNUT STREET	30	40	60	70	100	3	4	5	6	7
FAMILY	FONTAINE															
	GREEN															
	HATHAWAY															
	MITCHELL															
	YEARDON															
HOURS	3															
	4															
	5															
	6															
	7															
GALLONS	30															
	40															
	60															
	70															
	100															

LOGIC PROBLEM 155

While on a long car trip to visit relatives, Joe and his four children played Twenty Questions: one person selected an object and revealed to the others the category—animal, vegetable, or mineral—into which it fell. The guessers were then permitted to ask up to 20 yes-or-no questions in order to identify the object. During the course of the trip, each person got to select a word three times; each selected a different "animal" (Barbra Streisand, eyelash, feather, milk, or wombat), a different "vegetable" (baseball bat, book, rose, taffy, or zucchini), and a different "mineral" (cement, gold, handcuffs, salt, or telephone). Joe especially likes this game, since it is the only one that holds his kids' attention for more than 20 minutes! From the information provided, determine the animal, vegetable, and mineral object chosen by each person.

1. The person who chose baseball bat selected neither feather nor milk. The one who picked baseball bat (who isn't Dina) selected neither cement nor handcuffs as his or her mineral word.

2. Oberton (who didn't select rose) didn't choose handcuffs (which wasn't the mineral chosen by the person who picked book) or cement.

3. Dina and Mary are the one who chose feather and the one who picked wombat, in some order.

4. Mary's mineral was neither salt nor telephone.

5. The one who selected eyelash is neither the one who picked taffy (who isn't Joe) nor the one who chose zucchini.

6. Neither Sal nor the one who selected Barbra Streisand chose rose (which wasn't selected by the person whose mineral was salt).

7. The one who selected Barbra Streisand and the one who picked eyelash chose cement and handcuffs as their minerals, in some order.

		ANIMAL					VEGETABLE					MINERAL				
		BARBRA STREISAND	EYELASH	FEATHER	MILK	WOMBAT	BASEBALL BAT	BOOK	ROSE	TAFFY	ZUCCHINI	CEMENT	GOLD	HANDCUFFS	SALT	TELEPHONE
PERSON	DINA															
	JOE															
	MARY															
	OBERTON															
	SAL															
MINERAL	CEMENT															
	GOLD															
	HANDCUFFS															
	SALT															
	TELEPHONE															
VEGETABLE	BASEBALL BAT															
	BOOK															
	ROSE															
	TAFFY															
	ZUCCHINI															

LOGIC PROBLEM 156   HABITAT IS WHERE IT'S AT

Built in Montreal for the Expo 67 as a model of futuristic living, the individual units of architect Moshe Safdie's Habitat complex are made from identical prefabricated cubes fitted together to create a testament to the powers of reinforced concrete. Yet the Habitat is not without its problems—yesterday, for example, Pierre and four other Habitat dwellers, each of whom resides in a different apartment (1A, 2B, 3C, 4D, or 5E), became disoriented while trying to return to their homes, the result being that each accidentally entered a different one of the same five apartments. Each person's confusion stemmed from a different source (one was momentarily thrown by the Habitat's new coat of paint). From the information provided, determine the reason why each person became disoriented, the apartment in which each actually lives, and the apartment each entered by accident.

1. Jean-Luc, who became confused when he entered via the seldom-used back entrance from the Habitat parking lot, lives in and mistakenly entered apartments 1A and 2B, in some order.

2. Simone lives in apartment 5E, but she accidentally entered apartment 4D.

3. Mimi and the one who became disoriented after stopping to talk to a neighbor are the one who mistakenly entered apartment 3C and the one who lives in apartment 3C, in some order.

4. The one whose view was obscured by an armful of groceries accidentally wound up in apartment 1A. Angelique dwells in apartment 4D.

5. The one who lives in apartment 2B became distracted by the Muzak in the elevator and got off on the wrong floor.

6. One person mistakenly entered and lives in apartments 2B and 5E, in some order.

		REASON					LIVES					ENTERED				
		ARMFUL OF GROCERIES	DISTRACTED BY MUZAK	NEW COAT OF PAINT	TALKED TO NEIGHBOR	USED BACK ENTRANCE	1A	2B	3C	4D	5E	1A	2B	3C	4D	5E
PERSON	ANGELIQUE															
	JEAN-LUC															
	MIMI															
	PIERRE															
	SIMONE															
ENTERED	1A											
	2B											
	3C											
	4D											
	5E											
LIVES	1A											
	2B											
	3C											
	4D											
	5E											

The cover story of this month's issue of *Suspended Animation* magazine features five pairs of husband-and-wife cartoonists. After years of turning out a daily comic strip, each couple has recently been awarded their very own animated television program, each of which has a different title and features the cartoon character that made its creators famous. These artists are truly drawn to success! From the information provided, can you determine the husband (Art, Drew, Knox, Moe, or Ozzie) and wife (Faye, Gina, Kelly, Ruby, or Zoe) who created each character (no two couples created the same character), as well as the show in which the character now appears?

1. Neither Moe (who isn't Faye's husband) nor Ozzie (who isn't the one who created Mr. Muggs) is working on *Toon in Tomorrow*. The show featuring Dizzy Dupree is neither *Disorder in the Court* nor *Monkey Business*.

2. Gina didn't create Peabody. Kelly and her husband (who isn't Moe) aren't the cartoonists who created Egbert. Ruby (who draws the character Dizzy Dupree) isn't one of the cartoonists working on *Toon in Tomorrow*.

3. Ozzie's character (who isn't Nemo) isn't the one starring in *Mouseterpiece Theatre*. Kelly is neither the one who created Nemo nor the one who created Peabody. *Week Daze*, which isn't Zoe's show, is neither the show featuring Egbert nor the one whose main character is Peabody. Drew isn't the animator of *Week Daze*.

4. Zoe is neither Ozzie's wife nor the creator of *Monkey Business*. Mr. Muggs is neither Art's creation nor the star of *Week Daze* (which isn't the show Gina draws). Dizzy Dupree isn't on *Week Daze*.

		WIFE					CHARACTER					SHOW				
		FAYE	GINA	KELLY	RUBY	ZOE	DIZZY DUPREE	EGBERT	MR. MUGGS	NEMO	PEABODY	DISORDER IN THE COURT	MONKEY BUSINESS	MOUSETERPIECE THEATRE	TOON IN TOMORROW	WEEK DAZE
HUSBAND	ART															
	DREW															
	KNOX															
	MOE															
	OZZIE															
SHOW	DISORDER/COURT															
	MONKEY BUSINESS															
	MOUSETERPIECE															
	TOON IN . . .															
	WEEK DAZE															
CHARACTER	DIZZY DUPREE															
	EGBERT															
	MR. MUGGS															
	NEMO															
	PEABODY															

Julie was badly bitten by the "theater bug" several years ago and has since become quite active in her community drama group. From 2012 through 2014, she landed starring roles in *Show Boat* and four other musical productions. On each play's opening night, a different member of her family (two are her daughter and her mother) was in the audience to show support, each sitting in a different seat (1A, 4C, 5A, 6D, or 8F) in the theater. For Julie, there really is no business like show business! From the information provided, can you determine the year in which each play was performed (apart from the one show she did the first year she joined the group, Julie performed in two plays each year), as well as the relative who attended opening night and the seat in which he or she sat?

1. Julie's husband (who did not sit in seat 4C) attended the opening night of *Bye Bye Birdie*. Julie's son (who sat in seat 5A) attended a performance in an earlier year than at least one other relative.

2. The family member who attended *Brigadoon* sat in seat 8F. The three female members of Julie's family attended the two plays that ran in 2013 and *Oklahoma!*, in some order.

3. Julie's sister sat in seat 1A. One of Julie's children attended the opening performance of *Carousel* (which wasn't the 2012 production).

		YEAR					RELATIVE					SEAT				
							DAUGHTER	HUSBAND	MOTHER	SISTER	SON	1A	4C	5A	6D	8F
PLAY	BRIGADOON															
	BYE BYE BIRDIE															
	CAROUSEL															
	OKLAHOMA!															
	SHOW BOAT															
SEAT	1A															
	4C															
	5A															
	6D															
	8F															
RELATIVE	DAUGHTER															
	HUSBAND															
	MOTHER															
	SISTER															
	SON															

During a recent dig on the distant Isle of Estria, archaeologists were thrilled to unearth five completely intact ancient Estrian masks! Each mask was made of a different material and decorated with a different type of ornament. Through a new and highly accurate electrocarbon-dating technique, it was established that each was created in a different year (from oldest to youngest, 1500 B.C., 1400 B.C., 1250 B.C., 1100 B.C., or 1000 B.C.). Further study at the Institute for Estrian Studies revealed that these masks (each of which was worn either on a feast day or during a ceremonial rite) served to identify the rank of the wearer within the hierarchy of the culture (each masks signifies a different rank—from lowest to highest, hunter, warrior, medicine man, oracle, and chief). From the information provided, determine the year the mask of each material was created, the type of decoration used on each, and the rank each designated.

1. The mask decorated with feathers doesn't designate the rank of chief. The mask adorned with terra-cotta pieces was worn on feast days.

2. The mask inlaid with colored sand (which wasn't the chief's) isn't made of leather. The leather mask, which was only worn during ceremonial rites, isn't decorated with stone beads.

3. The mask made of grass (which wasn't worn by the hunter) designated a lower rank than the mask covered with stone beads, which designated the rank immediately below the one represented by the mask made in 1400 B.C.

4. The masks signifying the three lowest ranks are, in some order, the one made from an ocean shell (which is exactly 150 years older than the grass mask), the mask decorated with wooden beads, and the one created in 1500 B.C.

5. The clay mask wasn't worn by the chief. The mask worn by the medicine man was made exactly 150 years after the one made of dried tree bark.

		MATERIAL					DECORATION					RANK				
		BARK	CLAY	GRASS	LEATHER	OCEAN SHELL	COLORED SAND	FEATHERS	STONE BEADS	TERRA COTTA	WOODEN BEADS	HUNTER	WARRIOR	MEDICINE MAN	ORACLE	CHIEF
YEAR	1500 B.C.															
	1400 B.C.															
	1250 B.C.															
	1100 B.C.															
	1000 B.C.															
RANK	HUNTER															
	WARRIOR															
	MEDICINE MAN															
	ORACLE															
	CHIEF															
DECORATION	COLORED SAND															
	FEATHERS															
	STONE BEADS															
	TERRA COTTA															
	WOODEN BEADS															

LOGIC PROBLEM 160

Xavier is a great architect—of dollhouses! Indeed, his elaborate and beautiful designs are much sought after by collectors—but five of his recent creations went not to strangers but to members of his own family. Each dollhouse was created in a different basic style from a different hardwood, and Xavier added to each a different decorative feature, although not necessarily one of its period or style. Each magnificent masterpiece was given to a different relative, who was struck speechless with wonder at its beauty. From the information provided, determine the style of the dollhouse made of each type of hardwood and the feature Xavier added to each building, as well as the relative who received each masterpiece.

1. Xavier's daughter isn't the one who received the dollhouse whose design included a skylight. Neither Xavier's mother nor his daughter is the relative who was given the Tudor mansion.

2. Of the Georgian structure and the building constructed from maple wood, one was Xavier's gift to his wife, and the other featured parquet floors.

3. Neither the mahogany dollhouse nor the Queen Anne mansion is the one Xavier gave to his aunt. Xavier didn't give the cherry-wood structure (which isn't the Victorian dollhouse) to either his cousin or his aunt.

4. The Gothic and Georgian houses are the dollhouse made of oak and the one with the gargoyle, in some order. The Queen Anne dollhouse (which isn't made of cherry wood) isn't the one that features the cupola.

5. The building with flying buttresses, the Victorian mansion (which isn't made of mahogany), and the structure created from birch wood were given to Xavier's aunt, his cousin, and another relative, in some order. The cherry-wood dollhouse isn't the Gothic design.

		HARDWOOD					FEATURE					RELATIVE				
		BIRCH	CHERRY	MAHOGANY	MAPLE	OAK	CUPOLA	FLYING BUTTRESS	GARGOYLE	PARQUET FLOORS	SKYLIGHT	AUNT	COUSIN	DAUGHTER	MOTHER	WIFE
STYLE	GEORGIAN															
	GOTHIC															
	QUEEN ANNE															
	TUDOR															
	VICTORIAN															
RELATIVE	AUNT															
	COUSIN															
	DAUGHTER															
	MOTHER															
	WIFE															
FEATURE	CUPOLA															
	FLYING BUTTRESS															
	GARGOYLE															
	PARQUET FLOORS															
	SKYLIGHT															

LOGIC PROBLEM 161

The Institute for Rhinoceros Studies has just completed a weekend-long lecture series showcasing the work of five prominent zoologists, including the renowned Professor Childs. Each zoologist had spent the last year studying the grazing habits of a different species of rhinoceros (one studied the black rhinoceros) and, in particular, tracking the movements of a single rhino, each of whom has been given a different, friendly name. Each researcher's presentation consisted of a different number of slides (30, 40, 50, 60, or 70). From the information provided, identify the zoologist who studied each species of rhinoceros and the rhino in that group on which each focused, as well as the number of slides each showed.

1. Professor Bates didn't show either exactly 10 fewer or exactly 10 more slides than did his colleague who studied Gus. Professor Bates showed fewer slides than the researcher who studied the white rhinoceroses (which isn't the species of the one named Cupid).

2. The zoologist who studied the Sumatran rhinoceroses showed exactly 20 fewer slides than the one who studied the rhino named Queenie.

3. The researcher who studied the rhino nicknamed Flo showed fewer slides than Professor Gruber but exactly 10 more slides than the one who studied the Javan rhinoceroses.

4. Professor Jessup, who studied the Indian rhinoceroses, showed exactly 30 more slides than the researcher who studied Gus. The main subject of Professor Wilkins's study was either Lucky or Queenie.

		SPECIES					RHINO					SLIDES				
		BLACK	INDIAN	JAVAN	SUMATRAN	WHITE	CUPID	FLO	GUS	LUCKY	QUEENIE	30	40	50	60	70
ZOOLOGIST	BATES															
	CHILDS															
	GRUBER															
	JESSUP															
	WILKINS															
SLIDES	30															
	40															
	50															
	60															
	70															
RHINO	CUPID															
	FLO															
	GUS															
	LUCKY															
	QUEENIE															

LOGIC PROBLEM 162

BIDS IN TOYLAND

An avid toy collector, Milton was thrilled to hear that several rare toys from the '50s and '60s were to be auctioned off at Sotheby's. Reviewing the catalog, Milton found five different toys (including the Treasure Island Play Set) that he felt would complement his collection perfectly. Each of the toys was introduced in a different year (1959, 1960, 1961, 1962, or 1963) by a different toy company. When the gavel came down on the final sale, Milton had acquired all five of his choices, paying a different price for each ($350, $400, $450, $500, or $550). From the information provided, determine the company that manufactured each toy, the year of its release, and the price Milton paid for each.

1. The toy Milton bought for $550, which is neither Wrestling Robots nor the toy made by Wonder World, wasn't introduced in 1962.

2. The toy released in 1963 is neither the one made by Gleeco nor the one for which Milton paid $550. The toy introduced by Pennywhistle in 1959 sold for less than the Sergeant Steve Starcruiser doll.

3. Milton paid more for the Magic Phone (which wasn't made by Playtime) than he did for the toy manufactured by Funtastic. The Playtime toy wasn't released in 1960.

4. Lights Fantastic (which wasn't made by Playtime) was made at some point after the toy for which Milton paid $400. Sergeant Steve Starcruiser wasn't created in 1961.

5. The toy Milton bought for $350 (which wasn't made by Funtastic) isn't Lights Fantastic (which wasn't introduced in 1963). Milton didn't pay $450 for the Wonder World toy. The Gleeco toy (which wasn't made in 1960) isn't Wrestling Robots.

		TOY					YEAR					PRICE				
		LIGHTS FANTASTIC	MAGIC PHONE	SGT. STEVE STARCRUISER	TREASURE ISLAND PLAY SET	WRESTLING ROBOTS	1959	1960	1961	1962	1963	$350	$400	$450	$500	$550
COMPANY	FUNTASTIC															
COMPANY	GLEECO															
COMPANY	PENNYWHISTLE															
COMPANY	PLAYTIME															
COMPANY	WONDER WORLD															
PRICE	$350															
PRICE	$400															
PRICE	$450															
PRICE	$500															
PRICE	$550															
YEAR	1959																
YEAR	1960																
YEAR	1961																
YEAR	1962																
YEAR	1963																

While ringing up customers at Green Scene Garden Supply, Philip the salesclerk made a remarkable observation: each of the next five people standing in line seemed to be wearing a T-shirt with a different pro-weed saying! Intrigued, he asked each person to explain his or her attire, whereupon he learned that not only did each plan on cultivating a different type of weed (one is wild carrot) in his or her yard, but each was also buying a different item designed to promote weed growth! Quickly hiding the herbicide behind his counter, Philip wished them luck in their weed-growing endeavors. From the information provided, determine the weed each person (including Donald) is cultivating, the pro-weed saying (one is "Weeds: We're plants too!") on each person's T-shirt, and the item each bought.

1. Neil stood immediately in front of the one who is cultivating ragweed and immediately behind the one who purchased the special weed soil.

2. The one wearing the T-shirt with the saying "Save the weeds!" stood somewhere behind the one buying the weed seeds, who stood immediately behind the one who bought the specially formulated fertilizer.

3. The one wearing the "Weeds are our friends" T-shirt stood immediately in front of Sheila, who stood immediately in front of the one cultivating cattails.

4. Alan, who was first in line, was not the one buying a product for his or her dandelions. The person buying the supply of mulch was neither the one wearing the "Stop the weed whacking!" T-shirt (who isn't Alan) nor the one wearing the "Save the weeds!" T-shirt.

5. Mary, who was standing at the tail end of the line buying a product for her thistles, was not the one wearing the "No more Weed-B-Gone!" shirt. Mary wasn't the one in line to buy plant food.

		WEED					SAYING					ITEM				
		CATTAIL	DANDELION	RAGWEED	THISTLE	WILD CARROT	NO MORE WEED-B-GONE!	SAVE THE WEEDS!	STOP THE WEED WHACKING!	WEEDS ARE OUR FRIENDS	WEEDS: WE'RE PLANTS TOO!	FERTILIZER	MULCH	PLANT FOOD	SEEDS	SOIL
PERSON	ALAN															
	DONALD															
	MARY															
	NEIL															
	SHEILA															
ITEM	FERTILIZER															
	MULCH															
	PLANT FOOD															
	SEEDS															
	SOIL															
SAYING	NO MORE															
	SAVE THE															
	STOP THE															
	WEEDS ARE OUR															
	WEEDS: WE'RE															

LOGIC PROBLEM 164   SCULPTURESQUE

Monica has enjoyed great success as a sculptor, but her recent elemental series has elevated her to the realm of greatness. Monica carved five different-titled sculptures, each from a different material (including marble). Each sculpture required a different number of hours to complete, and Monica finished each outstanding piece of artwork in a different month (March through July). Soon to be unveiled is Monica's goddess series, which will represent the different religions of the world. From the information provided, can you determine the material from which Monica carved each sculpture, as well as the number of hours required to complete each and the month in which she finished that masterpiece?

1. Monica spent progressively more hours each month working on each sculpture. She completed Earth the month after Air but the month before the sculpture that took her exactly 125 hours to finish.

2. Fire (which was carved from alabaster) required exactly 50 more hours to complete than did the bronze masterpiece, which took exactly 50 more hours to finish than did the clay sculpture.

3. Monica finished the wood sculpture (which required exactly 50 hours to complete) the month after Water but the month before the bronze piece. The number of hours Monica required to complete Life was exactly five times that needed to finish Air.

		ALABASTER	BRONZE	CLAY	MARBLE	WOOD						MARCH	APRIL	MAY	JUNE	JULY
SCULPTURE	AIR															
	EARTH															
	FIRE															
	LIFE															
	WATER															
MONTH	MARCH															
	APRIL															
	MAY															
	JUNE															
	JULY															
HOURS												

LOGIC PROBLEM 165

Although initially regarded as shocking and inappropriate, Dadaism, the notorious "anti-art" movement of the '20s, has since been embraced by the art community as an important and influential style. So, when offered a chance to show several Dadaist sculptures created by some of the movement's biggest names, New York's Museum of Modern Art jumped at the chance. The MoMA curators were somewhat disappointed to discover that these works were not, in fact, made by the famous artists themselves, but by some of their lesser-known relatives. Each of the five artists had used the Dadaist "ready-made" technique, transforming ordinary objects into art by changing the context in which they are viewed. Each person's sculpture is composed of a different number of a different common object (one artist used snorkels). When the works were delivered, the MoMA curators had to admit that the artists had inherited some of their famous relatives' talent, and happily agreed that the show would go on. From the information provided, determine the number of the object each artist (identified by first and last names—one surname is Duchamp) used in his or her sculpture.

1. The paint-roller sculpture contains exactly two more pieces than the work created by the person surnamed Arp and exactly twice as many objects as Lucy's sculpture (which isn't the one made from cheese graters).

2. Clyde, who created neither the cheese-grater sculpture nor the one composed of shoehorns, used exactly one more object than Lucy (who isn't the artist surnamed Tzara).

3. Darla, whose last name is neither Ernst nor Tzara, used more objects than the artist surnamed Ball. Wilma, who isn't surnamed Ernst, used more objects than Uriah. The least number of objects used by any sculptor is 5, and the most used is 12.

4. The gravy-boat sculpture contains exactly twice as many pieces as Clyde's work. Neither the artist surnamed Ball nor the one surnamed Ernst worked with shoehorns.

		LAST NAME					NUMBER					OBJECT				
		ARP	BALL	DUCHAMP	ERNST	TZARA						CHEESE GRATERS	GRAVY BOATS	PAINT ROLLERS	SHOEHORNS	SNORKELS
FIRST NAME	CLYDE															
	DARLA															
	LUCY															
	URIAH															
	WILMA															
OBJECT	CHEESE GRATERS															
	GRAVY BOATS															
	PAINT ROLLERS															
	SHOEHORNS															
	SNORKELS															
NUMBER																

LOGIC PROBLEM 166 SURFIN' SURFARI

Gidget and four of her friends had a fabulous time catching the waves at the beach on Saturday. Experienced surfers all, they had carefully waxed their boards, each of which is known by a different affectionate nickname (one surfer calls his or her board "Moon Doggie"), in preparation for the big day. While shooting the curls, each surfer attempted a different maneuver. After several wipeouts (no two surfers fell the same number of times), each showed off a near-perfect execution of the maneuver. Waterlogged and exhausted after a long day of sun and surf, the five friends can hardly wait for their next wet 'n' wild adventure. From the information provided, can you determine the nickname of each surfer's board, as well as the maneuver each attempted and the number of wipeouts (3, 4, 5, 6, or 7) each endured?

1. Either Slade or the surfer who attempted the 360 is the owner of the surfboard nicknamed "Surf Master" (who wiped out six times).

2. Larue (who didn't try the reverse take-off) and the owner of "Big Kahuna" are the friend who had five wipeouts and the surfer who perfected the turn-around, in some order.

3. Of Sandi and the person who calls his or her board "Hawaiian Tropic," one attempted the 360, and the other fell three times.

4. If Hobie is the person who perfected the crossover, then the surfer who perfected the reverse take-off wiped out four times; otherwise, Hobie is the one who tried the roller coaster, and the friend who perfected the reverse take-off fell five times.

5. Slade had fewer wipeouts than the surfer who nicknamed his or her surfboard "Boogie Board," who wiped out exactly one time fewer than Sandi.

		BOARD					MANEUVER					WIPEOUTS				
		BIG KAHUNA	BOOGIE BOARD	HAWAIIAN TROPIC	MOON DOGGIE	SURF MASTER	CROSSOVER	REVERSE TAKE-OFF	ROLLER COASTER	360	TURN-AROUND	3	4	5	6	7
SURFER	GIDGET															
	HOBIE															
	LARUE															
	SANDI															
	SLADE															
WIPEOUTS	3															
	4															
	5															
	6															
	7															
MANEUVER	CROSSOVER															
	REVERSE															
	ROLLER COASTER															
	360															
	TURN-AROUND															

A NEW LEASE ON LIFE LOGIC PROBLEM 167

Earlier this week, Bonnie visited five apartments she'd seen listed in the real-estate section of her local paper. Her search took her to five different streets, where each apartment she saw had a different monthly rent ($450, $550, $650, $700, or $800). Each unit had a different feature that Bonnie found particularly attractive, but also a different drawback (basement apartment, fifth-floor walk-up, no pets, no window in bedroom, or too far from work). After carefully weighing her options, Bonnie finally put a down payment on the apartment that best suited her needs. From the information provided, determine the monthly rent of the apartment on each street (one is Arbor Place) and the attraction and drawback of each place, as well as the unit Bonnie ultimately opted to rent.

1. The five apartments are the one on Lager Street, the one that doesn't allow pets, the one with the $650 rent, the one with the doorman, and the one Bonnie ended up renting.

2. The apartment Bonnie selected (which costs less than $700 per month) isn't the one she considered too far from work. Bonnie didn't choose the unit with the lovely fireplace.

3. The apartment Bonnie opted to rent (which isn't the one on Rutherford Avenue) isn't the one with a garden (which doesn't cost $700 per month).

4. Four of the apartments are the one on Palm Boulevard (which doesn't rent for $800 per month), the one that doesn't have a window in the bedroom, the $550-per-month unit, and the one Bonnie selected.

5. The basement apartment (which costs more than $650 per month) has a dishwasher.

6. The $550-per-month unit (which isn't the one that bans pets) isn't the one on Benson Road (which isn't the apartment conveniently close to public transportation).

		RENT					ATTRACTION					DRAWBACK				
		$450	$550	$650	$700	$800	DISHWASHER	DOORMAN	FIREPLACE	GARDEN	PUBLIC TRANSPORTATION	BASEMENT APARTMENT	FIFTH-FLOOR WALK-UP	NO PETS	NO WINDOW IN BEDROOM	TOO FAR FROM WORK
STREET	ARBOR PLACE															
	BENSON ROAD															
	LAGER STREET															
	PALM BOULEVARD															
	RUTHERFORD AVE.															
DRAWBACK	BASEMENT APT.															
	FIFTH-FLOOR															
	NO PETS															
	NO WINDOW															
	TOO FAR															
ATTRACTION	DISHWASHER															
	DOORMAN															
	FIREPLACE															
	GARDEN															
	PUBLIC TRANSP.															

LOGIC PROBLEM 168 CHRISTMAS WITH THE DRAGONS

He thought it would take forever, but at long last, Gargouille the dragon finished grading his students' papers and set off for home to enjoy a good, old-fashioned, dragon Christmas. He was very excited to see his four siblings (two of whom—Fafnir and Smaug—are males, and two of whom—Jormungand and Vermithrax—are females) and show them the neat present he had bought for their parents. It turned out that each dragon had purchased a different present (including gag "Smoking Section" place mats) for the folks. After they enjoyed their Christmas feast and decorated the tree (each dragon hung a different number of ornaments), each of the siblings led the family in a different traditional, dragon-style, Christmas carol (including that old classic, "All I Want for Christmas Is My Two Front Fangs"). From the information provided, determine the number of ornaments (5, 10, 15, 20, or 25) each dragon hung, the present each gave, and the carol each sang.

1. Jormungand hung exactly 15 more ornaments than the one who gave a claw sharpener (who didn't sing "Fiery the Snowman").

2. The one who brought the automatic cave-door opener (who isn't Vermithrax) hung exactly 5 more ornaments than Gargouille. The dragon who sang "Silent Knight" hung exactly 5 fewer ornaments than the one who sang "O Lizard Town of Bethlehem."

3. Vermithrax hung exactly 5 fewer ornaments than the one who sang "Here Comes Santa Claws" (who isn't the one who gave the wing brush) and exactly 5 more ornaments than the one who gave the scale shiner.

4. Smaug hung exactly 5 fewer ornaments than did his brother who sang "Fiery the Snowman."

		FAFNIR	GARGOUILLE	JORMUNGAND	SMAUG	VERMITHRAX	CAVE-DOOR OPENER	CLAW SHARPENER	PLACE MATS	SCALE SHINER	WING BRUSH	ALL I WANT FOR CHRISTMAS	FIERY THE SNOWMAN	HERE COMES SANTA CLAWS	O LIZARD TOWN OF BETHLEHEM	SILENT KNIGHT
ORNAMENTS	5															
	10															
	15															
	20															
	25															
CAROL	ALL I WANT FOR															
	FIERY THE															
	HERE COMES															
	O LIZARD TOWN															
	SILENT KNIGHT															
PRESENT	CAVE-DOOR															
	CLAW SHARPENER															
	PLACE MATS															
	SCALE SHINER															
	WING BRUSH															

LOGIC PROBLEM 169

Although Norman the numismatist has many rare and valuable coins in his collection, he is still most fond of the five coins his great-aunt Millicent Moneypenny gave him when he was growing up. Each coin is of a different grade (in order from lowest to highest, fine, very fine, extremely fine, uncirculated, or proof), and Norman acquired each in a different year (1964, 1965, 1966, 1967, or 1969). Aware of each coin's sentimental, if not necessarily monetary, value, Norman carefully stores each one in a different type of container. From the information provided, can you determine the grade of each coin (no two of which are the same denomination) and the year each was acquired, as well as the container in which each is stored?

1. The dime, quarter, and half dollar are the one stored in the album, the extremely fine coin, and the one acquired in 1969, in some order. The penny and the nickel are, in some order, the one acquired in 1966 and the coin that is exactly one grade higher than the dime but exactly one grade lower than the coin stored in the velvet pouch (which isn't a penny or a nickel).

2. The half dollar is of a lower grade than at least one other coin. Norman acquired the penny in a year ending with an odd digit. The coin stored in the metal cabinet is of a lower grade than at least two other coins.

3. Norman received the coin with the lowest grade exactly two years after the one he keeps stored in a glass jar. The very-fine coin was acquired exactly two years before the one stored in a special coin envelope (which is not the nickel).

		GRADE					YEAR					CONTAINER				
		FINE	VERY FINE	EXTREMELY FINE	UNCIRCULATED	PROOF	1964	1965	1966	1967	1969	ALBUM	CABINET	ENVELOPE	JAR	POUCH
COIN	DIME															
	HALF DOLLAR															
	NICKEL															
	PENNY															
	QUARTER															
CONTAINER	ALBUM															
	CABINET															
	ENVELOPE															
	JAR															
	POUCH															
YEAR	1964															
	1965															
	1966															
	1967															
	1969															

LOGIC PROBLEM 170 WHAT'S IN A NAME?

In feudal times, a person's surname was derived from his or her trade. That all changed when several rebellious youngsters refused to go into the family business and decided instead to try their hands at new occupations. Each of five young men in the medieval village of Bryertown, for example, shocked his family by choosing a field outside of the family business—each man selected a different family trade of one of the other four men—with the result that no man's surname appeared in the name of his occupation. Eventually, each young man's skeptical parents admitted that their son displayed strong aptitudes for his new craft (blacksmith, glovemaker, stonemason, weaver, or woodcarver), as each finished his apprenticeship in a different, comparatively short amount of time (8, 10, 14, 16, or 20 months). Each of these highly skilled workers went on to make quite a name for himself as a master of his trade! From the information provided, determine the trade chosen by each young man (identified by first and last names), as well as the number of months his apprenticeship lasted.

1. Giles entered the family profession of the one who became a woodcarver. The young man surnamed Weaver had a longer apprenticeship than the one surnamed Mason.

2. The apprenticeship of the one whose last name was Glover was longer than that of the young man surnamed Weaver. Mr. Carver, who isn't Orville, chose the family profession of the one who became a glovemaker.

3. Mr. Smith was an apprentice for exactly six months longer than Dunston. Giles took exactly six months longer to master his craft than Mr. Mason. Mr. Carver's apprenticeship lasted exactly twice as long as that of the woodcarver.

4. The person who studied Terrence's family trade (which isn't woodcarving) is either Orville or Mr. Smith. Wallace excelled as a stonemason.

		LAST NAME					TRADE					MONTHS				
		CARVER	GLOVER	MASON	SMITH	WEAVER	BLACKSMITH	GLOVEMAKER	STONEMASON	WEAVER	WOODCARVER	8	10	14	16	20
FIRST NAME	DUNSTON															
	GILES															
	ORVILLE															
	TERRENCE															
	WALLACE															
MONTHS	8															
	10															
	14															
	16															
	20															
TRADE	BLACKSMITH															
	GLOVEMAKER															
	STONEMASON															
	WEAVER															
	WOODCARVER															

LOGIC PROBLEM 171

Jake and his fiancée had so much fun registering at First Impressions, a boutique specializing in china patterns with designs by great artists, that they immediately recommended it to four other couples. Each couple selected a design by a different artist (including Pisarro), ordering either four, six, or eight place settings. From the information provided, determine the man (Alex, Brad, Greg, Jake, or Stewart) and woman (Alicia, Elaine, Monica, Nadine, or Suzanna) who make up each couple, the artist's design they selected, and the number of place settings they ordered.

1. Brad and his fiancée (who aren't the couple who selected the Monet pattern) ordered exactly four more place settings than Nadine and her fiancé.

2. Exactly one couple ordered eight place settings. Of the other four couples, Monica and her fiancé ordered the same number of settings as Stewart and his fiancée, while Nadine and her fiancé ordered the same number of settings as the couple who ordered the Seurat design.

3. Two couples—Greg and his fiancée and Elaine and her fiancé—ordered the same number of settings. Suzanna and her fiancé ordered the same number of settings as another couple who selected the Renoir china.

4. Alex and his fiancée ordered exactly two more place settings than the couple who chose the Degas pattern.

		WOMAN					DESIGN					SETTINGS		
		ALICIA	ELAINE	MONICA	NADINE	SUZANNA	DEGAS	MONET	PISARRO	RENOIR	SEURAT			
MAN	ALEX													
	BRAD													
	GREG													
	JAKE													
	STEWART													
SETTINGS														
DESIGN	DEGAS													
	MONET													
	PISARRO													
	RENOIR													
	SEURAT													

LOGIC PROBLEM 172

When the town of Rome, Georgia, opened its Cosmopolitan Opera House six years ago, the founders vowed to bring the greatest operas of the world to their community. So far, they have made good on their promise, bringing in great directors and performers from around the globe. Indeed, in each of five of the past six years (2009, 2010, 2011, 2013, and 2014), a different prima donna has graced the stage of Rome's fledgling opera house, each traveling from a different country to appear in a different opera. From the information provided, can you determine the prima donna who visited Rome each year, the opera in which she performed, and the country from which she traveled?

1. Josephine visited Rome exactly one year before Maria. The guest soloist from Italy appeared exactly one year before the one who performed in *Otello*.

2. The prima donna who appeared in *The Marriage of Figaro* isn't the one from Austria. The *Don Giovanni* performer isn't from Argentina.

3. Arabella is either the soloist from Spain or the one who visited in 2014, or both. The prima donna from Argentina is either Lucretia or the one who appeared in a 2011 performance, or both.

4. *Madama Butterfly* was performed in 2013.

5. Volante visited Rome at some point before Lucretia and at some point after Arabella. *Carmen* was staged the year before the prima donna from France made her appearance but at some point after *The Marriage of Figaro*.

		ARABELLA	JOSEPHINE	LUCRETIA	MARIA	VOLANTE	CARMEN	DON GIOVANNI	MADAMA BUTTERFLY	MARRIAGE OF FIGARO	OTELLO	ARGENTINA	AUSTRIA	FRANCE	ITALY	SPAIN
YEAR	2009															
	2010															
	2011															
	2013															
	2014															
COUNTRY	ARGENTINA															
	AUSTRIA															
	FRANCE															
	ITALY															
	SPAIN															
OPERA	CARMEN															
	DON GIOVANNI															
	M. BUTTERFLY															
	MARRIAGE															
	OTELLO															

LOGIC PROBLEM 173

It has been an extraordinary year for "Lucky" Penny Mazel; not only did she get to appear on five of her favorite television game shows, she also won the grand prize on each program! Each show has a different host and airs on a different channel (2, 4, 5, 7, or 9), and each awarded Penny a different prize for her excellent performance as a contestant. Although obviously thrilled, Penny is a bit tired from her whirlwind victories and plans to take the next year off to enjoy her winnings! From the information provided, can you determine the channel on which each show is broadcast, the host of that program, and the prize that Penny won on each?

1. The three game shows that air during the day are the one hosted by Jack Gates, the one shown on the next higher channel than the one on which *On a Roll* is broadcast, and the one that awarded Penny a new Porsche. The two game shows that air during the evening are the one hosted by Gwen Hart and the one on which Penny won $50,000.

2. *Beginner's Luck* is not the program on which Penny won an all-expenses-paid Hawaiian vacation.

3. *Anyone's Guess* airs on a higher-numbered channel than *Bet the Bank* but on a lower-numbered channel (but not the next lower channel) than the show on which Penny won a Porsche. *Beginner's Luck* (which isn't hosted by Gwen Hart) airs on a higher-numbered channel (but not the next higher channel) than the program hosted by Whit Masterson.

4. Bruce Warner (who hosts a daytime show) isn't the host of the program on which Penny won a computer. The show that awarded the computer airs on the next lower channel than the one on which *The Quiet Game* is broadcast.

5. Jack Gates, on whose program Penny won the entertainment center, is the host of neither *Beginner's Luck* nor *On a Roll*. Neither Veronica Starr nor Whit Masterson hosts either *On a Roll* or *Bet the Bank*. Veronica Starr's program airs on either the next higher or the next lower channel than the one on which Whit Masterson's show is broadcast.

		SHOW					HOST					PRIZE				
		ANYONE'S GUESS	BEGINNER'S LUCK	BET THE BANK	ON A ROLL	THE QUIET GAME	BRUCE WARNER	GWEN HART	JACK GATES	VERONICA STARR	WHIT MASTERSON	COMPUTER	ENTERTAINMENT CENTER	$50,000	HAWAIIAN VACATION	PORSCHE
CHANNEL	2															
	4															
	5															
	7															
	9															
PRIZE	COMPUTER															
	ENTERTAINMENT															
	$50,000															
	HAWAIIAN															
	PORSCHE															
HOST	BRUCE WARNER															
	GWEN HART															
	JACK GATES															
	VERONICA STARR															
	WHIT MASTERSON															

LOGIC PROBLEM 174 — SORRY, WRONG NUMBER

The accounting firm of Potter & Peters gets its fair share of wrong numbers, as Leo and the four other receptionists who work there can certainly attest. Over the course of three days (Wednesday through Friday), each receptionist received a call from someone trying to reach a different firm (one person asked for the firm of Pilsner & Patton), each of which conducts a different type of business (one is a law office). From the information provided, determine the receptionist who took the call asking for each company and the type of business in which that company engages, as well as the day the call came in.

1. Exactly two wrong numbers came in on Wednesday—the one from a caller asking for the firm of Peterson & Porter and the one taken by Kay.

2. The caller who was trying to reach the publishing company, whose call wasn't taken by Tracy, didn't ask for the firm of Pippin & Prosky. Antoinette's wrong number (which was the only wrong number of the day) came on a later day of the week than the call for the dentist's office.

3. Three of the calls were the one Kay took (which wasn't from a person asking for the firm of Pucket & Prentice), the one for the publishing company, and the one that asked for the firm of Pepper & Pickney.

4. The call asking for the firm of Pippin & Prosky and the one for the construction company were taken by Antoinette and Basil, in some order.

5. Two wrong numbers that came on the same day were the one for the firm of Pepper & Pickney and the one for the florist. Kay didn't take the call asking for the dentist's office.

		PEPPER & PICKNEY	PETERSON & PORTER	PILSNER & PATTON	PIPPIN & PROSKY	PUCKET & PRENTICE	CONSTRUCTION	DENTIST	FLORIST	LAW	PUBLISHING	WEDNESDAY	THURSDAY	FRIDAY
	NAME						BUSINESS					DAY		
RECEPTIONIST	ANTOINETTE													
	BASIL													
	KAY													
	LEO													
	TRACY													
DAY	WEDNESDAY													
	THURSDAY													
	FRIDAY													
BUSINESS	CONSTRUCTION													
	DENTIST													
	FLORIST													
	LAW													
	PUBLISHING													

Archaeology can be a highly competitive field—a lesson that the five ambitious graduate students in Dr. McCoy's archaeology seminar have learned all too well! On a recent dig, each student tried a bit too hard to impress the professor; each claimed to have discovered a different type of bone (one was a humerus), which each attributed to a different, prehistoric creature (including the little-known mendacedon). But when each discovery was cleaned and proudly displayed to Dr. McCoy, it was revealed to be a different, disappointingly modern object. Although each student gets an A for effort, they all clearly have a lot left to learn. From the information provided, determine the bone each student claimed to find and the creature to which it allegedly belonged, as well as the object each had actually "discovered."

1. The one who unearthed an ordinary stick (who isn't Sara) isn't the one who claimed to have found the mandible. Aaron is neither the one who found the supposed ulna nor the one who attributed his or her bone to the ancient peccarosaurus (which wasn't the find that turned out to be handlebars from a bicycle).

2. The supposed vagaridactyl bone is neither the handlebars nor the fishing rod. The discovery revealed to be a broken fishing rod is neither the one found by Oscar nor the one purportedly from a ludificasaurus (which wasn't the femur). The ludificasaurus bone isn't the one that was actually a rusted car antenna.

3. Sara (who didn't discover the peccarosaurus bone) didn't find either the handlebars or the trowel lost by another student. Aaron (who didn't find the ludificasaurus bone) isn't the one who claimed to have found the fibula. Heidi didn't find the mandible (which wasn't the handlebars) or the fibula.

4. The purported femur (which wasn't the handlebars) is neither Oscar's discovery nor the one theorized to have come from the improbusaurus. Neither the improbusaurus bone (which wasn't the lost trowel) nor the ludificasaurus bone (which wasn't Lola's find) was the ulna. Lola didn't unearth the fishing rod.

5. Sara didn't find the fibula. Oscar is neither the one who found the vagaridactyl bone nor the one who found the lost trowel. The fishing rod wasn't the alleged mandible.

		BONE					CREATURE					OBJECT				
		FEMUR	FIBULA	HUMERUS	MANDIBLE	ULNA	IMPROBUSAURUS	LUDIFICASAURUS	MENDACEDON	PECCAROSAURUS	VAGARIDACTYL	ANTENNA	FISHING ROD	HANDLEBARS	STICK	TROWEL
STUDENT	AARON															
STUDENT	HEIDI															
STUDENT	LOLA															
STUDENT	OSCAR															
STUDENT	SARA															
OBJECT	ANTENNA															
OBJECT	FISHING ROD															
OBJECT	HANDLEBARS															
OBJECT	STICK															
OBJECT	TROWEL															
CREATURE	IMPROBUSAURUS															
CREATURE	LUDIFICASAURUS															
CREATURE	MENDACEDON															
CREATURE	PECCAROSAURUS															
CREATURE	VAGARIDACTYL															

LOGIC PROBLEM 176   WHEN IN PALINDROME . . .

"So many dynamos!" exclaimed Regdell Ledger book critic Sara Varas in her review of the five latest best-sellers from Palindrome Press. Each of these new releases (including the sentimental pet biography *Tess, a Basset*) is a different length, and each was penned by a different, highly acclaimed author (two of whom—Bob and Otto—are men, and three of whom—Eve, Hannah, and Lil—are women). "They're so great," Sara raved, "you'll want to read them backward and forward!" From the information provided, can you determine each author's first and last names (one surname is Emufume), as well as the title of each one's novel and the number of pages (121, 222, 323, 424, or 525) it contains?

1. Bob's work is longer than the book of poetry entitled *Yo, Banana Boy!* but exactly 101 pages shorter than the book written by the one surnamed Kinnik.

2. The book penned by Ms. Seles is shorter than Lil's offering but exactly 101 pages longer than the book of memoirs entitled *Martini Tram*.

3. The book written by the one surnamed Trebert is shorter than the detective novel *L.A. Usual*.

4. Bob's book is either exactly 101 pages longer or exactly 101 pages shorter than Otto's, which is either exactly 202 pages longer or exactly 202 pages shorter than the book penned by the one surnamed Drassard (who isn't Lil).

5. Eve's travelogue, *Sail On, Olias*, is not 222 pages long.

		DRASSARD	EMUFUME	KINNIK	SELES	TREBERT	L.A. USUAL	MARTINI TRAM	SAIL ON, OLIAS	TESS, A BASSET	YO, BANANA BOY!	121	222	323	424	525
FIRST NAME	BOB															
	EVE															
	HANNAH															
	LIL															
	OTTO															
PAGES	121															
	222															
	323															
	424															
	525															
TITLE	L.A. USUAL															
	MARTINI TRAM															
	SAIL ON, OLIAS															
	TESS, A BASSET															
	YO, BANANA BOY!															

LOGIC PROBLEM 177

Five of the residents of Scotland Road held a tag sale last Sunday. As the neighbors were setting out their goods, each person noticed a different object being sold by one of the other four that was perfect for his or her own home. Although each of the five items was already marked with a different price ($6, $7, $8, $9, or $10), each owner agreed to sell the item to his or her neighbor at discount (except for the two items that were sold for $3, each item was marked down to a different price). From the information provided, match the buyer and seller in each transaction and determine the original price and reduced price ($2, $3, $4, or $5) of the item each person bought.

1. Guiseppe received exactly $2 more for an item than he spent on an item; the original price of the item he sold was exactly $3 more than the original price of the item he purchased.

2. The item Flora purchased was originally priced exactly $2 higher than the marked price of the item Arnie sold. Lester didn't originally charge $7 for the item his friend bought.

3. The original price of the item Lester purchased was exactly $2 less than the original price of the item that was reduced to $2. The item Flora bought was originally priced at $8.

4. Arnie spent exactly $2 more for an item than he received for an item. Valeria was asking for exactly $1 less for the item she sold than the original price of the item she purchased.

5. Either Flora bought an item from Valeria, or Valeria bought an item from Flora. Valeria didn't purchase an item from Guiseppe.

		SELLER					ORIGINAL PRICE					REDUCED PRICE				
		ARNIE	FLORA	GUISEPPE	LESTER	VALERIA	$6	$7	$8	$9	$10	$2	$3	$3	$4	$5
BUYER	ARNIE															
	FLORA															
	GUISEPPE															
	LESTER															
	VALERIA															
REDUCED	$2															
	$3															
	$3															
	$4															
	$5															
ORIGINAL	$6															
	$7															
	$8															
	$9															
	$10															

LOGIC PROBLEM 178 RACK 'N' ROLL

On Saturdays, Nat plays pool with his friends at Bookman's Billiard Hall. Although nine ball has always been their game of choice, he and his five fellow pool sharks (two of whom—Anthony and Mark—are men, and three of whom—Elsie, Johnette, and Lita—are women) decided to do something different for last night's gathering; each player researched a different pool game (one is forty-one), which he or she then taught to the others. Throughout the course of the evening, each player made an impressive trick shot—or lucky shot, as some of the others claimed—which he or she promptly christened with a different, snazzy name (one is Levitation). As the night wore on, their pool-shooting skills waned; in the last few games they played, each player scratched with a different ball (numbered 10 through 15). At this, the pool players took their cue and headed home. From the information provided, determine the game each player taught the others and the trick shot he or she invented, as well as the number of the ball with which he or she scratched.

1. Lita, who didn't choose the game of eight ball, surprised everyone with the trick shot she named The Master. Anthony isn't the one who selected the game called rotation.

2. The person who invented the Big Sneaky maneuver (which wasn't Nat's trick shot) scratched with the ball numbered exactly 1 lower than that missed by the person who chose the game of cowboy.

3. Elsie, who wanted to play the game called Mr. and Mrs., scratched with the 15 ball. Elsie didn't create the shot called Ziparoo.

4. Johnette and Mark are the one who chose the game called line-up and the one who invented Through the Woods (who scratched with the ball numbered exactly 1 higher than the one who chose line-up), in some order.

5. The person who chose eight ball scratched with the ball numbered exactly 1 higher than that missed by the person who created the shot called Bongo's Revenge but exactly 1 lower than the scratched ball of Ziparoo's inventor.

6. No two women scratched with consecutively numbered balls.

		GAME						TRICK SHOT						BALL					
		COWBOY	EIGHT BALL	FORTY-ONE	LINE UP	MR. AND MRS.	ROTATION	BIG SNEAKY	BONGO'S REVENGE	LEVITATION	THE MASTER	THROUGH THE WOODS	ZIPAROO	10	11	12	13	14	15
PLAYER	ANTHONY																		
	ELSIE																		
	JOHNETTE																		
	LITA																		
	MARK																		
	NAT																		
BALL	10																		
	11																		
	12																		
	13																		
	14																		
	15																		
TRICK SHOT	BIG SNEAKY																		
	BONGO'S																		
	LEVITATION																		
	THE MASTER																		
	THROUGH THE																		
	ZIPAROO																		

LOGIC PROBLEM 179

Ever since her first child was knee-high, Lisa has kept a yearly record of her sons' heights. Now that her five sons are older (each is a different age—13, 15, 17, 19, or 21 years old), Lisa has a difficult time accurately measuring them, since each is over six feet tall! Lisa, who stood on a stepladder to attain this year's measurements, noted that each son is a different height (6′1″, 6′2″, 6′3″, 6′4″, or 6′5″). As she transferred the measurements to her record book, Lisa noticed that each of the five had also been a different height (6′1″, 6′2″, 6′3″, 6′4″, or 6′5″) in 2013. Probably due to Lisa's somewhat inaccurate measuring technique, each son's 2014 height was not always greater than his 2013 height. From the information provided, determine the age of each of Lisa's sons and the height each measured in 2013 and 2014.

1. Ivan, who measured 6′3″ in 2014, is 2 years younger than his brother who measured 6′3″ in 2013.

2. According to his mother's measurements, Will (who is 2 years older than Salvatore) was taller in 2013 than in 2014.

3. Matthew's 2013 height was exactly 1″ greater than Salvatore's 2014 height. Matthew's height in 2013 is the same as his 19-year-old brother's height in 2014.

4. Benjamin is 2 years older than a brother who measured taller in 2014 than in 2013. At least one of Lisa's sons measured the same height in both years.

		AGE					2013 HEIGHT					2014 HEIGHT				
		13	15	17	19	21	6′1″	6′2″	6′3″	6′4″	6′5″	6′1″	6′2″	6′3″	6′4″	6′5″
SON	BENJAMIN															
	IVAN															
	MATTHEW															
	SALVATORE															
	WILL															
2014 HEIGHT	6′1″															
	6′2″															
	6′3″															
	6′4″															
	6′5″															
2013 HEIGHT	6′1″															
	6′2″															
	6′3″															
	6′4″															
	6′5″															

LOGIC PROBLEM 180   CLEARLY NOT CLAIRVOYANT

After reading an article on how to develop extrasensory perception, Reese, who has always been fascinated with things psychic, hung a shingle outside her door advertising herself as a fortune teller. Her first customers were five pregnant friends (including Mandy), each of whom was due to give birth in early April and wanted to find out the gender of her child. Summoning all of her mental power, Reese made her best prediction for each woman's expected bundle (or bundles—Reese was convinced that each of two women were having twins) of joy. She predicted that each of two of the women would have a boy, one would have a girl, one would have twin girls, and one would have twins of opposite genders. As it turned out, however, when each woman finally did give birth (no two did so on the same date), only one woman had the same number of babies as Reese had predicted! From the information provided, determine the date (the 1st through 5th of April) each woman gave birth, the gender or genders Reese had predicted for each one's child or children, and the actual gender or genders of each woman's offspring (one woman had a boy, one had a girl, one had twin boys, one had twins of opposite genders, and one had triplets, all boys).

1. Sasha and Kayla gave birth on the 1st and 5th, in some order. Any babies that Reese predicted for Sasha were of the same gender, but this was the opposite gender of any babies she actually had. Similarly, any babies that Reese predicted for Kayla were of the same gender, but this was the opposite gender of any babies she actually had. Kayla is the only person who had the same number of babies as Reese had predicted.

2. Reese predicted that the women who gave birth on the 2nd and the 3rd would each have at least one girl.

3. The total number of boys born to the women who gave birth on the 1st and 2nd is equal to the total number of boys born to the women who gave birth on the 4th and 5th.

4. Of the two women whom Reese predicted would each give birth to a single boy, one gave birth the day after Jacqui, and the other gave birth the day after a woman (but not Erin) whom Reese predicted would have two babies.

		DATE					PREDICTED					ACTUAL				
		1st	2nd	3rd	4th	5th	BOY	BOY	GIRL	TWIN GIRLS	TWINS BOY/GIRL	BOY	GIRL	TRIPLET BOYS	TWIN BOYS	TWINS BOY/GIRL
WOMAN	ERIN															
WOMAN	JACQUI															
WOMAN	KAYLA															
WOMAN	MANDY															
WOMAN	SASHA															
ACTUAL	BOY																
ACTUAL	GIRL																
ACTUAL	TRIPLET BOYS																
ACTUAL	TWIN BOYS																
ACTUAL	TWINS BOY/GIRL																
PREDICTED	BOY																
PREDICTED	BOY																
PREDICTED	GIRL																
PREDICTED	TWIN GIRLS																
PREDICTED	TWINS BOY/GIRL																

LOGIC PROBLEM 181

Len loves to travel, but he always struggles with the ever-changing exchange rates in the countries he visits. In fact, when caught without his trusty guidebooks and exchange tables, Len has been known to make some fairly costly miscalculations. On five recent trips, for example, Len did some rather exorbitant tipping—in each of the five countries he visited (including Australia), he gave a tip to a different person (one is a cab driver) which he later calculated to be worth a different, rather staggering amount in dollars. In spite of his monetary misadventures, Len had a wonderful time in each country, and he didn't let his tipping troubles deter him from the purpose of his visit (each trip was made for a different reason—one was to visit the museums). He has also been fortunate that the people he encountered in his travels have all been extremely friendly—not to mention appreciative! From the information provided, determine the reason Len traveled to each country, as well as the tip (in U.S. dollars) he gave to each person.

1. Len's five vacations were the trip to Argentina, his Italian vacation, the one on which he took a bicycle tour of the countryside, the one on which he overtipped a bellhop, and the one on which he mistakenly tipped $25 (which was the smallest of the five tips). Len's largest tip was $75.

2. Italy wasn't the country in which he gave an extremely generous tip to a waiter. The relaxing beach vacation (which wasn't in Italy) was neither the one on which he overtipped the doorman nor the one on which he gave the barber a tremendous tip.

3. The difference between the tip Len left in Spain and the one he gave to the waiter is equal to the difference between the waiter's tip and the one he gave on his beach vacation (which wasn't to Spain).

4. The tip Len gave while on the bicycle tour (which wasn't given to a waiter) was less than the one he left in Spain. The tip Len gave to the waiter was larger than the one he gave while on his shopping expedition.

5. The barber didn't receive a tip during Len's shopping vacation. The tip Len left in France was exactly $10 more than the one from his vacation to visit his relatives.

6. The total of Len's tips was $250.

		REASON					PERSON					TIP				
		BEACH	BICYCLE TOUR	MUSEUMS	RELATIVES	SHOPPING	BARBER	BELLHOP	CAB DRIVER	DOORMAN	WAITER					
COUNTRY	ARGENTINA															
	AUSTRALIA															
	FRANCE															
	ITALY															
	SPAIN															
TIP																
PERSON	BARBER															
	BELLHOP															
	CAB DRIVER															
	DOORMAN															
	WAITER															

LOGIC PROBLEM 182

Once a year, Cub Scout Pack 238 holds an awards ceremony to honor its scouts and den leaders. During this event, scouts are given merit badges and those who have earned new ranks are advanced; in addition, special awards are given to those scouts who have shown exceptional ability in a particular aspect of their scout training. At this year's gathering, each of six scouts, each of whom is a different rank (from lowest to highest, tiger, bobcat, wolf, bear, lion, or webelo), was presented with a different award as his den leader proudly looked on. From the information provided, can you determine the rank of each scout, his den leader (no two have the same den leader—one is Mr. Shaw), and the award (one is for leadership skills) he won?

1. Mr. Bergman's scout (who isn't Marcus) didn't win the swimming award. Billy, who isn't in Mr. Bergman's den, isn't the one who was rewarded for excellent safety skills. Raphael isn't the one who received the fitness award.

2. The scout with superb camping skills has a lower rank than the scout in Ms. Witt's den (who isn't Dennis). Ms. Vane's scout has a higher rank than Julio.

3. The tiger, bobcat, and wolf scouts are Gino, the one in Mr. Parsons' den, and the one who won the safety award, in some order.

4. The bear, lion, and webelo scouts are Dennis, Mr. Bergman's scout, and the one who received the hiking award, in some order.

5. The scout who was rewarded for his excellent swimming skills (who isn't Gino) is exactly one rank higher than Billy but exactly one rank lower than the scout in Ms. Cortez's den.

		RANK						DEN LEADER						AWARD					
		TIGER	BOBCAT	WOLF	BEAR	LION	WEBELOS	MR. BERGMAN	MS. CORTEZ	MR. PARSONS	MR. SHAW	MS. VANE	MS. WITT	CAMPING	FITNESS	HIKING	LEADERSHIP	SAFETY	SWIMMING
SCOUT	BILLY																		
	DENNIS																		
	GINO																		
	JULIO																		
	MARCUS																		
	RAPHAEL																		
AWARD	CAMPING																		
	FITNESS																		
	HIKING																		
	LEADERSHIP																		
	SAFETY																		
	SWIMMING																		
DEN LEADER	MR. BERGMAN																		
	MS. CORTEZ																		
	MR. PARSONS																		
	MR. SHAW																		
	MS. VANE																		
	MS. WITT																		

Last Saturday afternoon, the Foreston community recreation center held a swim meet in which over a hundred students from area high schools competed in various events. After the competition, the tired swimmers piled into the center's cafeteria for a pizza party. Five friends (including Tom) sitting at the same table observed that they had each chosen a different variety of pizza (one chose deluxe). As they chatted, they also learned that, while each had participated in only one race that afternoon, none of them had participated in the same event (one swam in the relay race), and that each had finished in a different place (from highest to lowest, first through fifth) in his or her event. In fact, it looked like the only thing they had in common was a love of swimming—and pizza! From the information provided, can you match each swimmer with his or her event, place of finish, and variety of pizza?

1. Harry finished his race in a lower place than the swimmer who ate mushroom pizza, who finished exactly two places lower than the one who did the backstroke.

2. The freestyle swimmer, who finished fourth, did not order a cheese pizza.

3. The swimmer who did the butterfly (who didn't finish last) finished exactly one place below Amanda. Joy finished lower than at least one other swimmer.

4. The swimmer who ate cheese pizza finished exactly two places lower than the swimmer who ate pepperoni pizza (who did not finish first in his or her race).

5. The swimmer who did the breaststroke finished in a higher place than the one who ate onion pizza, who finished exactly one place higher than Helen.

		EVENT					FINISH					PIZZA				
		BACKSTROKE	BREASTSTROKE	BUTTERFLY	FREESTYLE	RELAY	FIRST	SECOND	THIRD	FOURTH	FIFTH	CHEESE	DELUXE	MUSHROOM	ONION	PEPPERONI
SWIMMER	AMANDA															
	HARRY															
	HELEN															
	JOY															
	TOM															
PIZZA	CHEESE															
	DELUXE															
	MUSHROOM															
	ONION															
	PEPPERONI															
FINISH	FIRST															
	SECOND															
	THIRD															
	FOURTH															
	FIFTH															

LOGIC PROBLEM 184

When gossip columnist Louella Hopper received birth announcements from five happy couples, she had to smile—it had been her scoop on the surprise weddings of these couples the previous year that had made her career! She well remembered the night the five couples had gotten married—she had been putting the final touches on her column when she received a hot tip that each of five heiresses had broken up with her wealthy fiancé in order to elope with an honest but penniless newspaper reporter! Louella used her sources to find out the different time of each secret wedding and dropped in on each happy couple just as they were exchanging vows. Once they were officially man and wife, each couple was pleased to talk to Louella, telling her of the different, unusual way they had met. In writing her column that night, Louella used a different adjective to describe each heiress and a different adjective to describe each reporter (she described one as "gruff"). From the information provided, match each heiress with her reporter husband (identified by the adjectives Louella used to describe them), as well as the time (7:30, 8:00, 8:30, 9:00, or 9:30) each couple was married and the way they originally met.

1. The "screwy" heiress and her groom were married at some point earlier in the evening than the future parents of the 7-pound baby but later than at least one other couple.

2. The "crusty" reporter and his bride, who met when they were mistakenly issued tickets for the same seat on the train, weren't married at 8:00, but they were married exactly 30 minutes after the "zany" heiress and her groom.

3. The "wisecracking" reporter and his bride were married exactly 30 minutes before the ones who met when their golf balls were accidentally switched and exactly 30 minutes after the future parents of Baby Cuddles.

4. The "sardonic" reporter was not married at 9:30. The couple who met while sharing a taxi ride in the rain, whose automated spaghetti twirler went kerflooey during Louella's visit, were married exactly 30 minutes before the "irascible" newspaperman and his bride.

		REPORTER					TIME					MET				
		CRUSTY	GRUFF	IRASCIBLE	SARDONIC	WISECRACKING	7:30	8:00	8:30	9:00	9:30	FENDER BENDER	GOLF BALLS SWITCHED	SAME TRAIN TICKETS	SPILLED SOUP	TAXI RIDE
HEIRESS	ECCENTRIC															
	MADCAP															
	SCREWY															
	WACKY															
	ZANY															
MET	FENDER BENDER															
	GOLF BALLS															
	SAME TRAIN															
	SPILLED SOUP															
	TAXI RIDE															
TIME	7:30															
	8:00															
	8:30															
	9:00															
	9:30															

This is part 1 of a two-part puzzle. It is necessary to work back and forth between this part and part 2 on page 193 in order to solve the puzzle.

A whole year has passed since gossip columnist Louella Hopper broke the stories of the five runaway heiresses who married reporters, and although she has moved on to other gossip items, she still remembers these couples fondly, so it was with great delight that she received a birth announcement from each. Each had just become the proud parents of a bouncing baby (including Baby Nugget), each of whom weighs a different amount (7, 8, 10, 11, or 13 pounds). When Louella came for a visit to see the baby, each couple showed her around their fully automated kitchen, and even though a different labor-saving appliance (including an automatic ketchup squirter) malfunctioned while she was there, Louella had a wonderful time. From the information provided, determine the weight in pounds of each heiress's baby, as well as the appliance that malfunctioned during Louella's visit.

1. The baby belonging to the couple whose automatic toast butterer went berserk weighs exactly 2 pounds more than the offspring of the "zany" heiress.

2. The "eccentric" heiress and her husband, whose electric banana peeler went out of control, were married exactly one hour after the ones who met during a mild fender bender (who are the proud parents of Baby Poopsie).

3. The couple whose automated pancake flipper went out of whack (whose baby weighs more than Baby Binky) were married exactly one hour before the couple who met when the heiress accidentally spilled soup on the reporter at a fancy restaurant.

4. The heiress who was married at 9:30 (who isn't the one Louella described as "madcap") gave birth to the 11-pound baby. Louella described Baby Snookums's mother as "wacky" in her original article.

| | | WEIGHT IN POUNDS | | | | | BABY | | | | | APPLIANCE | | | | |
		7	8	10	11	13	BINKY	CUDDLES	NUGGET	POOPSIE	SNOOKUMS	BANANA PEELER	KETCHUP SQUIRTER	PANCAKE FLIPPER	SPAGHETTI TWIRLER	TOAST BUTTERER
HEIRESS	ECCENTRIC															
	MADCAP															
	SCREWY															
	WACKY															
	ZANY															
APPLIANCE	BANANA PEELER															
	KETCHUP															
	PANCAKE FLIPPER															
	SPAGHETTI															
	TOAST BUTTERER															
BABY	BINKY															
	CUDDLES															
	NUGGET															
	POOPSIE															
	SNOOKUMS															

*This is part 2 of a two-part puzzle. It is necessary to work back and forth between this part and part 1 on page 192 in order to solve the puzzle.

LOGIC PROBLEM 186 RAGS TO RICHES

Although now in his nineties, shoe-polish magnate Sanford Klomp still recalls his shoe-shining days on the streets of Chicago as a young boy. In fact, he insists that he was inspired to found his own company when, over the course of one remarkable year, he shined the shoes of five wealthy and famous businessmen (including John D. Rockefeller), each in a different month. Each of these great men gave Sanford a large tip ($10, $18, $20, $28, or $36) and advised him to follow his dreams. Although it was many years ago, Sanford remembers every detail as if it were yesterday—right down to the type of shoes each man wore (no two wore the same type—one wore oxfords). Sanford soon followed in his customers' footsteps and climbed to the top of the business world! From the information provided, can you determine the millionaire whose shoes Sanford shined each month (May through September), as well as the type of shoes each wore and the tip each gave Sanford?

1. The five famous millionaires, in order from the first Sanford met to the last, are J.P. Morgan, the one who gave him the $20 tip, the one who wore stogies, Andrew Carnegie, and the one who wore wingtips.

2. Sanford shined the balmorals at some point earlier in the year than the brogans but later in the year than at least one other pair of shoes.

3. Sanford's customer in September (who wasn't Henry Ford) gave him exactly $8 less than the one whose shoes he shined in May but exactly $10 more than his August customer.

4. Neither H.L. Hunt nor Henry Ford wore the stogies.

		MILLIONAIRE					SHOES					TIP				
		ANDREW CARNEGIE	HENRY FORD	H.L. HUNT	JOHN D. ROCKEFELLER	J.P. MORGAN	BALMORALS	BROGANS	OXFORDS	STOGIES	WINGTIPS	$10	$18	$20	$28	$36
MONTH	MAY															
	JUNE															
	JULY															
	AUGUST															
	SEPTEMBER															
TIP	$10															
	$18															
	$20															
	$28															
	$36															
SHOES	BALMORALS															
	BROGANS															
	OXFORDS															
	STOGIES															
	WINGTIPS															

BIDDING FOR BACHELORS — LOGIC PROBLEM 187

The community of Lake Forest is raising money for the preservation of its historic landmarks. One of last week's fund-raising events was a "bachelor auction," in which five single men (Adam, Brad, Josh, Steve, and Trent) generously volunteered to put themselves on the auction block to be bid upon for a date. To sweeten the deal, each of five popular restaurants (one is Clarissa's) graciously agreed to donate a romantic dinner for two to a different bachelor and his top bidder. The competition was fierce, but in the end, each bachelor was snapped up by a different woman for a different, generous price ($70, $80, $90, $100, $110). From the information provided, can you determine the woman (Anna, Erica, Holly, Lisa, or Tammy) who successfully bid on each bachelor, the restaurant in which they dined, and the amount of each woman's bid?

1. Tammy bid $100 for a date with Josh, but they are neither the couple who dined at Donetto's nor the pair who ate at Town Fare.

2. Trent and his date had such a good time at the Manor House that they decided to go out again next week.

3. The $70 bachelor and his date ordered lobsters at the Seafood Shanty. Lisa (who didn't bid $70) went out with Adam, but they did not dine at Town Fare.

4. Anna bid $110 for her bachelor.

5. Erica didn't go out with Brad, who was auctioned off for $80.

		ADAM	BRAD	JOSH	STEVE	TRENT	CLARISSA'S	DONETTO'S	MANOR HOUSE	SEAFOOD SHANTY	TOWN FARE	$70	$80	$90	$100	$110
WOMAN	ANNA															
	ERICA															
	HOLLY															
	LISA															
	TAMMY															
BID	$70															
	$80															
	$90															
	$100															
	$110															
RESTAURANT	CLARISSA'S															
	DONETTO'S															
	MANOR HOUSE															
	SEAFOOD SHANTY															
	TOWN FARE															

LOGIC PROBLEM 188   COMMERCIAL SUCCESSES

Tonight on Inside Entertainment, don't miss our special feature "Before They Were Stars!" We'll give you an exclusive inside look at the very first television appearances of five of today's most well-known faces. Before becoming household names, these celebrities (each of whom currently has a different profession—one is a sitcom star) started out in commercials. In fact, each one first appeared in a commercial for a different company (one was Viking Burger). From these humble beginnings—each performer was given just one line in his or her debut commercial— these superstars launched themselves to the very top of the entertainment world. Don't miss your only chance to see them "Before They Were Stars!" From the information provided, can you determine the current profession of each celebrity, as well as the company each endorsed and the line (no two had the same line) each delivered in his or her first commercial appearance?

1. Robert Craig (who isn't the movie star) shouted "Who wants to limbo?" in his very first television appearance.

2. Susan Tomaling isn't the news anchor (who isn't the celebrity whose first job was in an Atomic Cola commercial). Howard O'Brien isn't the one who delivered the line "Don't miss the party!"

3. If Chloe Wofford is the sportscaster, then she is the star who uttered the line "Save us, Value Man!"; otherwise, she is the one who exclaimed "Now that's a great deal!" Susan Tomaling appeared in a Mattress Planet ad.

4. Neither Chloe Wofford (who isn't the one who appeared in a commercial for The Shoe Shack) nor Susan Tomaling is the sportscaster.

5. The talk-show host isn't the former Wonder Weeder spokesperson. Susan Tomaling (who started her career with the words "To pay more would be a crime") isn't the movie star, who once endorsed The Shoe Shack.

6. Talk-show host Allen Konigsberg didn't appear in the Atomic Cola commercial.

		PROFESSION					COMPANY					LINE				
		MOVIE STAR	NEWS ANCHOR	SITCOM STAR	SPORTSCASTER	TALK-SHOW HOST	ATOMIC COLA	MATTRESS PLANET	THE SHOE SHACK	VIKING BURGER	WONDER WEEDER	DON'T MISS THE PARTY!	NOW THAT'S A GREAT DEAL!	SAVE US, VALUE MAN!	TO PAY MORE WOULD BE A CRIME	WHO WANTS TO LIMBO?
CELEBRITY	ALLEN KONIGSBERG															
	CHLOE WOFFORD															
	HOWARD O'BRIEN															
	ROBERT CRAIG															
	SUSAN TOMALING															
LINE	DON'T MISS...															
	NOW THAT'S..															
	SAVE US...															
	TO PAY MORE..															
	WHO WANTS TO...															
COMPANY	ATOMIC COLA															
	MATTRESS PLANET															
	THE SHOE SHACK															
	VIKING BURGER															
	WONDER WEEDER															

LOGIC PROBLEM 189

One of the job hazards of the business traveler is the dreaded red-eye flight; the late evening/early morning arrivals and departures take their toll on even the most experienced passengers. Currently, each of five weary, bleary-eyed travelers with early-morning meetings is waiting to board his or her flight, each of which is bound for a different airport (one is O'Hare) in his or her destination city. Each flight has a different number (181, 281, 381, 481, or 581), and each is scheduled to take off at a different time (1:00, 1:30, 2:00, 3:00, or 3:30) in the wee hours of the morning. At this point, the travelers can't wait to get onto their planes and get some sleep! From the information provided, determine the airport to which each person is flying, as well as his or her flight number and departure time.

1. Lenny isn't the one flying to Heathrow Airport (which isn't flight 481). Flight 181 will be landing at Kennedy Airport.

2. Carla's flight is leaving at some point before both Lenny's and Mallory's but at some point after Stephanie's. Flight 381 isn't taking off at 1:30 a.m.

3. Jasper isn't the one flying into Ronald Reagan International Airport. The flight headed to LAX (Los Angeles International Airport) is leaving at 1:30 a.m.

4. Mallory's flight is numbered exactly 100 higher than Carla's but exactly 100 lower than Jasper's.

5. Lenny's flight has a higher number than Stephanie's. Mallory's flight (which isn't the latest one) is scheduled to take off at some point after Lenny's.

		AIRPORT				FLIGHT NUMBER					DEPARTURE TIME				
		HEATHROW	KENNEDY	LAX	O'HARE	RONALD REAGAN	181	281	381	481	581	1:00	1:30	2:00	3:00	3:30
PERSON	CARLA															
	JASPER															
	LENNY															
	MALLORY															
	STEPHANIE															
DEPARTURE	1:00															
	1:30															
	2:00															
	3:00															
	3:30															
FLIGHT NO.	181															
	281															
	381															
	481															
	581															

LOGIC PROBLEM 190   NOTHING UP MY SLEEVE . . .

Last Friday night, The Magic Palace hosted a spectacular night of magic featuring the talents of five up-and-coming magicians who amazed the audience with their awe-inspiring illusions. Each magician (including Merlin) performed a different illusion, and then capped the show off with a spectacular finale: before the very eyes of the stunned audience, each magician caused a different object to disappear! From the information provided, can you determine the order in which each magician performed his or her illusion and the object each caused to disappear?

1. The magician who caused a statue of Harry Houdini to disappear wowed the audience by sawing a woman in half. Neither Enchantra nor the third performer is the illusionist who turned doves into butterflies. Carnack wasn't the second magician to perform.

2. Neither the illusionist who made a Harley Davidson motorcycle disappear (who didn't pull items from a suitcase) nor Mephisto is the magician who turned a wand into a bouquet of roses (who performed fourth).

3. Enchantra (who isn't the illusionist who levitated his or her assistant) performed either immediately before or immediately after the one who caused a black panther to disappear (who isn't Carnack).

4. The first performer (who isn't Raven) caused a small tree to disappear, but didn't transform a flock of doves into butterflies.

5. The magician who pulled a seemingly endless supply of items from a small suitcase didn't perform last. Raven (who didn't make a motorcycle disappear) wasn't the fourth performer (who isn't the one who made a birdcage disappear).

		MAGICIAN					ILLUSION					OBJECT				
		CARNACK	ENCHANTRA	MEPHISTO	MERLIN	RAVEN	LEVITATED ASSISTANT	PULLED ITEMS FROM SUITCASE	SAWED WOMAN IN HALF	TURNED DOVES TO BUTTERFLIES	TURNED WAND TO ROSES	BIRDCAGE	MOTORCYCLE	PANTHER	STATUE	TREE
ORDER	FIRST															
	SECOND															
	THIRD															
	FOURTH															
	FIFTH															
OBJECT	BIRDCAGE															
	MOTORCYCLE															
	PANTHER															
	STATUE															
	TREE															
ILLUSION	LEVITATED															
	PULLED ITEMS															
	SAWED WOMAN															
	TURNED DOVES															
	TURNED WAND															

LOGIC PROBLEM 191

The classic-car competition is always an exciting part of the Woodbury Auto Show. This year, the crowd was especially impressed by five outstanding entries, each of which was manufactured in a different year (1929, 1933, 1937, 1941, or 1945). Each car has a different owner, each of whom is particularly proud of a different feature (one is the stylish grille) of his or her car. As these classic-car owners know, they don't make 'em like they used to! From the information provided, can you determine the owner of each car, as well as the year in which it was made and that car's special feature?

1. Ms. Bell's car is newer than at least one other vehicle. The car with the attractive headlights is older than at least one other vehicle.

2. The 1945 model is neither the car with the snazzy wheel design (which isn't the one that belongs to Mr. Robinson) nor the Nash.

3. The Studebaker is newer than Mr. Francis's car, which is exactly four years newer than the car with the like-new engine.

4. Ms. Ford's car is older than the Nash but newer than the car with the fully restored interior.

5. The DeSoto is older than Mr. Barker's Hudson, which is exactly four years older than the Oldsmobile.

		CAR					YEAR					FEATURE				
		DeSOTO	HUDSON	NASH	OLDSMOBILE	STUDEBAKER	1929	1933	1937	1941	1945	ENGINE	GRILLE	HEADLIGHTS	INTERIOR	WHEEL DESIGN
OWNER	MR. BARKER															
	MS. BELL															
	MS. FORD															
	MR. FRANCIS															
	MR. ROBINSON															
FEATURE	ENGINE															
	GRILLE															
	HEADLIGHTS															
	INTERIOR															
	WHEEL DESIGN															
YEAR	1929															
	1933															
	1937															
	1941															
	1945															

LOGIC PROBLEM 192 JUICY FUN

This weekend, five friends and natural-beverage lovers made the long trek to the nation's capital for the International Juice Festival! Saturday's unveiling of the latest juice-making technology was exciting enough, but the real highlight of the weekend proved to be Sunday afternoon, when each of the five friends (three of whom—Ingrid, Loretta, and Norma—are women, and two of whom—Orville and Rodney—are men) had the honor of sampling a different new juice blend (three of which—banana-kiwi, papaya-strawberry, and plum-tangerine—are fruit blends, and two of which—asparagus-spinach and broccoli-carrot—are vegetable blends), each flavored with a different spice. So delicious were the various combinations that each person let out a different spontaneous exclamation (one shouted "yummy!") after tasting it. From the information provided, determine the juice blend each friend sampled and the spice it contains, as well as the spontaneous exclamation each juice provoked.

1. Either the friend who shouted "savory!" or the person who exclaimed "flavorful!" is the one who sampled the broccoli-carrot juice. Neither Ingrid (who drank a fruit juice) nor Rodney pronounced his or her juice blend to be "flavorful!"

2. Norma pronounced her juice sample (which isn't the blend that contains allspice) to be "delicious!" The juices that provoked exclamations of "savory!" and "pungent!" are vegetable blends.

3. The plum-tangerine juice isn't the beverage containing nutmeg. The ginger-flavored sample is a fruit-juice blend. A woman declared her juice blend to be "pungent!"

4. The papaya-strawberry blend (which wasn't sampled by Orville) was flavored with cinnamon. Neither Norma (whose drink doesn't contain either cinnamon or ginger) nor Rodney is the person who tasted the juice flavored with anise.

		JUICE BLEND					SPICE					EXCLAMATION				
		ASPARAGUS-SPINACH	BANANA-KIWI	BROCCOLI-CARROT	PAPAYA-STRAWBERRY	PLUM-TANGERINE	ALLSPICE	ANISE	CINNAMON	GINGER	NUTMEG	DELICIOUS!	FLAVORFUL!	PUNGENT!	SAVORY!	YUMMY!
FRIEND	INGRID															
	LORETTA																
	NORMA																
	ORVILLE																
	RODNEY																
EXCLAMATION	DELICIOUS!																
	FLAVORFUL!																
	PUNGENT!																
	SAVORY!																
	YUMMY!																
SPICE	ALLSPICE																
	ANISE																
	CINNAMON																
	GINGER																
	NUTMEG																

LOGIC PROBLEM 193

Although the next Winter Olympics are still a few years away, the training and tryouts for the next generation of hopefuls is already well underway. Last weekend, six top-ranked American skiers (no two hold the same rank) gathered on a Vermont mountaintop for the preliminary tryouts for downhill and slalom skiing. In addition to demonstrating his or her skill in one of these events, each skier (including Owen) spent the day perfecting a different type of turn. Though actual tryouts are still far in the future, the six hopefuls have clearly shown that they have the Olympic spirit—each person managed to beat his or her previous record with a personal-best time of a different number of seconds (55, 58, 59, 62, 64, or 65)! From the information provided, determine each skier's national rank (second, third, fifth, seventh, ninth, or tenth), the type of turn (one is the Telemark) each practiced, and the number of seconds each took to finish the course.

1. The person who practiced the stem turn (who is ranked higher than Heather) took longer to finish than at least two other skiers. Linus took longer to finish than at least one other skier.

2. The person who practiced the christie turn (who was exactly 3 seconds faster than the skier ranked second) is ranked exactly two places lower than the one who completed the course in 55 seconds.

3. Donovan (who isn't the third-ranked skier) isn't the one who practiced the tempo turn.

4. The person who achieved a personal best of 64 seconds is ranked exactly two places higher than the one who practiced the tempo turn. Heather was exactly 1 second faster than a downhill skier. The one who finished in 65 seconds competed in the slalom event.

5. Zoe isn't the one who practiced the jump turn (who didn't complete the course in 58 seconds). Kate (who isn't ranked exactly two places lower than Zoe) is a slalom skier. The one ranked ninth is a downhill skier.

6. Zoe is ranked exactly three places lower, and took exactly 1 second fewer to finish the course, than the skier who practiced the snowplow turn.

		RANK						TURN						SECONDS					
		SECOND	THIRD	FIFTH	SEVENTH	NINTH	TENTH	CHRISTIE	JUMP	SNOWPLOW	STEM	TELEMARK	TEMPO	55	58	59	62	64	65
SKIER	DONOVAN																		
	HEATHER																		
	KATE																		
	LINUS																		
	OWEN																		
	ZOE																		
SECONDS	55																		
	58																		
	59																		
	62																		
	64																		
	65																		
TURN	CHRISTIE																		
	JUMP																		
	SNOWPLOW																		
	STEM																		
	TELEMARK																		
	TEMPO																		

LOGIC PROBLEM 194   SORELLE de ITALIA

Once a month, Marie and four of her coworkers have a girls' night out at Scungilli's Italian Restaurant. After a hard week of work, the five women (including Ms. Zabaglione) enjoy a relaxing dinner with appetizers, wine, and, of course, dessert. Usually, the women order Scungilli's famous chocolate cheesecake, but last night they wanted to try something new, so each woman ordered a different type of coffee and a different dessert (exactly three of which—biscotti, cannoli, and spumoni—have nuts). Coincidentally, the dessert each woman ordered is the same as the last name of one of the other four! From the information provided, determine the coffee and dessert ordered by each woman (identified by first and last names).

1. In exactly one case, a woman whose surname is the same as a dessert containing nuts also ordered a dessert that contains nuts.

2. Ms. Zeppoli ordered a decaffeinated cappuccino. Sally enjoyed zeppolis for dessert. The dessert selected by the woman who ordered a latte is the same as Theresa's last name.

3. Ms. Cannoli had biscotti for dessert and sat next to Louisa Biscotti at the table. Ms. Spumoni isn't the woman who ordered espresso.

4. One woman ordered spumoni and regular cappuccino. Doreen had hazelnut coffee.

		LAST NAME					COFFEE					DESSERT				
		BISCOTTI	CANNOLI	SPUMONI	ZABAGLIONE	ZEPPOLI	DECAFFEINATED CAPPUCCINO	ESPRESSO	HAZELNUT	LATTE	REGULAR CAPPUCCINO	BISCOTTI	CANNOLI	SPUMONI	ZABAGLIONE	ZEPPOLI
FIRST NAME	DOREEN															
	LOUISA																
	MARIE																
	SALLY																
	THERESA																
DESSERT	BISCOTTI																
	CANNOLI																
	SPUMONI																
	ZABAGLIONE																
	ZEPPOLI																
COFFEE	DECAF. CAPP.																
	ESPRESSO																
	HAZELNUT																
	LATTE																
	REGULAR CAPP.																

Kevin had been planning his chess tournament for months, so when he discovered, on the morning of the competition, that his little brother had "borrowed" several pieces from one of his chess sets, he flew into a panic. At his parents' suggestion, he reluctantly replaced the missing pieces with action figures from his brother's rather impressive collection. As it turned out, the replacement figures were such a huge hit that this special set was used in all five rounds of the tournament! In each round, a different player used the set, secretly thrilled to have an excuse to play with some of his or her favorite toys again. In fact, each player had a different favorite action figure, which each assigned to represent a different crucial piece (one was the king). The event was such a success that all of the players have vowed to raid their old toy chests to make the next tournament an all-action-figure event! From the information provided, determine the action figure chosen by the player (one is Margaret) who used the set in each round, as well as the chess piece it represented.

1. The replacement queen was selected for the round immediately following the one in which Reid selected his favorite action figure. Ashley (who isn't the one who chose Darth Vader) chose her favorite toy in an earlier round than at least one other person.

2. The person who chose a character to replace the rook played exactly two rounds before Kevin (who picked G.I. Joe), who played in an earlier round than at least one other person.

3. He-Man was chosen by a player exactly three rounds before someone chose a replacement for the knight. The replacement bishop was chosen exactly two rounds before the Batman figure.

4. Whitney (who isn't the player who selected Mr. Spock) used the set the round before the person who replaced the knight with his or her favorite toy.

5. If He-Man was used in round four, then Whitney chose the Darth Vader figure; otherwise, He-Man was chosen by Reid, and Whitney didn't select Darth Vader.

		PLAYER					ACTION FIGURE					PIECE				
		ASHLEY	KEVIN	MARGARET	REID	WHITNEY	BATMAN	DARTH VADER	G.I. JOE	HE-MAN	MR. SPOCK	BISHOP	KING	KNIGHT	QUEEN	ROOK
ROUND	1															
	2															
	3															
	4															
	5															
PIECE	BISHOP															
	KING															
	KNIGHT															
	QUEEN															
	ROOK															
FIGURE	BATMAN															
	DARTH VADER															
	G.I. JOE															
	HE-MAN															
	MR. SPOCK															

LOGIC PROBLEM 196 ASTRONOMIC LICENSE

At the conclusion of their section on astronomy, the students in Ms. Wheeler's eighth-grade science class were required to give presentations on astronomic subjects of their choice. Inspired by the theme, five students (three of whom—Arthur, Greg, and Owen—are boys, and two of whom—Felicia and Rhonda—are girls) chose to discuss a different aspect of a different planet in our solar system (in order from nearest to farthest from the sun, Mars, Jupiter, Saturn, Uranus, or Neptune). To add visual interest to his or her project, each student used a different object (including a volleyball) to represent the planet he or she discussed. While noting the objects did not necessarily correspond to the relative size of the planets, Ms. Wheeler gave each project an A for effort! From the information provided, can you determine the aspect (one is orbiting satellites) of each planet each student discussed and the object each used to illustrate his or her report?

1. The three boys are the one who talked about planetary atmosphere, the one who discussed Neptune, and the one who used a baseball to represent his planet.

2. The planet chosen by the girl who discussed surface features is closer to the sun than the planet one girl represented with an orange.

3. Owen's planet is the next farther from the sun than the world represented by a grapefruit.

4. Felicia, who chose to discuss either Saturn or Uranus, isn't the student who discussed planetary rotation (who isn't the one who used a beachball to illustrate his or her report).

5. The planet chosen by the boy who discussed planetary orbit is the next closer to the sun than Rhonda's planet but farther from the sun than Arthur's planet.

		PLANET					ASPECT					OBJECT				
		MARS	JUPITER	SATURN	URANUS	NEPTUNE	ATMOSPHERE	ORBIT	ROTATION	SATELLITES	SURFACE FEATURES	BASEBALL	BEACHBALL	GRAPEFRUIT	ORANGE	VOLLEYBALL
STUDENT	ARTHUR															
	FELICIA															
	GREG															
	OWEN															
	RHONDA															
OBJECT	BASEBALL															
	BEACHBALL															
	GRAPEFRUIT															
	ORANGE															
	VOLLEYBALL															
ASPECT	ATMOSPHERE															
	ORBIT															
	ROTATION															
	SATELLITES															
	SURFACE															

Five truck drivers from Nashville have chosen to take advantage of a great sale on tires at Smitty's Trucking, which specializes in accommodating the needs of semitrailers. Replacing all of the tires on a semi is a big job, so the five truckers had plenty of time to get acquainted as they waited for the servicemen at Smitty's to finish with their rigs. The drivers discovered that each regularly hauls a different product to a different city (in one case, Louisville) and that each makes a different number of stops (1 through 5) to unload or pick up freight before reaching his or her destination, where each leaves the remaining portion of his or her load. There is at least one thing, however, that the truckers have in common—they all love their jobs, and none of them want to retire anytime soon! From the information provided, determine the product each driver hauls, as well as the number of stops he or she makes en route to his or her final destination.

1. Sherlyn, who hauls fresh produce, stops fewer times than Grace.

2. The truck driven to Lexington stops either exactly three more or exactly three fewer times than the one driven to Knoxville.

3. Grace makes either exactly three more stops or exactly three fewer stops than Casey.

4. The one who drives to Chattanooga stops exactly two fewer times than the one who transports lumber (who isn't Casey).

5. Travis (who isn't the one who carries furniture) stops fewer times on his journey than the one who delivers loads of clothing (who isn't the one who drives to Memphis) but more times than Grace.

6. The truck used to haul toys (which isn't driven by Travis or Michael) stops more often than the one driven to Knoxville but fewer times than at least one other rig.

		PRODUCT					STOPS					DESTINATION				
		CLOTHING	FRESH PRODUCE	FURNITURE	LUMBER	TOYS	1	2	3	4	5	CHATTANOOGA	KNOXVILLE	LEXINGTON	LOUISVILLE	MEMPHIS
DRIVER	CASEY															
	GRACE															
	MICHAEL															
	SHERLYN															
	TRAVIS															
DESTINATION	CHATTANOOGA															
	KNOXVILLE															
	LEXINGTON															
	LOUISVILLE															
	MEMPHIS															
STOPS	1															
	2															
	3															
	4															
	5															

After months of diligently pursuing her day job, Samantha was thrilled when her agent called to tell her she was scheduled to audition for five of New York's most prominent choreographers. The only catch was that, unfortunately, all five auditions were on the same day! To make matters worse, each audition (each of which was scheduled for a different time—10:30 a.m., 12:00 p.m., 1:45 p.m., 3:00 p.m., or 4:30 p.m.) was to be held in a different area of Manhattan. Not one to be intimidated, Samantha merely focused on giving the performances of her life. Thanks to her remarkable footwork both in the studio and on the street, she managed to arrive at each appointment on time and so impressed the legendary choreographers that she must now decide which of the five different jobs (one is a Broadway musical) she is going to accept! From the information provided, determine the time of Samantha's audition with each choreographer (one is Isadora Pavlova) and the neighborhood where each was held, as well as the job she was offered after each audition.

1. Samantha's 3:00 p.m. audition (which was held on the Upper West Side) wasn't for the role in a music video. The audition for Martha Robbins wasn't the last one of the day. Jerome Tharp isn't the one Samantha met first.

2. Her Greenwich Village appointment (which wasn't at 4:30 p.m.) isn't the one where she was offered a film role. Twyla Graham (who didn't meet with Samantha at 10:30 a.m.) isn't the one casting the ballet.

3. Samantha's ballet audition was held in Murray Hill. She met E.M. Duncan in Chelsea before she auditioned for at least one other choreographer. The dance-company audition wasn't Samantha's first. She didn't audition for Twyla Graham at 3:00 p.m.

4. The film audition was scheduled for earlier than the music-video audition but later than the one held in Midtown. Jerome Tharp isn't the one Samantha met in Murray Hill.

		CHOREOGRAPHER					NEIGHBORHOOD					JOB				
		E.M. DUNCAN	ISADORA PAVLOVA	JEROME THARP	MARTHA ROBBINS	TWYLA GRAHAM	CHELSEA	GREENWICH VILLAGE	MIDTOWN	MURRAY HILL	UPPER WEST SIDE	BALLET	DANCE COMPANY	FILM	MUSICAL	MUSIC VIDEO
TIME	10:30 a.m.															
	12:00 p.m.															
	1:45 p.m.															
	3:00 p.m.															
	4:30 p.m.															
JOB	BALLET															
	DANCE COMPANY															
	FILM															
	MUSICAL															
	MUSIC VIDEO															
NEIGHBOR.	CHELSEA															
	GREENWICH VILL.															
	MIDTOWN															
	MURRAY HILL															
	UPPER WEST SIDE															

At her bridal shower on Sunday, Alexis received every appliance and utensil she could possibly need to equip her new kitchen! For example, each of her five closest relatives (including Nora) gave Alexis a different type of pan and brought a different utensil for the bride's wishing well. Now that she has such a wide array of kitchenware, all Alexis has to do is teach her future husband how to cook! From the information provided, determine each woman's relationship to Alexis (no two are related to her in the same way), as well as the type of pan and the utensil she gave.

1. Terry is either the woman who gave the omelet pan or the one who gave the paella pan. Alexis's cousin is either the woman who gave the Bundt pan or the one who gave the muffin pan.

2. Alexis's mother (who isn't Suzanne) gave her the jelly-roll pan. Her grandmother put the wooden spoon into the wishing well.

3. The woman who brought the corkscrew for the wishing well didn't give Alexis the omelet pan. Suzanne (who isn't Alexis's sister) gave the bride-to-be the pastry brush.

4. The woman who brought the whisk for the wishing well gave Alexis the Bundt pan. Lindsey isn't Alexis's sister.

5. Rosemary, who didn't give her niece the Bundt pan, isn't the woman who put the spatula in the wishing well.

		RELATIONSHIP					PAN					UTENSIL				
		AUNT	COUSIN	GRANDMOTHER	MOTHER	SISTER	BUNDT	JELLY ROLL	MUFFIN	OMELET	PAELLA	CORKSCREW	PASTRY BRUSH	SPATULA	WHISK	WOODEN SPOON
WOMAN	LINDSEY															
	NORA															
	ROSEMARY															
	SUZANNE															
	TERRY															
UTENSIL	CORKSCREW															
	PASTRY BRUSH															
	SPATULA															
	WHISK															
	WOODEN SPOON															
PAN	BUNDT															
	JELLY ROLL															
	MUFFIN															
	OMELET															
	PAELLA															

LOGIC PROBLEM 200   PEACHES AND CREAMS

For her birthday last month, Eartha's sister bought her a complete massage and citrus-herbal facial at Pamper Yourself, a high-priced, all-natural spa. Although she certainly can't afford regular visits, Eartha hoped that a trip to the Nature's Gifts boutique would prolong the pampering to which she had so quickly become accustomed. As an introduction to their wares, she purchased the Total Body Basket, a sampler that includes small bottles of five of the most popular Nature's Gifts products. Each beauty product comes in a bottle that contains a different number (2, 3, 4, 5, or 6) of ounces of all-natural ingredients, including a different fruit extract (one is mango) and a different herb (calendula, eryngo, fraxinella, lespedeza, or philodendron). Thoroughly pleased with her purchase, Eartha would be rushing out to buy more, if she weren't so completely relaxed! From the information provided, determine the number of ounces of each product Eartha purchased, as well as the fruit and herb in each.

1. The quince body wash, which isn't in the two-ounce bottle, contains either eryngo or calendula.

2. Eartha's basket contains four ounces of the papaya product. The bubble bath is in a five-ounce bottle.

3. The shampoo contains lespedeza. Eartha bought more of the eryngo product than of both the facial mask and the one containing avocado.

4. The six-ounce bottle contains an extract of the herb philodendron. The hand lotion isn't the product made with coconut.

		OUNCES					FRUIT					HERB				
		2	3	4	5	6	AVOCADO	COCONUT	MANGO	PAPAYA	QUINCE	CALENDULA	ERYNGO	FRAXINELLA	LESPEDEZA	PHILODENDRON
PRODUCT	BODY WASH															
	BUBBLE BATH															
	FACIAL MASK															
	HAND LOTION															
	SHAMPOO															
HERB	CALENDULA															
	ERYNGO															
	FRAXINELLA															
	LESPEDEZA															
	PHILODENDRON															
FRUIT	AVOCADO															
	COCONUT															
	MANGO															
	PAPAYA															
	QUINCE															

LOGIC PROBLEM 201

Six to eight weeks after placing his order, Clifford Dunlop finally received his very own Junior Sleuth Detective Kit! Complete with magnifying glass and fedora, the kit was everything Clifford had hoped for, and he was anxious to start his first investigation. Although no crime had yet been committed, Clifford thought it would be a good idea to have the fingerprints of his family members on file—just in case. Surreptitiously, Clifford began dusting the house and, sure enough, he found five different prints, each in a different location and each belonging to a different family member. He was able to discern that each print came from a different finger, each of which he assigned a different number (from lowest to highest, pinkie, ring, middle, index, and thumb). Further examination showed that each person (three of whom—Baxter, Jim, and Teddy—are men, and two of whom—Marilyn and Shirley—are women) has a different pattern of fingerprint (one is an ulnar loop). The rest of the family need not fear, now that Detective Dunlop is on the case! From the information provided, determine the location where Clifford found each person's print, the finger from which it came, and that person's fingerprint pattern.

1. The fingerprint found on the drinking glass is not the double loop (which doesn't belong to Shirley). Clifford discovered a woman's pinkie print.

2. One of the prints Clifford found was Teddy's thumbprint. The index finger is not the one that provided the arch-patterned print. Clifford lifted Marilyn's print from a doorknob.

3. The whorl print was assigned a higher number than Baxter's print but a lower number than the one found on the window.

4. The tented-arch print was numbered at least two lower than the one found on the nightstand (which wasn't the thumbprint).

5. Neither Baxter's fingerprint nor Shirley's fingerprint was either the one Clifford found on the cabinet or the one he lifted from the nightstand.

		LOCATION					FINGER					PATTERN				
		CABINET	DOORKNOB	GLASS	NIGHTSTAND	WINDOW	PINKIE	RING	MIDDLE	INDEX	THUMB	ARCH	DOUBLE LOOP	TENTED ARCH	ULNAR LOOP	WHORL
PERSON	BAXTER															
	JIM															
	MARILYN															
	SHIRLEY															
	TEDDY															
PATTERN	ARCH															
	DOUBLE LOOP															
	TENTED ARCH															
	ULNAR LOOP															
	WHORL															
FINGER	PINKIE															
	RING															
	MIDDLE															
	INDEX															
	THUMB															

LOGIC PROBLEM 202

ITS BEEP IS WORSE
THAN ITS BYTE

The only thing Jake wanted for his birthday was a virtual pet, and, as it turned out, the electronic toys were virtually the only gifts he received! Each of five guests at Jake's birthday party bought him a different brand of virtual pet. Although he was thrilled at first, Jake's foray into electronic-pet ownership has certainly taught him the meaning of responsibility. This afternoon alone, each of the five pets required his immediate attention, and his parents watched with amusement as he rushed to keep up with them all. To further complicate matters, each pet needed Jake's assistance with a different problem (one was stuck in a virtual tree), as was signaled by a different number (2 through 6) of beeps. Eventually, he was able to meet all of their needs, and, with each virtual creature sleeping peacefully, Jake's parents agreed to pet-sit for the rest of the evening so he could take a much-needed nap! From the information provided, determine the relative who gave Jake each pet, as well as the number of beeps each made to signal its problem.

1. Rachel's gift (which isn't Spot 6.0) didn't beep six times (which isn't the signal for needing a walk). The pet that was feeling a little bit sick (which isn't Virtual Vinnie) wasn't Gina's gift.

2. Both the pet given by Barbara and the one that made two beeps are rechargeable and must be plugged in every night. The Maritochi pet (which beeped six times) is battery-operated and cannot be recharged.

3. Cyber Friend (which beeped more times than the pet given by Carl) emitted exactly one beep fewer than the one that was hungry. Tad didn't buy Maritochi.

4. Neither the pet that wanted to play (which beeped exactly two fewer times than Robo Pet) nor Spot 6.0 is rechargeable.

		BARBARA	CARL	GINA	RACHEL	TAD	2	3	4	5	6	HUNGRY	NEEDED WALK	SICK	STUCK IN TREE	WANTED TO PLAY
			RELATIVE					BEEPS					PROBLEM			
PET	CYBER FRIEND															
	MARITOCHI															
	ROBO PET															
	SPOT 6.0															
	VIRTUAL VINNIE															
PROBLEM	HUNGRY															
	NEEDED WALK															
	SICK															
	STUCK IN TREE															
	WANTED TO PLAY															
BEEPS	2															
	3															
	4															
	5															
	6															

LOGIC PROBLEM 203

Ray normally likes to spend his Sundays relaxing with a big cup of coffee and the big Sunday newspaper, but last Sunday it seemed as if the phone never stopped ringing! Fortunately, it was all good news, as each of five of Ray's friends (including Grant) with whom he seldom has the opportunity to speak called and talked to Ray for a different period of time (9:45-10:15 a.m., 10:20-10:40 a.m., 10:50-11:40 a.m., 12:10-12:50 p.m., or 1:00-2:00 p.m.). Each had exciting news about a different big change in his or her life (one friend called to report the birth of a baby). Since Ray was usually in the middle of an article when the phone rang, each friend had to wait through a different number of rings (2 through 6) before Ray picked up the phone. Although he didn't make it all the way through the paper, Ray was happy to spend the better part of his Sunday catching up on the news that really matters the most. From the information provided, determine the time each friend spent on the phone with Ray, the number of rings before Ray answered, and the good news each friend called to report.

1. The person who called to say that he or she is moving waited through exactly twice as many rings as Julie (who spent exactly twice as many minutes talking to Ray as the person who waited through five rings but fewer minutes than at least one other friend).

2. Mary (who lives in Dubuque) had to wait through more phone rings than Winnie but fewer rings than the friend who called to announce that he or she had won the lottery.

3. The friend from Waterloo, who just received a promotion at work, called immediately before the one who waited through four rings before Ray answered.

4. Ray's lucky lottery-winning friend (who called after at least one other person) had to wait through exactly twice as many rings as Alonzo.

5. Ray's friend from Cedar Rapids called to announce that he or she had gotten engaged.

		ALONZO	GRANT	JULIE	MARY	WINNIE	2	3	4	5	6	BABY	ENGAGED	JOB PROMOTION	MOVING	WON LOTTERY
		FRIEND					RINGS					GOOD NEWS				
TIME	9:45-10:15 a.m.															
	10:20-10:40 a.m.															
	10:50-11:40 a.m.															
	12:10-12:50 p.m.															
	1:00-2:00 p.m.															
GOOD NEWS	BABY															
	ENGAGED															
	JOB PROMOTION															
	MOVING															
	WON LOTTERY															
RINGS	2															
	3															
	4															
	5															
	6															

LOGIC PROBLEM 204   LUGGING THE LUGGAGE

Although being a porter in a train station can be exhausting work, Harold loves the flurry of activity as passengers rush in and out en route to faraway places. Just today, he helped five travelers (including Gary), each of whom was transporting a different, very heavy piece of luggage. As he helped them with their baggage, each person chatted with Harold about his or her destination (each was headed to a different city—one is Cincinnati). After escorting each passenger to his or her train, each of which was departing from a different-numbered track (6, 8, 11, 13, or 16), Harold wished them well in their journeys and returned to his post, eager to see where his next encounter would take him. From the information provided, determine each passenger's destination, the track from which each left, and the type of luggage each carried.

1. Erin and Morgan are the one with the large knapsack and the one whose train left from a track numbered exactly five lower than that of the Chicago-bound train, in some order.

2. Drake (who was neither the one with the wardrobe trunk nor the one with the duffel bag) wasn't the passenger bound for Dallas (whose track number was lower than that of the person going to St. Louis). The one who needed help with a heavy duffel bag didn't leave from track 6.

3. Erin left from a track numbered exactly two lower than that of the person with the footlocker. Olivia wasn't the one traveling to Dallas.

4. The track number from which the person with the knapsack departed is higher than the sum of the track numbers of both Drake and the person who went to Wichita.

5. The track number sought by the one with the duffel bag was lower than that of the traveler with the portmanteau.

		CHICAGO	CINCINNATI	DALLAS	ST. LOUIS	WICHITA	6	8	11	13	16	DUFFEL BAG	FOOTLOCKER	KNAPSACK	PORTMANTEAU	WARDROBE TRUNK
PASSENGER	DRAKE															
	ERIN															
	GARY															
	MORGAN															
	OLIVIA															
LUGGAGE	DUFFEL BAG															
	FOOTLOCKER															
	KNAPSACK															
	PORTMANTEAU															
	WARDROBE TRUNK															
TRACK	6															
	8															
	11															
	13															
	16															

As part of their unit on American dramatists, five students in Ms. DuBois's English class elected to write their papers about playwright Thomas Lanier Williams, better known as Tennessee Williams. Each young scholar wrote about a different play (two of which—*Cat on a Hot Tin Roof* and *The Night of the Iguana*—have animals in their titles, and three of which—*The Glass Menagerie, The Rose Tattoo,* and *A Streetcar Named Desire*—do not), and each received a different grade on his or her paper (from highest to lowest, A, B+, B, B-, or C+). Ms. DuBois explained that the marks would have been higher, were it not for the fact that each student had given a different, incorrect explanation for why the playwright had adopted the name Tennessee (one thought that he was named after beloved cartoon character Tennessee Tuxedo). From the information provided, determine the play about which each student wrote, the grade he or she received, and the erroneous explanation each provided for the playwright's name.

1. Both Stanley and the one who reported that the playwright took his name from his favorite snack—Tennessee Red peanuts—wrote about plays with animals in their titles.

2. The report on *The Night of the Iguana* received a grade of B-. Blanche did not write about *The Glass Menagerie.*

3. The student who reported on *A Streetcar Named Desire* thought that the playwright took his name from the beautiful song of the Tennessee warbler.

4. Maggie received a higher grade on her paper than the one (who didn't write about a play with an animal in the title) who thought that the playwright had taken his name from country-and-western singer Tennessee Ernie Ford.

5. Stella received a B on her paper. The report on *Cat on a Hot Tin Roof* did not receive a grade of B+.

6. Blanche (who did not receive the lowest grade) reported that the playwright took his name from his favorite dance—the Tennessee Waltz.

7. Brick didn't think the playwright was named after either Tennessee Red peanuts or Tennessee Ernie Ford.

		PLAY					GRADE					EXPLANATION				
		CAT ON A HOT TIN ROOF	THE GLASS MENAGERIE	THE NIGHT OF THE IGUANA	THE ROSE TATTOO	A STREETCAR NAMED DESIRE	A-	B+	B	B-	C+	TENNESSEE ERNIE FORD	TENNESSEE RED PEANUT	TENNESSEE TUXEDO	TENNESSEE WALTZ	TENNESSEE WARBLER
STUDENT	BLANCHE															
	BRICK															
	MAGGIE															
	STANLEY															
	STELLA															
EXPLANATION	TENN. ERNIE FORD															
	TENN. RED PEANUT															
	TENN. TUXEDO															
	TENN. WALTZ															
	TENN. WARBLER															
GRADE	A-															
	B+															
	B															
	B-															
	C+															

LOGIC PROBLEM 206

For its energetic and talented staff of waiters, the Starlight Diner is more than just a job—it's an adventure! In addition to dressing as different rock'n'roll stars from the '50s, five of the food servers currently in the restaurant's employ are frequently called upon to step up to the microphone and perform for the delighted crowd of diners. Although the job is demanding, all the hard work is definitely paying off for these young waiters; yesterday, each of the five was rewarded for a remarkable performance of a different song (one was "Rock Around the Clock") with a different, impressive total amount ($100, $150, $175, $225, or $250) in tips. From the information provided, determine the costume worn by each waiter, the song he sang, and the total amount he earned in tips yesterday. (Note: The song each waiter sang is not necessarily related to the star whom he impersonated.)

1. The waiter who sang "Volare" (who didn't work the lunch shift yesterday) made more in tips than Harold, who sang "Chantilly Lace." Ira wears the Elvis Presley costume.

2. The waiter who dresses as Bobby Darin made exactly $50 less than the one who wears the Ricky Nelson costume. Eric only worked the dinner shift yesterday.

3. Philip earned $100 in tips. The waiter dressed as Jerry Lee Lewis, who earned $225 over the course of his lunch shift yesterday, isn't the one who sang "Johnny B. Goode."

4. The man who sang "Johnny B. Goode" earned more tip money than the one who dressed as Buddy Holly. Stan isn't the one who sang "Summertime Blues."

		COSTUME					SONG					TIPS				
		BOBBY DARIN	BUDDY HOLLY	ELVIS PRESLEY	JERRY LEE LEWIS	RICKY NELSON	CHANTILLY LACE	JOHNNY B. GOODE	ROCK AROUND THE CLOCK	SUMMERTIME BLUES	VOLARE	$100	$150	$175	$225	$250
WAITER	ERIC															
	HAROLD															
	IRA															
	PHILIP															
	STAN															
TIPS	$100															
	$150															
	$175															
	$225															
	$250															
SONG	CHANTILLY LACE															
	JOHNNY B. GOODE															
	ROCK AROUND															
	SUMMERTIME															
	VOLARE															

LOGIC PROBLEM 207

It seems that wedding bells have been ringing non-stop for Chad's coworkers at Papyrus Publishing; in the past year, in fact, five employees have gotten married and asked Chad to be a member of their wedding parties! While thrilled for his friends, the string of weddings has meant that Chad, who is usually more comfortable in a T-shirt and jeans, has had an unprecedented five occasions to don a tuxedo! Not one to be intimidated, Chad did a little comparison-shopping and eventually found great deals on five different designer tuxedos. For each wedding, he rented a tuxedo from a different formal-wear shop (including Mr. Tuxedo) using a coupon offering a different discount (one was 15% off the price of a rental). Although he had never worn a tux before in his life, Chad has certainly received a crash course, as each groom had selected a different style (one is notch) for the wedding party. From the information provided, determine the designer and style of the tuxedo Chad rented from each shop, as well as the coupon he used in each store.

1. The five tuxedos are the Perry Ellis (which isn't the one for which Chad received a specially priced two-evening rental), the peak tuxedo, the one he rented at Tuxedo Junction, the one he rented at a $20 discount, and the one in the Southbridge style.

2. The Ralph Lauren shawl tux wasn't the one rented from Fiesta Formal.

3. The style of the tuxedo Chad rented from Dress for Less (which wasn't the Oscar de la Renta rental) is either peak or Southbridge.

4. The Christian Dior tuxedo was neither the one with which Chad received his own free pair of cuff links nor the two-evening rental. He didn't get the free cuff links with the cutaway tux.

5. The Bill Blass evening wear (which wasn't offered at $20 off) is neither the peak-styled tux nor the rental for which Chad invited several other guests to participate in a group discount.

6. Chad and his fellow groomsmen got a group discount at King Tux (which isn't the store where he rented the Perry Ellis tuxedo).

		DESIGNER					STYLE					COUPON				
		BILL BLASS	CHRISTIAN DIOR	OSCAR DE LA RENTA	PERRY ELLIS	RALPH LAUREN	CUTAWAY	NOTCH	PEAK	SHAWL	SOUTHBRIDGE	15% OFF	FREE CUFF LINKS	GROUP DISCOUNT	$20 OFF	TWO-EVENING RENTAL
SHOP	DRESS FOR LESS															
	FIESTA FORMAL															
	KING TUX															
	MR. TUXEDO															
	TUXEDO JUNCTION															
COUPON	15% OFF															
	FREE CUFF LINKS															
	GROUP DISCOUNT															
	$20 OFF															
	TWO-EVENING															
STYLE	CUTAWAY															
	NOTCH															
	PEAK															
	SHAWL															
	SOUTHBRIDGE															

LOGIC PROBLEM 208

Eminent psychologist Dr. Somnolus has been conducting experiments on how stress levels affect sleep and dream activity. Dottie and the other four volunteers participating in the current study use Dr. Somnolus's stress-reducing relaxation techniques, then sleep through the night at the lab while the scientist collects data. Reviewing the results of last night's sleep, Dr. Somnolus noted that, upon waking, each person (no two of whom slept for the same number of hours) recalled a different dream and, as a result, awoke with a different feeling (one felt cheerful). Dr. Somnolus realizes that her subjects' interesting dreams have the potential to take her and her work just about anywhere! From the information provided, determine the number of hours (5 through 9) each subject slept last night, the dream each had (one dreamed of being a baseball star), and the feeling each experienced upon awakening.

1. Gilbert slept for exactly one hour longer than the one who dreamt about swimming across the ocean but for exactly one hour shorter than the person who awoke feeling tranquil.

2. Rita slept for exactly one hour longer than the subject who awoke feeling confident. The subject who felt exhilarated upon waking slept for more than five hours.

3. The person who dreamed about playing golf on the moon didn't sleep for nine hours.

4. The one who met the president in his or her dream got exactly one hour fewer of sleep than the one who awoke feeling refreshed, who got less sleep than Amos.

5. The subject who reported dreaming about sky-diving with a flock of sheep slept longer than Preston but not as long as the person who awoke feeling refreshed.

		HOURS					DREAM					FEELING				
		5	6	7	8	9	BECAME BASEBALL STAR	MET PRESIDENT	PLAYED GOLF ON MOON	SKY-DIVED WITH SHEEP	SWAM ACROSS OCEAN	CHEERFUL	CONFIDENT	EXHILARATED	REFRESHED	TRANQUIL
SUBECT	AMOS															
	DOTTIE															
	GILBERT															
	PRESTON															
	RITA															
FEELING	CHEERFUL															
	CONFIDENT															
	EXHILARATED															
	REFRESHED															
	TRANQUIL															
DREAM	BECAME BASEBALL															
	MET PRESIDENT															
	PLAYED GOLF															
	SKY-DIVED															
	SWAM ACROSS															

LOGIC PROBLEM 209

While strolling through his castle on Monday evening, King Bramwell noticed several important repairs and preparations (such as cleaning the ballroom) that had to be completed before his annual midsummer ball that weekend. He immediately summoned his five servants (two of whom—Constance and Rosalind—are women, and three of whom—Dudley, Irwin, and Norman—are men) and assigned each a different task to complete within the following four days. And indeed, by the end of the week, King Bramwell was so pleased with the work that had been done that he granted each servant a different reward of his or her choosing (one asked for a raise), putting a king-sized smile on each servant's face! From the information provided, determine the number of days (1 through 4) it took each servant to complete his or her task and the reward each chose in return for his or her good service.

1. The servant who decorated the courtyard (who isn't Irwin) received a horse as a reward.

2. Constance requested either a horse or some extra vacation time in return for her fine work. The servant who secured the keep (who didn't ask to attend the ball) completed his or her job in fewer days than the retainer who requested more vacation time.

3. Dudley refilled the moat with fresh water. Norman, who asked that his family be permitted to dine at the royal table, isn't the servant who secured the keep.

4. A woman required exactly two days to repair the drawbridge.

5. The person who was rewarded with an invitation to the ball did his or her special duty in fewer days than the person who requested dinner with the royal family. Only one servant completed his or her assigned task in exactly one day.

6. The retainer who refilled the moat took longer to complete his or her task than the one who asked to be paid with a horse. Rosalind isn't the one who repaired the drawbridge.

		TASK					DAYS				REWARD				
		CLEAN BALLROOM	DECORATE COURTYARD	REFILL MOAT	REPAIR DRAWBRIDGE	SECURE THE KEEP					ATTEND BALL	FAMILY DINNER	HORSE	RAISE	VACATION
SERVANT	CONSTANCE														
	DUDLEY														
	IRWIN														
	NORMAN														
	ROSALIND														
REWARD	ATTEND BALL														
	FAMILY DINNER														
	HORSE														
	RAISE														
	VACATION														
DAYS															

LOGIC PROBLEM 210   CORPS CORRESPONDENCE

Caroline and four other former Peace Corps volunteers have maintained enduring friendships with one another in the years since their service together ended. Last week, various letters crossed in the mail as each of the five sent a letter on a different weekday addressed to a different one of the other four. In addition to reminiscing about their last reunion, each person's letter provided an update about a different recent development in his or her life. From the information provided, can you determine the sender of the letter mailed on each weekday and the personal news it contained, as well as identify the recipient of that letter?

1. Jerry mailed his letter at some point earlier in the week than the person who wrote to Maggie.
2. The letter containing news of an engagement was mailed the day after the one addressed to Morton, which was mailed either exactly two days before or exactly two days after the letter that Morton sent.
3. The person who wrote about plans to move to California mailed his or her letter at some point later in the week than the one addressed to Caroline.
4. Maggie's letter announcing the birth of her new baby was mailed at some point earlier in the week than the letter containing news of a promotion.
5. The recipient of the letter announcing an upcoming visit mailed his or her own letter exactly two days after Lauren, who mailed her letter exactly three days before the person who wrote to Caroline.

		CAROLINE	JERRY	LAUREN	MAGGIE	MORTON	BABY	ENGAGED	MOVING	PROMOTION	VISITING	CAROLINE	JERRY	LAUREN	MAGGIE	MORTON
		SENDER					NEWS					RECIPIENT				
WEEKDAY	MONDAY															
	TUESDAY															
	WEDNESDAY															
	THURSDAY															
	FRIDAY															
RECIPIENT	CAROLINE															
	JERRY															
	LAUREN															
	MAGGIE															
	MORTON															
NEWS	BABY															
	ENGAGED															
	MOVING															
	PROMOTION															
	VISITING															

LOGIC PROBLEM 211

Enthusiasm toward soccer continues to grow in the United States. Now, even semi-pro farm clubs, such as the Kalamazoo Kickers, search the globe for the best recruits they can find. The Kickers are fortunate to have signed a new star player for each of the past five seasons (2010 through 2014), each of whom hails from a different South American country (including Peru). The team's goal-oriented recruitment policy has certainly scored points with the fans—as they kick off the new season, attendance at their games is up over 50 percent! From the information provided, can you identify the home country of each Kickers star (identified by first and last names—one first name is Guillermo, and one surname is Cruz), as well as the year in which he signed with the team?

1. The one surnamed Lopez signed with the team at some point after the player from Uruguay, who isn't the one surnamed Allende.

2. The one surnamed Braga joined the team the year after Jaime (whose last name isn't Tiant), who signed the year after the player surnamed Allende.

3. Pablo signed with the Kickers the year after the player surnamed Tiant, who was recruited the year after the player from Argentina.

4. The player from Chile isn't the team's most recent recruit.

5. Marcel was signed exactly two years after Luis but the year before the Colombian player.

		LAST NAME					COUNTRY					YEAR				
		ALLENDE	BRAGA	CRUZ	LOPEZ	TIANT	ARGENTINA	CHILE	COLOMBIA	PERU	URUGUAY	2010	2011	2012	2013	2014
FIRST NAME	GUILLERMO															
	JAIME															
	LUIS															
	MARCEL															
	PABLO															
YEAR	2010															
	2011															
	2012															
	2013															
	2014															
COUNTRY	ARGENTINA															
	CHILE															
	COLOMBIA															
	PERU															
	URUGUAY															

LOGIC PROBLEM 212 — A SNOWBALL'S CHANCE

As part of their preparations for the Snowball Fight of the Century, Eliot and his five siblings put the finishing touches on their snow forts. Using some felt and paste, each child had created a flag bearing a different emblem for his or her fort. Once the flags were in place, each child set to fortifying his or her position by making a different whole number of snowballs. After several hours, however, the shivering children unanimously agreed to save the fight for another day and went inside the warm house for a hot-chocolate break, where each child eagerly selected a different flavor of hot chocolate from the varieties Mom offered. From the information provided, can you determine the emblem emblazoned on each child's flag and the number of snowballs each made, as well as the flavor (one is raspberry) of hot chocolate each child drank?

1. A total of 100 snowballs was created by the six children. The child who made the most snowballs created exactly twice as many as one sibling, exactly three times as many as another sibling, exactly four times as many as yet another sibling, and exactly six times as many as the child who made the fewest snowballs.
2. Helen (who didn't make the most snowballs) made exactly twice as many snowballs as Olivia. The child whose emblem is an ice skate (who enjoyed a steaming cup of cinnamon hot chocolate) created an odd number of snowballs.
3. The child who made the fifth-greatest number of snowballs (whose flag features a snowman) consumed a cup of mocha hot chocolate. After making the third-greatest number of snowballs, Glenn enjoyed his warming cup of vanilla hot chocolate.
4. Rebecca didn't drink a cup of mocha hot chocolate. Helen's flag isn't the one bearing a picture of a pine tree or the one featuring a snowflake. The child who made the fewest snowballs drank a cup of Irish-cream hot chocolate, while the sibling who created the most snowballs enjoyed a cup of butterscotch hot chocolate.
5. Larry (whose emblem isn't a pine tree) made exactly twice as many snowballs as another child. The one whose emblem is an icicle made exactly half as many snowballs as the child whose emblem is a sled.

		EMBLEM						SNOWBALLS				HOT CHOCOLATE					
		ICE SKATE	ICICLE	PINE TREE	SLED	SNOWFLAKE	SNOWMAN					BUTTERSCOTCH	CINNAMON	IRISH CREAM	MOCHA	RASPBERRY	VANILLA
CHILD	ELIOT																
	GLENN																
	HELEN																
	LARRY																
	OLIVIA																
	REBECCA																
HOT CHOC.	BUTTERSCOTCH																
	CINNAMON																
	IRISH CREAM																
	MOCHA																
	RASPBERRY																
	VANILLA																
SNOWBALLS																		

After spending a week at magical Walt Disney World, Tammy and Tony were reluctant to return to the old grind. While in Disney World, they spent idyllic mornings exploring the Magic Kingdom where, on each day (Wednesday through Sunday) of their vacation, they met a different Disney character (including Mickey Mouse himself) in a different area of the theme park. After spending their afternoons visiting the other parks within the Disney World complex, Tammy and Tony wiled away their evenings exploring Epcot, where each night they ate an authentic dinner in a different country (including Norway) in the World Showcase. Fortunately, Tammy and Tony have resolved to bring a little of that vacation spirit back with them—even if it means wearing their mouse ears to work! From the information provided, can you determine, for each day, the character Tammy and Tony met in each area (one is Liberty Square) of the Magic Kingdom, as well as the country in the World Showcase where they dined?

1. Tammy and Tony met Donald Duck on the day they dined in Morocco, which was at some point earlier in the week than both the day they ate in Germany and the day they met a character in Adventureland.

2. Tammy and Tony met Goofy exactly two days after they met a character in Frontierland.

3. They met one character in Fantasyland the day after they encountered Pluto but the day before they dined in Japan.

4. Tammy and Tony ate in France exactly two days before they met a character in Tomorrowland.

5. On Wednesday morning, Tammy and Tony met Minnie Mouse; they didn't eat in France that evening.

		CHARACTER					AREA					COUNTRY				
		DONALD DUCK	GOOFY	MICKEY MOUSE	MINNIE MOUSE	PLUTO	ADVENTURELAND	FANTASYLAND	FRONTIERLAND	LIBERTY SQUARE	TOMORROWLAND	FRANCE	GERMANY	JAPAN	MOROCCO	NORWAY
DAY	WEDNESDAY															
	THURSDAY															
	FRIDAY															
	SATURDAY															
	SUNDAY															
COUNTRY	FRANCE															
	GERMANY															
	JAPAN															
	MOROCCO															
	NORWAY															
AREA	ADVENTURELAND															
	FANTASYLAND															
	FRONTIERLAND															
	LIBERTY SQUARE															
	TOMORROWLAND															

LOGIC PROBLEM 214

A LITTLE ELF GOES
A LONG WAY

While Santa Claus has the entire year to rest and relax until Christmas, the elves must work year-round to make all of the toys in time for delivery. The Clauses, however, appreciate all the care and effort their helpers put in to making toys for all the good little boys and girls and firmly believe in rewarding the elves for their hard work. Since five elves, each of whom specializes in a different toy (one makes wooden airplanes), have already more than tripled their production and easily exceeded their monthly quotas, each has earned a different bonus reward from head elf himself—Santa Claus! Each worker made a different number (2,000, 2,500, 3,000, 3,500, or 4,000) of toys, causing Santa to think that, at this rate, all the toys may well be finished by Thanksgiving! From the information provided, determine the number and type of toys each elf made and his or her bonus.

1. Blip made more toys than at least two other elves. Herbie made more toys than the one who received a new set of tools.

2. The train-making elf produced exactly 500 fewer toys than Mitzi. Pixel made at least 1,000 more toys than the elf who received extra cookies at dinner.

3. The doll maker didn't receive the tool set. The elf who makes wooden soldiers isn't the one who received a ride in Santa's sleigh. Clarice doesn't specialize in trains.

4. Neither the elf who makes cars (who produced neither the most nor the fewest toys) nor the one who makes soldiers (who completed either 3,000 or 3,500 toys) is the one who received a vacation to the South Pole.

5. The elf who received a new snowsuit from Mrs. Claus produced an extraordinary 4,000 toys.

		NUMBER					TOYS					BONUS				
		2,000	2,500	3,000	3,500	4,000	AIRPLANES	CARS	DOLLS	SOLDIERS	TRAINS	EXTRA COOKIES	NEW SNOWSUIT	RIDE IN SLEIGH	SET OF TOOLS	VACATION TO SOUTH POLE
ELF	BLIP															
	CLARICE															
	HERBIE															
	MITZI															
	PIXEL															
BONUS	EXTRA COOKIES															
	NEW SNOWSUIT															
	RIDE IN SLEIGH															
	SET OF TOOLS															
	VACATION															
TOYS	AIRPLANES															
	CARS															
	DOLLS															
	SOLDIERS															
	TRAINS															

In the town of Piney Ridge, Thanksgiving is celebrated the traditional way—with a full spread of roasted turkey, chestnut stuffing, sweet-potato pie, cranberry sauce, and homemade pumpkin pie. Almost as important as Thanksgiving itself, however, is the annual Thanks-For-Giving Tree-Trimming Contest held the following day on the town green. This year, the fierce competition resulted in a five-way tie between different local groups. Each prize-winning group decorated a different type of tree and, in addition to several pounds of tinsel, each put up a different number of strings of lights (2, 3, 4, 5, or 6) and added a different number of ornaments (45, 50, 55, 60, or 65) to their tree. After the prizes were handed out, the town's mayor flipped the switch to light the newly decorated trees, which will be on display through Christmas. From the information provided, can you determine the type of tree each group decorated, as well as the number of strings of lights and the number of ornaments adorning each?

1. The Girl Scouts, who used two strings of lights, used at least 10 more ornaments than the 4-H Club but fewer ornaments than the group who decorated the Douglas fir.

2. The blue spruce (which sports 45 ornaments) was dressed with exactly twice as many strings of lights as the Fraser fir (which wasn't adorned with 50 ornaments).

3. The 4-H Club used at least two fewer strings of lights than the Humane Society. Neither the 4-H Club nor the Humane Society is the group who trimmed the Scotch pine.

4. The Boy Scouts used exactly twice as many strings of lights as the number adorning the balsam fir. The Rotary Club didn't use five strings of lights on their tree.

		TREE					LIGHTS					ORNAMENTS				
		BALSAM FIR	BLUE SPRUCE	DOUGLAS FIR	FRASER FIR	SCOTCH PINE	2	3	4	5	6	45	50	55	60	65
GROUP	BOY SCOUTS															
	4-H CLUB															
	GIRL SCOUTS															
	HUMANE SOCIETY															
	ROTARY CLUB															
ORNAMENTS	45															
	50															
	55															
	60															
	65															
LIGHTS	2															
	3															
	4															
	5															
	6															

LOGIC PROBLEM 216

In an effort to promote interest in the traditional art of storytelling, the Riverton Council for the Arts sponsored a day-long festival of workshops for amateur storytellers. The curious townsfolk who showed up in droves were both entertained and instructed by the various demonstrations. Each of the five storytellers (including Tim) who led a workshop, one after another, began with a short, fictional story about a different, zany adventure (one was about time travel) to showcase a different aspect of effective story narration (including gesturing). These would-be storytellers were so inspired by the festival that many of them have gone on to achieve great success—but, of course, that's another story! From the information provided, can you determine the order in which each presenter led a workshop, as well as the adventure described in each one's story and the narrative technique it presented for discussion?

1. Celia told a story immediately before the person who handled the topic of thematic continuity (who isn't Jerry) but immediately after the one who told about wild creatures encountered on a camping trip.

2. Celia isn't the presenter who conveyed the importance of voice modulation in storytelling.

3. Jerry gave his presentation immediately after the one whose story centered on an African safari but immediately before the one who highlighted the importance of descriptive fillers in storytelling.

4. The fourth presenter of the day was neither the one who focused on the importance of plot development nor the one who stressed voice modulation.

5. Lydia lectured at some point before Marjorie (who didn't tell the story about joining the circus) but at some point after the one who told of a picnic—and unexpected swimming adventure—at the lake.

6. Celia (who didn't tell the circus story) didn't discuss the use of descriptive fillers.

		PRESENTER					ADVENTURE					NARRATIVE TECHNIQUE				
		CELIA	JERRY	LYDIA	MARJORIE	TIM	CAMPING	CIRCUS	PICNIC	SAFARI	TIME TRAVEL	DESCRIPTIVE FILLERS	GESTURING	PLOT DEVELOPMENT	THEMATIC CONTINUITY	VOICE MODULATION
ORDER	FIRST															
	SECOND															
	THIRD															
	FOURTH															
	FIFTH															
TECHNIQUE	DESCRIPTIVE											
	GESTURING											
	PLOT DEVELOP.											
	THEMATIC											
	VOICE MODUL.											
ADVENTURE	CAMPING						
	CIRCUS						
	PICNIC						
	SAFARI						
	TIME TRAVEL						

Always on the lookout for great bargains, Lyn and four of her friends were excited to see an advertisement for Willard's Furniture Warehouse—"High-quality furniture at rock-bottom prices!" Eager to check out the new store, each person (including Kirk and Patsy) shopped at Willard's on a different day (Monday, Tuesday, Thursday, Friday, or Saturday) last week. No one walked away empty-handed—each purchased a different piece of furniture (one bought an ottoman) at a different low, low price ($50, $100, $200, $250, or $300). These smart shoppers were thrilled to learn that, as Willard always says, Great furniture doesn't have to cost an arm and a leg! From the information provided, determine the day on which each person purchased his or her piece of furniture and the price he or she paid.

1. The person who purchased the daybed spent exactly twice as much as the friend who bought the roll-top desk on Monday but less than the one who has more letters in his or her first name than the one who spent $250.

2. Angela bought her piece at some point before the person who purchased the armoire (who spent exactly $50 less than the one who made his or her purchase on Saturday).

3. The one who shopped on Friday spent exactly $50 less, and has fewer letters in his or her first name, than the person who purchased the armoire.

4. Drew bought his piece exactly two days before the one who spent $50 (who isn't the one who bought a davenport).

		PERSON					PIECE					PRICE				
		ANGELA	DREW	KIRK	LYN	PATSY	ARMOIRE	DAVENPORT	DAYBED	OTTOMAN	ROLL-TOP DESK	$50	$100	$200	$250	$300
DAY	MONDAY															
	TUESDAY															
	THURSDAY															
	FRIDAY															
	SATURDAY															
PRICE	$50															
	$100															
	$200															
	$250															
	$300															
PIECE	ARMOIRE															
	DAVENPORT															
	DAYBED															
	OTTOMAN															
	ROLL-TOP DESK															

LOGIC PROBLEM 218

I DREAM OF GENIE

In the *Tales of the Arabian Nights*, the royal sultan has vowed to dispose of each of his wives because of the infidelity of the first—but the wise Scheherazade contrived to tell a story every evening for 1,001 nights until he revoked his decree. Unfortunately, when she came to the final five nights, Scheherazade found she was running a bit low on material. Recalling how the sultan had particularly enjoyed the tale of Aladdin and his wonderful lamp, she spent each of the remaining nights recounting a similar tale about a different humble hero (three of whom—Abdul, Jafar, and Sharif—are from Baghdad, and two of whom—Hamal and Kasim—are from Tabriz) who had freed a genie trapped in a different item. In gratitude, each genie granted his deliverer a different wish, and the five heroes lived in comfort for the rest of their days. In the end, of course, the sultan was so entertained by Scheherazade's stories that he spared her life—provided she promise to tell him a bedtime story every night! From the information provided, determine the hero of the story Scheherazade told each night (997th through 1,001st), as well as the item from which he freed the genie and the wish he was granted as a reward.

1. Two men from Baghdad were the hero of the last tale (who didn't find the magic lantern) and the one who wished for a flying carpet.

2. The hero who wished for a sultan's palace is either Jafar (who wasn't the hero of the 999th tale) or the one who freed a genie from a bottle.

3. Abdul isn't the one who wished for untold wealth. The 998th tale featured a hero from Tabriz.

4. Jafar isn't the one who released a genie from a mirror. The hero of the 999th tale wished for eternal life.

5. The tale of the hero who received a flying carpet was told before at least two other stories.

6. The tale of Abdul was told at least two nights after the story about the hero who received a sultan's palace.

7. Sharif, who freed a genie from a jar, was either the hero of the 997th story or the one who received a swift Arabian stallion. The genie in the ring was released by a man from Tabriz.

8. The tale of Hamal was told either the night before or the night after the story of the hero who found the magic lantern.

		HERO					ITEM					WISH				
		ABDUL	HAMAL	JAFAR	KASIM	SHARIF	BOTTLE	JAR	LANTERN	MIRROR	RING	ETERNAL LIFE	FLYING CARPET	SULTAN'S PALACE	SWIFT ARABIAN STALLION	UNTOLD WEALTH
NIGHT	997th															
	998th															
	999th															
	1,000th															
	1,001st															
WISH	ETERNAL LIFE															
	FLYING CARPET															
	SULTAN'S PALACE															
	SWIFT ARABIAN															
	UNTOLD WEALTH															
ITEM	BOTTLE															
	JAR															
	LANTERN															
	MIRROR															
	RING															

LOGIC PROBLEM 219

It was a busy morning at the post office, where five patrons were standing in a single-file line at the window awaiting its 9:00 a.m. opening. The five were waiting to turn in change of address forms, as each was moving from one address to another (one person was moving from Countryside Drive, and one was moving to 26th Avenue). Next stop for all five is the cable company, so they won't have to do without their MTV! From the information provided, determine each person's position in line, as well as his or her old and new addresses.

1. Ruby was standing behind, but not immediately behind, the person moving to Washington Place (who isn't Sydney).

2. The person from Cleveland Drive was standing immediately between the person moving to Kellogg Avenue and Jeb, in some order.

3. The person moving to Forrest Street was closer to the front of the line than Sophie. At least one person was standing between Sophie and the one moving to Forrest Street.

4. The person moving from Garden Drive was standing immediately between Ruby and the person moving to Sunset Road, in some order.

5. The person moving from Poplar Street was standing immediately between Duffy and the person moving from Monroe Terrace, in some order.

		DUFFY	JEB	RUBY	SOPHIE	SYDNEY	CLEVELAND DRIVE	COUNTRYSIDE DRIVE	GARDEN DRIVE	MONROE TERRACE	POPLAR STREET	FORREST STREET	KELLOGG AVENUE	SUNSET ROAD	26th AVENUE	WASHINGTON PLACE
		PERSON					OLD ADDRESS					NEW ADDRESS				
POSITION	FIRST															
	SECOND															
	THIRD															
	FOURTH															
	FIFTH															
NEW ADDRESS	FORREST STREET															
	KELLOGG AVENUE															
	SUNSET ROAD															
	26th AVENUE															
	WASHINGTON PL.															
OLD ADDRESS	CLEVELAND DRIVE															
	COUNTRYSIDE DR.															
	GARDEN DRIVE															
	MONROE TERRACE															
	POPLAR STREET															

LOGIC PROBLEM 220 KABLINKEE!

Kablinkee is a fun and fast-paced dice game in which players are awarded points for rolling certain patterns of numbers on the five dice. Last evening, Cliff and four of his friends sharpened their pencils, handed out the score pads, and settled down for a game or two. On each person's first roll, he or she rolled a different pattern (one is the Arugula), each of which was worth a different number (15, 20, 25, 30, or 35) of bonus points. The game proceeded until all the score sheets were filled and the numbers were tallied; at the end, each person had a different final score (150, 170, 190, 210, or 230 points). The first game went so well that they played another, each person trying to roll the rare Kablinkeesaurus, worth 700 bonus points! From the information provided, determine the bonus points each player was awarded for his or her opening roll, as well as each player's final score.

1. The player who rolled the Country Club (which occurs when the total of the numbers on the five dice equals 13) had a final score that was at least 40 points lower than that of the person whose first roll was worth 30 bonus points.

2. Stuart's bonus was worth more points than the Percolator (which entails rolling only odd numbers) but fewer points than at least one other roll.

3. When the same number appears on all five dice, a Kablinkee has been rolled; the person who rolled a Kablinkee was awarded exactly 5 more bonus points than the person whose final score was 210 points. The Maestro roll isn't worth 30 bonus points.

4. Jodie's final score was exactly 40 points higher than Lisa's final score.

5. The roll worth 35 bonus points was achieved by the person whose final score was exactly 20 points higher than that of the person who rolled a Percolator (who isn't Jodie).

6. Klaus's first roll was worth exactly 15 more bonus points than that of the person (who didn't roll a Percolator) who earned 170 points by the end of the game.

		ROLL					BONUS POINTS					FINAL SCORE				
		ARUGULA	COUNTRY CLUB	KABLINKEE	MAESTRO	PERCOLATOR	15	20	25	30	35	150	170	190	210	230
PLAYER	CLIFF															
	JODIE															
	KLAUS															
	LISA															
	STUART															
FINAL SCORE	150															
	170															
	190															
	210															
	230															
BONUS PTS.	15															
	20															
	25															
	30															
	35															

LOGIC PROBLEM 221

At the Perfect Match Dating Service, candidates are matched up with their ideal date by the company's own personal Cupid, manager Marvin Jessup. Marvin bases his decisions on the multiple-choice survey candidates fill out when they arrive and on the "video classified" each records. Today, for instance, he considered five applications, noting that each person had filled out a different number (10, 11, 12, 14, or 15) of A answers, a different number (12, 13, 15, 16, or 17) of B answers, and a different number (14, 15, 16, 17, or 18) of C answers on his or her multiple-choice survey. It was not until he watched each person's video, however, that the answer jumped out at him: Beth and Franz are ideal for each other, Kathleen and Sidney are a perfect match, and Tara—Tara is the woman of Marvin's dreams! From the information provided, determine the number of A, B, and C answers each person filled out on his or her survey.

1. Franz (who didn't have the most B answers) had fewer C answers than the person who had 11 A answers. One person had exactly 1 A answer more than the one who had 12 B answers.

2. Kathleen (who isn't the one who had exactly 1 C answer more than the one who had 12 A answers) had exactly 1 A answer fewer, but exactly 1 C answer more, than the one who had 17 B answers.

3. Sidney (who had fewer C answers than the one who had 15 A answers) had exactly 1 A answer more than the one who had 16 C answers.

4. Beth had exactly 1 C answer more than the one who had exactly 1 B answer more than Beth.

5. Tara (who had fewer C answers than the one who had 14 A answers) had exactly 1 B answer fewer than the one who had 15 C answers.

		A ANSWERS					B ANSWERS					C ANSWERS				
		10	11	12	14	15	12	13	15	16	17	14	15	16	17	18
PERSON	BETH															
	FRANZ															
	KATHLEEN															
	SIDNEY															
	TARA															
C ANSWERS	14															
	15															
	16															
	17															
	18															
B ANSWERS	12															
	13															
	15															
	16															
	17															

LOGIC PROBLEM 222   A LOTTO MONEY

With the 20-state Superball Lotto jackpot now at a record $250 million, people are flocking to local lottery outlets in hopes of drawing the winning ticket. For their shot at the enormous jackpot, William and four of his friends purchased a single ticket to share amongst themselves. Each person selected a different Lotto number (11, 16, 28, 37, or 44), to which they added the number 5 as their sixth "Superball" number, representing the number of people sharing the ticket. In addition to the joint ticket, each friend also purchased a different number of tickets from a different local store (one was Quik Stop), "just in case." From the information provided, determine the Lotto number each friend chose for their shared ticket, as well as the number of tickets each purchased individually from each store.

1. No one purchased fewer than 9 tickets or more than 24 tickets. The difference between the number of tickets purchased by any two people is at least 3. Neither Melinda (who didn't buy her tickets at Dairy Market) nor Jolene is the one who purchased his or her tickets at SuperShop (who didn't choose lucky number 44).

2. The friend who chose number 44 purchased more tickets than the person who bought his or her tickets at Country Grocer (who didn't choose an even number as his or her lotto number) but fewer tickets than at least one other person. The one who purchased his or her tickets at Dairy Market chose a lower number than Erica but a higher number than at least one other person.

3. The one who purchased the most tickets bought exactly twice as many as the one who bought the second-fewest number of tickets. The person who purchased the second-greatest number of tickets (who didn't choose number 44) bought exactly twice as many as the one who got the fewest tickets (who didn't choose number 28).

4. Neither Jolene nor the friend who went to Country Grocer purchased the fewest tickets. The person who bought his or her tickets at Walt's Mart didn't buy the most tickets.

5. The SuperShop shopper purchased fewer tickets than the friend who chose number 16 but more tickets than the one who went to Dairy Market (who isn't Thomas).

		NUMBER					STORE					TICKETS				
		11	16	28	37	44	COUNTRY GROCER	DAIRY MARKET	QUIK STOP	SUPERSHOP	WALT'S MART					
FRIEND	ERICA															
	JOLENE															
	MELINDA															
	THOMAS															
	WILLIAM															
TICKETS																
STORE	COUNTRY										
	DAIRY MARKET					
	QUIK STOP					
	SUPERSHOP					
	WALT'S MART					

LOGIC PROBLEM 223

The crew at All-Star Fences, a local construction company specializing in the installation and maintenance of private-property fences, had a busy week repairing five fences, each at a different address in town (125 Chestnut Street, 140 Camden Lane, 155 Lexington Court, 230 Fields Road, or 260 Water Shadow Place). Except for the two fences the team repaired on Wednesday, they mended one fence on each day from Tuesday through Friday. Each job involved a different type of fence (three of which—chain link, wire mesh, and wrought iron—are metal fences, and two of which—split rail and white picket—are wooden fences), and in each case, a different length (10, 12, 15, 20, or 25 feet) of the fence needed to be replaced. All-Star's customers aren't on the fence about the company's repairs—the quality of their work has no boundaries! From the information provided, can you determine the address at which the fence repaired on each day is located, as well as the length in feet of the segment of fence that needed replacing for each job?

1. One of the Wednesday jobs required the replacement of a 12-foot segment of fence at an address with a house number under 200.

2. The replacement piece of wooden fence repaired the day before the wrought-iron fence was exactly 10 feet longer than the segment of wooden fence used at 260 Water Shadow Place.

3. The white-picket fence and the one made from wire mesh are the one repaired on Thursday (which required a segment of fence exactly 5 feet shorter than the one used at 155 Lexington Court) and the one located at 125 Chestnut Street, in some order.

4. The segment of the split-rail fence that needed to be replaced was exactly 5 feet shorter than the segment of metal fence replaced on Tuesday (which wasn't the day the crew worked at 230 Fields Road).

5. The difference between the house number of the address where the chain-link fence is located and that of the address where the replaced segment of fence was next-larger than the chain-link segment, is less than 90.

		FENCE					ADDRESS					FEET				
		CHAIN LINK	SPLIT RAIL	WHITE PICKET	WIRE MESH	WROUGHT IRON	125 CHESTNUT STREET	140 CAMDEN LANE	155 LEXINGTON COURT	230 FIELDS ROAD	260 WATER SHADOW PLACE	10	12	15	20	25
DAY	TUESDAY															
	WEDNESDAY															
	WEDNESDAY															
	THURSDAY															
	FRIDAY															
FEET	10															
	12															
	15															
	20															
	25															
ADDRESS	125 CHESTNUT															
	140 CAMDEN LANE															
	155 LEXINGTON															
	230 FIELDS ROAD															
	260 WATER SHAD.															

LOGIC PROBLEM 224   INVENTORY ADJUSTMENT

Her recent promotion to Office Manager of GlobalCorp has given Jackie a crash course in supply-side economics. Part of her new position is ordering office supplies for the entire company, and last week six department heads came to her with requests. Each department (one is the computer department) asked for a different number (30, 40, 50, 70, 80, or 90) of legal pads, a different number (20, 30, 50, 60, 70, or 80) of manila envelopes, and a different number (40, 50, 60, 70, 90, or 100) of red pens. Having finally moved into her new office, Jackie is anxious to fill the requests—just as soon as she can find a pencil! From the information provided, determine the number of legal pads, manila envelopes, and red pens each department ordered.

1. No department requested the same number of any two items. The department that requested 50 manila envelopes (which asked for fewer legal pads than at least one other department) needed exactly 10 more red pens than the public-relations department.

2. The department that asked for 90 legal pads needed exactly 10 fewer manila envelopes than the department that ordered 90 red pens (which requisitioned more legal pads than the marketing department).

3. The department that needed 50 red pens wanted fewer manila envelopes than the art department (which requested fewer red pens than the personnel department).

4. The accounting department asked for more legal pads than the one that requested 30 manila envelopes (which ordered exactly 10 more red pens than the department that needed 40 legal pads).

5. The department that ordered 60 red pens wanted exactly 20 fewer legal pads than the department that asked for 60 manila envelopes (which needed exactly 20 more red pens than the department that ordered 90 legal pads).

		LEGAL PADS						MANILA ENVELOPES						RED PENS					
		30	40	50	70	80	90	20	30	50	60	70	80	40	50	60	70	90	100
DEPARTMENT	ACCOUNTING																		
	ART																		
	COMPUTER																		
	MARKETING																		
	PERSONNEL																		
	PUB. RELATIONS																		
RED PENS	40																		
	50																		
	60																		
	70																		
	90																		
	100																		
ENVELOPES	20																		
	30																		
	50																		
	60																		
	70																		
	80																		

LOGIC PROBLEM 225

Every year, the Vaniteaux International Fashion Show provides up-and-coming designers a chance to model their latest designs for some of the world's most influential critics. This year, five young designers were thrilled when a critic for *Haute Couture* magazine made a different, favorable comment about each one's new line! Each person had created a line of clothing featuring a different type of outfit rendered in a different material. With reviews like these, the Vaniteaux runway is sure to lead to fashionable career takeoffs for all five designing superstars! From the information provided, determine the designer who created each line of clothing and the material in which each was rendered, as well as the favorable comment (one person's line was described as "eye-pleasing") each received from the *Haute Couture* critic.

1. Paolo Ferrari didn't design the cashmere line. The jackets weren't described as "handsome." Yves St. Denis, who didn't employ silk, didn't present the line of tailored suits (which weren't characterized as "elegant").

2. The cocktail dresses weren't called "splendid." Donna Vitali, who used neither cotton nor cashmere, did not design the evening gowns. Satin wasn't used for the cocktail dresses.

3. Rory Bean, who isn't the one who used cotton fabric, didn't create a new line of jackets. The items rendered in silk weren't the ones described as "lovely" (which wasn't the epithet used to describe the cocktail dresses). Calvin Phelps didn't create the line of clothing described as "handsome" (which wasn't the remark made about the evening gowns).

4. Yves St. Denis, who didn't employ cotton in his designs, isn't the one whose line was called "elegant." Neither tailored suits nor cocktail dresses were part of the Paolo Ferrari line. The silk wardrobe, which wasn't created by Calvin Phelps, wasn't called "handsome."

5. Neither the cocktail dresses nor the evening gowns were pronounced "elegant." The cashmere wardrobe wasn't designed by Yves St. Denis. Neither Rory Bean's collection nor the polyester line was called "handsome."

6. Satin wasn't the material used to create the leisure-wear collection. The line of tailored suits wasn't the one described as "splendid" (which wasn't the epithet used to describe the polyester clothing). Donna Vitali didn't design jackets or tailored suits.

		CLOTHING					MATERIAL					COMMENT				
		COCKTAIL DRESSES	EVENING GOWNS	JACKETS	LEISURE WEAR	TAILORED SUITS	CASHMERE	COTTON	POLYESTER	SATIN	SILK	ELEGANT	EYE-PLEASING	HANDSOME	LOVELY	SPLENDID
DESIGNER	CALVIN PHELPS															
	DONNA VITALI															
	PAOLO FERRARI															
	RORY BEAN															
	YVES ST. DENIS															
COMMENT	ELEGANT															
	EYE-PLEASING															
	HANDSOME															
	LOVELY															
	SPLENDID															
MATERIAL	CASHMERE															
	COTTON															
	POLYESTER															
	SATIN															
	SILK															

LOGIC PROBLEM 226 DUET PART 1: SHOW TOONS*

Tired of being typecast, many animated characters, against the wishes of their agents, are attempting to break out of the cartoon industry and try their luck in other dramatic forms. Surprisingly enough, they have footsteps in which to follow, as years ago, each of six characters who were told by cartoon executives that they'd never get live work landed a role in a different musical (one is *Les Misérables*). Each role began in a different month and lasted a different number (4, 5, 7, 8, 9, or 10) of weeks. Those successes have encouraged others in the field to free themselves from the corner into which they've been drawn. From the information provided, determine the month (June through November) each character began performing in each musical, as well as the number of weeks of his or her engagement.

1. The television role for which Loony Goon auditioned had exactly one line fewer than the role sought by the character who began performing in a musical in September (who did so for exactly one week fewer than the one who auditioned for the role of Troubled Teen on one program). The Troubled Teen role had exactly one line more than the part Mr. Goop wanted.

2. Margie Muffen's desired role had exactly one line more than did the part of Plumber. The character who took to the stage in June spent more time in the theater than both Margie Muffen and the one who auditioned for a part on *Law & Order*.

3. The one who performed in the musical *Evita* was up for a role that had exactly two fewer lines than the part on *NYPD Blue*.

4. Jiggly Jalopy, who got a role in a musical in November, spent exactly one week more on the stage than the one who hoped to appear in *Party of Five*.

		MUSICAL					MONTH						WEEKS					
		EVITA	JEKYLL & HYDE	LES MISERABLES	MISS SAIGON	THE PHANTOM OF THE OPERA	SUNSET BOULEVARD	JUNE	JULY	AUGUST	SEPTEMBER	OCTOBER	NOVEMBER	4	5	7	8	9	10
CHARACTER	JIGGLY JALOPY																		
	LOONY GOON																		
	LOOPY LARRY																		
	MARGIE MUFFEN																		
	MR. GOOP																		
	SLAPPY FROG																		
WEEKS	4																		
	5																		
	7																		
	8																		
	9																		
	10																		
MONTH	JUNE																		
	JULY																		
	AUGUST																		
	SEPTEMBER																		
	OCTOBER																		
	NOVEMBER																		

This is part 1 of a two-part puzzle. It is necessary to work back and forth between this part and part 2 on page 235 in order to solve the puzzle.

Upon the successful completion of their roles in musicals, the six cartoon characters wanted to try their hands at dramatic television, so each auditioned for a different role on a different, prime-time TV program (one is *The X-Files*). Even though they were bit parts that had a different, seemingly insignificant number of lines (1, 2, 4, 5, 6, or 7), the characters were confident that landing these roles would open the door for animated actors everywhere! From the information provided, determine the role on each program for which each character auditioned and the number of lines that part had.

1. Loony Goon isn't the character who tried out for *Touched by an Angel*, who took to the stage in October for exactly one week more than Slappy Frog but for fewer weeks than at least one other. The character who opened in October is not the one who sang in *The Phantom of the Opera*.

2. The one who got a part in a musical in August (who wasn't engaged there for seven weeks) was up for a TV part that had exactly one line more than the part of the Bus Driver (which was sought by a character who spent more weeks in the theater than the one who started in August).

3. The one who sang onstage in *Sunset Boulevard* auditioned for the part of Cashier #3, which had fewer lines than the part sought by the *Miss Saigon* actor, who sang onstage for fewer weeks than the character who audition for *ER*.

4. After four weeks on stage, Loopy Larry was up for a part with exactly one line more than the role of the Journalist (which was sought by a character who was in a musical for fewer weeks than the one who auditioned for the four-line part).

5. The one who began his or her stint in the stage musical *Jekyll & Hyde* in July (which didn't last for ten weeks) did so for exactly one week more than another character. The character who auditioned for the role of the Concerned Parent did not have the shortest theatrical engagement.

		ROLE						PROGRAM						LINES					
		BUS DRIVER	CASHIER #3	CONCERNED PARENT	JOURNALIST	PLUMBER	TROUBLED TEEN	ER	LAW & ORDER	NYPD BLUE	PARTY OF FIVE	TOUCHED BY AN ANGEL	THE X-FILES	1	2	4	5	6	7
CHARACTER	JIGGLY JALOPY																		
	LOONY GOON																		
	LOOPY LARRY																		
	MARGIE MUFFEN																		
	MR. GOOP																		
	SLAPPY FROG																		
LINES	1																		
	2																		
	4																		
	5																		
	6																		
	7																		
PROGRAM	ER																		
	LAW & ORDER																		
	NYPD BLUE																		
	PARTY OF FIVE																		
	TOUCHED BY																		
	THE X-FILES																		

*This is part 2 of a two-part puzzle. It is necessary to work back and forth between this part and part 1 on page 234 in order to solve the puzzle.

LOGIC PROBLEM 228 NETWORKING

Every year during ratings-sweeps period, television networks try to attract new viewers to their shows by broadcasting special "crossover" episodes in which characters from one hit show appear on another program. This year, the National Broadcasting Conglomerate is planning guest appearances on five of its top-rated shows. Each show has a different star, each of whom plays a character with a different profession. Due to some quick thinking and intricate plotting by the series' writers, each program's star will appear on a different one of the other four shows. Although critics scoff at this bonanza of crossovers, real television fans are in for happy days! From the information provided, determine the role played by the star of each series, as well as the show on which each will appear as a guest.

1. The actor who portrays a detective in his or her weekly series will guest star on *Practice Makes Perfect*. The main character of *Losing Patients* is a psychiatrist.

2. Cedric Howe (who is neither the actor who portrays a single parent nor the one who plays a traffic cop) is the star of the show Victor Walsh will visit.

3. The star of *Family Business* (who isn't Laura Pontz) will make a guest appearance on *Losing Patients*.

4. The performer who plays the single parent (who isn't Peter Santos) will guest star on Jasmine French's program (which isn't the series called *Overboard*). Jasmine French will make a special appearance on the show about a small-town lawyer.

5. The regular star of *On the Job* will guest star on the program whose leading man or woman is scheduled to make an appearance on *Family Business*.

		ROLE					SERIES					GUEST				
		DETECTIVE	LAWYER	PARENT	PSYCHIATRIST	TRAFFIC COP	FAMILY BUSINESS	LOSING PATIENTS	ON THE JOB	OVERBOARD	PRACTICE MAKES PERFECT	FAMILY BUSINESS	LOSING PATIENTS	ON THE JOB	OVERBOARD	PRACTICE MAKES PERFECT
STAR	CEDRIC HOWE															
	JASMINE FRENCH															
	LAURA PONTZ																
	PETER SANTOS																
	VICTOR WALSH																
GUEST	FAMILY BUSINESS																
	LOSING PATIENTS																
	ON THE JOB																
	OVERBOARD																
	PRACTICE MAKES																
SERIES	FAMILY BUSINESS																
	LOSING PATIENTS																
	ON THE JOB																
	OVERBOARD																
	PRACTICE MAKES																

Even though baseball season is officially over, Sports Etcetera sporting goods sought to extend the season a little longer last week by inviting five minor-league baseball players, each of whom plays a different position (one is the first baseman) for a different team, for a week of autographs and questions. Young Donald Ortiz, thrilled with the thought of meeting five of his idols, went to Sports Etcetera on four different days in order to obtain the treasured autographs. When he finally met each hero, Donald nearly swooned with delight as he handed each player a different item (in one case, a player's photograph) to be signed. Gazing happily at his prized treasures, Donald can hardly wait for next year's season to arrive! From the information provided, determine each player's team (one is the Pratt Penguins) and position, as well as the item he autographed.

1. Neither Roger Merrick (who autographed Donald's bat) nor Jackson Butler is the man who plays for the Oswego Ospreys. Lenny Ayala (whom Donald met on the first day) isn't the man who plays catcher for his team.

2. Neither the player who signed Donald's baseball (whom he met on the fourth day) nor Alan Dykstra is the man who plays for the Wichita Redwings (who isn't Roger Merrick). Donald met both the player who signed his pennant and Eddie Armstrong on the same day.

3. Donald met the shortstop (who isn't the all-star from the Kansas City Suns) on his third visit to Sports Etcetera. Donald met the Topeka Flyers player on the first day, and he met the pitcher on the fourth day.

4. On the second day (which is the only day on which Donald met two players), Donald met both the left fielder and the one who signed a page in his autograph book.

		TEAM					POSITION					ITEM				
		KANSAS CITY SUNS	OSWEGO OSPREYS	PRATT PENGUINS	TOPEKA FLYERS	WICHITA REDWINGS	CATCHER	FIRST BASEMAN	LEFT FIELDER	PITCHER	SHORTSTOP	AUTOGRAPH BOOK	BASEBALL	BAT	PENNANT	PHOTOGRAPH
PLAYER	ALAN DYKSTRA															
	E. ARMSTRONG															
	JACKSON BUTLER															
	LENNY AYALA															
	ROGER MERRICK															
ITEM	AUTOGRAPH BOOK															
	BASEBALL															
	BAT															
	PENNANT															
	PHOTOGRAPH															
POSITION	CATCHER															
	FIRST BASEMAN															
	LEFT FIELDER															
	PITCHER															
	SHORTSTOP															

LOGIC PROBLEM 230 CHILD'S PLAY

When the sun made an unexpected appearance last weekend, the unseasonably warm weather drove some neighborhood children out of doors to take advantage of what may have been their last chance this years to use the playground in the park! Each of the six children (four of whom—Cindy, Elise, Lana, and Millie—are girls, and two of whom—Joseph and Vince—are boys) was accompanied to the park by a different person, and, except for the two children who rode the seesaw, each child played on a different piece of playground equipment. It didn't feel warm for long, however, and each child stayed at the park for a different number (25, 35, 45, 55, 65, or 75) of minutes before runny noses caused them to head home for soup and hot cocoa. From the information provided, determine the companion each child brought to the park, the playground equipment on which he or she played, and the number of minutes each spent there before returning home.

1. The four girls are Elise, the one who spent time in the sandbox, the one who came with her brother, and the one who played for exactly 10 minutes longer than Joseph.

2. Cindy played in the park for more than twice as long as both the child who arrived with his or her mother and the one accompanied by his or her father.

3. The ones who were accompanied by a friend, a father, and a sister are Millie, the child who slipped down the slide, and the one who stayed for 35 minutes, in some order.

4. The child who played at the park with his or her cousin stayed for at least twice as long as Vince. The one who frolicked on the swings didn't stay for as long as the child who clambered on the jungle gym.

5. The average of the combined times spent by the two children who rode the seesaw is equal to the time spent at the park by the child who went with his or her friend. The one who came to the park with an older brother stayed exactly 10 fewer minutes than a girl but exactly 10 minutes longer than a boy.

		COMPANION						EQUIPMENT						MINUTES					
		BROTHER	COUSIN	FATHER	FRIEND	MOTHER	SISTER	JUNGLE GYM	SANDBOX	SEESAW	SEESAW	SLIDE	SWINGS	25	35	45	55	65	75
CHILD	CINDY																		
	ELISE																		
	JOSEPH																		
	LANA																		
	MILLIE																		
	VINCE																		
MINUTES	25																		
	35																		
	45																		
	55																		
	65																		
	75																		
EQUIPMENT	JUNGLE GYM																		
	SANDBOX																		
	SEESAW																		
	SEESAW																		
	SLIDE																		
	SWINGS																		

LOGIC PROBLEM 231

When their 13th-century castle was purchased and turned into a theme hotel, the six resident ghosts (each of whom is one of three types of spirit—poltergeist, specter, or wraith) who had haunted the fortress for hundreds of years suddenly found themselves looking for a new place to live. Eager for a change of scenery, the six incorporeal beings (including Ileana) settled on suburban America. Each selected a different house, each of which has a different number (626, 930, 1218, 1453, 1687, or 2750) and is located on a different street. While all of the houses are spacious—each has either four, five, or six bedrooms—and loaded with the customary amenities, each spirit made his or her final decision based on a different, slightly less traditional feature (one has a revolving bookcase, perfect for waylaying unsuspecting mortals). From the information provided, determine the number and street (one is Silver Street) on which each spirit's new house is located, as well as the special feature that attracted his or her attention.

1. House number 1687 and the one on Mason Road (which are inhabited by a specter and a poltergeist, in some order) have the same number of bedrooms; none of the other four houses have this number of bedrooms.

2. Jed's new abode and the one on Wingate Circle are the only two homes that have four bedrooms. The house with the creaking staircase has fewer bedrooms than Danica's.

3. Three houses containing the same number of bedrooms are the one affected by cold drafts (which isn't inhabited by a wraith), Horace's, and the one on Greenwood Way.

4. Petra's new home, which has more bedrooms than any other spirit's abode, isn't the one at 1218 Park Lane recently inhabited by a ghost. Petra, who isn't a wraith, isn't the spirit whose new home has banging shutters.

5. Both the house on Oak Terrace and the one that boasts a large, dark attic are inhabited by wraiths. A specter lives in the lowest-numbered house. Marvin, the one who chose the house with loose floorboards, and the ghost living in house number 2750 are all poltergeists.

6. Danica doesn't haunt house number 930.

		NUMBER						STREET						FEATURE					
		626	930	1218	1453	1687	2750	GREENWOOD WAY	MASON ROAD	OAK TERRACE	PARK LANE	SILVER STREET	WINGATE CIRCLE	ATTIC	BANGING SHUTTERS	COLD DRAFTS	CREAKING STAIRCASE	LOOSE FLOORBOARDS	REVOLVING BOOKCASE
SPIRIT	DANICA																		
	HORACE																		
	ILEANA																		
	JED																		
	MARVIN																		
	PETRA																		
FEATURE	ATTIC																		
	BANGING																		
	COLD DRAFTS																		
	CREAKING																		
	LOOSE FLOOR.																		
	REVOLVING																		
STREET	GREENWOOD WAY																		
	MASON ROAD																		
	OAK TERRACE																		
	PARK LANE																		
	SILVER STREET																		
	WINGATE CIRCLE																		

LOGIC PROBLEM 232

Several times each year, Enid gets together with a group of her friends who share her enthusiasm for spelunking, or cave exploration. Each time they meet, the six end up talking well into the night about the various exciting caves they have recently explored. Last night's get-together was no exception, as each person described in detail a breathtaking series of rock formations he or she had stumbled upon in a different cave (including Tom Thumb Cavern). Each exploration occurred in a different month (May through October), and no two friends described the same type of formation (one told of beautiful stalagmites). Caving in to their love of spelunking, the six have already begun laying the groundwork for their next expeditions! From the information provided, determine the month in which the cave exploration described by each person took place and the type of impressive formation he or she saw there.

1. Linoch Falls Cave was explored the month after the one in which a spectacular flowstone formation was observed.

2. Sheila went spelunking the month before her friend observed the gypsum flowers but the month after Destiny's Cavern was explored.

3. Bo, who isn't the one who saw the drapery formation, isn't the person who explored Boer's Cavern (which wasn't visited in May).

4. Kirk observed a spectacular natural formation exactly three months after someone else explored Bent Knee Cave.

5. The gypsum flowers (which weren't seen in October) weren't found in Symmes Ridge Cave.

6. Abundant stalactites were seen in the cave explored the month after Boer's Cavern but the month before the one described by Kim.

7. The cave with the helictites was explored the month after the one Dennis described but the month before Symmes Ridge Cave (which wasn't explored by Sheila).

		BO	DENNIS	ENID	KIM	KIRK	SHEILA	BENT KNEE CAVE	BOER'S CAVERN	DESTINY'S CAVERN	LINOCH FALLS CAVE	SYMMES RIDGE CAVE	TOM THUMB CAVERN	DRAPERY	FLOWSTONE	GYPSUM FLOWERS	HELICTITES	STALACTITES	STALAGMITES
MONTH	MAY																		
	JUNE																		
	JULY																		
	AUGUST																		
	SEPTEMBER																		
	OCTOBER																		
FORMATION	DRAPERY																		
	FLOWSTONE																		
	GYPSUM FLOW.																		
	HELICTITES																		
	STALACTITES																		
	STALAGMITES																		
CAVE	BENT KNEE																		
	BOER'S																		
	DESTINY'S																		
	LINOCH FALLS																		
	SYMMES RIDGE																		
	TOM THUMB																		

LOGIC PROBLEM 233

Scientists from the Fradell Institute recently reported conclusive evidence confirming the existence of extra-terrestrial life forms—and their habitation of Earth! In a recent press conference, it was disclosed that alien beings from the Plexas galaxy had visited five different Earth islands in the 14th century. Each island was visited in a different year (1301 through 1399) for a different, whole number of months, and the experts say that the alien creatures escaped detection by disguising themselves as a different type of indigenous life form. Ironically, the scientists claim that the visitors in their natural form were already fairly inconspicuous, since they bear a strong resemblance to moss! From the information provided, determine the year in which the aliens resembling each life form arrived, the island they visited, and the number of months they stayed.

1. One group of aliens arrived in 1323. The beings who resided in Sri Lanka aren't the ones who masqueraded as radishes. One island was inhabited for exactly five months.

2. The creatures who inhabited our planet for exactly three months (who didn't live in Maui) arrived exactly 23 years before the ones who disguised themselves as dragonflies.

3. The visitors who stayed for the shortest time didn't arrive in 1340. The aliens who resided in Ireland stayed on Earth for exactly half as long as the ones who landed in 1384.

4. Except for the first two digits, the arrival year of the visitors to Maui added to the arrival year of another group of aliens (who stayed for seven months) is equal to the arrival year of the creatures posing as bats.

5. The aliens who pretended to be jellyfish lived on Earth for exactly three months longer than the ones who arrived in Cuba (but not in 1348).

6. Except for the first two digits, the arrival year of the visitors to Borneo added to the arrival year of another group of aliens (who looked like orchids) is equal to the arrival year of the visitors who stayed for exactly four months.

7. The first aliens to arrive stayed exactly one month longer than the ones who were the last to arrive. The aliens who spent the longest amount of time on Earth landed exactly two years before the ones who had the shortest stay.

		LIFE FORM					ISLAND					MONTHS				
		BATS	DRAGONFLIES	JELLYFISH	ORCHIDS	RADISHES	BORNEO	CUBA	IRELAND	MAUI	SRI LANKA					
YEAR																
MONTHS																
ISLAND	BORNEO															
	CUBA															
	IRELAND															
	MAUI															
	SRI LANKA															

LOGIC PROBLEM 234

A FINE ROMANCE

Although they have enjoyed great success as directors of romance movies, five filmmakers are hoping to reach new audiences with their latest features. Each movie, while technically another romance, incorporates elements of a different genre (one is a Western) into its story line as well. Courting favorable reviews, each director had a different promotional item bearing the title of his or her film (no two have the same title) sent out to film critics a few weeks before its release. With their big dates coming up, these directors are hoping that the audience's response will be love at first sight! From the information provided, determine the genre of the movie (one is *Kiss of an Angel*) each director made, as well as the promotional item distributed for each.

1. *The Embrace* is a romantic action movie that will soon be appearing in a theater near you. *Forever Paradise* is not a horror film. Neither the action movie nor the mystery film is the one for which Anita Beakist had special bottles of a supposed love potion sent to the critics.

2. The horror movie isn't the one for which candy hearts imprinted with the name of the movie (which isn't *The Embrace*) were sent to critics. Lottie Hart didn't direct either the mystery or the suspense movie (neither of which was promoted with candy hearts).

3. The promotional item for *Love on the Nile* was a box of chocolates.

4. Neither the silk roses nor the book of love poems was the item distributed to promote Ed Schmaltz's movie. Neither Lacey Arrow's movie, *Chance Encounter*, nor Lily Valentine's movie was promoted with silk roses (which wasn't the gimmick used to promote the action movie).

		MOVIE					GENRE					PROMOTIONAL ITEM				
		CHANCE ENCOUNTER	THE EMBRACE	FOREVER PARADISE	KISS OF AN ANGEL	LOVE ON THE NILE	ACTION	HORROR	MYSTERY	SUSPENSE	WESTERN	CANDY HEARTS	CHOCOLATES	LOVE POEMS	LOVE POTION	SILK ROSES
DIRECTOR	ANITA BEAKIST															
	ED SCHMALTZ															
	LACEY ARROW															
	LILY VALENTINE															
	LOTTIE HART															
ITEM	CANDY HEARTS															
	CHOCOLATES															
	LOVE POEMS															
	LOVE POTION															
	SILK ROSES															
GENRE	ACTION															
	HORROR															
	MYSTERY															
	SUSPENSE															
	WESTERN															

LOGIC PROBLEM 235

After a long day of hiking and fishing, five friends on a camping trip gathered around the campfire and took turns spooking each other with scary stories about monsters who prey on unsuspecting campers. Each person described a different monster who crept up to a camper as he or she was performing a different activity (in one case, gathering firewood), but just when it seemed the monsters would get the best of their would-be victims, each hero managed to find a different way to frighten the monster away (one used the flash on his or her camera to startle the beast). From the information provided, determine the monster each camper described, the activity in which its unsuspecting victim was engaged, and the item each hero used to escape the monster's clutches.

1. Lionel's story featured the fiendish ape-man. The hero of one story drove off the dreadful campfire spook by scaring it away with a flashlight.

2. Neither Alice nor Curtis is the person who told the tale of the giant squirrel who chased campers through the woods.

3. The monster who stalked the flower-picking camper was chased away with bug spray.

4. Lionel's monster was frightened away by a fizzy can of soda pop. Neither Joanita's monster (who was attracted to the singing of camp songs) nor Curtis's monster was the one driven off by flaming marshmallows.

5. Trudy told the story about the frightening river griffin, which wasn't the monster attracted to whispering.

6. Alice isn't the storyteller who described the hideous tree brute. Lionel's monster had a habit of scaring hikers.

		MONSTER					ACTIVITY					ITEM				
		APE-MAN	CAMPFIRE SPOOK	GIANT SQUIRREL	RIVER GRIFFIN	TREE BRUTE	GATHERING FIREWOOD	HIKING	PICKING FLOWERS	SINGING CAMP SONGS	WHISPERING	BUG SPRAY	CAMERA FLASH	FLAMING MARSHMALLOWS	FLASHLIGHT	SODA POP
CAMPER	ALICE															
	CURTIS															
	JOANITA															
	LIONEL															
	TRUDY															
ITEM	BUG SPRAY															
	CAMERA FLASH															
	FLAMING															
	FLASHLIGHT															
	SODA POP															
ACTIVITY	GATHERING WOOD															
	HIKING															
	PICKING FLOWERS															
	SINGING SONGS															
	WHISPERING															

LOGIC PROBLEM 236   SUPERMARKET STAND-IN

Fifteen years ago, Lloyd and Andrew opened up a supermarket which, after many years of hard work, has become quite profitable. Retired for several years now, Lloyd still fills in at the store when his services are needed. Last week, for instance, Lloyd felt like he was back to the old grind when, each weekday Andrew called and asked him to fill in for a different employee who needed the day off for a different reason. Lloyd performed a different job (including displaying the produce) each day. From the information provided, determine the worker (one is Marie) Lloyd replaced on each weekday and his or her job, as well as the reason (one had to meet someone at the airport) for each person's absence.

1. Both Sam (who is neither the one who had a dental appointment nor the one who took a day off to house hunt) and Hilda worked on both Monday (which is the day Lloyd stocked shelves) and Tuesday. Lloyd took his mid-morning break with both Cheryl and Tim on Monday.

2. When Lloyd arrived at the store on Tuesday, Cheryl told him that he would be replacing the employee who had taken his or her cat to the veterinarian.

3. On Wednesday, Lloyd filled in for the person who unloads the trucks (who didn't go to the dentist) and had lunch with Sam (who isn't the worker who experienced car problems on Thursday).

4. On Thursday, Lloyd worked the cash register and took his morning break with Cheryl. Tim isn't the employee who works at the customer-service counter.

		WORKER					JOB					REASON				
		CHERYL	HILDA	MARIE	SAM	TIM	CASH REGISTER	CUSTOMER SERVICE	DISPLAY PRODUCE	STOCK SHELVES	UNLOAD TRUCKS	AIRPORT	CAR TROUBLE	DENTIST	HOUSE HUNTING	VETERINARIAN
WEEKDAY	MONDAY															
	TUESDAY															
	WEDNESDAY															
	THURSDAY															
	FRIDAY															
REASON	AIRPORT															
	CAR TROUBLE															
	DENTIST															
	HOUSE HUNTING															
	VETERINARIAN															
JOB	CASH REGISTER															
	CUSTOMER															
	DISPLAY															
	STOCK SHELVES															
	UNLOAD TRUCKS															

LOGIC PROBLEM 237

As a dedicated practitioner of tantra yoga, Drew has repeatedly urged five of his college friends (including Heather), each of whom has a different, high-stress profession, to visit his ashram. Although they were all somewhat skeptical at first, each one eventually signed up for a different workshop that lasts a different number of weeks (6, 8, 10, 12, or 14) and teaches a different type of yoga. Although their courses are not yet complete, the five have already started feeling the physical and spiritual benefits, and Drew is thrilled that his friends have finally agreed to give inner peace a chance! From the information provided, can you determine each person's profession (one is a surgeon) and the type of yoga (one is jnana) each chose, as well as the number of weeks each workshop lasts?

1. The attorney's karma workshop lasts longer than Will's course (which isn't the shortest).

2. Maxwell finds his hatha workshop to be a great relief from his work as an advertising executive.

3. The air-traffic controller isn't the one taking the 12-week raja workshop. Jon's course lasts for 8 weeks.

4. Gina, who finds her job as a stockbroker very stressful, is enrolled in the 10-week workshop (which isn't the one that teaches bhakti yoga).

		PROFESSION					YOGA					WEEKS				
		ADVERTISING EXECUTIVE	AIR-TRAFFIC CONTROLLER	ATTORNEY	STOCKBROKER	SURGEON	BHAKTI	HATHA	JNANA	KARMA	RAJA	6	8	10	12	14
PERSON	GINA															
	HEATHER															
	JON															
	MAXWELL															
	WILL															
WEEKS	6															
	8															
	10															
	12															
	14															
YOGA	BHAKTI															
	HATHA															
	JNANA															
	KARMA															
	RAJA															

LOGIC PROBLEM 238 COMPUTER CRAZE

Dexter is currently shopping for a computer, and when he found the sales circular for Circuit World in last Sunday's newspaper, he immediately headed down there to examine the five different models (one was a Harvard computer) on sale. While each machine comes loaded with a different word-processing package, Dexter's real interest was in the different piece of hardware featured on each computer and the amount of RAM memory it has (each has a different amount of RAM—16, 28, 32, 64, or 128 gigabytes). From the information provided, can you determine the word-processing package, featured piece of hardware (camera, DVD-ROM, scanner, sub woofer, or zip drive), and amount of RAM each computer has?

1. Neither the Packard computer (which features a scanner) nor the Orange computer is the machine equipped with Macroletter 3.0. Neither the computer featuring the zip drive nor the one that comes with the camera is the computer equipped with Notetaker 4.0 (which isn't the Packard computer).

2. LetterWriter 2000 is loaded on the machine featuring the DVD-ROM. The computer in the package including the sub woofer (which isn't the one made by Orange) has 64 gigabytes of RAM. The Writer's Workshop 2.0 software is included with the computer with 16 gigabytes of RAM.

3. The Matrix computer (which doesn't have a zip drive) has 32 gigabytes of RAM. Office Keeper 4.1 is loaded on the Omega computer, which doesn't have 128 gigabytes of RAM.

		PACKAGE					HARDWARE					RAM				
		LETTERWRITER 2000	MACROLETTER 3.0	NOTETAKER 4.0	OFFICE KEEPER 4.1	WRITER'S WORKSHOP 2.0	CAMERA	DVD-ROM	SCANNER	SUB WOOFER	ZIP DRIVE	16	28	32	64	128
COMPUTER	HARVARD															
COMPUTER	MATRIX															
COMPUTER	OMEGA															
COMPUTER	ORANGE															
COMPUTER	PACKARD															
RAM	16															
RAM	28															
RAM	32															
RAM	64															
RAM	128															
HARDWARE	CAMERA															
HARDWARE	DVD-ROM															
HARDWARE	SCANNER															
HARDWARE	SUB WOOFER															
HARDWARE	ZIP DRIVE															

LOGIC PROBLEM 239

After living with roommates for years, Jamie enjoys the peace and quiet of her new apartment. In some ways, though, it seems like she still has roommates—she keeps getting mail for the unit's previous tenants! This week alone, junk mail addressed to five people (including Franklin) has been sent to Jamie's address, as each person was sent an application for a different credit card (one is Passway) and a catalog for a different store (exactly three of which—Arcadia, Fashion Exchange, and Threads—are clothing stores). It seems as if everyone is getting mail at Jamie's apartment—except for Jamie herself! From the information provided, can you determine the person (identified by first and last names—one surname is Santangelo) to whom each credit-card application and each catalog (one is Array of Appliances) was addressed?

1. The application for the U.S. Unlimited credit card (which wasn't addressed to Georgette) wasn't sent to the person surnamed Papadamaki (whose name was on the Fashion Exchange catalog).

2. Neither Thomas nor the person to whom the Supercard application was addressed (who isn't the one surnamed Zelinski) was sent a clothing catalog.

3. Beth, which wasn't the name on the catalog from Threads, got the application for the CreditPlus card. The person surnamed Gentle received a clothing-store catalog.

4. The person to whom the Visions credit-card application was sent isn't the addressee for either the Fashion Exchange catalog or the Purley Discount catalog.

5. The three clothing catalogs were addressed to Apostolia, the person surnamed Ozeri, and the one to whom the U.S. Unlimited application was sent.

		LAST NAME					CREDIT CARD					CATALOG				
		GENTLE	OZERI	PAPADAMAKI	SANTANGELO	ZELINSKI	CREDITPLUS	PASSWAY	SUPERCARD	U.S. UNLIMITED	VISIONS	ARCADIA	ARRAY OF APPLIANCES	FASHION EXCHANGE	PURLEY DISCOUNT	THREADS
FIRST NAME	APOSTOLIA															
	BETH															
	FRANKLIN															
	GEORGETTE															
	THOMAS															
CATALOG	ARCADIA															
	ARRAY OF APPLI.															
	FASHION EX.															
	PURLEY DISC.															
	THREADS															
CREDIT CARD	CREDITPLUS															
	PASSWAY															
	SUPERCARD															
	U.S. UNLIMITED															
	VISIONS															

LOGIC PROBLEM 240

Although the real moneymaker for Henry's farm is the vegetables he grows, he originally got into farming because of his love of animals. Currently, he has a full barn, as each of his five sows has recently become the proud mother of a different number (4, 6, 8, 10, or 12) of piglets! Each of the five sows (each of whom is a different breed—one is a Duroc) is kept in a different pen (3 through 7), and Henry always remembers to bring each sow her favorite treat, which she gets in addition to her regular feed. On the days the sows get their favorite food (no two have the same favorite—one is sweet corn), they truly eat like pigs! From the information provided, determine the breed of the sow in each pen and the number of piglets in her litter, as well as each sow's favorite treat.

1. The sow who gave birth to 12 piglets (who isn't the Berkshire) doesn't care for bananas (which is the favorite snack of the sow in pen seven).

2. The Chester White had more piglets than at least one other sow. The one who enjoys snacking on fish is in a pen numbered exactly two higher than the one holding the Berkshire (who didn't have 6 piglets).

3. The Hampshire pig is in a higher-numbered pen than the sow who gave birth to 8 piglets.

4. The Poland China (who didn't have 10 piglets) isn't the sow who dotes on apples (who is in a lower-numbered pen than the Berkshire).

5. The number of piglets each sow has is higher than her pen number. The sow in pen seven isn't the Hampshire, who gave birth to fewer piglets than the sow who likes to eat tomatoes.

		PEN					PIGLETS					TREAT				
		3	4	5	6	7	4	6	8	10	12	APPLES	BANANAS	FISH	SWEET CORN	TOMATOES
BREED	BERKSHIRE															
	CHESTER WHITE															
	DUROC															
	HAMPSHIRE															
	POLAND CHINA															
TREAT	APPLES															
	BANANAS															
	FISH															
	SWEET CORN															
	TOMATOES															
PIGLETS	4															
	6															
	8															
	10															
	12															

At Bayside College, the hallowed halls echo with the traditions of decades past—and one of the most popular with the students is the week of Halloween pranks! This year, a group of students really outdid themselves, "borrowing" five model skeletons that normally reside in the biology building and dressing each as a different, well-known school official (including the college president). Each skeleton was then propped in an amusing pose at a different location on campus. The skeletons were easily identified by the different room number (101, 102, 104, 105, or 106) stamped on each one's arm bone and were returned to their proper classrooms. The school officials took plenty of good-natured ribbing, though, thanks to the "humerus" antics of this skeleton crew! From the information provided, determine the name of the school official represented by the skeleton from each room and the location where each was propped.

1. The skeleton disguised as Mr. Fortescue (which wasn't the one propped up in the library with a copy of *Gray's Anatomy*) is from a room numbered higher than 102.

2. Mr. Henkels' imposter wasn't the skeleton found saluting the flagpole in the main quadrangle. The skeleton found in the cafeteria contemplating a burger and fries isn't stamped with number 105.

3. The skeleton found in the philosophy building poring over the works of Nietzsche has a lower number than the one dressed as the admissions director. Ms. Sanders, who isn't the admissions director or the provost, isn't the one whose look-alike is stamped with number 101.

4. The skeleton who represented the dean is numbered exactly two higher than the one who was discovered on a stationary bike in the gymnasium.

5. Ms. McGee isn't the football coach. The skeleton found sitting in the cafeteria (who bears neither the highest nor the lowest room number) wasn't dressed like Mr. Fortescue.

6. The skeleton who bears number 101 (who wasn't discovered in the philosophy building) wasn't dressed as Mr. Rathburn, who isn't the provost. The skeleton mimicking the provost was borrowed from the room numbered exactly one higher than the one from which the skeleton in the main quadrangle was taken.

		NAME					SCHOOL OFFICIAL					LOCATION				
		MR. FORTESCUE	MR. HENKELS	MS. McGEE	MR. RATHBURN	MS. SANDERS	ADMISSIONS DIRECTOR	DEAN	FOOTBALL COACH	PRESIDENT	PROVOST	CAFETERIA	GYMNASIUM	LIBRARY	MAIN QUADRANGLE	PHILOSOPHY BUILDING
ROOM	101															
	102															
	104															
	105															
	106															
LOCATION	CAFETERIA															
	GYMNASIUM															
	LIBRARY															
	MAIN QUAD.															
	PHILOSOPHY															
OFFICIAL	ADMISSIONS DIR.															
	DEAN															
	FOOTBALL COACH															
	PRESIDENT															
	PROVOST															

LOGIC PROBLEM 242

Although it only debuted in January, the new children's game show *It's a Wise Child* is already one of the biggest hits of the season! To celebrate their success, the producers have invited the five highest-scoring contestants back to the show for a special championship episode. Each contestant (three of whom—Buddy, Holden, and Seymour—are boys, and two of whom—Franny and Phoebe—are girls) had appeared on the program during a different month (January through May) and had reigned as the show's champion for a different number of days. Although all five are widely knowledgeable about a variety of subjects, each child admitted to program host Jerome David that he or she had a different favorite category (one is literature). From the information provided, determine the month in which each contestant originally appeared on the show, the number of days (3 through 7) he or she was champion, and each one's favorite category.

1. Seymour (who didn't appear on the program in May) was champion for fewer days than the January contestant but for more days than at least one other child.

2. The three boys are the one whose favorite category is science, the one who first appeared in May, and the one who had the longest winning streak.

3. Buddy isn't the one who prefers the history category. The contestant who was champion for four days wasn't on the show in April.

4. Buddy competed in an earlier month than the one whose favorite category is geography. The child who prefers the music category won for five straight days.

5. The winning streak of the geography buff (who isn't Phoebe) lasted longer than that of the March contestant but was shorter than Holden's streak.

		MONTH					DAYS					CATEGORY				
		JANUARY	FEBRUARY	MARCH	APRIL	MAY	3	4	5	6	7	GEOGRAPHY	HISTORY	LITERATURE	MUSIC	SCIENCE
CONTESTANT	BUDDY															
	FRANNY															
	HOLDEN															
	PHOEBE															
	SEYMOUR															
CATEGORY	GEOGRAPHY															
	HISTORY															
	LITERATURE															
	MUSIC															
	SCIENCE															
DAYS	3															
	4															
	5															
	6															
	7															

LOGIC PROBLEM 243

The five young women who recently moved into an apartment together at 240 Morningside Drive wanted to add some personal touches to the living room they now share. As each person has a collection of a different type of object (in one case, crystals) that she has been accumulating for years, they decided the living room would be the perfect place to display them. Since none of the women owned any furniture on which to set the bric-a-brac, however, the group went to a yard sale and purchased an old shelving unit with five shelves, thus granting each woman a different shelf for her collection. Although the wood on the antique piece was in less-than-perfect condition, each woman creatively covered the flaws by laying a furniture scarf made from a different material (including velveteen) on her designated shelf. Pleased with the results of their efforts, the roommates are certain that if only they could find a couch and a coffee table, the room would *really* start to come together! From the information provided, determine the shelf (1 through 5) on which each roommate has her collection displayed and the type of scarf on which it rests.

1. Becky's collection is beautifully arranged on shelf one. Marcia's knickknacks rest on a printed cotton scarf.

2. The collection of ceramic turtles is displayed on shelf two. Shelf four is covered by a lace scarf.

3. Robyn, who collects paperweights, isn't the woman who placed a silk scarf on her shelf.

4. Trish's collection, which is on neither shelf two nor shelf five, isn't the lovely assortment of seashells owned by one of the roommates.

5. Paige's collection of thimbles rests on a rayon scarf, but not on shelf five.

		ROOMMATE					COLLECTION					SCARF				
		BECKY	MARCIA	PAIGE	ROBYN	TRISH	CERAMIC TURTLES	CRYSTALS	PAPERWEIGHTS	SEASHELLS	THIMBLES	COTTON	LACE	RAYON	SILK	VELVETEEN
SHELF	1															
	2															
	3															
	4															
	5															
SCARF	COTTON															
	LACE															
	RAYON															
	SILK															
	VELVETEEN															
COLLECTION	CERAMIC TURTLES															
	CRYSTALS															
	PAPERWEIGHTS															
	SEASHELLS															
	THIMBLES															

With dozens of stars set to perform astounding feats, this year's *Circus of the Stars* will be the tent pole holding up the United Broadcasting Company's spring sweeps programming! Thrilled executives reported this week that the star of each of the network's five highest-rated shows has agreed to participate. Since each celebrity (including Whitney Marks) is set to perform a different, breathtaking act in a different one of the circus's five rings, this year's broadcast promises to be the greatest TV show on Earth! From the information provided, can you determine the act (one is the tightrope) that will be performed by the star in each ring, as well as the hit show on which he or she normally appears?

1. The star of *Shop Talk*, who isn't Hank Rialto, will appear in a lower-numbered ring than Greg Benz. Both *Law of Averages* and *Life Lines* are hour-long dramas.

2. Neither Dylan McCrae (who won't be performing in ring one) nor Ashley Fowler is the celebrity who will perform the human-cannonball act. The lion tamer, who won't appear in the highest-numbered ring, isn't Ashley Fowler (who isn't the *Baker's Dozen* star).

3. The star who will walk on hot coals will appear in the ring numbered exactly one higher than that in which the star of *Law of Averages* will perform.

4. Both Ashley Fowler (who will perform in a ring numbered at least two higher than that in which Greg Benz will appear) and the trapeze artist (who isn't the *Baker's Dozen* star) appear in half-hour sitcoms.

5. The ring in which the star of *Life Lines* will appear has a lower number than that in which the *Baker's Dozen* star will perform and is numbered exactly one lower than that in which the *Odd Jobs* star will appear.

		HUMAN CANNONBALL	LION TAMING	TIGHTROPE	TRAPEZE	WALK ON HOT COALS	ASHLEY FOWLER	DYLAN McCRAE	GREG BENZ	HANK RIALTO	WHITNEY MARKS	BAKER'S DOZEN	LAW OF AVERAGES	LIFE LINES	ODD JOBS	SHOP TALK
	ACT						STAR					SHOW				
RING	1															
	2															
	3															
	4															
	5															
SHOW	BAKER'S DOZEN															
	LAW OF AVERAGES															
	LIFE LINES															
	ODD JOBS															
	SHOP TALK															
STAR	ASHLEY FOWLER															
	DYLAN McCRAE															
	GREG BENZ															
	HANK RIALTO															
	WHITNEY MARKS															

LOGIC PROBLEM 245

At the headquarters of Wicks Candle Company, visitors get a hands-on lesson in the intricacies of making candles. So it was that, on Saturday, Victor and four of his friends spent the day learning about candles and making some of their own! During the process, each friend fashioned a different number (2 through 6) of candles, opting to improve them with a different scent (one was patchouli) from the hundreds of available varieties. One thing's for sure—no mere electric light can hold a candle to the friends' new sources of illumination! From the information provided, can you determine the number of candles made by each person (identified by first and last names) and the scent each chose?

1. Dominique (who isn't the person who made sandalwood-scented candles) isn't surnamed Candela.

2. The friend who made bayberry-scented candles made exactly one candle fewer than Walter, who made exactly one candle fewer than the person surnamed Bougie.

3. The one surnamed Kerze made exactly one more candle than Stefan, who made more candles than the person surnamed Vela. Louisa made more candles than the one who made jasmine-scented candles.

4. The person surnamed Candela made three candles, while another person made four jasmine-scented candles.

5. The one who made lavender-scented candles made exactly one candle more than the person surnamed Kaars but exactly one candle fewer than the friend surnamed Kerze.

	LAST NAME					CANDLES					SCENT				
	BOUGIE	CANDELA	KAARS	KERZE	VELA	2	3	4	5	6	BAYBERRY	JASMINE	LAVENDER	PATCHOULI	SANDALWOOD
FIRST NAME DOMINIQUE															
LOUISA															
STEFAN															
VICTOR															
WALTER															
SCENT BAYBERRY															
JASMINE															
LAVENDER															
PATCHOULI															
SANDALWOOD															
CANDLES 2															
3															
4															
5															
6															

LOGIC PROBLEM 246   SUPER MARIO DAY

March 10th is Mario Day: the abbreviation for the month of March (MAR) added to the date of the 10th spells MAR10, causing Marios around the world to celebrate! This year, each of five enthusiastic Marios had been arranging a different, special event (one was going to throw a party) to celebrate his name day—but, due to circumstances beyond his control, each of the five had to postpone the festivities to a different date (11th through 15th). This hasn't dampened the spirits of the Marios, who plan to glory in Mariosity; each man admires a different, famous Mario (one is race car driver Mario Andretti) who will be present in spirit for the celebration. From the information provided, determine the famous namesake admired by the Mario with each surname (one is Bumoni), as well as the event he has planned for the date on which he will celebrate Mario Day.

1. Mario Ramirez, who has always admired singer Mario Lanza, will celebrate the occasion on a later date than Mario Ortega, who is planning to take a day off from work for this special occasion.

2. The Mario who plans to see a movie to celebrate Mario Day (but not on March 12th) will do so on an earlier date than the man who loves the books written by Mario Puzo (who isn't Mario Hellman). The man who respects politician Mario Cuomo will celebrate Mario Day the day after the one who likes Mario Puzo's books.

3. The Mario who enjoys the work of actor Mario Van Peebles will celebrate the holiday on March 13th.

4. The man treating himself to a nice dinner (who isn't surnamed Ramirez) will celebrate earlier in the week than Mario Scarano (who isn't the one buying himself a present).

		NAMESAKE					EVENT					DATE				
		MARIO ANDRETTI	MARIO CUOMO	MARIO LANZA	MARIO PUZO	MARIO VAN PEEBLES	DAY OFF	DINNER	MOVIE	PARTY	PRESENT	11th	12th	13th	14th	15th
SURNAME	BUMONI															
	HELLMAN															
	ORTEGA															
	RAMIREZ															
	SCARANO															
DATE	11th															
	12th															
	13th															
	14th															
	15th															
EVENT	DAY OFF															
	DINNER															
	MOVIE															
	PARTY															
	PRESENT															

The Karlovs are notorious horror-movie buffs, so when a horror convention came to the Prescott Center in town, the entire family packed into the car and headed to the arena. Once there, the Karlovs found themselves in horror heaven; not only were some of their favorite scary movie stars signing autographs, but there were hundreds of vendors selling posters, scripts, and other movie memorabilia. Their collective spines tingled, however, when they reached the booth selling model kits of famous movie monsters, whereupon each person was suddenly possessed by the desire to purchase a different model kit (one chose a replica of the alien from the popular *Alien* movie series). Although they hadn't much experience with models, the Karlovs refused to be frightened by the number of pieces to be assembled (no two models had the same number of parts), nor could they rest in peace until their monstrous creations were completed. Finally, each Karlov placed his or her sinister masterpiece in a different room in their house (one person placed it in his or her bedroom), warning visitors that, in the Karlov home, no place is safe! From the information provided, can you determine the number of pieces (144, 167, 190, 213, or 236) in the monster model created by each person, as well as the room in which each model is displayed?

1. Gail's model has fewer pieces than the one kept in the living room, which has fewer pieces than the detailed model of the prehistoric pterodactyl Rodan. The replica of Freddy Krueger from the *Nightmare on Elm Street* series is comprised of fewer pieces than the one of King Kong.

2. Neither Randy (who didn't build the King Kong model) nor the one who built Freddy Krueger made the model with the fewest pieces. Pearl, who isn't the person who made the model of the Gill-Man from *The Creature from the Black Lagoon*, isn't the person who placed the replica in his or her home office. The replica kept in the basement is comprised of more than 144 pieces.

3. The model kept in the kitchen has neither 144 nor 236 pieces. Jed's model is comprised of fewer pieces than Omar's but more components than Gail's, which has more pieces than the model kept in the Karlovs' basement.

		MODEL					PIECES					ROOM				
		ALIEN	FREDDY KRUEGER	GILL-MAN	KING KONG	RODAN	144	167	190	213	236	BASEMENT	BEDROOM	KITCHEN	LIVING ROOM	OFFICE
PERSON	GAIL															
	JED															
	OMAR															
	PEARL															
	RANDY															
ROOM	BASEMENT															
	BEDROOM															
	KITCHEN															
	LIVING ROOM															
	OFFICE															
PIECES	144															
	167															
	190															
	213															
	236															

LOGIC PROBLEM 248   RIGHT UP YOUR ALLOY

The department of metallurgy at Gurnisson University has just experienced a number of exciting breakthroughs. By working with a different combinations of metals, each of five scientists (including Dr. Pushkin) created a different, innovative alloy. Much to the delight of the discovering scientist, each alloy exhibits a different, advantageous property (one doesn't rust or tarnish, keeping its luster without fail). Rather than naming the alloys after themselves, each scientist has humbly christened his metallic creation with a different, creative name. The industrial world is sure to embrace these new compounds, which are mixed blessings of the best kind! From the information provided, can you determine the mixture of metals (bismuth and chromium, bismuth and iron, chromium and iron, iron and tin, or magnesium and tin) used by each scientist to create his or her alloy (including additon), as well as its particular property?

1. Dr. Axis didn't make the alloy with high electrical resistance. The creator of the exceptionally lightweight alloy didn't use chromium.
2. Both the maker of malgamite (which is very strong) and Dr. McNeal used tin.
3. Neither blendium nor the alloy with a low melting point contains iron.
4. Bismuth was used to make both combinal (which has a high electrical resistance) and Dr. Vittorio's alloy.
5. Dr. Zeemu created emixion.

		METALS					ALLOY					PROPERTY				
		BISMUTH AND CHROMIUM	BISMUTH AND IRON	CHROMIUM AND IRON	IRON AND TIN	MAGNESIUM AND TIN	ADDITON	BLENDIUM	COMBINAL	EMIXION	MALGAMITE	DOES NOT RUST	HIGH ELECTRICAL RESISTANCE	LIGHTWEIGHT	LOW MELTING POINT	STRONG
SCIENTIST	DR. AXIS															
	DR. McNEAL															
	DR. PUSHKIN															
	DR. VITTORIO															
	DR. ZEEMU															
PROPERTY	DOES NOT RUST															
	HIGH ELECTRICAL															
	LIGHTWEIGHT															
	LOW MELTING															
	STRONG															
ALLOY	ADDITON															
	BLENDIUM															
	COMBINAL															
	EMIXION															
	MALGAMITE															

Musicians know how difficult gaining a following can be without getting airplay on radio stations; so, several budding young talents (including Pam) decided to take matters into their own hands by sending demo tapes to radio stations around the country. Although they sent out hundreds of tapes, each person only managed to get one song (no two of which have the same title) played, each on a different radio station. While some might consider this a small victory, these musicians have been greatly encouraged by their successes—in fact, each performer is currently putting the finishing touches on his or her first music video! From the information provided, determine the song recorded by each musician (identified by first and last names—two surnames are Barran and Esopo) and the radio station on which it aired.

1. The five musicians are Bittina, the one surnamed Rowley, the performer surnamed Garrison, the one who sings "Five Days in Cleveland" (which wasn't played on KRYX), and the one whose song was played on WYJM.

2. Gloria wrote the song entitled "Mikey's Tale." None of the musicians have the same first- and last-name initials.

3. "Let's Play Cricket" (which isn't the song performed by the musician surnamed Persaud) isn't the tune that was broadcast on KRYX. Either Bittina or Eugene is surnamed Rowley. A demo version of "Knockin' on My Door" was heard on WBQO.

4. Rodney isn't the one whose song was played on WUNH. Bittina was thrilled when she heard her song on KNTP. Eugene isn't the one who recorded "Have Some Cake."

		LAST NAME					SONG					STATION				
		BARRAN	ESOPO	GARRISON	PERSAUD	ROWLEY	FIVE DAYS IN CLEVELAND	HAVE SOME CAKE	KNOCKIN' ON MY DOOR	LET'S PLAY CRICKET	MIKEY'S TALE	KNTP	KRYX	WBQO	WUNH	WYJM
FIRST NAME	BITTINA															
	EUGENE															
	GLORIA															
	PAM															
	RODNEY															
STATION	KNTP															
	KRYX															
	WBQO															
	WUNH															
	WYJM															
SONG	FIVE DAYS IN...															
	HAVE SOME CAKE															
	KNOCKIN' ON...															
	LET'S PLAY...															
	MIKEY'S TALE															

LOGIC PROBLEM 250 COPY TALK

Next month, Branford Beene, owner and manager of the Copy Connection, is taking a three-week vacation, leaving Dean, his assistant manager, in charge. To make sure that he could handle the assignment, Branford let Dean take a "trial run" this morning, leaving him alone in the front of the store. Things ran pretty smoothly all morning, even when Dean had six customers at once. Each person (including Holly) ordered copies of a different document (including a flyer). To further complicate matters, each customer selected a different size of paper (from smallest to largest, monarch, statement, crescent, executive, letter, or legal) and a different color of paper. Branford was so impressed by how well Dean handled the rush that he wishes he had ten more just like him! From the information provided, can you determine the document each customer brought in to be copied, as well as the size and color (one is gray) of the paper each selected?

1. The copies made on the largest-sized paper (which weren't the ones ordered by Arte) were neither the ones made on yellow paper nor the ones printed on orange paper. Moe didn't select the monarch paper.

2. The size chosen by Freida is next-larger than that used for the red copies but next-smaller than the paper used to copy a newsletter. Glenn (who selected neither the largest-sized nor the smallest-sized paper) isn't the one who had a poster copied.

3. The green paper used for Nora's copies is exactly four sizes larger than that used to print the résumé. The invitations (which weren't copied on orange paper) were printed on statement paper.

4. The blue paper is next larger than that ordered by Moe but next-smaller than the paper ordered by the fledgling theater director for his or her programs.

		DOCUMENT						SIZE						COLOR				
		FLYER	INVITATION	NEWSLETTER	POSTER	PROGRAM	RÉSUMÉ	MONARCH	STATEMENT	CRESCENT	EXECUTIVE	LETTER	LEGAL	BLUE	GRAY	GREEN	ORANGE	RED	YELLOW
CUSTOMER	ARTE																		
	FREIDA																		
	GLENN																		
	HOLLY																		
	MOE																		
	NORA																		
COLOR	BLUE																		
	GRAY																		
	GREEN																		
	ORANGE																		
	RED																		
	YELLOW																		
SIZE	MONARCH																		
	STATEMENT																		
	CRESCENT																		
	EXECUTIVE																		
	LETTER																		
	LEGAL																		

LOGIC PROBLEM 251

This week, our entire town was glued to their television sets for the highly anticipated premiere of the four-part miniseries based on the epic novel *The Oddity*. The reason for all the hype was that the series was filmed on location only a few miles away on the edge of our rural neighborhood! Furthermore, since production had been short a few cast members during filming, local townsfolk were employed in bit parts. Thus, four of our neighborhood friends (including Leo) made their small-screen debuts this past week, each appearing in an episode that aired on a different night and portraying a different character (no two of whom had the same occupation). Many of the people in town hope that the high ratings the miniseries achieved will encourage other television producers to film in our area—in fact, several of my neighbors have signed up for acting classes, just in case! From the information provided, determine the episode (1 through 4) in which each person appeared, the role he or she played, and that character's profession.

1. The episode in which one of our townsfolk portrayed a servant aired at some point before the one in which Nilda appeared, which aired immediately before the one featuring the character named Xenakis.

2. The local who portrayed Heredia made his or her debut in an earlier episode than the one who played a guard at the palace, whose episode was shown at some point earlier in the week than Troy's.

3. Sondra had two lines in her scene, while neither the one who portrayed Robos (who wasn't the street vendor) nor the person who appeared in the third installment had any speaking parts.

4. Nilda isn't the person who was cast as Zados (who is neither the person who portrayed a messenger nor the one who was a convincing street vendor).

		PERSON				ROLE				PROFESSION			
		LEO	NILDA	SONDRA	TROY	HEREDIA	ROBOS	XENAKIS	ZADOS	GUARD	MESSENGER	SERVANT	STREET VENDOR
EPISODE	1												
	2												
	3												
	4												
PROFES.	GUARD												
	MESSENGER												
	SERVANT												
	STREET VENDOR												
ROLE	HEREDIA												
	ROBOS												
	XENAKIS												
	ZADOS												

LOGIC PROBLEM 252

On a recent trip to Ichluga, I could not help but be impressed by the richness of the small republic's sense of history and tradition. The past is kept alive in the country's various statues, monuments, and even currency. I returned home with five different coins (including the dagmeluach), which together provide a primer in Ichlugan history and geography. Each coin features an obverse portrait of a different one of the republic's rulers, each of whom is identified by both name and number (I through V), and on the reverse, a depiction of a different Ichlugan building (one is the House of Parliament). These informative coins are invaluable for outsiders like myself, who can barely make heads or tails of Ichluga's history! From the information provided, can you determine the number of the ruler (two of whom—Cedric and Rufus—are kings, and three of whom—Imogene, Wilhemina, and Xanthe—are queens) whose portrait appears on the obverse side and the building depicted on the reverse side of each coin?

1. The monarch who appears on the arenque had a lower number than Queen Xanthe but a higher number than at least one other ruler.

2. The ruler featured on the coin that depicts Cabrini Castle had a higher number than the monarch who appears on the ringa, who had a higher number than Queen Wilhemina. King Cedric's number is at least three higher than that of another monarch.

3. The king whose portrait graces the sild had a number exactly one lower than that of another king. Donago Monument doesn't appear on the reverse side of the ringa. The monarch pictured on the nishin doesn't have the highest number.

4. The monarch whose face appears on the obverse side of the coin that depicts the clock tower in Ichluga's capital city had a higher number than King Rufus but a lower number than the ruler who appears on the same coin as Fyrement Cathedral.

		RULER					NUMBER					BUILDING				
		CEDRIC	IMOGENE	RUFUS	WILHEMINA	XANTHE	I	II	III	IV	V	CABRINI CASTLE	CLOCK TOWER	DONAGO MONUMENT	FYREMENT CATHEDRAL	HOUSE OF PARLIAMENT
COIN	ARENQUE															
	DAGMELUACH															
	NISHIN															
	RINGA															
	SILD															
BUILDING	CABRINI CASTLE															
	CLOCK TOWER															
	DONAGO															
	FYREMENT															
	HOUSE OF															
NUMBER	I															
	II															
	III															
	IV															
	V															

LOGIC PROBLEM 253

In an attempt to boost sales, the president of Colorific Crayons asked five of his top executives to come up with exciting new colors to add to their upcoming holiday line. So, during the last board meeting, each of the five presented a prototype crayon that is not only a different new color, but also sports an exciting new feature to make it even more irresistible to budding artists. After the presentation, the eight members of the board voted on their favorites, so that each new crayon received a different number (2, 4, 5, 6, or 8) of votes. Thrilled at how well his employees rose to the occasion, the president assured the company's top brass that the new holiday gift pack is sure to make a lot of green! From the information provided, can you determine the color (one is electric turtle) and special feature of the crayon pitched by each employee, as well as the number of votes each received?

1. The off-magenta crayon received either exactly two more votes or exactly two fewer votes than another crayon. The new scented crayon is either the lovely shade called crustacean or the one named off-magenta.

2. Carmine's crayon received exactly one vote fewer than the one that glows in the dark. The chutney-colored crayon received exactly twice as many votes as the one with the calligraphic tip.

3. The crayon proposed by Holly received exactly one more vote than the off-magenta one. Neither Ginger nor Merle is the designer of the erasable crayon.

4. The crayon that received exactly two fewer votes than the one Amber created isn't the proposed I-can't-believe-it's-not-butter crayon, which isn't Holly's new color. Ginger's crayon (which isn't the one that received exactly two fewer votes than Amber's) isn't the one that contains glitter.

		COLOR					FEATURE					VOTES				
		CHUTNEY	CRUSTACEAN	ELECTRIC TURTLE	I-CAN'T-BELIEVE-IT'S-NOT-BUTTER	OFF-MAGENTA	CALLIGRAPHIC TIP	ERASABLE	GLITTER	GLOW-IN-THE-DARK	SCENTED	2	4	5	6	8
EMPLOYEE	AMBER															
	CARMINE															
	GINGER															
	HOLLY															
	MERLE															
VOTES	2															
	4															
	5															
	6															
	8															
FEATURE	CALLIGRAPHIC TIP															
	ERASABLE															
	GLITTER															
	GLOW-IN-THE-DARK															
	SCENTED															

LOGIC PROBLEM 254

EXTRA CREDIT WHERE CREDIT IS DUE

After a semester of being stumped by Professor Urqhardt's notorious extra-credit questions, which were always packed with obscure and arcane facts, five determined students spent most of the week before his final exam holed up in the university library, filling their heads with the minutiae of European history. Fortunately, their hard work paid off; each of the five was able to correctly answer a different one of the five extra-credit questions—in each case proving to be the only one in the class to do so! Each question dealt with a different, little-known individual (one is Pallida de Muse), each of whom lived in a different century (15th through 19th) and earned distinction through a different, unusual accomplishment. While all of his students are amazed at Professor Urqhardt's encyclopedic knowledge of history, they are glad that his class is now a thing of the past! From the information provided, can you determine the historical figure each student correctly identified, his or her accomplishment, and the century in which each lived?

1. The 18th-century figure whom Errol identified is neither the one famed for building the first bowling alley nor the one whose pioneering work in soil additives allowed him or her to grow a giant radish.

2. The person who invented shrubbery stakes lived in an earlier century than Ashley di Ponte.

3. Oswald answered a question about a figure from a later century than the one who built the first bowling alley.

4. The first person ever to name his or her dog "Rover" (who wasn't the one identified by Bobbie) lived in an earlier century than—but not the century immediately before—the one in which Basset Basile lived but in a later century than the historical figure whom Rachel correctly identified.

5. Sheba answered a question about the person who domesticated the peacock, who did not live in the 17th century.

6. Efemera Equerrius, who did not grow a giant radish, lived in a later century than Victor Stavinere.

		FIGURE					ACCOMPLISHMENT					CENTURY				
		ASHLEY di PONTE	BASSET BASILE	EFEMERA EQUERRIUS	PALLIDA de MUSE	VICTOR STAVINERE	DOMESTICATED THE PEACOCK	FIRST BOWLING ALLEY	GREW GIANT RADISH	NAMED DOG ROVER	SHRUBBERY STAKES	15th	16th	17th	18th	19th
STUDENT	BOBBIE															
	ERROL															
	OSWALD															
	RACHEL															
	SHEBA															
CENTURY	15th															
	16th															
	17th															
	18th															
	19th															
ACCOMPLISH.	DOMESTICATED															
	FIRST BOWLING															
	GREW GIANT															
	NAMED DOG															
	SHRUBBERY															

LOGIC PROBLEM 255

When the newest module in the popular role-playing series Creatures & Caverns hit the shelves last month, Kitty rushed to her local gaming store to buy the new scenario. Set in a land called Felindar, the new "Furry Fury" fantasy world is inhabited entirely by felines. Anxious to explore the uncharted terrain, Kitty and four of her friends each created a different character (one designed a fearsome serval caterwauler), choosing from the hundreds of possible combinations of breeds and abilities. Meeting at the Scratching Post Inn, the players set out on their first adventure. Although it took some time to adjust to being feline adventurers, each person's character quickly earned enough experience points to attain a different experience level (from lowest to highest, pussywillow, kitten, catechumen, cub, or dewclaw). Their travels, however, were not without their perils—the inexperienced characters ran into some dangerous situations, and as a result, each has a different number of lives remaining. With danger lurking in every alley of Felindar, this troop of cat fighters will have to take every precaution to ensure that curiosity doesn't get the best of them! From the information provided, determine the cat character created by each player and his or her experience level, as well as the number of lives (5 through 9) each has remaining.

1. Thanks to a knowledge of magic and spells, the lynx catalyst has attained a higher experience level than at least one other character but a lower experience level than the character who still has all nine of his or her lives.

2. Claudia's character has a lower experience level than the caracal meowtlaw, who has a lower experience level than the character who has seven of his or her lives intact.

3. Purvis's cat character has exactly one more life remaining than the shifty caracal meowtlaw (which wasn't created by Christopher), who has more lives left than the character who has earned the rank of cub.

4. Christopher's character has fewer lives remaining than the noble puma purrtector (who isn't played by Lionel).

5. Claudia's character (who isn't the puma) has exactly one more life remaining than the ocelot hunter, who has exactly one more life left than the character who has attained the rank of kitten.

		CAT CHARACTER					EXPERIENCE LEVEL					LIVES				
		CARACAL MEOWTLAW	LYNX CATALYST	OCELOT HUNTER	PUMA PURRTECTOR	SERVAL CATERWAULER	PUSSYWILLOW	KITTEN	CATECHUMEN	CUB	DEWCLAW	5	6	7	8	9
PLAYER	CHRISTOPHER															
	CLAUDIA															
	KITTY															
	LIONEL															
	PURVIS															
LIVES	5															
	6															
	7															
	8															
	9															
EXPERIENCE	PUSSYWILLOW															
	KITTEN															
	CATECHUMEN															
	CUB															
	DEWCLAW															

LOGIC PROBLEM 256

Centuries ago, in the Far East country of Nepal, there lived a wise man by the name of Siddhartha. Each of five pilgrims (three of whom—Apu, Naji, and Sanjay—were men, and two of whom—Arothana and Manjula—were women) from villages near and far sought him out to ask advice about a different subject. Each person found Siddhartha sitting under a different type of tree (one was a banyan tree), and, as was his way, Siddhartha told each a different *jataka*, or fable, meant to enlighten and teach valuable life lessons. The pilgrims went home much wiser, content that Siddhartha's knowledge would serve them well, both in this life and in the next! From the information provided, determine the question that plagued each pilgrim (one wanted to know about discipline), the type of tree under which he or she found Siddhartha sitting, and the *jataka* (one was "Fear Maker and Little Archer") the guru told each.

1. The three male seekers of enlightenment were the one who found Siddhartha sitting under a mango tree, the person to whom the guru told the story of "Prince Five-Weapons and Sticky-Hair," and the man who had a question about meditation.

2. The two women who sought out Siddhartha were the one who was told the *jataka* of "The Bull Called Delightful" and the person who wanted knowledge about nirvana.

3. Neither Arothana nor Sanjay found the wise man sitting under a bodhi tree.

4. Of the person who found Siddhartha under a deodar tree (who wasn't the pilgrim who was seeking enlightenment on the subject of marriage) and the one to whom the sage told the *jataka* of "The Shovel Wise Man," one was a man, and the other was a woman.

5. The five seekers of enlightenment were the one who found Siddhartha under a bodhi tree, the woman who had a question about karma, the person to whom the wise man told the fable "King Goodness the Great," the one who found the guru seated under a cycad tree, and Naji.

6. Apu is neither the person who was told the *jataka* of "Prince Five-Weapons and Sticky-Hair" (which wasn't told under the cycad tree) nor the one who sought information on meditation (who wasn't told the tale "The Shovel Wise Man").

		QUESTION					TREE					JATAKA				
		DISCIPLINE	KARMA	MARRIAGE	MEDITATION	NIRVANA	BANYAN	BODHI	CYCAD	DEODAR	MANGO	BULL CALLED DELIGHTFUL	FEAR MAKER & LITTLE ARCHER	KING GOODNESS THE GREAT	PRINCE FIVE-WEAPONS	THE SHOVEL WISE MAN
PILGRIM	APU															
	AROTHANA															
	MANJULA															
	NAJI															
	SANJAY															
JATAKA	BULL CALLED															
	FEAR MAKER															
	KING GOODNESS															
	PRINCE FIVE															
	THE SHOVEL															
TREE	BANYAN																
	BODHI																
	CYCAD																
	DEODAR																
	MANGO																

On Thursday, Elizabeth rushed straight from work to the Ivory Tower bookstore to pick up her reserved copy of *The Alabaster Figurine*, the seventh book in the Inspector Black series. As an avid fan of the Inspector, Elizabeth was anxious to reacquaint herself with her favorite detective and the colorful cast of supporting characters she has come to know and love. Each of six minor characters (three of whom—Carmine, Kelly, and Lincoln—are men, and three of whom—Fawn, Hazel, and Scarlet—are women) assists the Inspector through his or her work in a different profession (one is a laboratory technician), and each was introduced in a different one of the first six novels in the series. While Elizabeth delves into the new novel, can you determine the order in which each book (including *The Lady in the Mink Coat*) in the Inspector Black series was published and the character who was introduced in each, as well as the occupation of each recurring character?

1. The book in which Hazel was introduced was published immediately before the one in which the Inspector makes the acquaintance of a helpful police officer but immediately after *Clean Slate* hit the bookstores.

2. The artist made his or her debut appearance in *The Canary's Cage*, which was published at some point before the novel in which the woman who works as a psychic first appeared.

3. *Marooned* isn't the first Inspector Black novel. The third book in the series is entitled *The Caller at Midnight*.

4. The book in which the insurance appraiser was introduced was published immediately before the one in which Kelly first appeared but immediately after *Marooned* was released.

5. Scarlet works as a landscaper. Carmine made his first appearance in the fourth novel in the series. Fawn was introduced in *The Jade Monkey*.

		BOOK					CHARACTER						OCCUPATION					
		THE CALLER AT MIDNIGHT	THE CANARY'S CAGE	CLEAN SLATE	THE JADE MONKEY	THE LADY IN THE MINK COAT	MAROONED	CARMINE	FAWN	HAZEL	KELLY	LINCOLN	SCARLET	ARTIST	INSURANCE APPRAISER	LABORATORY TECHNICIAN	LANDSCAPER	POLICE OFFICER	PSYCHIC
ORDER	FIRST																		
	SECOND																		
	THIRD																		
	FOURTH																		
	FIFTH																		
	SIXTH																		
OCCUPATION	ARTIST																		
	INS. APPRAISER																		
	LAB. TECHNICIAN																		
	LANDSCAPER																		
	POLICE OFFICER																		
	PSYCHIC																		
CHARACTER	CARMINE																		
	FAWN																		
	HAZEL																		
	KELLY																		
	LINCOLN																		
	SCARLET																		

LOGIC PROBLEM 258

Business has been brisk at Time & Again, the secondhand watch store located in Brownsville's antique district. Nestled between the consignment dress shop Clothes Encounters and the furniture outlet Unfinished Business, the store can be hard to spot, but it does have a loyal base of customers that is constantly expanding. This afternoon, for example, Justin, the store's owner, sold five different antique pocket watches to five different first-time visitors. Since the store is absolutely full of clocks, Justin couldn't help but notice that each purchase was made at a different time (9:00 a.m., 10:00 a.m, 12:00 p.m., 2:00 p.m., or 3:00 p.m.). Now that sales are picking up and word of Time & Again is spreading, those big department stores had better watch out! From the information provided, determine the time at which each customer (identified by first and last names—one first name is Quinn, and one surname is Allen) purchased a watch.

1. Nancy isn't the person who purchased the Waltham William Emery pocket watch at 2:00 p.m. Fanny bought a watch at 10:00 a.m.

2. Victoria Embers isn't the person who made his or her purchase exactly one hour after the customer surnamed Merrick. The Elgin Veritas timepiece was bought exactly one hour before the customer surnamed Lewiston made a purchase.

3. The customer who purchased the Bunn Special 60-Hour pocket watch (who isn't Nancy) did so at some point earlier in the day than the person who picked out the Longines 15J watch (who isn't the customer surnamed Devlin) but at some point later in the day than the person who bought the Hamilton 992E timepiece.

4. Victoria didn't buy a watch at 12:00 p.m. At least one person purchased a timepiece at some point earlier in the day than the one surnamed Merrick (who isn't Chuck).

		FIRST NAME					SURNAME					WATCH				
		CHUCK	FANNY	NANCY	QUINN	VICTORIA	ALLEN	DEVLIN	EMBERS	LEWISTON	MERRICK	BUNN SPECIAL 60-HOUR	ELGIN VERITAS	HAMILTON 992E	LONGINES 15J	WALTHAM WILLIAM EMERY
TIME	9:00 a.m.															
	10:00 a.m.															
	12:00 p.m.															
	2:00 p.m.															
	3:00 p.m.															
WATCH	BUNN SPECIAL															
	ELGIN VERITAS															
	HAMILTON 992E															
	LONGINES 15J															
	WALTHAM WILLIAM															
SURNAME	ALLEN															
	DEVLIN															
	EMBERS															
	LEWISTON															
	MERRICK															

LOGIC PROBLEM 259

At Calbert Associates, employees have to act fast if they want to reserve the best weeks of the year for their vacation time—a lesson that six of the company's most recent hires learned all too well. Each person dawdled when the time came to sign up for vacation and, as a result, was unable to schedule his or her two weeks off next year for the summer months. Instead, each person had to settle for one week in the first half of the year and one week toward the end of the year. No two people will be on vacation at the same time next year. Far from being disappointed by this turn of events, however, the Calbert Associate employees are looking forward to leaving the snow and rain behind to travel to sunny locations during the off-season! From the information provided, determine the starting date of the first week (January 1, January 8, January 15, January 29, February 5, or February 12) and second week (October 1, October 8, October 15, October 22, October 29, or November 5) of each employee's vacation. (Note: January and October each have 31 days.)

1. No employee has arranged to start his or her two weeks of vacation on the same numbered date. Dorothy's second week of vacation begins exactly one week before Scott's.

2. The employee who is going on vacation on February 12 has arranged his or her second vacation week to begin exactly one week before Jake's second vacation week.

3. Michele's second week of vacation begins earlier than Tiffany's but exactly one week after that of the person who has also scheduled time off starting on January 8.

4. Harry (whose first vacation week is earlier in the year than Jake's) arranged to begin his second vacation week later than the person whose first vacation week starts exactly one week after Harry's.

5. The employee whose second vacation begins on October 22 arranged to begin his or her first vacation week later than Michele.

		FIRST WEEK						SECOND WEEK					
		JANUARY 1	JANUARY 8	JANUARY 15	JANUARY 29	FEBRUARY 5	FEBRUARY 12	OCTOBER 1	OCTOBER 8	OCTOBER 15	OCTOBER 22	OCTOBER 29	NOVEMBER 5
EMPLOYEE	DOROTHY												
	HARRY												
	JAKE												
	MICHELE												
	SCOTT												
	TIFFANY												
SECOND WEEK	OCTOBER 1												
	OCTOBER 8												
	OCTOBER 15												
	OCTOBER 22												
	OCTOBER 29												
	NOVEMBER 5												

MUSIC TO THEIR EARS

After a successful winter tour following the release of their indie-label debut album, the Breakers have been caught in a whirlwind bidding war among five prominent record labels (including Wild Heart Records). The group was approached by a different representative from each company who, anxious to sign the quartet, proffered the group a contract worth a different amount ($10 million, $11 million, $12 million, $13 million, or $14 million). In addition, each representative offered a different, tempting incentive. Pleased to have gotten the big break for which they've worked all these years, the Breakers accepted one of the offers, and now all the members agree that their careers are finally on the right track! From the information provided, can you determine the record company for whom each representative works, as well as the amount of money and the incentive each offered the Breakers?

1. The Breakers didn't accept Ms. Rochester's offer (which didn't include a signing bonus as an incentive), which was for either exactly $1 million dollars more or exactly $1 million less than that offered by the representative who gave the group a chance to produce.

2. Ms. Thornton (who added an open-ended record deal to sweeten the contract) offered the group either exactly $1 million more or exactly $1 million less than Mr. Davidson; neither agent is the representative for DreamWeaver Records.

3. Ms. Wilder (who offered the group exactly $1 million less than the person who signed the Breakers) is neither the representative who offered the Breakers absolute artistic freedom (whose offer wasn't accepted) nor the one who offered them an escape clause.

4. Mr. Mathews offered the group exactly $1 million more than the representative for Star Bright Records but exactly $1 million less than the person who offered them a $500,000 signing bonus. Ms. Wilder isn't the person who added a signing bonus (who isn't the representative for Lone Star Records).

5. The representative from Odyssey Records (whose bid wasn't accepted) didn't offer the group either $13 million or $14 million.

		REPRESENTATIVE					AMOUNT					INCENTIVE				
		MR. DAVIDSON	MR. MATHEWS	MS. ROCHESTER	MS. THORNTON	MS. WILDER	$10 MILLION	$11 MILLION	$12 MILLION	$13 MILLION	$14 MILLION	ARTISTIC FREEDOM	CHANCE TO PRODUCE	ESCAPE CLAUSE	OPEN-ENDED RECORD DEAL	SIGNING BONUS
COMPANY	DREAMWEAVER															
	LONE STAR															
	ODYSSEY															
	STAR BRIGHT															
	WILD HEART															
INCENTIVE	ARTISTIC															
	CHANCE TO															
	ESCAPE CLAUSE															
	OPEN-ENDED															
	SIGNING BONUS															
AMOUNT	$10 MILLION															
	$11 MILLION															
	$12 MILLION															
	$13 MILLION															
	$14 MILLION															

LOGIC PROBLEM 261

After retiring from the Air Force, Jeremiah Traeger launched a new career as an aerial stunt coordinator. His fledgling business is really taking off, too, now that he has been asked to supervise the stunts in five upcoming movies (including *Wild Blue Yonder*). Under Jeremiah's direction, each film will feature a different talented stunt pilot (including Hannah Lin) performing a different daring maneuver in a different World War II aircraft. With his new career off to such a promising start, it seems that, for Jeremiah, there will be nothing but blue skies from now on! From the information provided, can you determine the stunt pilot who will fly the airplane (one is the Supermarine Spitfire) used in each movie, as well as the maneuver he or she will perform?

1. Orson Greco will perform a scene in *The Fighting 52nd*, but won't be flying the Hawker Typhoon.

2. Blake Mason (who will perform a spin) isn't the pilot of the Hawker Typhoon. The pilot of the Fairey Swordfish isn't the one who will execute the falling-leaf stunt.

3. *The Sky's the Limit* (which isn't the film that requires a pilot to perform a roll) and *Operation Eagle* are the movie in which the figure-eight maneuver will appear and the flick featuring the stunt flying of Frances Forester, in some order.

4. The Hawker Hurricane (which will appear in *Winged Victory*) and the Hawker Sea Fury are the plane Alex Roth will fly and the one in which a pilot will perform a loop, in some order.

5. *Winged Victory* is neither the movie requiring the falling-leaf stunt (which won't be performed by Frances Forester) nor the one whose climactic scene features a roll.

		PILOT					AIRPLANE					MANEUVER				
		ALEX ROTH	BLAKE MASON	FRANCES FORESTER	HANNAH LIN	ORSON GRECO	FAIREY SWORDFISH	HAWKER HURRICANE	HAWKER SEA FURY	HAWKER TYPHOON	SUPERMARINE SPITFIRE	FALLING LEAF	FIGURE EIGHT	LOOP	ROLL	SPIN
MOVIE	THE FIGHTING 52nd															
	OPERATION EAGLE															
	THE SKY'S THE LIMIT															
	WILD BLUE YONDER															
	WINGED VICTORY															
MANEUVER	FALLING LEAF															
	FIGURE EIGHT															
	LOOP															
	ROLL															
	SPIN															
AIRPLANE	FAIREY SWORDFISH															
	HAWKER HURRICANE															
	HAWKER SEA FURY															
	HAWKER TYPHOON															
	SUPERMARINE															

In addition to treating a full schedule of patients, the Center for Holistic Medicine offers free consultations for new clients. This morning, five newcomers (including Tanner) arrived at the office wanting to see if the ancient Chinese treatment of acupuncture could, in conjunction with more traditional therapy, be used to treat a different condition (in one case, arthritis). Although all five had to wait before being seen, each passed the time by reading a magazine devoted to a different type of healing. Eventually, each had the opportunity to consult a different doctor (including Dr. Nissar), who, after examining the patient, recommended scheduling a different number of acupuncture sessions (1 through 5) to treat his or her condition. Even though they're still sticking with their regular physicians, the new clients of the Center for Holistic Medicine are willing to give the acupuncturists a chance to pinpoint the source of their troubles! From the information provided, determine the magazine (one is *Reflexology Today*) read by the patient who consulted each doctor and his or her complaint, as well as the number of sessions recommended to treat it.

1. After speaking with a doctor, the person who read *Chakra Digest* scheduled at least three sessions to treat his or her pulled hamstring. Richard (who booked more than one acupuncture session) read *Modern Kinesiology*.

2. Dr. Siabhan recommended four treatment sessions for his patient (who didn't have a backache). The person who gets frequent headaches saw Dr. Lee.

3. The five patients are the one who saw Dr. Chow, the person who scheduled the most appointments, Linda, the patient who read *Healing Herbs*, and the one with a sore back.

4. Audrey (whose doctor recommended three acupuncture sessions) read neither *Healing Herbs* nor *Myotherapy Monthly*.

5. The five doctors are the one who prescribed the fewest sessions, the specialist who evaluated Boyce, Dr. Drexel (who didn't recommend two sessions), the healer who saw the person with asthma, and the one who evaluated the patient who read *Myotherapy Monthly*.

		MAGAZINE					DOCTOR					COMPLAINT					SESSIONS				
		CHAKRA DIGEST	HEALING HERBS	MODERN KINESIOLOGY	MYOTHERAPY MONTHLY	REFLEXOLOGY TODAY	CHOW	DREXEL	LEE	NISSAR	SIABHAN	ARTHRITIS	ASTHMA	BACKACHE	FREQUENT HEADACHES	PULLED HAMSTRING	1	2	3	4	5
PATIENT	AUDREY																				
	BOYCE																				
	LINDA																				
	RICHARD																				
	TANNER																				
SESSIONS	1															
	2															
	3															
	4															
	5															
COMPLAINT	ARTHRITIS										
	ASTHMA										
	BACKACHE										
	FREQUENT										
	PULLED										
DOCTOR	CHOW					
	DREXEL					
	LEE					
	NISSAR					
	SIABHAN					

For the past several years, the Jonses have been cultivating a keen interest in modern art by frequenting galleries and exhibits to learn as much as possible about today's up-and-coming talent. They have even begun collecting the works of a few of their favorite artists to display in their home. Although their collection is still fairly small, they have acquired a different piece in each of the past six years (2009 through 2014) and are quite pleased with the variety they have achieved. Each piece the Jonses own was produced by a different artist (including Ivan Edwards) in a different medium (one is an oil painting). Recognizing that each piece of artwork has a unique, commanding presence, the Jonses have displayed each work in a different, prominent location in their home. From the information provided, determine the artist responsible for the work in each location in the Jonses' house and the year in which each piece was produced.

1. The Jonses purchased the work displayed in the master bedroom (which wasn't made by Medrie McDaniel) exactly two years before they bought the sculpture, which was exactly two years before they acquired the Piper Dolan piece.

2. The woodcarving was purchased the year before the artwork currently found in the living room.

3. The work by Medrie McDaniel (which isn't the sculpture) was obtained the year after the Jonses bought the metal-cast piece.

4. The artwork in the study was procured exactly two years before Wallace Keegan's work (which isn't the piece in the dining room), which was exactly two years before the Jonses bought the watercolor.

5. The photograph owned by the Jonses wasn't obtained the year before the piece created by Anton Casper, which is on display in the front hall of their home.

6. The artwork by Finola Hirsch (which isn't the metal cast) was purchased exactly three years before the family acquired the work displayed in the guest bedroom.

		WORK						LOCATION						YEAR					
		METAL CAST	OIL PAINTING	PHOTOGRAPH	SCULPTURE	WATERCOLOR	WOODCARVING	DINING ROOM	FRONT HALL	GUEST BEDROOM	LIVING ROOM	MASTER BEDROOM	STUDY	2009	2010	2011	2012	2013	2014
ARTIST	ANTON CASPER																		
	FINOLA HIRSCH																		
	IVAN EDWARDS																		
	MEDRIE McDANIEL																		
	PIPER DOLAN																		
	W. KEEGAN																		
YEAR	2009																		
	2010																		
	2011																		
	2012																		
	2013																		
	2014																		
LOCATION	DINING ROOM																		
	FRONT HALL																		
	GUEST BEDROOM																		
	LIVING ROOM																		
	MASTER BED.																		
	STUDY																		

LOGIC PROBLEM 264

"When your copier jams, you call a repair man; when gremlins take over your fax machine, you call us," explained Dagmar Olafsen, one of the five members of Gremlin Grabbers. This unusual pest-control agency has recently risen to prominence after helping five large corporations with their "technical difficulties." According to Dagnar's account, each company had been experiencing all manner of mechanical problems before they called Gremlin Grabbers. A different agent responded to each company's call, whereupon each discovered a different number of gremlins (14, 18, 22, 26, or 30) lurking in the corridors at each business. "The key to eradicating gremlin infestation is to locate the nest," Dagmar continued, adding that, in each company, the nest was found in a different location (including the supply room). In closing, said Dagmar, "If gremlins are giving you grief, don't give up—get Gremlin Grabbers!" From the information provided, can you determine the number of gremlins that plagued the company (one is GlobalCorp) investigated by each agent, as well as the location of the gremlin nest at each business?

1. Exactly three of the agents—Stig, the person who rid a company of 14 gremlins, and the one who discovered a nest under the office copy machine—are founding members of Gremlin Grabbers, while the remaining two—Rocco and the one who chased the gremlins out of Ianuzzi & Swift—were recently hired as a result of booming business.

2. Both Ivor and the agent who found the gremlin nest in an elevator shaft were able to rapidly locate the nest and remove the gremlins during a single visit, while both the agent who assisted Ianuzzi & Swift and the specialist who discovered the nest in a staff lounge took longer to locate the source of the problem and made multiple visits in order to ensure a gremlin-free zone. Alma (who didn't remove the fewest gremlins) didn't oust pesky critters from the office of Ianuzzi & Swift (which didn't have the largest gremlin problem).

3. The nest one founding member discovered in an air-conditioning duct housed exactly 4 fewer gremlins than the one a recently hired agent found at WorldCo. Stig didn't discover the largest group of gremlins.

4. Intellinet was plagued by exactly 4 more gremlins than the company that had a nest in its elevator shaft. Omicron Industries didn't have either the most or the fewest gremlins.

		COMPANY					GREMLINS					LOCATION				
		GLOBALCORP	IANUZZI & SWIFT	INTELLINET	OMICRON INDUSTRIES	WORLDCO	14	18	22	26	30	AIR-CONDITIONING	ELEVATOR SHAFT	STAFF LOUNGE	SUPPLY ROOM	UNDER COPY MACHINE
AGENT	ALMA															
	DAGMAR															
	IVOR															
	ROCCO															
	STIG															
LOCATION	AIR-CONDITIONING															
	ELEVATOR SHAFT															
	STAFF LOUNGE															
	SUPPLY ROOM															
	UNDER COPY															
GREMLINS	14															
	18															
	22															
	26															
	30															

LOGIC PROBLEM 265

In order to get some hands-on experience before receiving their master's degrees, six marine-biology students at Thoreau University signed up for internships over the winter break. Each student did field work at a laboratory located in a different state, where he or she studied the microscopic algae and protozoa that comprise plankton. Since the study lasted only four weeks, each soon-to-be scientist focused on a different, single organism (one was the crustacean known as the copepod). There was much to learn, and with the help of the astute scientists on site, all six of the students soaked up an ocean of practical knowledge! From the information provided, determine the organism studied by each student (identified by first and last names) and the state in which he or she interned.

1. Neither Avi (who wasn't in North Carolina) nor William is the one who studied krill. Zed didn't go to Florida, which isn't where barnacle larva was examined. The student surnamed Barrie didn't go to Massachusetts.
2. The student surnamed Rome (who wasn't in California or Oregon) is either Avi, Sterling, or Zed. The arrowworm was studied in either California, North Carolina, or Oregon. Either Emily or William examined the sea snail.
3. Neither Darren (who isn't surnamed Cerullo or Godmun) nor Sterling (who didn't study krill) was the California intern. Avi isn't the student who went to Massachusetts.
4. Neither Emily nor the student surnamed Barrie is either the Oregon intern or the North Carolina intern. The student surnamed Rome isn't the one who focused on the hydromedusa (which wasn't the organism studied in Florida).
5. Zed didn't go to Massachusetts (which isn't where either barnacle larva or the sea snail was studied) or California. Neither the student surnamed Wachtel (who didn't look at krill) nor the one surnamed Godmun studied in Florida.
6. The student surnamed Barrie (who is neither Avi nor William) didn't research krill (which wasn't the organism studied in Louisiana). The North Carolina intern isn't surnamed Godmun or Rome.
7. Five students are the one surnamed Godmun (who isn't Emily), the one surnamed Rasmussen (who didn't go to Massachusetts), the one surnamed Wachtel (who didn't go to North Carolina), Zed (who isn't the student surnamed Cerullo), and the one who examined barnacle larva.

		LAST NAME						ORGANISM						STATE					
		BARRIE	CERULLO	GODMUN	RASMUSSEN	ROME	WACHTEL	ARROWWORM	BARNACLE LARVA	COPEPOD	HYDROMEDUSA	KRILL	SEA SNAIL	CALIFORNIA	FLORIDA	LOUISIANA	MASSACHU-SETTS	NORTH CAROLINA	OREGON
FIRST NAME	AVI																		
	DARREN																		
	EMILY																		
	STERLING																		
	WILLIAM																		
	ZED																		
STATE	CALIFORNIA																		
	FLORIDA																		
	LOUISIANA																		
	MASSACHUSETTS																		
	NORTH CAROLINA																		
	OREGON																		
ORGANISM	ARROWWORM																		
	BARNACLE LARVA																		
	COPEPOD																		
	HYDROMEDUSA																		
	KRILL																		
	SEA SNAIL																		

LOGIC PROBLEM 266 TROUBLED TIMES

After years of tinkering with his homemade time machine, Professor Walter J. Entwhistle proudly demonstrated his prototype to his colleague, Dr. Maureen Fellner—although the demonstration didn't exactly go as planned. At Dr. Fellner's request, the professor attempted to transport them back in time to witness five different historic events (including the original premiere of *Hamlet*), but each time they arrived instead in a different year (1460, 1520, 1580, 1640, or 1760). To make matters worse, one of the two made a different careless mistake during each trip, which had a different, rather alarming result when they returned to the present (in one case, the planet was ruled by giant slugs). With such a powerful invention, the future is sure to hold great things for Professor Entwhistle! From the information provided, can you determine the year to which the pair accidentally traveled when trying to witness each event, as well as the mistake they made in each year (on one trip, Dr. Fellner left her wristwatch behind) and the result it had in the present?

1. The pair's ill-fated trip to watch the *Mayflower* landing is either the one on which Professor Entwhistle fed part of his sandwich to a flock of birds or the one on which they taught some of the locals the Macarena.

2. The five trips are the one on which Dr. Fellner picked a flower, the one on which they tried to hear Lincoln deliver the Gettysburg Address, the trip to 1760, the one from which they returned to find light bulbs growing on trees (which wasn't their journey to 1520), and the one on which the Professor thoughtlessly swatted a fly.

3. The colleagues' failed trip to see Queen Elizabeth I's coronation was neither the one that resulted in pink skies nor the one that resulted in talking llamas. The mistake that led to the evolution of talking llamas (which wasn't the swatted fly) took place in a later year than the one they visited while trying to watch the *Mayflower* land but an earlier year than the one they encountered while trying to hear the Gettysburg Address.

4. Their trip to watch Michelangelo paint the Sistine Chapel ceiling landed them in a year exactly 60 years before that from which they returned to find that the most popular sporting event on Earth was the robot Olympics, which was exactly 120 years before they taught their hosts the Macarena (which wasn't on their trip to Queen Elizabeth I's coronation).

		EVENT					MISTAKE					RESULT				
		CORONATION	GETTYSBURG ADDRESS	HAMLET PREMIERE	MAYFLOWER LANDING	SISTINE CHAPEL	FED BIRDS	LEFT WRISTWATCH	PICKED FLOWER	SWATTED FLY	TAUGHT MACARENA	GIANT SLUGS	LIGHT-BULB TREES	PINK SKY	ROBOT OLYMPICS	TALKING LLAMAS
YEAR	1460															
	1520															
	1580															
	1640															
	1760															
RESULT	GIANT SLUGS															
	LIGHT-BULB TREES															
	PINK SKY															
	ROBOT OLYMPICS															
	TALKING LLAMAS															
MISTAKE	FED BIRDS															
	LEFT WRISTWATCH															
	PICKED FLOWER															
	SWATTED FLY															
	TAUGHT MACARENA															

While performing research for the Human Genome Project—a massive scientific effort dedicated to mapping out the genetic makeup of humankind—each of five geneticists (three of whom—Dr. Estecado, Dr. Garvey, and Dr. Klotz—are women, and two of whom—Dr. Russell and Dr. Zelenka—are men) "discovered" a different brand-new gene carried by a different chromosome. For ease of description, each gene was given a different number-letter designation (BQ1L6, HRO7, M32ST, PGG84, or TUN9). Further study revealed that each gene controls a different trait not originally thought to be hereditary. Without a doubt, this important new information will be passed down to a new generation of scientists! From the information provided, determine the gene discovered by each geneticist and the numbered chromosome (2, 5, 11, 14, or 17) on which it was found, as well as the heredity trait it controls.

1. Two of the genes discovered by women are the one that causes a paralyzing fear of pickles and the gene whose chromosome is numbered exactly 3 lower than the one on which the gene M32ST was found.

2. The gene BQ1L6 was discovered by a male geneticist. Neither Dr. Russell nor Dr. Garvey is the one who discovered the gene on chromosome 17.

3. The gene that controls a person's affinity for Taco Bell is on the chromosome numbered exactly 3 higher than that on which the gene discovered by Dr. Estecado was found. The gene TUN9 wasn't found on chromosome 2.

4. The gene that controls a person's ability to do the chicken dance is on the chromosome numbered exactly 6 higher than the one on which the gene PGG84 was found but on a lower-numbered chromosome than the one on which the gene discovered by Dr. Garvey was found.

5. The gene discovered by Dr. Zelenka (which isn't the one that provides an immunity to March Madness) is on the chromosome numbered exactly 3 higher than that on which the gene that imparts an innate knowledge of *Mannix* episodes was found but on a lower-numbered chromosome than at least one other newly discovered gene.

		GENE					CHROMOSOME					TRAIT				
		BQ1L6	HRO7	M32ST	PGG84	TUN9	2	5	11	14	17	CHICKEN DANCE	FEAR OF PICKLES	MANNIX EPISODES	MARCH MADNESS	TACO BELL
GENETICIST	DR. ESTECADO															
	DR. GARVEY															
	DR. KLOTZ															
	DR. RUSSELL															
	DR. ZELENKA															
TRAIT	CHICKEN DANCE															
	FEAR OF PICKLES															
	MANNIX EPISODES															
	MARCH MADNESS															
	TACO BELL															
CHROMOSOME	2															
	5															
	11															
	14															
	17															

LOGIC PROBLEM 268

The Regency Inn was proud to host last month's Electronics Expo 2015, a four-day conference at which interested technophiles gathered to meet and exchange ideas. Besides the chance to check out the latest gadgetry, there were six seminars that focused on the impact of various technologies on society. Each seminar (one is "Superconductors and You") was held at a different time, and no more than two discussions were held on the same day. Each talk was hosted by a different expert (including Lindsey) in his or her field. After so much serious discussion, the attendees were glad to let loose during the final night's party and do the Electric Slide! From the information provided, determine the order in which the seminars were held and the person (identified by first and last names) who hosted each discussion.

1. The seminar hosted by the person surnamed Hyatt was given at some point after "The History of Solid-State Electronics." "Practical Solar Energy" was held at some point after, and on the same day as, the person surnamed Bernier's discussion; these two seminars were both held before lunch, but weren't offered on the last day of the conference.

2. Olympia (who isn't the one surnamed Devine) hosted her seminar before lunch. Olympia wasn't scheduled to host the first seminar. Zoe's discussion was held on the same day as the one entitled "What's New in Oscilloscopes."

3. Cyril (who isn't surnamed Monaco) held his seminar at some point before, and on the same day as, the person surnamed Pinchbeck; these two seminars were both held after lunch. The fourth seminar (which was held after lunch) was the only one scheduled that day.

4. "The Future of Silicon" seminar (which wasn't hosted by the one surnamed Monaco) was held immediately before the speech by the person surnamed Ruegger but immediately after Kamil's discussion; these three seminars were held on different days of the conference. The one surnamed Ruegger didn't speak on the last conference day. "A Hard-Wired World" (which wasn't the seminar hosted by Foster) wasn't the last discussion of the conference.

		SEMINAR						FIRST NAME						LAST NAME					
		THE FUTURE OF SILICON	A HARD-WIRED WORLD	THE HISTORY OF SOLID-STATE	PRACTICAL SOLAR ENERGY	SUPERCONDUC-TORS AND YOU	WHAT'S NEW IN OSCILLOSCOPES	CYRIL	FOSTER	KAMIL	LINDSEY	OLYMPIA	ZOE	BERNIER	DEVINE	HYATT	MONACO	PINCHBECK	RUEGGER
ORDER	FIRST																		
	SECOND																		
	THIRD																		
	FOURTH																		
	FIFTH																		
	SIXTH																		
LAST NAME	BERNIER																		
	DEVINE																		
	HYATT																		
	MONACO																		
	PINCHBECK																		
	RUEGGER																		
FIRST NAME	CYRIL																		
	FOSTER																		
	KAMIL																		
	LINDSEY																		
	OLYMPIA																		
	ZOE																		

THE THREE MOUSEKETEERS · LOGIC PROBLEM 269

Faced with constant royal intrigues and the stirrings of social unrest, life in the 1600s was difficult for French noblemice. Living in such uncertain times, the rodent nobility needed a champion. Enter the famed Three Mouseketeers—Aramouse, Athmouse, and Porthmouse—royal guardsmice to King Louis XIII's favorite pet rodent, Pierre LeMouse. The daring exploits of these resolute rodents quickly became legendary; in fact, in one memorable week, each Mouseketeer rescued each of five noblemice (three of whom—Bellamouse, Julirat, and Mouseleine—are female, and two of whom—R'Atagnan and Ratspierre—are male) from a different one of the same five hazards. These and other exciting tales have been chronicled in the novel *The Three Mouseketeers*, written by that world-famous author, Alexandre Dumouse! From the information provided, can you determine the hazard from which each noblemouse was rescued by Aramouse, Athmouse, and Porthmouse?

1. No noblemouse was rescued from the same hazard by Aramouse as he or she was by Athmouse. Aramouse rescued a male noblemouse from the clutches of the evil Cardinal Chatelieu. The mouse Porthmouse saved from humans was prevented from eating bad fromage by the timely intervention of Aramouse.

2. Bellamouse isn't the female noblemouse Aramouse rescued from humans. The one Porthmouse saved from eating bad fromage was rescued from a mousetrap by Athmouse.

3. Porthmouse rescued R'Atagnan from a mousetrap. Neither Mouseleine (who was prevented from eating bad fromage by Athmouse) nor Ratspierre is the one Porthmouse rescued from Cardinal Chatelieu.

4. Aramouse rescued Julirat from a mousetrap. Athmouse prevented a female noblemouse (but not Julirat) from washing down the Paris sewers. Neither R'Atagnan nor Bellamouse is the one rescued from the city sewers by Aramouse.

		ARAMOUSE					ATHMOUSE					PORTHMOUSE				
		BAD FROMAGE	CARDINAL CHATELIEU	HUMANS	MOUSETRAP	PARIS SEWERS	BAD FROMAGE	CARDINAL CHATELIEU	HUMANS	MOUSETRAP	PARIS SEWERS	BAD FROMAGE	CARDINAL CHATELIEU	HUMANS	MOUSETRAP	PARIS SEWERS
NOBLEMOUSE	BELLAMOUSE															
	JULIRAT															
	MOUSELEINE															
	R'ATAGNAN															
	RATSPIERRE															
PORTHMOUSE	BAD FROMAGE															
	CARDINAL															
	HUMANS															
	MOUSETRAP															
	PARIS SEWERS															
ATHMOUSE	BAD FROMAGE															
	CARDINAL															
	HUMANS															
	MOUSETRAP															
	PARIS SEWERS															

LOGIC PROBLEM 270

As a teller at Citizens Federal Bank in Decatur, Sydney is quite familiar with the late-afternoon Friday crowd who rush to deposit their paychecks before the bank closes at 6:00 p.m. This Friday, in the last hour of her shift, she waited on seven of these regular customers, each of whom works for a different, nearby business (including Joe's Auto Body). After taxes, each person's paycheck was made out for a different amount ($350, $380, $390, $430, $450, $500, or $530), and of that sum, each person requested a different amount ($20, $60, $80, $110, $120, $140, or $150) in cash before depositing the remainder into his or her account. From the information provided, determine the business that employs each of Sydney's customers, the amount of each one's paycheck, and the amount of cash requested by each person.

1. Evan (who deposited exactly $390 of his paycheck) requested less cash than Felix. The customer who works at Expert Construction requested less cash than the person with the $380 paycheck.

2. Darcie's paycheck was for a lower amount than that of the customer who requested $60 in cash. Blythe's check was for a higher amount than the one brought in by Gabrielle, who requested more cash than the DataWorld employee.

3. The customer who works at Prestige Travel (who deposited exactly $280 of his or her paycheck) requested less cash than the person with the $450 paycheck. Adam's paycheck was for less money the customer who requested $80 (who doesn't work for Lacy's department store).

4. Cliff (who deposited exactly $320 of his paycheck) earned more than a customer who requested either exactly $30 more or exactly $30 less than the employee of Memories Photography. Felix earned less than the customer who requested $20 in cash.

5. The DataWorld employee had a paycheck for a higher amount than did the Lacy's employee. The employee of Pro Fitness didn't get paid $430.

		BUSINESS						PAYCHECK							CASH						
		DATAWORLD	EXPERT CONSTRUCTION	JOE'S AUTO BODY	LACY'S	MEMORIES PHOTOGRAPHY	PRESTIGE TRAVEL	PRO FITNESS	$350	$380	$390	$430	$450	$500	$530	$20	$60	$80	$110	$120	$140	$150
CUSTOMER	ADAM																					
	BLYTHE																					
	CLIFF																					
	DARCIE																					
	EVAN																					
	FELIX																					
	GABRIELLE																					
CASH	$20																					
	$60																					
	$80																					
	$110																					
	$120																					
	$140																					
	$150																					
PAYCHECK	$350																					
	$380																					
	$390																					
	$430																					
	$450																					
	$500																					
	$530																					

LOGIC PROBLEM 271

To dispel the myth that computer games are the exclusive realm of the adolescent male, *Gaming Monthly* ran a feature in last month's issue focusing on five women (including Phoebe) who are at the forefront of the game-design industry. These in-depth interviews revealed that each woman is currently working on a different game (two of which—Arcadia Prime and BioControl—are real-time strategy games, and three of which—Land's End, Necropolis, and Umbra—are role-playing games) and is responsible for a different aspect of that game's design. When asked how she got into the computer industry, each woman admitted that she had been hooked on games from an early age, spending countless hours playing a different, older title. Without a doubt, when it comes to playing and designing computer titles, these wired women are certainly game! From the information provided, determine the aspect of the game for which each woman is responsible, as well as the older game that most influenced her.

1. The five women are Leah, the one who obsessively played Super Mario Bros., the woman influenced by The Legend of Zelda, the BioControl designer, and the one working on Land's End.

2. Neither Arcadia Prime nor Umbra is the game Belinda is designing.

3. Four of the women are Gloria (who is working on a real-time strategy game), the one who was influenced by King's Quest, the computer-AI programmer, and the Super Mario Bros. fan.

4. Leah isn't the woman who spent an exorbitant amount of time playing Ultima (who is now producing a real-time strategy game). The level designer's project is a real-time strategy game.

5. The five women are the background artist, the story designer, the woman influenced by Zork, the one working on Necropolis, and Belinda.

6. The interface designer featured in the *Gaming Monthly* article isn't on the Necropolis team.

7. Tina (who is creating a role-playing game) isn't the woman working on Umbra (who isn't the story designer).

		GAME					ASPECT					INFLUENCE				
		ARCADIA PRIME	BIOCONTROL	LAND'S END	NECROPOLIS	UMBRA	BACKGROUND ART	COMPUTER AI	INTERFACE DESIGN	LEVEL DESIGN	STORY DESIGN	KING'S QUEST	THE LEGEND OF ZELDA	SUPER MARIO BROS.	ULTIMA	ZORK
WOMAN	BELINDA															
	GLORIA															
	LEAH															
	PHOEBE															
	TINA															
INFLUENCE	KING'S QUEST															
	THE LEGEND															
	SUPER MARIO															
	ULTIMA															
	ZORK															
ASPECT	BACKGROUND															
	COMPUTER AI															
	INTERFACE															
	LEVEL DESIGN															
	STORY DESIGN															

LOGIC PROBLEM 272   DINNERWARE DEBACLES

The organizers of the annual Pottsville Potluck Dinner tried to divide up the duties involved in planning and preparing for the event as evenly as possible. The real mathematical challenge came when Gordon and the other five planners went to the local supermarket to buy supplies for the dinner. Although they expected 75 people to attend, each found that the item he or she had been assigned to purchase (no two bought the same supply) only came in packages of a different multiple of ten. After some quick calculations, each one managed to leave the store with the appropriate amount of supplies—plus a few left over for next year's event! From the information provided, can you determine the quantity of each package in the item purchased by each person?

1. A package of plastic spoons contained fewer items than a package of napkins but more items than of the supply Tyler purchased. Felicity didn't buy napkins or spoons.

2. A single package of the supply Petra bought contained exactly twice as many items as a package of plastic forks, which contained more items than a package of the product bought by Josie. A package of the supply purchased by Mark contained fewer items than a package of plastic forks.

3. A package of Styrofoam plates (which wasn't the item Josie was assigned to bring) contained fewer than half as many pieces as a package of the supply Tyler bought. Felicity isn't the one who purchased plastic cups.

4. One of the items was sold only in 50-count packages. Felicity's designated item was sold in a larger quantity than the plastic bowls (which didn't come in packages of exactly 40).

5. The smallest number of items sold in a single package was exactly 20, and the largest number contained in one package was exactly 100. The total number of items contained in a single package of each of the six supplies was exactly 340.

		BOWLS	CUPS	FORKS	NAPKINS	PLATES	SPOONS						
PERSON	FELICITY												
	GORDON												
	JOSIE												
	MARK												
	PETRA												
	TYLER												
QUANTITY													

280

Madame Zelda's popular telephone hot line for psychic advice has been doing so well lately that the fortune teller had to hire six new psychics to help with the sheer volume of calls! Unfortunately, none of her protégés (each of whom assumed a different professional name—Astra, Crystal, Ebony, Jade, Miranda, or Zorah) has shown quite the flair for their work that their mentor possesses. In fact, they seem to be making quite a few mistakes. This morning, for example, each attempted to name the astrological sign of a different caller (no two guessed the same sign—Aquarius, Cancer, Leo, Libra, Sagittarius, or Scorpio)—but each guess was incorrect! Fortunately, the callers were willing to overlook these mistakes, since each was quite excited about the advice he or she was given on a matter pertaining to either romance or work. From the information provided, determine the astrological sign guessed by the psychic who spoke with each caller and that caller's actual sign (no two callers have the same sign—one is a Gemini).

1. The Capricorn caller is neither the person who was mistaken for a Scorpio (who asked about romance) nor the one who was thought to be a Sagittarius. Crystal incorrectly identified her caller as either a Scorpio or a Sagittarius.

2. Richard was misidentified as a Cancer. Zorah spoke with either Beth or Karen. Ebony didn't speak to the Pisces caller (who wanted to know if he or she was going to get a promotion at work).

3. Miranda didn't prognosticate her caller to be an Aquarius. Jade and the psychic who incorrectly called a client a Leo spoke with Axel and Beth, in some order. Astra spoke with either Dina or Richard.

4. Dina is neither the Aries caller (who asked about work) nor the Capricorn caller (who asked about romance). Axel (who is a Virgo), Karen, and Maurice all inquired about work-related matters.

5. Neither Dina (who isn't the Taurus caller) nor Karen is the Pisces caller. Dina isn't the caller misidentified as a Sagittarius (who asked about romance).

		PSYCHIC						GUESSED						ACTUAL					
		ASTRA	CRYSTAL	EBONY	JADE	MIRANDA	ZORAH	AQUARIUS	CANCER	LEO	LIBRA	SAGITTARIUS	SCORPIO	ARIES	CAPRICORN	GEMINI	PISCES	TAURUS	VIRGO
CALLER	AXEL																		
	BETH																		
	DINA																		
	KAREN																		
	MAURICE																		
	RICHARD																		
ACTUAL	ARIES																		
	CAPRICORN																		
	GEMINI																		
	PISCES																		
	TAURUS																		
	VIRGO																		
GUESSED	AQUARIUS																		
	CANCER																		
	LEO																		
	LIBRA																		
	SAGITTARIUS																		
	SCORPIO																		

LOGIC PROBLEM 274   BEAUTY IS IN THE EYES

The July issue of *A La Mode* fashion magazine contains a special section featuring makeovers of six lucky readers (including Patrice) done by world-renowned hair and makeup artists. The makeover spread, which appears in its entirety between pages 33 and 38 of the issue, features "before" and "after" photographs of the women, as well as an interview with the different makeup artist who worked his magic on each woman. The artists, however, claimed to have made only minor adjustments to bring out the natural beauty of the women—in fact, each cited a different element (exactly three of which—the eyelash curler, mascara, and under-eye cream—relate to the eyes) that he added to his subject's beauty regimen that created a world of difference in her appearance. From the information provided, can you determine the page on which each woman's pictures appear, the makeup artist (Frédéric, Jean Claude, Kevyn, Lorenzo, Pierre, or Rinalde) who worked with her, and the key element of each woman's new look?

1. Exactly one of the six pages between pages 33 and 38 features a full-page advertisement and doesn't have any makeover photographs.
2. The page depicting Pierre's handiwork is numbered exactly 1 lower than the one showing Doreen's makeover (which didn't feature a change in the appearance of her eyes) but exactly 1 higher than the one on which an artist describes his appearance-altering application of bronzer.
3. Of the makeover done by Rinalde and one featured on page 37, either both involve changes to the eyes, or neither involve changes to the eyes.
4. Kevyn (who didn't do Natalie's makeover) worked with a woman featured on a page numbered at least 2 lower than that showing the makeover of the woman for whom lip pencil was a key change.
5. The page on which Linda's pictures appear is numbered exactly 1 higher than the one featuring the woman on whom pink blush was used but exactly 1 lower than the full-page advertisement page.
6. Neither Celeste (whose makeover included a significant eye change) nor Frédéric's subject (who appears on a higher-numbered page than Celeste) is the woman on whom under-eye cream was used.
7. Amber (who didn't have her eyelashes curled) is the only woman pictured on page 38. The makeover performed by Lorenzo doesn't appear on page 35.

		PAGE						MAKEUP ARTIST						ELEMENT					
								FRÉDÉRIC	JEAN CLAUDE	KEVYN	LORENZO	PIERRE	RINALDE	BRONZER	EYELASH CURLER	LIP PENCIL	MASCARA	PINK BLUSH	UNDER-EYE CREAM
WOMAN	AMBER																		
	CELESTE																		
	DOREEN																		
	LINDA																		
	NATALIE																		
	PATRICE																		
ELEMENT	BRONZER																		
	EYELASH CURLER																		
	LIP PENCIL																		
	MASCARA																		
	PINK BLUSH																		
	UNDER-EYE																		
MAKEUP ARTIST	FRÉDÉRIC																		
	JEAN CLAUDE																		
	KEVYN																		
	LORENZO																		
	PIERRE																		
	RINALDE																		

LOGIC PROBLEM 275

As the receptionist for the successful real-estate firm of Glengarry Properties, Gil McCoy must keep track of the frequent comings and goings of the company's five agents. Today, for instance, each agent (three of whom—Dave, John, and Sheldon—are men, and two of whom—Georgia and Rikki—are women) left the office at a different time (10:00 a.m., 10:15 a.m., 10:30 a.m., 12:00 p.m., or 12:15 p.m.) to meet with a client. Fortunately, Gil was there to answer the many customer calls in the interim, so that when each agent returned at a different time (11:00 a.m., 11:15 a.m., 12:00 p.m., 12:45 p.m., or 1:00 p.m.), Gil was able to give each his or her messages (each received a different number of messages—4 through 8). In the sometimes turbulent world of real estate, Gil can rest assured that Glengarry's top agents are sold on his skill and professionalism! From the information provided, can you determine the times at which each agent left and returned, as well as the number of messages he or she received while out of the office?

1. The two women received consecutive numbers of messages. Rikki returned to the office exactly one hour after the agent who received eight messages.

2. The three men are the one who left at 10:00 a.m., the agent who got five calls while he was gone, and the person who returned at 12:00 p.m.

3. The salesperson who left at 10:15 a.m. was away from the office for at least 30 minutes longer than Sheldon.

4. Dave, who got exactly one more message than Rikki, left the office at some point after Georgia.

		LEFT					RETURNED					MESSAGES				
		10:00 a.m.	10:15 a.m.	10:30 a.m.	12:00 p.m.	12:15 p.m.	11:00 a.m.	11:15 a.m.	12:00 p.m.	12:45 p.m.	1:00 p.m.	4	5	6	7	8
AGENT	DAVE															
	GEORGIA															
	JOHN															
	RIKKI															
	SHELDON															
MESSAGES	4															
	5															
	6															
	7															
	8															
RETURNED	11:00 a.m.															
	11:15 a.m.															
	12:00 p.m.															
	12:45 p.m.															
	1:00 p.m.															

LOGIC PROBLEM 276

With many powerful talent scouts and producers in the audience, the Pflugerville International Comedy Pfestival is no laughing matter to the dozens of up-and-coming comedians who attend the annual event. This year's closing-night show at Lenny's Laff Shack was no exception, as the five comedians who performed did their side-splitting best to attract the attention of the various talent agents in the crowd. Each comic has a different type of routine (one sings humorous songs) that proved so popular with the audience that each was approached by an impressed scout after his or her act and offered an exciting new career opportunity. After years of trying to get into some funny business, these comedians are finally ready to stand up and be counted! From the information provided, can you determine the routine performed by each comedian (identified by first and last names) and the job offer he or she received?

1. Neither Donna (who doesn't specialize in political humor) nor the comedian surnamed Gould is the one who was offered his or her own sitcom. Donna is neither the performer surnamed Warrick nor the one who was offered a part in an upcoming commercial. The sitcom wasn't offered to the comic who delighted the crowd with his or her political humor.

2. The comedian surnamed Findlay (who wasn't offered a sitcom) is neither the one who does impressions nor the comic who uses props. The one surnamed Warrick (who doesn't do impressions) isn't the comedian who was offered a guest appearance on a late-night talk show.

3. Neither Michael nor the performer surnamed Warrick was offered a sitcom. Jackie is neither the ventriloquist (who wasn't the one given the chance to host an awards show) nor the props comedian (who wasn't offered a talk-show appearance). Neither Jackie nor the one surnamed Jarman is the comedian who does impressions (who isn't Michael).

4. Both Stephen and the future awards-show host are veterans of last year's Pfestival, whereas both Eric and the comedian surnamed Jarman made their festival debuts this year. Neither Eric (who isn't the one who was offered a voice-over role on a new animated series) nor Stephen is the comic surnamed Pressman.

		LAST NAME					ROUTINE					JOB OFFER				
		FINDLAY	GOULD	JARMAN	PRESSMAN	WARRICK	IMPRESSIONS	POLITICAL HUMOR	PROPS	SONGS	VENTRILOQUISM	ANIMATED SERIES	AWARDS SHOW	COMMERCIAL	SITCOM	TALK SHOW
FIRST NAME	DONNA															
	ERIC															
	JACKIE															
	MICHAEL															
	STEPHEN															
JOB OFFER	ANIMATED SERIES															
	AWARDS SHOW															
	COMMERCIAL															
	SITCOM															
	TALK SHOW															
ROUTINE	IMPRESSIONS															
	POLITICAL HUMOR															
	PROPS															
	SONGS															
	VENTRILOQUISM															

The living room of Joanie Cunningham's modest ranch house is full of trinkets from across the country. Years ago, her youngest son jokingly sent Joanie a troll doll from GatorTown in the Florida Everglades, but it soon became a serious tradition among her well-traveled grandchildren. Whenever they visit an unusual tourist spot, they send a souvenir to their grandmother, so by now she has quite a collection! Joanie treasures these ornaments, so she was thrilled when she recently received five new ones (exactly two of which—the snow globe and swizzle stick—are made from glass) from her loving progeny. Two gifts arrived in March, two in April, and one in May. Each tchotchke was purchased at a different roadside attraction located in a different state. Now, so many neighbors want to see all the baubles and gewgaws filling every available space in her home that Joanie is thinking of charging admission! From the information provided, determine the trinket (one is a googly-eyed rock) purchased at the roadside attraction in each state, as well as the month Joanie received it.

1. The knickknack from the giant Fiberglass Dandelion (which isn't the tourist spot in Kansas) didn't arrive in April.

2. Joanie received the ceramic frog (which was purchased in Missouri) the month after she got the trinket from the Kale Capital of the World (which isn't made from glass).

3. The tchotchke from Nebraska arrived in the same month as the thimble (which was at some point before Joanie received the glass souvenir bought at the Mystery Monster roadside attraction).

4. The snow globe arrived at some point after the knickknack from the Lincoln Log Village (which came in the same month as the trinket from Iowa). The swizzle stick isn't the tchotchke that Joanie got from the Lincoln Log Village.

5. The Haunted Recycling Center is in South Dakota.

		ATTRACTION					STATE					MONTH				
		FIBERGLASS DANDELION	HAUNTED RECYCLING	KALE CAPITAL OF THE WORLD	LINCOLN LOG VILLAGE	MYSTERY MONSTER	IOWA	KANSAS	MISSOURI	NEBRASKA	SOUTH DAKOTA	MARCH	MARCH	APRIL	APRIL	MAY
TRINKET	CERAMIC FROG															
	GOOGLY-EYED															
	SNOW GLOBE															
	SWIZZLE STICK															
	THIMBLE															
MONTH	MARCH															
	MARCH															
	APRIL															
	APRIL															
	MAY															
STATE	IOWA															
	KANSAS															
	MISSOURI															
	NEBRASKA															
	SOUTH DAKOTA															

LOGIC PROBLEM 278 FIXER-UPPERS

Last week, new homeowners Mellany and Giles Keiffer watched with interest as six new home-improvement shows made their debuts on the Do-It-Yourself network. Each show premiered on a different day (Monday through Saturday) and was hosted by a different person (including Liz Burke), and each offered tips on redecorating a different room in the house. While the Keiffers know there is room for improvement in their new home, they were absolutely floored by all the helpful tips the shows contained! From the information provided, determine the host of the show that aired on each day and the room discussed on each show.

1. If Vince Dalton hosted *From House to Home*, then *Room by Room* (which wasn't the show hosted by Cassidy Miles) focused on redecorating the kitchen; otherwise, Vince Dalton hosted *Room-lifts*, and *Making Your Dream a Home* spotlighted the kitchen.

2. The six shows are the one that featured a basement overhaul, *Your House and You*, the Saturday program, the one hosted by Beth Norton, *The Unique House*, and the show that gave pointers on the master bedroom.

3. The show hosted by Vince Dalton aired exactly two days after the one that featured a face-lift of the kitchen. Of Nat Wilson and Ken Pfeiffer, one hosted a show that aired at some point later in the week than the one that focused on the living room, and the other hosted either the show that aired on Saturday (which isn't the one that featured a makeover of the family room) or *Making Your Dream a Home*.

4. If Beth Norton's show spotlighted the bathroom, then *Making Your Dream a Home* aired on Tuesday; otherwise, Ken Pfeiffer hosted the show featuring new ideas for the bathroom, and *Making Your Dream a Home* aired at some point earlier in the week than the show that gave pointers on sprucing up the master bedroom (which isn't *Room-lifts*).

5. *Your House and You* didn't spotlight the living room. Of the show hosted by Beth Norton and the one that aired on Tuesday, one is *Room by Room*, and the other aired exactly two days before *Room-lifts* (which isn't the show that offered tips on redoing the bathroom).

		FROM HOUSE TO HOME	MAKING YOUR DREAM A HOME	ROOM BY ROOM	ROOM-LIFTS	THE UNIQUE HOUSE	YOUR HOUSE AND YOU	BETH NORTON	CASSIDY MILES	KEN PFEIFFER	LIZ BURKE	NAT WILSON	VINCE DALTON	BASEMENT	BATHROOM	FAMILY ROOM	KITCHEN	LIVING ROOM	MASTER BEDROOM
		SHOW						HOST						ROOM					
DAY	MONDAY																		
	TUESDAY																		
	WEDNESDAY																		
	THURSDAY																		
	FRIDAY																		
	SATURDAY																		
ROOM	BASEMENT																		
	BATHROOM																		
	FAMILY ROOM																		
	KITCHEN																		
	LIVING ROOM																		
	MASTER																		
HOST	BETH NORTON																		
	CASSIDY MILES																		
	KEN PFEIFFER																		
	LIZ BURKE																		
	NAT WILSON																		
	VINCE DALTON																		

Opera lovers rejoice—next month, six of the world's greatest sopranos will fly to glittery Las Vegas for one-night-only appearances! Each woman's performance is scheduled for a different date at a different world-class hotel, where she will perform breathtaking arias from the opera that made her famous (each will sing arias from a different opera—one is Giacomo Puccini's *La Bohème*). Opera buffs who were lucky enough to purchase tickets for these exclusive Las Vegas performances have really hit the jackpot! From the information provided, determine the date on which each diva will perform and the hotel where she's appearing, as well as the opera from which she will perform arias.

1. Serena Chase will perform exactly three days after the diva who will appear at the Bellagio. The woman who will sing arias from Giuseppe Verdi's *Aida* won't be the first diva to perform next month. Daniella Dubois will perform exactly eight days before the woman scheduled to appear at the Mandalay Bay Resort.

2. The diva who will sing arias from Verdi's *La Traviata* (who isn't Alexis Olsavsky) won't be performing at Caesars Palace. Margaret Whitmore's performance will be exactly eight days after the one at the MGM Grand Hotel. The performance featuring selections from Amilcare Ponchielli's *La Gioconda* will be exactly eight days after Katerina Cordova's.

3. Justine Whitley will perform exactly two days after the diva who will sing arias from Georges Bizet's *Carmen* (who isn't Alexis Olsavsky). Only one woman will perform on an odd-numbered date. Margaret Whitmore won't perform selections from *La Gioconda*. Daniella Dubois won't be appearing at the MGM Grand Hotel. Alexis Olsavsky won't be seen at the Bellagio.

4. Katerina Cordova won't perform arias from *Carmen*. The performance featuring selections from Puccini's *Tosca* will be exactly three days after the one at Caesars Palace. The date of the Mandalay Bay Resort performance is exactly twice that of the Bellagio performance. Daniella Dubois won't be appearing at the Bellagio. Justine Whitley won't sing arias from *La Traviata*.

5. The Bally's Las Vegas performance will be exactly eight days after the one featuring arias from *La Gioconda*. Serena Chase won't sing arias from *Aida*. Neither the performance at the Bellagio nor the one at the Mirage will feature selections from *La Traviata*.

		DATE					HOTEL						OPERA					
							BALLY'S LAS VEGAS	BELLAGIO	CAESARS PALACE	MANDALAY BAY RESORT	MGM GRAND	MIRAGE	AIDA	CARMEN	LA BOHÈME	LA GIOCONDA	LA TRAVIATA	TOSCA
DIVA	ALEXIS																	
	DANIELLA																	
	JUSTINE																	
	KATERINA																	
	MARGARET																	
	SERENA																	
OPERA	AIDA																	
	CARMEN																	
	LA BOHÈME																	
	LA GIOCONDA																	
	LA TRAVIATA																	
	TOSCA																	
HOTEL	BALLY'S LAS																	
	BELLAGIO																	
	CAESARS																	
	MANDALAY BAY																	
	MGM GRAND																	
	MIRAGE RESORT																	

LOGIC PROBLEM 280   OUT OF THE KITCHEN

It was a busy week for Cara and four of her friends, so, to save some time in the kitchen, each agreed to cook dinner for the other four one day that week. Each served a different meal, each of which was accompanied by a different beverage. From the information provided, can you determine the meal and beverage each person (identified by first and last names—one surname is Barrett) served?

1. The one surnamed Kerr (who is not the one who made quiche) is not the one who served iced tea.
2. The one surnamed Gray, who provided a substantial sandwich buffet, is neither Neil nor Polly.
3. The fish barbecue was served with wine.
4. Neither Stan Frost nor Polly is the one who served lemonade with the meal.
5. Neil, who served cola with his meal, is not the one who provided a salad bar.
6. Neither June nor Polly is the one surnamed Shaw, who served hamburgers and milk.

		LAST NAME					MEAL					BEVERAGE				
		BARRETT	FROST	GRAY	KERR	SHAW	FISH	HAMBURGERS	QUICHE	SALAD BAR	SANDWICHES	COLA	ICED TEA	LEMONADE	MILK	WINE
FIRST NAME	CARA															
FIRST NAME	JUNE															
FIRST NAME	NEIL															
FIRST NAME	POLLY															
FIRST NAME	STAN															
BEVERAGE	COLA															
BEVERAGE	ICED TEA															
BEVERAGE	LEMONADE															
BEVERAGE	MILK															
BEVERAGE	WINE															
MEAL	FISH															
MEAL	HAMBURGERS															
MEAL	QUICHE															
MEAL	SALAD BAR															
MEAL	SANDWICHES															

Last month, Catherine Knight (also known by her transpositional name, "Thinking Teacher"), professor of "Anagram-ology" at Burnt Siena University, received letters from five of her former students, all of whom now live in Canada. She was delighted to hear that each person has a different career, but she was also disappointed that no one entered a career that is anagram-related. As she sat down to write letters to each former student, she frequently referred to the letters that the five had written, noting the letter and number similarities and dissimilarities between the students' names, their five different house numbers, and their five different postal codes. From the information provided, determine each former student's profession (one is a stockbroker), his or her postal code (D3B 4H1, K1W 7C8, L4C 3E6, L8V 4N3, or M9S 4C5), and his or her house number (9, 75, 366, 743, or 851).

1. Kendra's postal code has no letters in common with her name. Hugh is the meteorologist.
2. Holly's postal code, which isn't L4C 3E6, has no digits in common with her house number, which is higher than that of the paralegal.
3. David's name has no letters in common with his profession or his postal code.
4. Jerry (whose postal code has no letters in common with his name) lives at 743 Oak Street. The dentist's house number doesn't have exactly three digits.
5. The address that has L8V 4N3 as its postal code has a higher house number than the journalist's address.

		PROFESSION					POSTAL CODE					HOUSE NUMBER				
		DENTIST	JOURNALIST	METEOROLOGIST	PARALEGAL	STOCKBROKER	D3B 4H1	K1W 7C8	L4C 3E6	L8V 4N3	M9S 4C5	9	75	366	743	851
STUDENT	DAVID															
	HOLLY															
	HUGH															
	JERRY															
	KENDRA															
HOUSE NO.	9															
	75															
	366															
	743															
	851															
POSTAL CODE	D3B 4H1															
	K1W 7C8															
	L4C 3E6															
	L8V 4N3															
	M9S 4C5															

LOGIC PROBLEM 282   PLANTS AND THINGS

In addition to having the best selection of gardening supplies in the tri-state area, the Green Thumb Nursery has an extensive inventory of flowering plants. Each of five customers, including Karen, went to the nursery to buy a different item and also purchased a different flowering plant. From the information provided, determine the item (one is a trowel) each customer (identified by first and last names—one surname is Crandell) went to purchase, as well as the flower she bought (one purchased carnations).

1. Four of the customers are the woman who selected lilies, Ms. Madsen, the one who went to buy potting soil, and Janice.
2. One woman, but not Janice, went for plant fertilizer and also ended up buying peonies.
3. Alice is the one surnamed Vincent.
4. Diana, who went shopping alone, bought irises.
5. Toni (who bought decorator rock for her flower bed, but not lilies) went shopping with Ms. Madsen.
6. Ms. Gallagher, who is not Janice, bought the asters.
7. Ms. Simpson went shopping with the woman who needed to buy flower pots.

		LAST NAME					ITEM					FLOWER				
		CRANDELL	GALLAGHER	MADSEN	SIMPSON	VINCENT	FERTILIZER	POTS	ROCK	SOIL	TROWEL	ASTERS	CARNATIONS	IRISES	LILIES	PEONIES
FIRST NAME	ALICE															
	DIANA																
	JANICE																
	KAREN																
	TONI																
FLOWER	ASTERS																
	CARNATIONS																
	IRISES																
	LILIES																
	PEONIES																
ITEM	FERTILIZER																
	POTS																
	ROCK																
	SOIL																
	TROWEL																

LOGIC PROBLEM 283

It's the end of the day, and Carl, a mailman for the town of Northport, has five deliveries to make before heading home. Each delivery consists of a different number of packages (5, 7, 9, 11, or 13) that will be delivered to the owner of a different Northport business. Each business (one is Joshua's Restaurant) has a different street address (1250 Clay Road, 1320 Miller Street, 2430 Tyler Boulevard, 3140 Elm Place, or 3510 Commerce Avenue). From the information provided, determine the number of packages to be delivered to each business, the proprietor (one is Ms. Lyman) of each business, and the street address of each business.

1. The street addresses of both Playclothes, Inc., and Ms. Brewster's business begin with the numeral 3. The street addresses of both Cinema One and Mr. Jacobson's business begin with the numeral 1.

2. Ms. Rice will receive exactly two fewer packages than the owner of Glassworks, who will receive exactly two fewer packages than the business located at 1250 Clay Road.

3. The street address of Mr. Orchard's business doesn't share the same first numeral with Glassworks. Mr. Orchard will receive exactly four more packages than the owner of the business located at 3510 Commerce Avenue.

4. The business located at 3140 Elm Place will receive the fewest packages.

5. The owner who will receive seven packages has a business with a lower-numbered street address than the business owned by Ms. Brewster.

6. Northport Design (which isn't the business owned by Mr. Orchard) is located at 2430 Tyler Boulevard.

		BUSINESS					PROPRIETOR					ADDRESS				
		CINEMA ONE	GLASSWORKS	JOSHUA'S RESTAURANT	NORTHPORT DESIGN	PLAYCLOTHES, INC.	MS. BREWSTER	MR. JACOBSON	MS. LYMAN	MR. ORCHARD	MS. RICE	1250 CLAY ROAD	1320 MILLER STREET	2430 TYLER BOULEVARD	3140 ELM PLACE	3510 COMMERCE AVENUE
PACKAGES	5															
	7															
	9															
	11															
	13															
ADDRESS	1250 CLAY ROAD															
	1320 MILLER ST.															
	2430 TYLER BLVD.															
	3140 ELM PLACE															
	3510 COMMERCE															
PROPRIETOR	MS. BREWSTER															
	MR. JACOBSON															
	MS. LYMAN															
	MR. ORCHARD															
	MS. RICE															

Jim takes great pride in his antique car, which has won many prizes in car shows around the country. Four of his friends also own beautiful antique automobiles, and they are quite a sight as they go for their Sunday drives together. Other people on the highway stare and wave, and many shout out appreciative comments to the drivers as they pass. Each person owns a different car, and each car was made in a different year. No two cars are painted the same color. From the information provided, determine the car (one is a Morgan) each person owns, as well as its year (1928, 1929, 1932, 1934, or 1935) of manufacture and color (one is blue).

1. The Bugatti is neither the red car nor the tan car.
2. Phyllis does not drive the newest car.
3. The Maserati, which is not yellow, is older than the tan car but newer than Helen's car.
4. Nicole's car, which is not the green one, is newer than the tan car but older than the Aston Martin.
5. The yellow car is older than the Bugatti.
6. Helen is not the one who owns the Alfa Romeo.
7. Neither Lionel's car nor the Aston Martin is green.

		CAR					YEAR					COLOR				
		ALFA ROMEO	ASTON MARTIN	BUGATTI	MASERATI	MORGAN	1928	1929	1932	1934	1935	BLUE	GREEN	RED	TAN	YELLOW
PERSON	HELEN															
	JIM															
	LIONEL															
	NICOLE															
	PHYLLIS															
COLOR	BLUE															
	GREEN															
	RED															
	TAN															
	YELLOW															
YEAR	1928															
	1929															
	1932															
	1934															
	1935															

LOGIC PROBLEM 285

In his capacity as Bridge Inspector for Basin County, Cam examined five different bridges last week. He drove all over the county to look at the bridges, and although each was completed in a different year and was designed by a different person, he found them all to be in excellent condition. Each is a different length and spans a different river. From the information provided, determine the river spanned by each bridge and the year in which it was completed (1982, 1984, 1986, 1988, or 1990), as well as its length in yards (700, 750, 800, 850, or 900) and designer.

1. The bridge completed in 1988 is shorter than the one over the Tualpa but longer than the one over the Florice river.

2. Of the bridge over the Molne and the one completed in 1984, one was designed by Lenoir and the other is exactly 50 yards longer than the bridge Ashley designed.

3. Of the bridges over the Chinapi and Ridalo rivers, one was designed by Ashley, and the other was completed in 1982.

4. The bridge that Volkov designed is exactly 50 yards shorter than the one spanning the Ridalo river.

5. The bridge completed in 1988 is either the one designed by Hackman or the one designed by Greig.

6. The 800-yard bridge was completed in either 1982 or 1990.

7. The 750-yard bridge was designed by either Hackman or Lenoir.

		YEAR					YARDS					DESIGNER				
		1982	1984	1986	1988	1990	700	750	800	850	900	ASHLEY	GREIG	HACKMAN	LENOIR	VOLKOV
RIVER	CHINAPI															
	FLORICE															
	MOLNE															
	RIDALO															
	TUALPA															
DESIGNER	ASHLEY															
	GREIG															
	HACKMAN															
	LENOIR															
	VOLKOV															
YARDS	700															
	750															
	800															
	850															
	900															

LOGIC PROBLEM 286   THE BOOK-EXCHANGE CLUB

Debra and five of her friends, all of whom are avid readers, have formed a book-exchange club in the small village of Fulham. At their first meeting last Thursday evening, the person surnamed Trabert spoke about a favorite writer. Each member then lent a book of a different literary genre to a different one of the other five members. The six (three of whom—Debra, Eliza, and Nina—are women, and three of whom—Joseph, Martin, and Rick—are men) plan to discuss the various merits of the books at their next meeting. From the information provided, determine the first and last names of each member, the literary genre of the book each lent at the meeting, and the genre of the book each borrowed at the meeting.

1. The member who lent the science-fiction book, who isn't Nina, borrowed the mystery.

2. Joseph borrowed a book from Mr. Varney (who is not the one who loaned the mystery). The person surnamed Shaw lent the book of poetry.

3. Ms. Foster, who isn't Debra, lent the biography to a woman.

4. Neither Rick nor Nina is the one surnamed Anders. Rick and Nina exchanged books.

5. Martin, who isn't the one who borrowed a book from Joseph, borrowed a western.

6. The person who borrowed the mystery isn't the one surnamed Kearney.

7. Eliza isn't the one who borrowed the romance.

		ANDERS	FOSTER	KEARNEY	SHAW	TRABERT	VARNEY	BIOGRAPHY	MYSTERY	POETRY	ROMANCE	SCIENCE FICTION	WESTERN	BIOGRAPHY	MYSTERY	POETRY	ROMANCE	SCIENCE FICTION	WESTERN
		LAST NAME						LENT						BORROWED					
FIRST NAME	DEBRA																		
	ELIZA																		
	JOSEPH																		
	MARTIN																		
	NINA																		
	RICK																		
BORROWED	BIOGRAPHY																		
	MYSTERY																		
	POETRY																		
	ROMANCE																		
	SCIENCE FICTION																		
	WESTERN																		
LENT	BIOGRAPHY																		
	MYSTERY																		
	POETRY																		
	ROMANCE																		
	SCIENCE FICTION																		
	WESTERN																		

LOGIC PROBLEM 287

Ten friends, each of whom has recently moved to a different city, have found e-mail to be useful in their correspondence. On Saturday, each of five of the friends (three of whom—Brett, Fritz, and Jasper—are men, and two of whom—Darla and Rebecca—are women) sent an e-mail message to a different one of the other five (two of whom—Chad and Ellis—are men, and three of whom—Karla, Lois, and Meryl—are women). From the information provided, determine the sender of the message from each city (Atlanta, Georgia, Billings, Montana, Dallas, Texas, Salem, Massachusetts, or Tampa, Florida), the recipient of that message, and the city in which it was received (Chicago, Illinois, Fargo, North Dakota, Lansing, Michigan, Norwalk, Connecticut, or Reno, Nevada).

1. Three of the senders are the man from Billings, the man who sent a message to Karla, and the man who sent his message to Norwalk.
2. Lois lives in Lansing. Fritz lives in Salem.
3. Rebecca, who sent a message to a man, isn't the one who sent a message to Reno.
4. The three messages sent to women were the one from Jasper, the one sent to Fargo (which wasn't sent from Tampa), and the one sent from a woman in Atlanta.
5. Ellis doesn't live in Norwalk. Karla didn't receive a message from Salem.
6. Meryl didn't receive a message from Billings.

		SENT FROM					RECIPIENT					RECEIVED IN				
		ATLANTA	BILLINGS	DALLAS	SALEM	TAMPA	CHAD	ELLIS	KARLA	LOIS	MERYL	CHICAGO	FARGO	LANSING	NORWALK	RENO
SENDER	BRETT															
	DARLA															
	FRITZ															
	JASPER															
	REBECCA															
RECEIVED IN	CHICAGO															
	FARGO															
	LANSING															
	NORWALK															
	RENO															
RECIPIENT	CHAD															
	ELLIS															
	KARLA															
	LOIS															
	MERYL															

LOGIC PROBLEM 288 GADABOUT

Last week was an unusually busy week for Annie. On each weeknight, she enjoyed a different activity with a different person (three of whom—Betty, Carol, and Sharon—are women, and two of whom—Bill and Jack—are men). Each person has a different relationship with Annie (one is her boyfriend). From the information provided, determine the weeknight on which Annie saw each person, his or her relationship to Annie, and the activity they shared (one was a PTA meeting).

1. Annie saw her mother on one of the nights, but not the night she played bridge.
2. Annie's evening with her coworker was at some point later in the week than her night out with Betty but at some point earlier in the week than her evening with Jack (which wasn't Friday).
3. Annie went out with Carol the day after she had plans with Sharon but the day before she attended her dance class, which isn't the activity she shared with her neighbor.
4. Sharon, who doesn't work with Annie, isn't the person who accompanied her to the ice-skating party on Wednesday.
5. Annie and her sister had a good time together, but not on Monday.
6. Bill is neither the person who joined Annie at the garden-club meeting nor the one who was her partner for a game of bridge.

		PERSON					RELATIONSHIP					ACTIVITY				
		BETTY	BILL	CAROL	JACK	SHARON	BOYFRIEND	COWORKER	MOTHER	NEIGHBOR	SISTER	BRIDGE GAME	DANCE CLASS	GARDEN CLUB MEETING	ICE SKATING PARTY	PTA MEETING
WEEKNIGHT	MONDAY															
	TUESDAY															
	WEDNESDAY															
	THURSDAY															
	FRIDAY															
ACTIVITY	BRIDGE GAME															
	DANCE CLASS															
	GARDEN CLUB															
	ICE SKATING															
	PTA MEETING															
RELATIONSHIP	BOYFRIEND															
	COWORKER															
	MOTHER															
	NEIGHBOR															
	SISTER															

LOGIC PROBLEM 289

Five members of the Randori Judo Club (three of whom—Jacques, Luke, and Nathan—are men, and two of whom—Kathleen and May—are women) entered a rousing local judo competition this past week. Competitors wore the regulation judo-gi (loose pants and jacket) tied with a colored belt denoting rank (from lowest to highest, white, yellow, orange, green, blue, brown, and black belt). Using a different judo throw to win his or her match, each Randori member earned a different honor (three of which—the gold, silver, and bronze medal—are medals, and two of which are promotions to the next higher judo rank) in the competition. Between the member's original ranks and their promotions, all seven belt colors were represented. From the information provided, can you determine the throw (one was Osoto Gari) each member used, as well as each member's original rank and the honor that was bestowed upon each?

1. The member who used the Hiza Guruma throw had a lower original rank than the member who used the De Ashi Hari throw, who had a lower original rank than the member who used the Ogoshi throw.

2. The three male Randori members are the one who used the Tsuri Komi Goshi throw, Luke, and the one who was promoted to green belt.

3. Kathleen, who entered the competition with the lowest rank, won the same type of honor as Nathan. Kathleen's throw wasn't the Hiza Guruma.

4. Prior to the competition, May had a higher belt than Luke.

5. The member who used the Tsuri Komi Goshi throw (who didn't start the competition with the highest belt) didn't win a bronze medal.

6. The three medalists were Jacques, the member who entered the competition as a blue belt, and the silver medalist.

		THROW					ORIGINAL RANK					HONOR				
		DE ASHI HARI	HIZA GURUMA	OGOSHI	OSOTO GARI	TSURI KOMI GOSHI										
MEMBER	JACQUES															
	KATHLEEN															
	LUKE															
	MAY															
	NATHAN															
HONOR												
ORIGINAL												

LOGIC PROBLEM 290   I DO BELIEVE IN SPOOKS

After Sean inherited Glenrock Castle from some distant Scottish relatives, he moved the entire structure from Scotland to his hometown of Passaic, New Jersey! He's delighted with his new home, although it did take him a little time to adjust to the castle's five resident ghosts (three of whom—Charles, Hector, and Joshua—are male, and two of whom—Eliza and Emmeline—are female). Day after day, each specter haunts a different room (one floats around the attic) at a different time of day (12:00 a.m., 2:00 a.m., 4:00 a.m., 5:00 p.m., or 10:00 p.m.), but the spirits are harmless as each performs a different activity. From the information provided, determine the time at which each ghost haunts his or her room, as well as the activity each performs.

1. Joshua (who appears at 5:00 p.m.) is neither the spirit who recites poetry nor the specter who dances.

2. The ghost who haunts the kitchen (who doesn't hum) isn't the one who appears at 12:00 a.m.

3. The laughing ghost is female.

4. The dancing ghost, who is not Emmeline, appears in the ballroom, but not at 10:00 p.m.

5. The male ghost who haunts the wine cellar isn't the spirit who hums or the phantom who sings.

6. Hector (who sings gustily) is neither the ghost who appears in the library at 4:00 a.m. nor the specter who shows up at 10:00 p.m. each night.

		TIME					ROOM					ACTIVITY				
		12:00 a.m.	2:00 a.m.	4:00 a.m.	5:00 p.m.	10:00 p.m.	ATTIC	BALLROOM	KITCHEN	LIBRARY	WINE CELLAR	DANCES	HUMS	LAUGHS	RECITES POETRY	SINGS
GHOST	CHARLES															
	ELIZA															
	EMMELINE															
	HECTOR															
	JOSHUA															
ACTIVITY	DANCES															
	HUMS															
	LAUGHS															
	RECITES POETRY															
	SINGS															
ROOM	ATTIC															
	BALLROOM															
	KITCHEN															
	LIBRARY															
	WINE CELLAR															

Fresh out of college, each of five journalism students from Scoop'em U found employment at a different newspaper (one is *Newsdesk*). For his or her first assignment, each covered a different event held on a different date last month. From the information provided, can you determine the paper for which each reporter works, as well as the event each covered (one is the Blueberry Bake-Off) and the date (8th, 10th, 15th, 21st, or 27th) each event took place?

1. Sam, who covered the event held on the 8th, is taller than the person who covered the Home & Garden Convention.

2. The reporter whose first assignment was on the 10th is younger than Kris.

3. Lena, who covered the opening of the Get Fit Aerobic-thon for her first assignment, is not the journalist who works for *Fresh Eye* (who covered the event held on the 21st).

4. The reporter who covered the County Chess Championship for *Home Digest* is shorter than the one who reported on the event held on the 27th.

5. Neither Tony, who works for *Scribblings*, nor Alex is the one whose first assignment was covering the Turtle Races on the 15th.

6. The journalist whose first assignment was the Home & Garden Convention is older than both Alex and the *Chat Box* reporter.

		PAPER					EVENT					DATE				
		CHAT BOX	FRESH EYE	HOME DIGEST	NEWSDESK	SCRIBBLINGS	BLUEBERRY BAKE-OFF	COUNTY CHESS CHAMPIONSHIP	GET FIT AREOBIC-THON	HOME & GARDEN CONVENTION	TURTLE RACES	8th	10th	15th	21st	27th
REPORTER	ALEX															
	KRIS															
	LENA															
	SAM															
	TONY															
DATE	8th															
	10th															
	15th															
	21st															
	27th															
EVENT	BLUEBERRY															
	COUNTY CHESS															
	GET FIT AREOBIC															
	HOME & GARDEN															
	TURTLE RACES															

LOGIC PROBLEM 292

The proofreading department at Papyrus Press can be a quiet place, but its employees like to show their individuality. Each of five proofreaders (including Nancy) owns a coffee mug featuring a different one of the five Marx Brothers (Chico, Groucho, Gummo, Harpo, or Zeppo), from which each drinks a different type of beverage. Each person's desk also bears a different personal object (exactly two of the personal items—the geranium and the violet—are plants). From the information provided, can you determine each person's beverage (one is juice) and the Marx brother on his or her mug, as well as the personal object (one is a photo of a dog) on his or her desk?

1. Of the two desks bearing plants, one is Greta's, and the other sports the Chico mug (which is neither Jack's mug nor the one containing Ovaltine).

2. One desk bears both a mug of coffee and the photo of an employee's child.

3. The owner of the Gummo mug, whose desk bears the geranium, is neither the proofreader who drinks cocoa nor the one who drinks Ovaltine.

4. The proofreader who displays a photo of his or her cat (who isn't the one who owns the Groucho mug) isn't Fred.

5. The owner of the Harpo mug has neither a photo of his or her child nor a photo of his or her cat.

6. The three people who display photos are Mildred, the one who drinks tea, and the one with the Zeppo mug.

		BEVERAGE					MARX BROTHER					OBJECT				
		COCOA	COFFEE	JUICE	OVALTINE	TEA	CHICO	GROUCHO	GUMMO	HARPO	ZEPPO	CAT'S PHOTO	CHILD'S PHOTO	DOG'S PHOTO	GERANIUM	VIOLET
PERSON	FRED															
PERSON	GRETA															
PERSON	JACK															
PERSON	MILDRED															
PERSON	NANCY															
OBJECT	CAT'S PHOTO															
OBJECT	CHILD'S PHOTO															
OBJECT	DOG'S PHOTO															
OBJECT	GERANIUM															
OBJECT	VIOLET															
MARX	CHICO															
MARX	GROUCHO															
MARX	GUMMO															
MARX	HARPO															
MARX	ZEPPO															

LOGIC PROBLEM 293

Most circuses own their own trains to get their performers from town to town, but if a performer is running late and the train leaves without him or her, he or she has to take a commuter train like everyone else! On my shift at the train station's newsstand last night, I saw each of five such circus performers (no two of whom have the same act—one is a fire-eater) scrambling to board a different train. All wore colorful circus garb, including a different hat, which was the trademark headgear of his or her troupe. From the information provided, match each performer with his or her train (8:03, 9:15, 10:27, 11:16, or 11:57), act, and hat (one is a tam-o'-shanter).

1. Bruce, who wore a Stetson, took the train that left immediately before Michael's (whose train departed before at least one other).

2. The performer wearing a beret (who isn't the juggler) left either immediately before or immediately after the clown.

3. Charles's train left at some point before the magician's train.

4. The performer wearing a fez left at some point before Rochelle (whose train left at 10:27). Paula's train left either immediately before or immediately after the one boarded by the acrobat (who was wearing a kepi).

		TRAIN					ACT					HAT				
		8:03	9:15	10:27	11:16	11:57	ACROBAT	CLOWN	FIRE-EATER	JUGGLER	MAGICIAN	BERET	FEZ	KEPI	STETSON	TAM-O'-SHANTER
PERFORMER	BRUCE															
	CHARLES															
	MICHAEL															
	PAULA															
	ROCHELLE															
HAT	BERET															
	FEZ															
	KEPI															
	STETSON															
	TAM-O'-SHANTER															
ACT	ACROBAT															
	CLOWN															
	FIRE-EATER															
	JUGGLER															
	MAGICIAN															

Recently, we decided to buy a new house, and last Sunday we looked at five potential new homes, all on scenic Caspin Lake. Each house has a different address (203, 303, 403, 503, or 603) on a different street. Each was shown to us by a different agent (including Ms. Ameling), who pointed out the picture window that gives each house a majestic view of the lake (each window faces a different direction). From the information provided, determine the address and street (one is Lodge Way) of the house shown by each agent, as well as the direction (east, south, southeast, southwest, or west) each picture window faces.

1. The address of the house on Grange Drive is either exactly 200 higher or exactly 200 lower than that of the house with the picture window that faces south.

2. The house at 603 isn't the one whose picture window faces west (which isn't the house shown by Ms. Vaness).

3. The house with the east-facing picture window is numbered exactly 100 higher than the house Ms. Callas showed and exactly 100 lower than the house on Castle Lane.

4. The house on Viking Hill, whose picture window faces southwest, is numbered exactly 100 lower than the house Mr. Trebor showed.

5. The house on Manor Road has a higher number than the house with the southeast-facing picture window (which was shown by Mr. Durward). The picture window in the house numbered 503 doesn't face southeast.

		STREET					AGENT					DIRECTION				
		CASTLE LANE	GRANGE DRIVE	LODGE WAY	MANOR ROAD	VIKING HILL	MS. AMELING	MS. CALLAS	MR. DURWARD	MR. TREBOR	MS. VANESS	EAST	SOUTH	SOUTHEAST	SOUTHWEST	WEST
ADDRESS	203															
	303															
	403															
	503															
	603															
DIRECTION	EAST															
	SOUTH															
	SOUTHEAST															
	SOUTHWEST															
	WEST															
AGENT	MS. AMELING															
	MS. CALLAS															
	MR. DURWARD															
	MR. TREBOR															
	MS. VANESS															

Dashing news reporter Ethan Fox was determined to launch his career into the big time by snagging interviews with five elusive art-loving philanthropists during last night's gala exhibit at the Gershwin Gallery. Ethan was able to approach each person at a different time (9:30, 9:35, 9:40, 9:45, or 9:50 p.m.), when he spotted each philanthropist relaxing in a corner with a glass of a different type of wine. Unfortunately for Ethan, when his cameraman moved in to get the perfect shot, each person, preferring to keep his or her identity private, managed to obscure his or her face with a different object. No sooner had Ethan blinked than each person ducked behind a different potted plant and retreated from the gallery, leaving Ethan wondering how to artfully fill out the rest of his report! From the information provided, determine the time at which each Ethan approached each person, the type of wine he or she was sipping, the obstruction (one was a scarf) that hid each from the camera, and the potted plant behind which each vanished.

1. The suspect drinking Chablis (who was obscured when a popping Champagne cork momentarily knocked the camera off kilter) was approached either exactly five minutes before or exactly five minutes after the one who ducked behind the mauna-loa plant.

2. The one drinking Riesling (who wasn't the one hidden by a hat flung over the camera) ducked behind a sago palm either exactly five minutes before or exactly five minutes after the one drinking zinfandel was approached by Ethan.

3. The Chardonnay sipper (who isn't the one who slipped behind the dumb cane) was approached exactly five minutes before the one who was eclipsed by a balloon in front of the camera lens before ducking behind a never-never plant.

4. The Gewurztraminer drinker was approached at some point after the one obscured by a paper streamer across the lens but exactly five minutes before the one who took cover behind a European fan palm (who wasn't drinking Chardonnay).

		WINE					OBSTRUCTION					PLANT				
		CHABLIS	CHARDONNAY	GEWURZTRAMINER	RIESLING	ZINFANDEL	BALLOON	CHAMPAGNE CORK	HAT	PAPER STREAMER	SCARF	DUMB CANE	EUROPEAN FAN PALM	MAUNA LOA	NEVER-NEVER PLANT	SAGO PALM
TIME	9:30															
	9:35															
	9:40															
	9:45															
	9:50															
PLANT	DUMB CANE															
	EUROPEAN FAN															
	MAUNA LOA															
	NEVER-NEVER															
	SAGO PALM															
OBSTRUCTION	BALLOON															
	CHAMPAGNE															
	HAT															
	PAPER STREAMER															
	SCARF															

LOGIC PROBLEM 296

Technology Chasers, an employment agency, had quite a good year. In each of five months (March through July), Ezra Pixel, a headhunter for Technology Chasers, placed five new employees (from lowest to highest position, programmer, computer graphicist, design engineer, systems analyst, or project manager) in different companies. Each person is working on a different software package (one is OPENINGS). From the information provided, determine the month each person was hired for each company, the position each holds, and the software on which each is working.

1. The Technocorp employee was hired at some point after the one working on APERTURES but at some point before the the project manager (who isn't responsible for GATEWAYS).

2. Neither Softworld employee (who wasn't hired in March) nor the Hypermax employee is the project manager. The one working on GATEWAYS (who wasn't hired last) was hired at some point after the one whose new position ranks immediately below that of the suspect working for Computron (who was hired earlier than the one working on ENTRANCES).

3. The Microcom employee works in a higher-ranked position than the person who was hired the month before the one working on PORTALS but a lower-ranked position than the employee who was hired at some point after the one working on the ENTRANCES software.

		COMPANY					POSITION					SOFTWARE				
		COMPUTRON	HYPERMAX	MICROCOM	SOFTWORLD	TECHNOCORP	PROGRAMMER	COMPUTER GRAPHICIST	DESIGN ENGINEER	SYSTEMS ANALYST	PROJECT MANAGER	APERTURES	ENTRANCES	GATEWAYS	OPENINGS	PORTALS
MONTH	MARCH															
	APRIL															
	MAY															
	JUNE															
	JULY															
SOFTWARE	APERTURES															
	ENTRANCES															
	GATEWAYS															
	OPENINGS															
	PORTALS															
POSITION	PROGRAMMER															
	COMP. GRAPHIC.															
	DESIGN ENG.															
	SYS. ANALYST															
	PROJECT MGR.															

LOGIC PROBLEM 297

While nowadays I am an expert on using my home computer and mobile devices, it wasn't always that way! I used to be terribly confused by technology, but one year a friend advised me to take some computer classes, and my life has never been the same. I took five classes (including "Key to Success"), each of which was held in a different month at a different university. Each class lasted a different number of days (3, 5, 8, 9, or 12). From the information provided, can you determine the course offered by each university, the month (April through August) in which each course was held, and the number of days it lasted?

1. The course taught at Ventnor University was held the month after the one offered by Durwood University.
2. The May course (which wasn't "Mac and Me") lasted exactly four days longer than the course offered at Kublin University.
3. The June course lasted longer than the August one.
4. The course held at Williams University (which didn't last eight days) was held at some point earlier in the year than "Stand by Your RAM" but at some point later in the year than the three-day class.
5. "Diskotheque" was shorter than the June course.
6. "Love Your Laptop" (which wasn't offered in June) lasted exactly four days fewer than the class taught at Amthor University.

		COURSE					MONTH					DAYS				
		DISKOTHEQUE	KEY TO SUCCESS	LOVE YOUR LAPTOP	MAC AND ME	STAND BY YOUR RAM	APRIL	MAY	JUNE	JULY	AUGUST	3	5	8	9	12
UNIVERSITY	AMTHOR															
	DURWOOD															
	KUBLIN															
	VENTNOR															
	WILLIAMS															
DAYS	3															
	5															
	8															
	9															
	12															
MONTH	APRIL															
	MAY															
	JUNE															
	JULY															
	AUGUST															

LOGIC PROBLEM 298

At a truck stop recently, I met five fellow truckers (each of whom has a different handle, or nickname—one is Rip Van Winkle). Even though each has been a trucker for several years (no two have been trucker for the same number of years), I got the feeling that all of them (including Marge) had once harbored dreams of being a train conductor, as each had named his or her truck after a different famous train (including the *Best Friend*). From the information provided, determine each trucker's handle, the name of his or her truck, and the number of years (14, 15, 16, 18, or 19) he or she has been trucking.

1. The driver of the *De Witt Clinton* has been driving for 19 years. The one with the handle of Grizzly Bear (who isn't Rita) has been driving for 18 years.
2. The one with the handle of Frosty the Snowman has been driving for exactly 1 year longer than the driver of *Old Ironsides*.
3. The one with the handle of Appleseed (who isn't Gladys) has been driving for exactly 2 more years than Frank (who drives the *Pontchartrain*).
4. Neither Tom (whose handle is the Big Bad Wolf) nor Rita is the one who drives the *John Bull*.

		HANDLE					TRUCK					YEARS				
		APPLESEED	BIG BAD WOLF	FROSTY THE SNOWMAN	GRIZZLY BEAR	RIP VAN WINKLE	BEST FRIEND	DE WITT CLINTON	JOHN BULL	OLD IRONSIDES	PONTCHARTRAIN	14	15	16	18	19
TRUCKER	FRANK															
	GLADYS															
	MARGE															
	RITA															
	TOM															
YEARS	14															
	15															
	16															
	18															
	19															
TRUCK	BEST FRIEND															
	DE WITT CLINTON															
	JOHN BULL															
	OLD IRONSIDES															
	PONTCHARTRAIN															

LOGIC PROBLEM 299

Clem's Postcard Shop is the ideal place for people who want to send postcards but don't like to travel! This afternoon, five customers (including Gerald) stopped by, each at a different time (1:00, 1:30, 2:00, 2:30, or 3:00 p.m.). Each bought a different postcard to send to a friend. From the information provided, determine the time that each customer (identified by first and last names—one surname is Halliday) came to the store, as well as the postcard he or she bought.

1. The one surnamed Settle (who didn't come at 1:30 p.m.) bought a postcard showing the Grand Canyon. Cora didn't stop by at 2:30 p.m.

2. Barry Baker is a frequent customer at Clem's. The one surnamed Markham bought a postcard showing the Eiffel Tower.

3. The one surnamed Greenaway came by at 2:00 p.m. The customer surnamed Settle came by exactly 30 minutes before the one who bought a postcard featuring the Taj Mahal.

4. Rose (whose last name isn't Greenaway) bought a postcard featuring the Brooklyn Bridge.

5. Ted came by at some point before the person who bought a postcard featuring Big Ben but after at least one other customer.

		BARRY	CORA	GERALD	ROSE	TED	BAKER	GREENAWAY	HALLIDAY	MARKHAM	SETTLE	BIG BEN	BROOKLYN BRIDGE	EIFFEL TOWER	GRAND CANYON	TAJ MAHAL
TIME	1:00 p.m.															
	1:30 p.m.															
	2:00 p.m.															
	2:30 p.m.															
	3:00 p.m.															
POSTCARD	BIG BEN															
	BROOKLYN															
	EIFFEL TOWER															
	GRAND CANYON															
	TAJ MAHAL															
LAST NAME	BAKER															
	GREENAWAY															
	HALLIDAY															
	MARKHAM															
	SETTLE															

LOGIC PROBLEM 300 **ARTISTIC SECRETS**

Lara's dream finally became a reality when several of her sculptures were chosen for display at the prestigious Halford Gallery of Fine Art. She invited five of her closest family members and friends to the show's opening. As a surprise for Lara, each of her loved ones joined the gallery's donor list by paying for a different level of membership (from lowest to highest, friend, booster, donor, angel, and benefactor). During each of the three half-hour intervals between 9:00 and 10:30 p.m., Lara spotted each of her loved ones engaged in conversation with a different one of five art connoisseurs who was attending the show, though Lara later learned that no two of her loved ones had spoken with any connoisseur more than once that evening. Lara suspected that her loved ones were doing their best to mold her career into a success! From the information provided, determine, for the person at each level of membership, the art connoisseur with whom each chatted at 9:00-9:30, 9:30-10:00, and 10:00-10:30 that evening.

1. Mrs. Fitzbudget conversed with the booster from 9:30 to 10:00. The art connoisseur with whom the booster spoke from 10:00 to 10:30 was not the same person who, from 9:00 to 9:30, chatted with the member who spoke with Mrs. Fitzbudget between 10:00 and 10:30.

2. The donor spoke with Count Avertovsky from 10:00 to 10:30. One art connoisseur chatted with the donor from 9:00 to 9:30 and the friend from 9:30 to 10:00.

3. The angel conversed with Ms. Silique from 9:30 to 10:00. The connoisseur with whom the angel spoke from 9:00 to 9:30 wasn't the person who, from 10:00 to 10:30, chatted with the member who spoke with Mr. Poddleway between 9:30 and 10:00.

4. One person spent the hour between 9:00 and 10:00 chatting first with Dr. Griffin and then with Count Avertovsky.

5. The membership level of the person who was with Dr. Griffin between 10:00 and 10:30 is either exactly one rank lower or exactly one rank higher than that of the person who was with Count Avertovsky from 9:00 to 9:30.

		9:00-9:30					9:30-10:00					10:00-10:30				
		COUNT AVERTOVSKY	MRS. FITZBUDGET	DR. GRIFFIN	MR. PODDLEWAY	MS. SILIQUE	COUNT AVERTOVSKY	MRS. FITZBUDGET	DR. GRIFFIN	MR. PODDLEWAY	MS. SILIQUE	COUNT AVERTOVSKY	MRS. FITZBUDGET	DR. GRIFFIN	MR. PODDLEWAY	MS. SILIQUE
MEMBERSHIP	FRIEND															
	BOOSTER															
	DONOR															
	ANGEL															
	BENEFACTOR															
10:00-10:30	CT. AVERTOVSKY															
	MRS. FITZBUDGET															
	DR. GRIFFIN															
	MR. PODDLEWAY															
	MS. SILIQUE															
9:30-10:00	CT. AVERTOVSKY															
	MRS. FITZBUDGET															
	DR. GRIFFIN															
	MR. PODDLEWAY															
	MS. SILIQUE															

LOGIC PROBLEM 301

Sofia can't wait to play her new video game, *Reality Bytes*. In it, she has the choice of playing one of five characters, each of whom is in a different type of debt, with the goal of getting out of debt. That shouldn't be too difficult, as each character receives a different salary ($40,000, $42,500, $47,500, $50,000, or $55,000) and works a different number of hours. Through diligent play, each character will eventually earn a different percent increase (8%, 10%, 12%, 16%, or 18%) in his or her salary. From the information provided, determine the number of hours per week (45, 55, 60, 65, or 75) each character works, his or her salary, and the percent increase each will receive, as well as each one's debt.

1. The character who makes $40,000 isn't the one with outstanding credit-card bills (who doesn't work 65 hours).

2. The character weighed down with car payments makes exactly $7,500 less than the person who will receive the 10% raise.

3. The salary of the character with student loans is exactly $5,000 more than that of the one who works 75 hours (whose raise will be exactly 4 percentage points lower than that of the character with student loans).

4. The one who will receive an 8% salary increase was not working the most number of hours. The future raise of the character making $42,500 is exactly 2 percentage points higher than that of the person making mortgage payments.

5. One character works exactly 15 more hours per week, but will receive a raise of exactly 2 fewer percentage points, than the one who has had several bad investments.

		SALARY					INCREASE					DEBT				
		$40,000	$42,500	$47,500	$50,000	$55,000	8%	10%	12%	16%	18%	BAD INVESTMENTS	CAR PAYMENTS	CREDIT CARD	MORTGAGE	STUDENT LOANS
HOURS	45															
	55															
	60															
	65															
	75															
DEBT	BAD INVESTMENTS															
	CAR PAYMENTS															
	CREDIT CARD															
	MORTGAGE															
	STUDENT LOANS															
INCREASE	8%															
	10%															
	12%															
	16%															
	18%															

LOGIC PROBLEM 302   WHISTLING IN THE DARK

Joe Porter, the longtime doorman at the Savoy Apartments, is well acquainted with most of the residents. In fact, so regular are their routines that he knows who's getting out of the elevator before he even sees their faces. Each resident leaves for work at a different time in the morning (5:45, 6:00, 6:15, 6:30, or 6:45), and each wears a different colored coat and carries a different item. Even more distinctive, each can always be heard whistling the score of a different Gilbert and Sullivan operetta. From the information provided, can you determine the time at which the person wearing each color of coat leaves for work, as well as the item he or she carries and the operetta he or she whistles?

1. The one who whistles *HMS Pinafore* leaves exactly 30 minutes after the woman who wears a camel-colored coat.

2. The resident who wears a russet-colored coat isn't the one who carries a briefcase.

3. The one who carries an umbrella leaves exactly 45 minutes after the woman who wears a sienna-colored coat.

4. The man who carries a knapsack leaves exactly 30 minutes before the resident who whistles *Patience*.

5. The resident who whistles *The Mikado* leaves at some point before the one who wears a maroon-colored coat but exactly 30 minutes after the one who carries a lunchbox (who isn't the resident who whistles *Iolanthe*).

6. The one who whistles *The Gondoliers* leaves at some point after the one who wears a taupe-colored coat.

		TIME					ITEM					OPERETTA				
		5:45	6:00	6:15	6:30	6:45	BRIEFCASE	KNAPSACK	LUNCHBOX	NEWSPAPER	UMBRELLA	THE GONDOLIERS	HMS PINAFORE	IOLANTHE	THE MIKADO	PATIENCE
COAT	CAMEL															
	MAROON															
	RUSSET															
	SIENNA															
	TAUPE															
OPERETTA	THE GONDOLIERS															
	HMS PINAFORE															
	IOLANTHE															
	THE MIKADO															
	PATIENCE															
ITEM	BRIEFCASE															
	KNAPSACK															
	LUNCHBOX															
	NEWSPAPER															
	UMBRELLA															

LOGIC PROBLEM 303

On a recent transcontinental train ride aboard the *Iron Rooster*, five veteran rail riders found themselves seated together in the dining car. Each one's berth is located in a different sleeping car (from front to back, A through E), and each has a different cabin number (5, 6, 7, 8, or 9). In addition to train buffs, they are all movie buffs as well, and each has a different favorite film (including *Murder on the Orient Express*) that features train travel. From the information below, determine each passenger's sleeping car, cabin number, and favorite film.

1. The passenger staying in cabin six of sleeper car A isn't the one whose favorite movie is *North by Northwest*. Nancy isn't in cabin five.

2. The cabin number of the one whose favorite film is *The General* (who isn't Gregory) is exactly one lower than that of the one whose favorite film is *The Great Train Robbery*.

3. The passengers in cars A and E are, in some order, Eloise and the one in the cabin that is numbered exactly two higher than the cabin of the passenger in car C.

4. The sleeping car occupied by the passenger staying in cabin seven (whose favorite film is *The Darjeeling Limited*) is somewhere in front of Truman's car. Truman's cabin is numbered exactly one lower than Otto's cabin.

		SLEEPER CAR					CABIN					FILM				
		A	B	C	D	E	5	6	7	8	9	THE DARJEELING LIMITED	THE GENERAL	THE GREAT TRAIN ROBBERY	MURDER ON THE ORIENT EXPRESS	NORTH BY NORTHWEST
PASSENGER	ELOISE															
	GREGORY															
	NANCY															
	OTTO															
	TRUMAN															
FILM	THE DARJEELING															
	THE GENERAL															
	THE GREAT															
	MURDER ON THE															
	NORTH BY															
CABIN	5															
	6															
	7															
	8															
	9															

LOGIC PROBLEM 304   HOUSING DEVELOPMENTS

It's Mandy's second week on the job as a real-estate agent, and just this afternoon she took five new clients to see houses in the prestigious neighborhood around Caspin Lake. Each client saw a different house (each of which has a different name), and each house has a different number of rooms (6, 7, 8, 10, or 11). Each client told Mandy that he or she was relocating to Caspin Lake from a different state (including Texas) for a different reason. Mandy is hoping these houses on the lake will help her reel in a big profit! From the information provided, determine the number of rooms in the house on each property (one is Chatsworth House), the state in which each client currently lives, and the reason each client gave for relocating.

1. The client who saw the house with eight rooms, who told Mandy he or she was moving for a change of scenery, is from a state that comes alphabetically after the state of the client who viewed Paramount.

2. The client who viewed Green Fields is relocating from Colorado. The house seen by the person from Vermont (who was moving to the area due to its climate) has more rooms than the house seen by the client from Maine and fewer rooms than at least one other house.

3. The Nook has exactly one more room than the house seen by the client who was relocating in order to attend graduate school at a local university.

4. The one who saw Tranquility is moving due to his or her job. Tranquility has either exactly one room fewer or exactly one room more than the house seen by the client who was moving to Caspin Lake to be closer to his or her family.

5. The client from Hawaii didn't see the ten-room house.

		PROPERTY					STATE					REASON				
		CHATSWORTH HOUSE	GREEN FIELDS	THE NOOK	PARAMOUNT	TRANQUILITY	COLORADO	HAWAII	MAINE	TEXAS	VERMONT	CHANGE OF SCENERY	CLIMATE	FAMILY	GRADUATE SCHOOL	JOB
ROOMS	6															
	7															
	8															
	10															
	11															
REASON	CHANGE/SCENERY															
	CLIMATE															
	FAMILY															
	GRADUATE															
	JOB															
STATE	COLORADO															
	HAWAII															
	MAINE															
	TEXAS															
	VERMONT															

LOGIC PROBLEM 305

I've seen some odd things in my years as a hostess at the Ivy Trellis restaurant, but the crew of guys from Piedmont Plumbing who came in last night for their holiday party really left a smile on my face. After enjoying an elegant dinner with their wives, each man searched in the pocket of his suit for his valet chit (each of which had a different number) and his coat-check chit (each of which had a differet number). Instead of the chits, the first thing that came out of each man's pocket was a different tool! I guess these guys really do take their work home with them! From the information provided, determine the order of departure (first through fifth) for the man carrying each tool, as well as the number (15, 16, 17, 19, or 20) of each man's valet chit and the number (11, 12, 14, 15, or 16) of each one's coat-check chit.

1. The valet number of the one who left fourth was either exactly 1 higher or exactly 1 lower than that of the one with the Phillips screwdriver (who left either immediately before or immediately after the one with valet chit 15). The one who left third didn't have coat check 11.

2. The coat-check number of the one with valet chit 19 was either exactly 1 higher or exactly 1 lower than the coat-check number of the only man wearing a red coat (who departed either immediately before or immediately after, and had a valet number either exactly 1 higher or exactly 1 lower than, the man carrying lineman's pliers).

3. The one with locking pliers left either immediately before or immediately after, had a valet number exactly 2 lower than, and a coat-check number exactly 1 lower than, the one with slip-joint pliers.

4. The one with the flat-head screwdriver left either immediately before or immediately after, and had a valet number that was exactly 1 lower than, the one with coat-check chit 12.

		TOOL					VALET					COAT CHECK				
		FLAT-HEAD SCREWDRIVER	LINEMAN'S PLIERS	LOCKING PLIERS	PHILLIPS SCREWDRIVER	SLIP-JOINT PLIERS	15	16	17	19	20	11	12	14	15	16
DEPARTURE	FIRST															
	SECOND															
	THIRD															
	FOURTH															
	FIFTH															
COAT CHECK	11															
	12															
	14															
	15															
	16															
VALET	15															
	16															
	17															
	19															
	20															

Alexander just had his first interview and is taking a tour of the company. He was amused to notice on five different desks, a mousepad decorated with a different cartoon mouse (one is Jerry). He also noted that each mousepad's owner has a monitor of a different size (13 in., 15 in., 17 in., 19 in., or 21 in.) and a calendar with one of three themes and one of three types. Being an observant fellow, he observed each person working on a different file. From the information provided, determine the size of each person's monitor, the mousepad and calendar (*Dilbert* desk, *Dilbert* wall, *Star Trek* desk, *Star Trek* planner, or *X-Files* wall) each has, and the name of the file on which each one was working.

1. Of the four people with their own offices, the one working on the "Doorstop" file has a calendar with the same theme as the owner of the Danger Mousepad, who has the same type of calendar as the one who uses the 15 in. monitor, whose calendar has the same theme as that belonging to the owner of the Minute Mousepad.

2. Alexander spotted the "Unhinged" file on a computer with a smaller monitor than that used by the Mickey Mousepad owner. The one working on "Unhinged" has a calendar with a different theme, but of the same type, as the owner of the Mickey Mousepad (whose calendar has the same theme as one other person's).

3. The calendars belonging to the author of the "Deadbolt" file (which wasn't on the computer with the 21 in. montor) and the owner of the Minute Mousepad have different themes, but are the same type.

4. The "Knock Knock" file was on a computer with a monitor exactly 2 in. smaller than that belonging to the person with the *Star Trek* planner.

5. The computer screen with the "Peephole" file is exactly 2 in. smaller than that used by the Mighty Mousepad's owner.

		MOUSEPAD					CALENDAR					FILE				
		DANGER MOUSE	JERRY MOUSE	MICKEY MOUSE	MIGHTY MOUSE	MINUTE MOUSE	DILBERT DESK	DILBERT WALL	STAR TREK DESK	STAR TREK PLANNER	X-FILES WALL	DEADBOLT	DOORSTOP	KNOCK KNOCK	PEEPHOLE	UNHINGED
MONITOR SIZE	13"															
	15"															
	17"															
	19"															
	21"															
FILE	DEADBOLT															
	DOORSTOP															
	KNOCK KNOCK															
	PEEPHOLE															
	UNHINGED															
CALENDAR	DILBERT DESK															
	DILBERT WALL															
	TREK DESK															
	TREK PLANNER															
	X-FILES WALL															

Five friends (including Ian) were put in charge of making bacon-lettuce-and-tomato sandwiches for an upcoming picnic. Each bought a different number (4, 5, 7, 8, or 9) of bacon packages, a different number (3 through 7) of heads of lettuce, and a different number (5 through 9) of tomatoes. From the information provided, can you determine the numbers of bacon packages, heads of lettuce, and tomatoes that each friend bought?

1. Jeremiah (who didn't buy 9 tomatoes) bought fewer heads of lettuce than the friend who purchased seven bacon packages.

2. The friend who bought five heads of lettuce purchased exactly one bacon package more than the friend who bought five tomatoes.

3. Maureen bought exactly one bacon package fewer than the friend who purchased six heads of lettuce.

4. Jeremiah bought exactly one bacon package fewer, and more tomatoes, than the friend who purchased seven heads of lettuce.

5. Larry bought exactly two more bacon packages than the friend who purchased eight tomatoes.

6. Karen didn't buy five bacon packages.

		BACON					LETTUCE					TOMATOES				
		4	5	7	8	9	3	4	5	6	7	5	6	7	8	9
FRIEND	IAN															
	JEREMIAH															
	KAREN															
	LARRY															
	MAUREEN															
TOMATOES	5															
	6															
	7															
	8															
	9															
LETTUCE	3															
	4															
	5															
	6															
	7															

After spending a few years working abroad as an illustrator, I'm excited to be moving back to my home state of Virginia. And I'm even more ecstatic that I've put aside enough money for a down payment on my first house! I attended five open houses this weekend. Each house that I toured is a different style (one is a Federal) and was built in a different year (1980, 1981, 1982, 1984, or 1985). Each house has a different asking price and has been on the market for a different number of months. I'll be taking all that into consideration as I draw up what I hope will be a winning bid! From the information provided, determine the year each style of house was built, the asking price ($396,000, $396,500, $397,500, $398,000, or $398,500) of each house, and the number of months (2, 4, 6, 9, or 11) each house has been on the market.

1. The house built in 1985 has been on the market for exactly two months longer than the house with the asking price of $396,000.

2. The Georgian house on Laurel Way was built at some point after the one that has been on the market for six months.

3. The house with the asking price of $396,500 is either exactly one year older or exactly one year younger, and has been on the market exactly two months longer, than the ranch house (whose asking price is exactly $1,500 lower than that of the house that has been on the market for two months).

4. The house that has been on the market for four months (which wasn't built in 1982) has a lower asking price than the one built in 1981 (which isn't the Colonial).

5. The house built in 1984 has been on the market for fewer months than the Victorian.

		STYLE					ASKING PRICE					MONTHS				
		COLONIAL	FEDERAL	GEORGIAN	RANCH	VICTORIAN	$396,000	$396,500	$397,500	$398,000	$398,500	2	4	6	9	11
YEAR	1980															
	1981															
	1982															
	1984															
	1985															
MONTHS	2															
	4															
	6															
	9															
	11															
ASKING PRICE	$396,000															
	$396,500															
	$397,500															
	$398,000															
	$398,500															

LOGIC PROBLEM 309

Bryan frequents many Internet forums. Just today, he spent he spent a different number of minutes in five different forums chatting with a different poster (Badenov, Chewbacca, Cyborg, Skeletor, or SpeedRacer). He uses a different user name (Agent99, Danno, Kojak, Serpico, or Starsky) on each forum. From the information provided, determine the poster with whom Bryan chatted under each user name, the forum (one is Techtalk) where each interview occurred, and the number of minutes (6, 9, 12, 15, or 18) Bryan chatted on each forum.

1. The poster with whom Bryan chatted as Agent99 has a user name with exactly one letter fewer, and chatted with Bryan for less time, than the one Bryan encountered on the Friendly Users forum.

2. The poster to whom Bryan spoke as Starsky has a user name with exactly one more letter, and chatted with Bryan for either exactly 3 more or exactly 3 fewer minutes, than the poster in on the Gigagab forum.

3. Bryan spent exactly 3 more minutes on the Speak PC forum than on the Cyberchat forum. The poster he spoke with on the Cyberchat forum has a user name with at least two more letters than the one in the Speak PC room. Bryan didn't chat with Badenov on the Speak PC forum.

4. The poster with whom Bryan chatted as Serpico has a user name with exactly one letter fewer, and chatted with Bryan for either exactly 3 more or exactly 3 fewer minutes, than the one to whom he spoke as Danno.

5. SpeedRacer chatted with Bryan for 6 minutes. Bryan identified himself as Kojak to a poster whose user name had fewer letters than the one with whom he chatted for 12 minutes.

		USER NAME					FORUM					MINUTES				
		AGENT99	DANNO	KOJAK	SERPICO	STARSKY	CYBERCHAT	FRIENDLY USERS	GIGAGAB	SPEAK PC	TECHTALK	6	9	12	15	18
POSTER	BADENOV															
	CHEWBACCA															
	CYBORG															
	SKELETOR															
	SPEEDRACER															
MINUTES	6															
	9															
	12															
	15															
	18															
FORUM	CYBERCHAT															
	FRIENDLY USERS															
	GIGAGAB															
	SPEAK PC															
	TECHTALK															

LOGIC PROBLEM 310

The Quincy quintuplets are huge fans of *The Mummy*, so for their annual Halloween party, the five siblings decided to dress as mummies! They really did their homework, as each costume was designed in accordance with the mummification process of a different Egyptian dynasty (from earliest to latest, 17th, 18th, 19th, 20th, or 21st), although each person had used a different number of rolls (2, 3, 4, 5, or 6) of a different, conventional wrapping material to complete the ensemble. Even though each sibling suffered a different mishap (one person spilled punch on his or her costume), the Quincy siblings were definitely the life of the party! From the information provided, determine the dynasty from which each mummy costume was modeled, the number of rolls of wrapping used for each, and the incident that befell each make-believe mummy.

1. The sibling who used two rolls of paper towels for his or her costume purported to be a mummy from a later dynasty than the person whose six rolls of wrapping somehow got caught in a door (who wasn't the person covered in shelf paper).

2. The person who was wrapped in masking tape had the embarrassing dilemma of being stuck to the wall. The person wrapped in gauze wasn't emulating the mummification process of the 17th dynasty.

3. The sibling who began to unravel in the middle of the party (who was dressed as an 18th-dynasty mummy) used more rolls of his or her wrapping than the person covered in crepe paper.

4. The 19th-dynasty mummy was composed of fewer rolls of wrapping than the person who was bound so tightly that he or she was unable to sit down.

		ROLLS					WRAPPING					INCIDENT				
		2	3	4	5	6	CREPE PAPER	GAUZE	MASKING TAPE	PAPER TOWELS	SHELF PAPER	CAUGHT IN DOOR	COULDN'T SIT	SPILLED PUNCH	STUCK TO WALL	UNRAVELED
DYNASTY	17th															
	18th															
	19th															
	20th															
	21st															
INCIDENT	CAUGHT IN DOOR															
	COULDN'T SIT															
	SPILLED PUNCH															
	STUCK TO WALL															
	UNRAVELED															
WRAPPING	CREPE PAPER															
	GAUZE															
	MASKING TAPE															
	PAPER TOWELS															
	SHELF PAPER															

Dirk Hanson is one of Broadway's most prolific actors—in the last seven years, he has starred in five different Broadway productions. He took over the role in each play on a different date and ended each run on a different date. From the information provided, determine the date on which each of Dirk's last five plays began (January 17, March 20, April 14, June 10, or June 23) and ended its run (January 10, January 20, February 23, March 14, or April 17).

1. Dirk's time in *Les Terribles* (which didn't begin or end on the 20th of any month) has no starting or ending date or starting or ending month in common with his time in *North Atlantic*.

2. Dirk's run in *North Atlantic* has exactly one date or month in common with his time starring in *Man of the Year*.

3. Dirk's time in *Monsieur Dragonfly* either began or ended in April. His *North Atlantic* run either began or ended on the 10th. *Cattle* is not the play Dirk left on the 17th.

4. One of Dirk's runs began on June 23 and ended on January 20, but this was not the time he spent starring in *Cattle*.

		DATE BEGAN					DATE ENDED				
		JANUARY 17	MARCH 20	APRIL 14	JUNE 10	JUNE 23	JANUARY 10	JANUARY 20	FEBRUARY 23	MARCH 14	APRIL 17
PLAY	CATTLE										
	LES TERRIBLES										
	MAN OF THE YEAR										
	M. DRAGONFLY										
	NORTH ATLANTIC										
DATE ENDED	JANUARY 10										
	JANUARY 20										
	FEBRUARY 23										
	MARCH 14										
	APRIL 17										

LOGIC PROBLEM 312

Priscilla Paisley was excited to get the galleys for her new guidebook *Islands in the Sun*. After going through the first five chapters, each of which describes a different island (exactly two of which—Maui and Oahu—are Hawaiian), she noticed that each was coded for proofreading with a with a different color (two of which—aqua and indigo—have a blue tint, two of which—rust and scarlet—have a red tint, and one of which—saffron—has a yellow tint). She called her editor and learned that each chapter was proofread by a different person. From the information provided, determine the island (one is New Zealand) described in each chapter (first through fifth), the proofreader who reviewed each chapter, and the color by which it was coded.

1. Both the first chapter (which wasn't coded indigo) and the second chapter describe Hawaiian islands.

2. The chapter proofread by Mr. Chaney (which is coded with a blue-tinted color) is exactly two chapters after the one proofread by Ms. Wolfe.

3. Of the two chapters describing Hawaii, one was proofread by Mr. Marcotte, and the other was coded scarlet.

4. Of the two chapters coded with a red-tinted color, one describes Jamaica, and the other discusses Maui.

5. The chapter proofread by Ms. Fehr, which isn't the one describing Tahiti, comes earlier in the manuscript than the one proofread by Mr. Vachon (which wasn't coded saffron).

6. Both the first chapter and the fourth chapter are coded with blue-tinted color.

		FIRST	SECOND	THIRD	FOURTH	FIFTH	MR. CHANEY	MS. FEHR	MR. MARCOTTE	MR. VACHON	MS. WOLFE	AQUA	INDIGO	RUST	SAFFRON	SCARLET
		CHAPTER					LAST NAME					COLOR				
ISLAND	JAMAICA															
	MAUI															
	NEW ZEALAND															
	OAHU															
	TAHITI															
COLOR	AQUA															
	INDIGO															
	RUST															
	SAFFRON															
	SCARLET															
LAST NAME	MR. CHANEY															
	MS. FEHR															
	MR. MARCOTTE															
	MR. VACHON															
	MS. WOLFE															

LOGIC PROBLEM 313

Last night was Stanley's first night as a security guard at the prestigious Egyptian Historical Museum. He noticed five employees, each of whom left a different number of minutes late, were carrying rather large packages. Eager to help, he offered his assistance to each person, each of whom gladly gave Stanley his or her package, no two of which were the same. The grateful employees (including a tour guide) led Stanley to their vehicles. Each employee owns a different vehicle (one is a station wagon). From the information provided, determine how many minutes late (15, 20, 30, 35, or 40) each employee left, the object each was carrying, and the vehicle each owns.

1. The employee who drives the pickup truck left exactly 10 minutes after the preparator but at some point before the one who was bringing home a bag of dirty laundry.

2. The one who owns a sedan left earlier than the employee transporting a collection of souvenir museum posters but later than the employee who had an armful of groceries.

3. The one who was transporting a rolled-up Oriental rug (who isn't the registrar) left exactly 20 minutes later than the conservator.

4. The designer left earlier than the employee who drives the Jeep. The employee who owns the van was the last to leave.

		CONSERVATOR	DESIGNER	PREPARATOR	REGISTRAR	TOUR GUIDE	GROCERIES	LAUNDRY BAG	POSTERS	RUB	TREE	JEEP	PICKUP TRUCK	SEDAN	STATION WAGON	VAN
MINUTES	15															
	20															
	30															
	35															
	40															
VEHICLE	JEEP															
	PICKUP TRUCK															
	SEDAN															
	STATION WAGON															
	VAN															
OBJECT	GROCERIES															
	LAUNDRY BAG															
	POSTERS															
	RUB															
	TREE															

LOGIC PROBLEM 314 EDITORIAL EXCHANGES

Five of the fine editors at Penny Press (three of whom—Alex, Pete, and Troy—are men, and two of whom—Michaela and Sara—are women) not only love their jobs but also enjoy creating puzzles in their spare time! Each editor creates two of five different types of puzzle (crosswords, crostics, fill-ins, logic problems, and word seeks), neither of which is the type used in the publication he or she edits at work (no two edit the same publication). Each type of puzzle is created by exactly two people. From the information provided, determine the two types of puzzle each editor creates in his or her spare time, as well as the publication (one is *Puzzler's Choice Crostics*) each edits.

1. Alex (who doesn't create logic problems or fill-ins) isn't the one who edits *Favorite Fill-In Puzzles*.

2. The woman who edits *Original Logic Problems* creates word seeks in her spare time.

3. Michaela (who edits *Quick & Easy Crosswords*) doesn't edit puzzles of the type created by either Troy or Sara. Both Sara and Troy provide Pete (who doesn't create logic problems) with the type of puzzle he uses in his publication.

4. Between them, the editors of *All-Star Word Seek Puzzles* and *Favorite Fill-In Puzzles* create four of the five types of puzzle.

		PUZZLES					PUBLICATION				
		CROSSWORDS	CROSTICS	FILL-INS	LOGICS	WORD SEEKS	ALL-STAR WORD SEEK PUZZLES	FAVORITE FILL-IN PUZZLES	ORIGINAL LOGIC PROBLEMS	PUZZLER'S CHOICE	QUICK & EASY CROSSWORDS
EDITOR	ALEX										
	MICHAELA										
	PETE										
	SARA										
	TROY										
PUBLICATION	ALL-STAR WORD										
	FAVORITE FILL-IN										
	ORIGINAL LOGIC										
	PUZZLER'S CHOICE										
	QUICK & EASY										

LOGIC PROBLEM 315

This Christmas, six couples who live on Bergen Street thought it would be fun to form a "Secret Santa" gift exchange. Each couple drew the name of a different couple from a hat and purchased a different gift for that couple. As it turned out, no couple received a gift from the couple for whom they had bought a gift, and no couple pulled their own name out of the hat. From the information provided, determine, for each couple, the gift they bought and the couple to whom it was given.

1. The Dales gave the computer game to the couple who purchased a gift for the Carneys. The Ashes gave a present to the couple who bought a present for the couple who gave the flowerpot.

2. The Brooks received a gift from the couple who received the picture frame. The Edens gave a gift to the couple who purchased a gift for the ones who gave the stationery.

3. The couple who gave the coffee mugs received a gift from the couple who received a gift from the Fosters. The ones who received the scented candles gave a gift to the Dales.

4. The Carneys gave a gift to the couple who bought a gift for the ones who gave a gift to the Ashes. The couple who received the flowerpot purchased a gift for the Fosters.

		COFFEE MUGS	COMPUTER GAME	FLOWERPOT	PICTURE FRAME	SCENTED CANDLES	STATIONERY	ASHES	BROOKS	CARNEYS	DALES	EDENS	FOSTERS
		GIFT						GIVEN TO					
COUPLE	ASHES												
	BROOKS												
	CARNEYS												
	DALES												
	EDENS												
	FOSTERS												
GIVEN TO	ASHES												
	BROOKS												
	CARNEYS												
	DALES												
	EDENS												
	FOSTERS												

LOGIC PROBLEM 316   MUMMY DEAREST

In the course of researching information about ancient Egypt for my senior thesis, I found five local archaeologists who are equally as fascinated with that subject. Each person has conducted extensive research on the history of a different Egyptian ruler (from latest to earliest reign, Amenhotep I, Thutmose I, Hatshepsut, Akhenaton, or Tutankhamun). Last year, each visited a number of prestigious colleges and universities and gave a different number of lectures (11, 13, 15, 18, or 21) on his or her favorite subject. In addition, each archaeologist has created a pamphlet of a different number of pages (3, 4, 5, 7, or 8) explaining in greater detail the highlights of the lecture. From the information provided, determine the number of lectures each archaeologist gave on his or her favorite Egyptian ruler and the number of pages in each person's pamphlet.

1. Mr. Franks gave exactly 2 fewer lectures than the one who wrote the five-page pamphlet but more lectures than the person who spoke about Tutankhamun.

2. One archaeologist gave 11 lectures on the Egyptian ruler who had the next earlier reign than the ruler studied by Mr. Ahrens.

3. The pamphlet highlighting the lecture on Thutmose I is exactly one page longer than the one created by Ms. Phillips.

4. The archaeologist who extensively researched the life of Akhenaton gave fewer lectures than Ms. Randal.

5. The pamphlet created by Mr. Ahrens is exactly one page shorter than the one featuring the Egyptian ruler who had the next earlier reign than the ruler studied by Mr. Turner (who gave more lectures than the archaeologist who lectured on Hatshepsut).

		RULER					LECTURES					PAGES				
		TUTANKHAMUN	AKHENATON	HATSHEPSUT	THUTMOSE I	AMENHOTEP I	11	13	15	18	21	3	4	5	7	8
CURATOR	MR. AHRENS															
	MR. FRANKS															
	MS. PHILLIPS															
	MS. RANDAL															
	MR. TURNER															
PAGES	3															
	4															
	5															
	7															
	8															
LECTURES	11															
	13															
	15															
	18															
	21															

LOGIC PROBLEM 317

Last Saturday, Armando and five of his friends (three of whom—Belinda, Josie, and Marcia—are women, and two of whom—David and Scott—are men) met at the Bowville Archery Range for target practice. Each archer took three practice shots, and each got a different total score. Scores are determined by the area in which each arrow lands: hitting the gold area in the center, or bull's-eye, is worth nine points, an arrow landing in the red ring around it is worth seven points, one hitting the blue area surrounding that is worth five points, a dart in the black ring is worth three points, one landing in the white area is worth one point, and an arrow landing in the green area, or apron, is worth zero points. Each person's arrows were marked with a different one of the six target colors so that they could be distinguished from those of the other archers. From the information provided, determine the color of the markings on each archer's arrows and the number of points (0, 1, 3, 5, 7, or 9) each scored for each of his or her three practice shots.

1. None of the archers hit the target in the area whose color corresponds to that of the markings on his or her arrows.

2. The only archer who hit the same colored area on the target more than once isn't the person who scored exactly 21 points. Josie, who scored exactly 8 points, has gold markings on her arrows.

3. David's total score was exactly 3 points higher than that of one of his friends but exactly 3 points lower than that earned by yet another of his companions.

4. The only three archers who hit the red area of the target are Belinda, the man who has blue markings on his arrows, and the one whose total score was exactly 15 points.

5. Scott has white markings on his arrows. One archer had a total score of exactly 14 points.

6. The total score of the woman who has black markings on her arrows was exactly 2 points higher than Marcia's total score.

7. Between them, the archers with the red markings and the green markings on their arrows scored three of the four total bull's-eyes.

| | | COLOR | | | | | | POINTS | | | | | |
		BLACK	BLUE	GOLD	GREEN	RED	WHITE	0	1	3	5	7	9
ARCHER	ARMANDO												
	BELINDA												
	DAVID												
	JOSIE												
	MARCIA												
	SCOTT												
POINTS	0												
	1												
	3												
	5												
	7												
	9												

LOGIC PROBLEM 318   BUMPER-TO-BUMPER

Since retro clothes and the music of the '60s and '70s have made such a comeback in recent years, the Gilded Age Nicknacks Company is now attempting to reproduce that success by marketing the fads of the '40s and '50s—including bumper stickers. After receiving their catalog, each of five residents of Marmalade Way (including Mr. McGregor) immediately ordered a replica of a different bumper sticker. When their new automobile adornments finally arrived, each resident affixed the new bumper sticker to his or her car in a different location (one placed the new sticker on the front bumper). From the information provided, can you determine the house (from west to east, 101, 103, 105, 107, or 109) of the person who ordered each bumper sticker, as well as the location on the car each placed his or her new sticker?

1. The house owned by the person who placed his or her new sticker on the left rear bumper of his or her car is somewhere to the west of Ms. Dryden's house. Ms. Laing's house is somewhere to the east of the house owned by the person who placed his or her new sticker on the trunk of his or her car.
2. The house owned by the person who ordered the "Forward with President Truman—No Retreat" bumper sticker is somewhere to the east of Mr. Quon's house.
3. The house owned by the person who placed his or her new bumper sticker on the right rear bumper of his or her car is somewhere to the west of the house owned by the one who ordered the "I Like Ike" bumper sticker.
4. Mr. Quon's house is somewhere to the east of the house owned by the one who ordered the original "School's Open, Drive Slowly" bumper sticker. The house owned by the person who placed his or her new sticker on the right rear bumper of his or her car is somewhere to the east of Ms. Laing's house.
5. The one who lives in house 101, who isn't Ms. Nightingale, isn't the one who ordered the "Phooey on Dewey" bumper sticker.
6. The house whose owner placed his or her new sticker on the rear window of his or her car (who isn't the one who ordered the "Think! Prevent Wallacitis" bumper sticker) is somewhere to the west of the house owned by the one who ordered the "School's Open, Drive Slowly" bumper sticker.

		PERSON					BUMPER STICKER					LOCATION				
		MS. DRYDEN	MS. LAING	MR. MCGREGOR	MS. NIGHTINGALE	MR. QUON	FORWARD WITH PRESIDENT	I LIKE IKE	PHOOEY ON DEWEY	SCHOOL'S OPEN, DRIVE SLOWLY	THINK! PREVENT WALLACITIS	FRONT BUMPER	LEFT REAR BUMPER	REAR WINDOW	RIGHT REAR BUMPER	TRUNK
HOUSE	101															
HOUSE	103															
HOUSE	105															
HOUSE	107															
HOUSE	109															
LOCATION	FRONT BUMPER															
LOCATION	LEFT REAR															
LOCATION	REAR WINDOW															
LOCATION	RIGHT REAR															
LOCATION	TRUNK															
STICKER	FORWARD WITH															
STICKER	I LIKE IKE															
STICKER	PHOOEY ON															
STICKER	SCHOOL'S OPEN															
STICKER	THINK! PREVENT															

On the day before Halloween last year, the Wrap It Up gift shop closed early so the employees could gather for an office party. Each of the five employees clocked out at a different time (2:00, 2:15, 2:30, 2:40, or 2:55 p.m.). While running errands for the party, each person visited a different DVD-rental store to return a different one of five mummy movies. While there, he or she also rented a different movie that one of the other four had returned. From the information provided, determine the time each employee clocked out to go to each DVD store, the movie each returned, and the one each rented.

1. The person who visited Video Venture clocked out at some point after (but not immediately after) the employee who rented *Abbott and Costello Meet the Mummy* but at some point before the one who rented *The Mummy's Hand*.

2. The person who trekked to Movie Hut (who clocked out after at least one other worker) isn't the employee who rented *The Mummy's Curse* (who isn't the one who returned *The Mummy's Shroud* to Rentarama).

3. The one who rented *The Mummy's Shroud* left work at some point before the employee who went to Discount Video but at some point after the person who returned *Dawn of the Mummy*.

4. The employee who went to Chart Topper (who didn't rent *The Mummy's Curse*) clocked out at some point after the one who returned *Dawn of the Mummy*.

5. The employee who returned *The Mummy's Curse* left work exactly 25 minutes after the person who rented *Dawn of the Mummy*.

		STORE					RETURNED					RENTED				
		CHART TOPPER	DISCOUNT VIDEO	MOVIE HUT	RENTARAMA	VIDEO VENTURE	ABBOTT & COSTELLO MEET	DAWN OF THE MUMMY	THE MUMMY'S CURSE	THE MUMMY'S HAND	THE MUMMY'S SHROUD	ABBOTT & COSTELLO MEET	DAWN OF THE MUMMY	THE MUMMY'S CURSE	THE MUMMY'S HAND	THE MUMMY'S SHROUD
TIME	2:00															
	2:15															
	2:30															
	2:40															
	2:55															
RENTED	ABBOTT & COST.															
	DAWN OF THE															
	MUMMY'S CURSE															
	MUMMY'S HAND															
	MUMMY'S SHROUD															
RETURNED	ABBOTT & COST.															
	DAWN OF THE															
	MUMMY'S CURSE															
	MUMMY'S HAND															
	MUMMY'S SHROUD															

ANSWERS

LOGIC PROBLEM 1

Times are 11:00 a.m., 11:00 a.m., 12:00 p.m., 4:00 p.m., and 7:00 p.m. (intro.). Eva isn't 7:00 [Bert (3)]; she's 4:00, so orange is 7:00 (1). Dan isn't 11:00 [earliest] (2); Ann and Cal are [only left], so Ann is black cherry (1). Dan's 12:00 [lemon-lime (3)]. Cal [11:00 [earliest]] isn't root beer (2); he's cola. Eva's root beer.

In summary:
11:00 a.m., Ann, black cherry
11:00 a.m., Cal, cola
12:00 p.m., Dan, lemon-lime
4:00 p.m., Eva, root beer
7:00 p.m., Bert, orange

LOGIC PROBLEM 2

Sidney [Sweden (1)] isn't Sally (1), Tess [Turkey (1)], Jane [Jim (2)], or Marj [Malta (2)]; he's Doris. Pete [Poland (3)] isn't Marj [Malta] or Tess [Turkey]; he's Sally. Morris isn't Marj (2); he's Tess. John's Marj. Jim's Spain.

In summary:
Doris, Sidney, Sweden
Jane, Jim, Spain
Marj, John, Malta
Sally, Pete, Poland
Tess, Morris, Turkey

LOGIC PROBLEM 3

Women are Ally and Brenda, and men are Clark, Larry, and Perry (intro.). Ms. Witt [St. Thomas (1)] (1) isn't Brenda [Eckert (2)]; she's Ally. Mr. Godwin isn't Perry or Larry [Antigua (3)] (1); he's Clark. Larry isn't Shelton (3); he's Malone. Perry's Shelton. Barbados isn't Brenda or Perry (2); it's Clark. St. Lucia isn't Perry (1); it's Brenda. Perry's Jamaica.

In summary:
Ally Witt, St. Thomas
Brenda Eckert, St. Lucia
Clark Godwin, Barbados
Larry Malone, Antigua
Perry Shelton, Jamaica

LOGIC PROBLEM 4

Ross isn't Kona, Kenya AA (1), house [Joey (2)], or Arabica [Monica (3)]; he's Colombian. Phoebe isn't Kona (1); she's Kenya AA. Chandler's Kona. Ross isn't cream and 1 sugar (1), cream only (2), black [Chandler (2)], or cream and 2 sugars [Monica (3)]; he's sugar only. Phoebe isn't cream and 1 sugar (3); she's cream only. Joey's cream and 1 sugar.

In summary:
Chandler, Kona, black
Joey, house blend, cream & 1 sugar
Monica, Arabica, cream & 2 sugars
Phoebe, Kenya AA, cream only
Ross, Colombian, sugar only

LOGIC PROBLEM 5

Wks. are 4, 5, 6, 7, and 8 (intro.). Val is 8, and Outward Bound is 4 (2). Sandy isn't 4, 5, or 7 (3); she's 6, so Yale's 7, and science camp's 8 (3). Yale isn't scout camp (3); he's music camp (1). Wallis isn't 4 (2); he's 5, so is scout camp (1). Tim's Outward Bound. Sandy's art classes.

In summary:
Sandy, art classes, 6
Tim, Outward Bound, 4
Val, science camp, 8
Wallis, Scout camp, 5
Yale, music camp, 7

LOGIC PROBLEM 6

One had cake (intro.), 2 had ice cream, and 2 had pie (2). Dog and garbage aren't ice cream (2); they're pie (3). Pie isn't Sam or Wilt (3); it's Babs and Pat (2). Pat isn't garbage (3); he's dog. Babs is garbage. Ice cream is dishes and porch (2). Dishes aren't Chris or Wilt (1); they're Sam. Porch isn't Wilt (1); it's Chris. Wilt is newspapers and cake.

In summary:
Babs, garbage, pie
Chris, porch, ice cream
Pat, dog, pie
Sam, dishes, ice cream
Wilt, newspapers, cake

LOGIC PROBLEM 7

Cole [Saturn (2)] isn't arts & crafts (1), drama [Tricia (2)], horseback riding [Ford (2)], or swimming (3); he's gymnastics. Swimming isn't Mazda or Volvo (3); it's Saab. Drama [Tricia] isn't Mazda (1); it's Volvo. Arts & crafts is Mazda, so isn't Allie or Lauren (1); it's Justin. Lauren isn't horseback riding (3); she's swimming. Allie's horseback riding.

In summary:
Allie, horseback riding, Ford
Cole, gymnastics, Saturn
Justin, arts & crafts, Mazda
Lauren, swimming, Saab
Tricia, drama, Volvo

LOGIC PROBLEM 8

Weekdays are Mon.-Fri., and times are 10:05, 10:07, 10:10, 10:13, and 10:15 (intro.). 10:13 isn't Mon. [1st], Tue., Fri. (1), or Wed. [no 10:11] (2); it's Thu., so cuttlebone's Tue. (1). Mon. isn't food dish [Fri. (1)], swing, or mirror (2); it's perch. Wed. isn't swing (2); it's mirror. Thu. [10:13] is swing, so Wed. is 10:15 (2). 10:05 isn't Tue. or Mon. [perch] (3); it's Fri. 10:07 isn't Mon. [perch] (2); it's Tue. 10:10 is Mon.

In summary:
Mon., 10:10, perch
Tue., 10:07, cuttlebone
Wed., 10:15, mirror
Thu., 10:13, swing
Fri., 10:05, food dish

LOGIC PROBLEM 9

Sol isn't yellow [Reggie (1)], blue, orange (2), or pink [Zach Acker (2)]; she's red. Tabi isn't blue (3); she's orange. Mindy's blue. Reggie isn't Sorkin, Hamilton (1), or Vernon (3); he's Mason. Tabi isn't Sorkin or Vernon (3); she's Hamilton. Sol isn't Sorkin (1); she's Vernon. Mindy's Sorkin.

In summary:
Mindy Sorkin, blue
Reggie Mason, yellow
Sol Vernon, red
Tabi Hamilton, orange
Zach Acker, pink

LOGIC PROBLEM 10

Sizes are 5, 5½, 6, 6½, and 7 (intro.). Oval [size 7 (1)] isn't Suzanne [size 5½ (1)], Gemma, Karen (2), or Margot [emerald (3)]; it's Beth. Marquise isn't Gemma or Karen (2); it's Suzanne. Brilliant isn't Karen (3); it's Gemma. Karen's pear, so isn't size 5 or 6 (2); she's size 6½. Margot isn't size 5 (3); she's size 6. Gemma's size 5.

In summary:
Beth, 7, oval
Gemma, 5, brilliant
Karen, 6½, pear
Margot, 6, emerald
Suzanne, 5½, marquise

LOGIC PROBLEM 11

Parcel post isn't 3rd [Celia, express (1)], 1st, 5th (2), or 4th [priority (3)]; it's 2nd, so Sara's 1st (2). 4th isn't Garrett [5th (2)] or Matt (3); it's Simon. Matt's 2nd. Garrett isn't 1st class (2); he's 3rd class. Sara's 1st class.

In summary:
1st, Sara, 1st class
2nd, Matt, parcel post
3rd, Celia, express
4th, Simon, priority
5th, Garrett, 3rd class

LOGIC PROBLEM 12

Women are Annie, Caitlin, and Marie, and men are Ben and Cole (intro.). Man who chose green isn't Cole Johnson (1); he's Ben. Cole Johnson isn't red (2), purple [Beech (2)], or yellow (3); he's blue. Marie isn't purple or red (2); she's yellow. Annie isn't purple (3); she's red. Caitlin's purple. Summers isn't Annie or Marie (1); he's Ben. Marie [yellow] isn't Ward (3); she's Hasmond. Annie's Ward.

In summary:
Annie Ward, red
Ben Summers, green
Caitlin Beech, purple
Cole Johnson, blue
Marie Hasmond, yellow

LOGIC PROBLEM 13

Amts. are $5-$9 (intro.). Stimson isn't $6, $9 (1), $7, or $8 (2); he's $5, so Waverly's $7, and Stimson's furniture painted (3). Carlson isn't $6 or $9 (1); he's $8, and isn't sweep garage (1), mow lawn (2), or wax car (4), so he's clean pool. $9 isn't garage (1) or car (4); it's lawn. $6 isn't garage (1); it's car. $7 is garage. Babcock isn't lawn (2); Greer is. Babcock's car.

In summary:
Babcock, car, $6
Carlson, pool, $8
Greer, lawn, $9
Stimson, furniture, $5
Waverly, garage, $7

LOGIC PROBLEM 14

Final scores are 43, 47, 52, 55, and 59 (intro.). Alberta [score 55 (4)] isn't goldfish pond [Irving (2)], covered bridge [score 43 (3)], windmill (4), or farmhouse [Deborah (5)]; she's 2-level hole. Gretchen [score 52 (1)] isn't bridge [score 43]; she's windmill. Chase's bridge. Deborah's score isn't 59 (5); it's 47. Irving's score is 59.

In summary:
Alberta, 2-level, 55
Chase, covered bridge, 43
Deborah, farmhouse, 47
Gretchen, windmill, 52
Irving, goldfish pond, 59

LOGIC PROBLEM 15

Bartolio fruit isn't 1st, 2nd (1), or 4th (4); it's 3rd, so Quirko's 1st, Distiana's 2nd (1), and Nexdour's 4th [last] (4), so Nodum's 2nd [only left before fruit [3rd]] (4). Asleo isn't 4th (2); he's 3rd, so water's 4th [last] (2). Mauli's 4th. Seeds aren't 1st (3); they're 2nd, so Farlu's 1st (3). Oil's 1st. Awavy's 3rd.

In summary:

Asleo, Awavy, bartolio fruit, 3rd

Mauli, Nexdour, klink water, 4th

Nodum, Distiana, germaine seeds, 2nd

Quirko, Farlu, Luxa oil, 1st

LOGIC PROBLEM 16

Riley isn't Nip-It [model car [Mayer (6)] (5)]; he's 10 free pinball games, and Harry's Nip-It (2). Duane [puzzle (1)] isn't Xenon (1), Black Knight [Scott (3)] (3), or Mousetrap [stickers (5)]; he's Funhouse [Burns (4)]. Scott [Black Knight] isn't stickers [Mousetrap]; he's cards. Collins is stickers. Riley's Xenon. Scott isn't Brian or Wade (3); he's Jason. Brian isn't stickers (5); Wade is. Brian's free games.

In summary:

Brian Riley, Xenon, free games

Duane Burns, Funhouse, jigsaw puzzle

Harry Mayer, Nip-It, model car

Jason Scott, Black Knight, baseball cards

Wade Collins, Mousetrap, stickers

LOGIC PROBLEM 17

Dugout isn't Evelyn, Mary Anne (1), Karen, or Alice (3); it's Carolyn. Quilted isn't Evelyn, Mary Anne, Carolyn (1), or Alice (6); it's Karen, so she used hearth crane, and Mary Anne made syrup (2). Candle-dipping isn't Alice (6) or Evelyn (7); it's Carolyn. Wool spinning isn't Evelyn (7); it's Alice. Evelyn made soap. Sod isn't Evelyn, Mary Anne, or Karen [quilted] (1); it's Alice. Cave isn't Evelyn or Mary Anne (7); it's Karen. Mary Anne [syrup] isn't bark hut (4); Evelyn is. Mary Anne's log cabin. Loom-user isn't Alice, Carolyn [dugout], or Evelyn [soap] (3); it's Mary Anne. Evelyn [bark, soap] isn't spinning wheel (4) or hominy block (5); she's spider. Carolyn [candle] isn't hominy block (5); Alice is. Carolyn's spinning wheel.

In summary:

Alice, sod house, hominy block, wool-spinning

Carolyn, dugout, spinning wheel, candle-dipping

Evelyn, bark hut, spider, soap-making

Karen, cave, hearth crane, quilting

Mary Anne, log cabin, loom, syrup making

LOGIC PROBLEM 18

Pounds were 20, 25, 30, 40, and 50 (intro.). Between them, ones with Yellow and Red Delicious picked 45 lbs. (5), so one picked 25 lbs. and the other 20 [only possible], but ones with Red Delicious didn't pick 20 lbs. (6); they picked 25 lbs., so ones with Yellow Delicious picked 20 lbs. (above), and Hancocks picked 20 lbs. [fewest] (6), so ones with Granny Smith picked 40 lbs. (2), Franklins picked Red Delicious, and Hancocks [Yellow Delicious] are going to bake apples (5). Franklins [25 lbs., Red Delicious] are going to make apple pie [only possible in (1)]. Gradys [red (1)] didn't pick 30 (1) or 40 lbs. [Granny Smith [green (2)]]; they picked 50 lbs. Judsons picked fewer lb. than ones who were going to make apple crisp, who picked fewer than ones with McIntosh (4), so Judsons didn't pick 40 lbs. [only fewer than 50 lbs.]; they picked 30 lbs., so ones going to make apple crisp picked 40 lbs., and ones with McIntosh picked 50 lbs [most] (above). Irvings picked 40 lbs. 30 lbs. of Empire were picked. Between them, Irvings [40 lbs.] and ones who are going to make apple coffeecake picked 70 lb. (3); ones who were going to make coffeecake picked 30 lbs. Gradys [50 lbs.] are going to make applesauce.

In summary:

Franklin, Red Delicious, 25, apple pie

Grady, McIntosh, 50, applesauce

Hancock, Yellow Delicious, 20, baked apples

Irving, Granny Smith, 40, apple crisp

Judson, Empire, 30, apple coffeecake

LOGIC PROBLEM 19

Doughnuts are 6, 12, 18, 24, and 36 (intro.). 6 doughnuts [least] isn't basket (1), gourds (2), wreath (3), or corn (7); it's mums. 12 doughnuts [more than only 6 doughnuts] isn't gourds (2), wreath [no 4 doughnuts] (3), or corn (7); it's basket, so Hubbard squash is 6 doughnuts (1). Ones with red apples [Franklins [Red Delicious], Gradys [McIntosh], and Judsons [Empire] (part 1)] ate a total of 54 doughnuts, and 1 ate 6 doughnuts [Hubbard squash], and another ate 12 doughnuts [basket] (1); the 3rd ate 36 doughnuts [54 [total] − 6 [Hubbard squash] − 12 [basket] = 36]. 18 doughnuts isn't gourds [more than Irvings [Granny Smith (part 1)], who are more than butternut squash (2), who didn't buy 6 doughnuts [Hubbard]] or corn [total of Franklins [Red Delicious] and Hancocks [Yellow Delicious (part 1)] (7), but Hancocks not 6 or 12 doughnuts [red (above)]]; it's wreath. Franklins [apple pie (part 1)] ate 6 doughnuts (3). Gradys [McIntosh, 50 lbs. [most] (part 1)] didn't eat

331

36 doughnuts (5); Judsons [Empire] did, so Gradys ate 12 doughnuts (above). Judsons [36 doughnuts] aren't butternut (2), spaghetti, or zucchini (6); they're acorn squash. Corn isn't 36 doughnuts [acorn] (7); it's 24 doughnuts. Gourds is 36 doughnuts. Hancocks [Yellow Delicious] didn't eat 24 doughnuts [corn] (7); they ate 18 doughnuts. Irvings ate 24 doughnuts. Irvings [Granny Smith, apple crisp (part 1)] aren't butternut (2) or zucchini (4); they're spaghetti. Hancocks [18 doughnuts] aren't zucchini (6); Gradys are. Hancocks are butternut.

In summary:
Franklin, 6, Hubbard, mums
Grady, 12, zucchini, basket
Hancock, 18, butternut, straw wreath
Irving, 24, spaghetti, Indian corn
Judson, 36, acorn, gourds

LOGIC PROBLEM 20

Women are Allison and Lori, and men are Bruno and Dexter (intro.). Dexter isn't 1st (4); he's 4th (1), so Bruno's 1st (1), and 7 yrs. old is 3rd [only possible in (4)], so Allison's 2nd, so radio's 1st (4). Lori's 3rd, and isn't newspaper or TV (2); she's magazine. Dexter [4th] isn't newspaper (3); Allison is. Dexter's TV. "Leon" isn't Dexter [4th] or Allison [newspaper] (3); it's Bruno. Allison [newspaper] isn't major in physical education (3); Dexter is. Allison's West Point.

In summary:
1st, Bruno, radio, Leon
2nd, Allison, newspaper, West Point
3rd, Lori, magazine, 7 years old
4th, Dexter, television, physical education

LOGIC PROBLEM 21

Weekdays are Mon.-Fri. (intro.) Mon. isn't Nesbitt (1), Townsend (4), Swartz (5), or Curie (6); it's Heath, and isn't Gladys (1), Ben (2), Mona (3), or Zelda (4), so is Roger. Mon. isn't stove & refrigerator (2), so Tue. isn't Nesbitt (1), Townsend (4), or Curie (6); it's Swartz. Floor waxed is Mon. (5). Fri. isn't Townsend (4) or Curie (6); it's Nesbitt, and isn't windows washed (1), patios washed (3), or floor waxed (5), so is garage cleaned. Ben's job is 2 before window washing (6), so Tue. or Wed., but not Wed. [Fri. garage]; Ben's job is Tue., Curie's Wed., and window washing's Thu. (6). Townsend's Thu.; Zelda's Fri. (4). Swartz [Ben] isn't stove & refrigerator cleaned (2); Curie is. Swartz is patios washed. Mona isn't wash windows (3); Gladys is. Mona's clean stove & refrigerator.

In summary:
Ben, Swartz, wash patios, Tue.
Gladys, Townsend, wash windows, Thu.
Mona, Curie, clean stove & refrigerator, Wed.
Roger, Heath, wax floors, Mon.
Zelda, Nesbitt, clean garage, Fri.

LOGIC PROBLEM 22

Fees are $420, $450, $480, $500, and $540 (intro.). $540 isn't fireplace (2), terrace (3), picture window (4), or cathedral ceiling (5); it's skylight. $500 isn't fireplace [lower than Sharon's, which isn't skylight (2)], window [lower than Contemporary, which isn't skylight (4)], or cathedral ceiling (5); it's terrace. Bryan's $540 [skylight] (3), and isn't Country French (1), Victorian (2), Art Deco (3), or Contemporary (4); it's Southwestern. $420 [lowest] isn't Rosalyn (1), Sharon (2), or Warren (5); it's Glen. Warren is lower than Art Deco but higher than cathedral ceiling, which isn't Glen [$420] (5); cathedral ceiling is $450, Warren's $480, and Art Deco's $500. Sharon [higher than 2 others (2)] is $500. Rosalyn's $450. Glen [$420] isn't fireplace (2); Warren is. Glen's window. Country French [lower than Rosalyn [$450] (1)] isn't Warren [$480] or Rosalyn (1); it's Glen. Warren [fireplace] isn't Victorian (2); Rosalyn is. Warren's Contemporary.

In summary:
Bryan, Southwestern, skylight, $540
Glen, Country French, picture window, $420
Rosalyn, Victorian, cathedral ceiling, $450
Sharon, Art Deco, terrace, $500
Warren, Contemporary, fireplace, $480

LOGIC PROBLEM 23

No one did both chores same night (intro.). Lance didn't cook Mon., Wed., Thu. (1), or Fri. [Vladimir (3)]; he cooked Tue. [fried chicken (3)] and cleaned Mon. [night one made hamburger (1)] (1). Calvin [cleaned night one made chicken fajitas (2)] didn't clean night Lance [fried chicken] cooked; he cooked night Lance cleaned [Mon.], and Christopher made chicken fajitas (4). Christopher [Calvin cleaned] didn't cook Wed. (1); Alonzo did. Christopher cooked Thu. Alonzo [cooked Wed.] didn't clean Wed. (intro.) or Tue. (5); Alonzo cleaned Fri. Christopher didn't clean Wed. (1); Vladimir did. Christopher cleaned Tue. Lasagna wasn't Fri. [Alonzo cleaned] (5); it were Wed. Chili was Fri.

In summary (day, cooked, cleaned up, entrée):
Mon., Calvin, Lance, cheeseburger
Tue., Lance, Christopher, fried chicken

Wed., Alonzo, Vladimir, lasagna
Thu., Christopher, Calvin, chicken fajitas
Fri., Vladimir, Alonzo, chili con carne

LOGIC PROBLEM 24

Yrs. are 1891-1895 (intro.). Horseback riders are 1891 or 1893 (3), but not 1893 [would have done horseshoe throwing, and potato-sack race ones would've worked 1892 (3), so parade ones would have worked 1891, Finches would have worked 1893, and ones who walked would have worked 1894 (4), so carriage ones would have been 1891, trolley ones would have been 1892, and Stoddards would have been 1893 [Finches] (1)]; horseback riders worked 1891, so are the Kings, and did dance (3). Ones who walked worked year after the Finches and 3 years after parade ones (4); parade ones worked 1892, Finches worked 1894, and ones who walked worked 1895. Carriage ones aren't 1892 [Stoddards would be 1894 [Finches] (1)]; they are 1893, so trolley ones are 1894, and Stoddards are 1895 (1). Wagon ones worked 1892, so Engels worked 1893, and ball-game ones worked 1894 (5). Beans worked 1892. Race ones didn't work 1895 (2); they worked 1893. Horseshoe ones worked 1895.

In summary:

1891, Kings, dance, horseback
1892, Beans, parade, wagon
1893, Engels, potato-sack race, carriage
1894, Finches, ball game, trolley
1895, Stoddards, horseshoe throwing, walked

LOGIC PROBLEM 25

Days off are Mon.-Fri., and yrs. are 5, 10, 15, 20, and 25 (intro.). Mon. isn't Bridget (1), Georgette (3), Paulette [Wed. (5)], or Fatima (6); she's Cherie. Cherie [Mon.] isn't Bigwigs (1), Worths [Georgette (3)], Van Snoots [Fri. (4)], or Moneypennys [Fatima (6)]; she's Bankses, so Georgette's Tue. (3). Paulette [Wed.] isn't Van Snoots [Fri.]; Bridget is. Paulette's Bigwigs. Fatima's Thu. Georgette's 10 yrs. fewer than Cherie [Banks] (3), so isn't 20 [no 30 yrs.], 5 [Fatima [Thu.] (2)], 25 [Bridget [Van Snoot]] or 15 yrs. [Bridget 25 yrs.]; she's 10 yrs., and Cherie's 20 yrs. (3). Paulette's 15 yrs.

In summary:

Bridget, Fri., Van Snoot, 25
Cherie, Mon., Banks, 20
Fatima, Thu., Moneypenny, 5
Georgette, Tue., Worth, 10
Paulette, Wed., Bigwig, 15

LOGIC PROBLEM 26

Mon. [1st] isn't 4 (1), 2, 6 (3), or 5 miles (4); it's 3 miles. 4 miles [woods (1)] is twig, and 2 miles is along beach (3). 5 miles [day after flower (4)] isn't around track [day after rock (2)] or through park (4); it's around the mall. 3 miles [Mon.] isn't around track (2); 6 miles is around the track, and 3 miles [Mon.] is through park, so picked flower is Tue., and 5 miles [mall] is Wed. (4). 2 miles, picked up rock, and around track are 3 consecutive days (2), so 2 miles isn't Thu. or Fri.; 2 miles [beach] is Tue., picked up rock's Wed., and around track [6 miles] is Thu. (2). Through woods [4 miles, twig] is Fri. Feather isn't Thu. [woods Fri.] (1); it's Mon. Robin's egg is Thu.

In summary:

Mon., park, 3, feather
Tue., beach, 2, flower
Wed., mall, 5, rock
Thu., track, 6, robin's egg
Fri., woods, 4, twig

LOGIC PROBLEM 27

Women are Annette, Cindy, Julie, Martha, and Paula, and men are Brad, David, Greg, Jason, and Nathan (intro.). Groom on 30th isn't Nathan (1), Brad (2), or Jason (3); he's David or Greg, but not David [Martha would be 23rd, and earrings would be 16th (5), so Brad would be 9th, Annette would be 16th, and brooch would be 23rd [only possible] (2), so Nathan and Julie [couple (1)] would be 2nd [only possible], so Jason would be 23rd, and handkerchief would be 30th [only possible] (3), so Cindy [pendant (2)] couldn't be 23rd [brooch], 30th [handkerchief], or 9th [Brad] (2), so couldn't be placed], so he's Greg. Annette [week before brooch, week after Brad (2)] isn't brooch (2) or handkerchief [week after Jason (3)]; she's earrings or veil, but not earrings [Martha [week after earrings, week before David (5)] would be brooch, Brad would be 2nd, Annette would be 9th, Martha would be 16th, and David would be 23rd (above), so Julie and Nathan [couple (above)] couldn't be placed (above)], so she's veil. Martha [week after earrings (5)] isn't brooch [week after Annette [veil] (2)] or earrings (5); she's handkerchief. Jason's bride [week before handkerchief [Martha] (3)] is earrings (5), so isn't Annette [veil], Cindy [pendant], or Martha [handkerchief]; she's Paula. Julie's brooch. Brad's bride isn't Annette (2) or Cindy (4); she's Martha. Jason and Paula [earrings] are the week before Martha and Brad [handkerchief] (3), who are the week before Annette [veil] (2) and David (5), who are the week before Julie and Nathan [brooch] (2);

333

Paula's 2nd, Martha's 9th, Annette's 16th, and Julie's 23rd (above). Cindy's 30th.

In summary:
Annette, May 16th, David, veil
Cindy, May 30th, Greg, pendant
Julie, May 23rd, Nathan, brooch
Martha, May 9th, Brad, handkerchief
Paula, May 2nd, Jason, earrings

LOGIC PROBLEM 28

Women are Cathy, Judy, and Rosa, men are Fred, Leo, Paul, and Tony, and fls. are 1st-7th (intro.). Five entered and exited as elevator rose and 2 as elevator dropped (intro.), for 7 people total; 1 person got on and 1 got off on each of the 7 fl. (intro.). Fred left as Paul entered, who left as Judy entered (5), so either all 3 went up, just Judy went down, or Paul and Judy went down, which isn't possible [one of 2 going down is Cathy (1)]; Judy went up or entered on 7th (1). Woman entered on 2nd fl. (4), but not Cathy [down 2 (1)] or Judy [after 2 others, so above 2nd, or at 7th (above)]; Rosa did [only woman left] [exited at 3rd (3)]. Cathy [down 2] didn't enter on the 7th, 6th (1), or 5th fl. [Rosa exited 3rd]; she entered on 4th or 3rd. Tony went up 2 fls. (2), so didn't enter on 7th, 6th, or 4th [would force exit on 6th, which isn't possible (2)]; he entered on 5th [exit on 7th (2)] or 3rd [exit 5th]. One who entered on 7th isn't Leo [1st (3)], Fred, Paul (above), Tony [5th or 3rd], or Cathy [4th or 3rd]; she is Judy. Paul exited on 7th (5). Tony [exit 7th or 5th] exited on 5th and entered on 3rd (above). Cathy [entered 3rd or 4th] entered on 4th and exited on 2nd (1). Fred entered before Paul (5); Fred entered on 5th and Paul on 6th. Fred exited on 6th (5). Leo [entered on 1st] exited on 4th [only other fl. left]. Judy exited on 1st.

In summary (person, entered, exited):
Cathy, 4th, 2nd
Fred, 5th, 6th
Judy, 7th, 1st
Leo, 1st, 4th
Paul, 6th, 7th
Rosa, 2nd, 3rd
Tony, 3rd, 5th

LOGIC PROBLEM 29

Men are Alex, Brian, Clint, Doug, and Evan, and women are Angie, Barbara, Carla, Dana, and Eileen (intro.). Five husbands are Alex, one who gave "S.W.A.K.", Eileen's (1), Clint [Angie (4)], and one who gave steamboat ride (4). Carla's "I'm Yours," and isn't Alex's wife (7); she's steamboat ride (above), and isn't married to Brian [New Orleans trip (6)] or

Doug (8), so Evan. Doug didn't give "S.W.A.K." (8); his wife is Eileen (above). Neither Alex nor Clint give "S.W.A.K." (above); Brian did (above), and isn't married to Barbara (3), so Dana. Alex is married to Barbara. Angie [Clint] isn't Alaskan excursion (2) or rafting trip [Barbara (5)]; she's golf weekend. Barbara [rafting] isn't "Luv U" (5) or "Hug Me" [Alaskan (2)]; she's "Be Mine." Angie [golf] isn't "Hug Me" [Alaskan]; Eileen is. Angie's "Luv U" heart.

In summary:
Alex & Barbara, "Be Mine," whitewater rafting
Brian & Dana, "S.W.A.K.," New Orleans Mardi Gras
Clint & Angie, "Luv U," golf weekend
Doug & Eileen, "Hug Me," Alaskan excursion
Evan & Carla, "I'm Yours," steamboat ride

LOGIC PROBLEM 30

Males are Hubert and Lucas, and females are Isabel, Julie, and Kirsten (intro.). There are 2 males (3), so 1 is father and 1 is son; there are 2 daughters [only possible (intro.)]. A male is truck (3); he's son, so is Lucas (5), so Hubert [only other male] is father, and has "DON'T LAUGH" bumper sticker (3). Lucas's truck is blue (6), but not navy (5) or delft (1); it's slate, and isn't "TEE TIME" (2), "RADIO ACTIVE" (5), or "I OWE, I OWE" (6); it's "TEAR ALONG." Delft [parent (1)] isn't Julie, Kirsten, Lucas (5), or Hubert ["DON'T LAUGH"] (6); it's Isabel, so she's "I OWE" (6). Kirsten's navy (6), and isn't "RADIO ACTIVE" (5); Julie is. Kirsten's "TEE TIME." Hubert isn't plum (2); he's cream. Julie's plum. Female sports car driver isn't Julie or Kirsten ["TEE TIME"] (2); she's Isabel. Compact car isn't Hubert [father] or Kirsten ["TEE TIME," so golf lover (2)] (4); it's Julie. Hubert [cream] isn't jeep (7); Kirsten is. Hubert's station wagon.

In summary:
Hubert, station wagon, cream, "DON'T LAUGH"
Isabel, sports car, delft blue, "I OWE, I OWE"
Julie, compact car, plum, "RADIO ACTIVE"
Kirsten, jeep, navy blue, "TEE TIME"
Lucas, truck, slate blue, "TEAR ALONG"

LOGIC PROBLEM 31

Men are Alex, Chad, Gary, John, and Mark, women are Belinda, Darlene, Hilda, Kathy, and Polly, and distances are 20, 40, 60, 80, and 100 mi. (intro.). 100 mi. isn't emerald & white (1), lime & ruby (2), cobalt & lavender (3), or ivory & sapphire (4); it's aqua & coral. 20 mi. isn't John (1), Gary (3), Alex (4), or Chad (5); it's Mark. 100 mi. isn't John (1), Alex [no 50 mi.] (4), or Chad (5); it's Gary. Belinda's twice as far as lime & ruby (2); she's 40 mi. or 80 mi., and lime & ruby is 20 mi. or 40 mi., respectively (2). Belinda [40 or 80 mi. (above)] isn't Mark [20 mi. [fewest]], Gary [100 mi., but no 50 mi.] (2), Alex [twice as far as ivory & sapphire (4)], or John (6); he's Chad. Alex's twice as far as ivory & sapphire (4); he went 40 mi. or 80 mi., and ivory & sapphire is 20 or 40 mi., respectively (4). Alex and Chad [Belinda] are 40 mi. and 80 mi., in some order (above). John isn't 40 or 80 mi. [Alex and Chad, in some order (above)]; he's 60 mi. Emerald & white is farther than John [60 mi.] (1); it's 80 mi. [only left farther than John]. Cobalt & lavender isn't 20 or 40 mi. [ivory & sapphire and lime & ruby, in some order (above)]; it's 60 mi. [John, only distance left]. Darlene [less than cobalt & lavender [60 mi.]] isn't aqua & coral [100 mi.], cobalt & lavender [60 mi.], emerald & white [80 mi.], or lime & ruby (3); it's ivory & sapphire. Hilda [less than John [60 mi.]] isn't aqua & coral [100 mi.], cobalt & lavender [60 mi.], or emerald & white [80 mi.]; it's lime & ruby. Darlene [ivory & sapphire] isn't Gary [aqua & coral], John [cobalt & lavender], or Alex (4); she's Mark. Alex [twice as far as ivory & sapphire [20 mi.] (4)] is 40 mi. Chad and Belinda are 80 mi. [emerald & white], and lime & ruby [Hilda] is 40 mi. [Alex] (2). Kathy's 20 mi. farther than Chad [80 mi.] (5); she's 100 mi. Polly's 60 mi.

In summary:

Alex, Hilda, 40, lime & ruby
Chad, Belinda, 80, emerald & white
Gary, Kathy, 100, aqua & coral
John, Polly, 60, cobalt & lavender
Mark, Darlene, 20, ivory & sapphire

LOGIC PROBLEM 32

Men are Alex, Carl, and David, women are Brenda, Elaine, and Faith, 2 won gold, 2 won silver, and 2 won bronze medals (intro.). Elaine won the same color medal as another female (2), but not gold [Mr. Lawson and diver (3)] or bronze [man (6)]; they both won silver. The hurdler [met Kramer before (6)] didn't win gold [Lawson [never met any of others (3)] and diver] or bronze (6); the hurdler won silver, so is female (above). Kramer and one who won same color medal as Kramer didn't win silver [hurdler] or bronze (6); they won gold [Lawson and diver], so Kramer is the diver. Ingles didn't win gold [Kramer and Lawson] or bronze (4); Ingles won silver, so is a woman. Gibson didn't win gold [Kramer and Lawson] or silver [Elaine] (2); she won bronze. Kramer [gold] isn't a woman [silver or Gibson (2)]; he's a man. Neither Brenda nor Hayes won gold [Mr. Kramer and Mr. Lawson], so the archer did (5) and is Lawson. David and the gymnast didn't win gold [diving and archery] or silver [women], so they won bronze (1) and the gymnast is Ms. Gibson. She isn't Elaine [silver] or Brenda (1); she's Faith. Brenda didn't win bronze [Faith and David], so Hayes did (5) and is David. Brenda won silver [only left] (5). She isn't the hurdler [silver] (5); Elaine [silver] is. David Hayes [bronze] isn't the fencer (4); he's the swimmer. The fencer won silver and is Brenda [only silver left]. She isn't Ingles (4); she's Johnson. Ingles is the hurdler [Elaine]. Carl isn't Lawson [archer] (1); Alex is. Carl is Kramer.

In summary:

Alex Lawson, archery, gold
Brenda Johnson, fencing, silver
Carl Kramer, diving, gold
David Hayes, swimming, bronze
Elaine Ingles, hurdles, silver
Faith Gibson, gymnastics, bronze

LOGIC PROBLEM 33

5th-place finisher isn't Wheel Deal (1), Chain Lightning (2), Holy Spokes (4), or Pedal Pushers (5); he's Tires Afire. Claudio's 4th, and one who went fastest through Queens is 3rd (3). One who went fastest through Manhattan [1 higher than Raul, 1 lower than Chain Lightning (2)] isn't 1st, 5th, or 3rd [Claudio 4th]; he is 2nd or 4th. If 4th, Raul would be 5th, leaving no place for one who went fastest through Brooklyn, who is 4th or 5th (4); one who went fastest through Manhattan is 2nd, Chain Lightning representative is 1st, and Raul is 3rd (2). Holy Spokes representative is 1st or 2nd (4); he's 2nd. Pedal Pushers representative is 1 higher than Pedro (5), so not 3rd [Claudio 4th]; he's 4th, and Pedro's 5th. Wheel Deal representative's 3rd. Andy isn't 2nd [Manhattan] (2); Greg is. Andy is 1st. One who went fastest through the Bronx isn't 1st [Andy] or 5th (1); he is 4th. One who went fastest through Brooklyn isn't 1st (4); he's 5th. One who went fastest through Staten Island is 1st.

In summary:

Andy, Chain Lightning, Staten Island, 1st
Claudio, Pedal Pushers, Bronx, 4th
Greg, Holy Spokes, Manhattan, 2nd
Pedro, Tires Afire, Brooklyn, 5th
Raul, Wheel Deal, Queens, 3rd

LOGIC PROBLEM 34

Regular drivers are Brady [camel caravan (6)], Crystal, Cyril, Georgette, and Nathan, and relief drivers are Arthur [mule train (1)], Rhonda [Nathan

(2)], Roger, Suzy, and Violet (intro.). Roger [panama hat (6)] isn't relief driver for riverboat (3), camel caravan (6), or minirail [derby (7)]; he's relief for stagecoach, and his regular driver isn't Cyril (3), Georgette (4), or Brady (6), so is Crystal. Relief driver on camel caravan [Brady] isn't Rhonda [Nathan]; she's Violet or Suzy. Sombrero isn't riverboat (3) or camel caravan [Violet or Suzy (above)] (5); it's mule train. Regular driver on mule train [sombrero, Arthur] isn't Nathan [Rhonda] or Cyril (3); that one's Georgette. Cyril isn't regular driver of riverboat (3); Nathan is. Cyril's minirail, and his relief isn't Violet (7), so is Suzy. Violet is Brady's relief. Nathan isn't helmet (2); Brady is. Nathan's turban.

In summary (regular driver, relief driver, transportation, hat):

Brady, Violet, camel caravan, helmet
Crystal, Roger, stagecoach, panama hat
Cyril, Suzy, minirail, derby
Georgette, Arthur, mule train, sombrero
Nathan, Rhonda, riverboat, turban

LOGIC PROBLEM 35

The fish and the brass paperweight were bought after the 2 on incoming (4), which were not bought in consecutive mos. (1); Aug. and Oct. must be on incoming, and the fish and brass paperweights are Nov. and Dec., in some order. Sept. isn't filing [then the ones bought in Nov. and Dec. would both be on outgoing, which isn't possible (1)]; it's outgoing. One of wood is bought before 2 others, but isn't incoming [Aug. and Oct.] (5); it's Sept. Wood [antique (2), Sept.] isn't dove (2), frog [mo. before filing (3), and Oct. is incoming], fish (4), or cat (5); it's unicorn. Aug. [incoming] isn't frog [Sept. outgoing] (3), fish (4), or cat (5); it's dove, and isn't made of lead (2), brass (4), or seashells (5); it's crystal. Fish isn't brass or lead [antique (2)] (4); it's seashells, and isn't Dec. (5), so is Nov., and 1 of brass is Dec. (above). Lead is Oct. Frog isn't Dec. (3); cat is. Frog is Oct. Filing is Nov. (3). Dec. is outgoing.

In summary:

August, dove, crystal, incoming
September, unicorn, wood, outgoing
October, frog, lead, incoming
November, fish, seashells, filing
December, cat, brass, outgoing

LOGIC PROBLEM 36

Quentin [basketball (3)] isn't IN (3), so isn't in (1); 5 coaches are Quentin, golf coach, Otis, Ms. Bennett, and IN (1, above). Simon isn't golf (5); he's IN [only

336

possible in (above)], and isn't golf (1), track [FL (5)], or swimming (6); he's volleyball, and isn't Ms. Bennett, Farson [ME (2)], Darcy (6), or Evans (7); he's Clinton. Otis isn't golf (1) or track [next to Simon Clinton (5), but Otis [end room (2)] is next to Farson (2)]; he's swimming. Ruth is AL (4), and isn't track (5); Paula is. Ruth's golf, and isn't Ms. Bennett (1); Paula is. Otis isn't Darcy (1) or Farson (2); he's Evans. Ruth [AL] isn't Farson [ME]; Quentin is. Ruth's Darcy. Otis is CO.

In summary:

Otis Evans, swimming, CO
Paula Bennett, track, FL
Quentin Farson, basketball, ME
Ruth Darcy, golf, AL
Simon Clinton, volleyball, IN

LOGIC PROBLEM 37

Cristina isn't banana nut, sourdough (1), or zucchini (5); she's rye or cinnamon raisin. Easter bread isn't Cristina [couldn't be rye (2) or cinnamon raisin (6), so couldn't be placed (above)], Johnny (1), Brad, or Ginger (6); it's Herb, and isn't rye (2), zucchini (3), or cinnamon (6), so is sourdough or banana nut. Herb isn't Eggers [couldn't be banana nut or sourdough (1), so couldn't be placed (above)], Batterson, Flournoy (3), or Needham (6); he's Wheaton, so isn't sourdough (4), so is banana nut. Sourdough isn't Eggers (1) or Wheaton (4); it's Batterson or Flournoy, so isn't Christmas [couldn't be Batterson or Flournoy (3), so couldn't be placed (above)], birthday (2), or Thanksgiving (4); it's Memorial Day, so isn't Batterson (7), so is Flournoy (above). Needham isn't rye or cinnamon raisin (6); it's zucchini. Batterson isn't rye (7); it's cinnamon raisin. Eggers is rye. Needham [zucchini] isn't Johnny (2), Cristina (5), or Brad (6); that one's Ginger, so isn't Christmas (3) or birthday (5), so is Thanksgiving. Batterson isn't Christmas (3); Eggers is. Batterson is birthday. Johnny isn't Batterson [birthday] or Eggers (2); he's Flournoy. Brad isn't Batterson [birthday] (5); Christina is. Brad is Eggers.

In summary:

Brad Eggers, rye, Christmas
Cristina Batterson, cinnamon, Grandma's birthday
Ginger Needham, zucchini, Thanksgiving
Herb Wheaton, banana, Easter
Johnny Flournoy, sourdough, Memorial Day

LOGIC PROBLEM 38

Irene's old no. is twice Hope's new no. (5), but not 2 Hill [Neil and Carolyn's new no. is 1 Fern (2)];

Irene's old no. is 10 Glen, and Hope's new no. is 5 East [only no. twice another]. Martin's new no. is 4 lower than Philip's (6), so either Philip's 13 and Martin's 9, or Philip's 9 and Martin's 5; either Philip or Martin moved to 9 Byrd. Oliver's new no. is higher than Laura's (1), so not 5 East [higher than 1 Fern [Carolyn]] or 7 Oak [higher than 1 Fern [Carolyn] and 5 East [Hope]]; it's 13 West. Philip moved to 9 Byrd, and Martin moved from 2 Hill to 5 East (6). Rex moved to 7 Oak [from 6 Dale (4)]. Rex's new no. [7 Oak] is 3 higher or 3 lower than Julia's old no. (3); Julia's old no. is 4 York. Oliver's old no. isn't 8 Sea [Laura's old no. would be 10 Glen [only higher than 8, Irene's old no.] (1)]; it's 4 York. Neil and Carolyn's old no. isn't 10 Glen [Irene's old no.]; Philip's is. Neil's old no. is 8 Sea. Laura is married to Rex.

In summary (husband, wife, old address, new address):

Martin, Hope, 2 Hill St., 5 East Hill
Neil, Carolyn, 8 Sea Ln., 1 Fern Rd.
Oliver, Julia, 4 York Way, 13 West Way
Philip, Irene, 10 Glen Ave., 9 Byrd St.
Rex, Laura, 6 Dale Rd., 7 Oak Ln.

LOGIC PROBLEM 39

Reg. pos. are 1st base, left field, pitcher, shortstop, 3rd base, and secondary pos. are catcher, 1st base, pitcher, right field, and 2nd base (intro.). No one has same reg. and secondary pos. (intro.). Lewis's reg. pos. is pitcher or 1st base [only 2 pos. that are also someone's secondary] (3), but not pitcher [no 1st name beginning with L] (2); Lewis's reg. pos. is 1st base, so Mickey's secondary pos. is 1st base (3). Chet's secondary pos. and Jordan's reg. pos. are pitcher [only pos. left that was both reg. and secondary] (3). Jordan's Jack [only 1st name beginning with J] (2). Jack [reg. pos. pitcher] plays right field as secondary pos., and Nelson plays left field as reg. pos. (1). Eric doesn't play catcher as secondary pos. (4); he plays 2nd base. Bob plays catcher as secondary pos. Bob isn't Collins, Nelson (1), or Miller (4); he's Lewis. Mickey isn't Miller (2) or Collins (5); he's Nelson. Chet isn't Collins (2); he's Miller. Eric's Collins, so his reg. pos. isn't 3rd base (5); it's shortstop. Chet Miller's reg. pos. is 3rd base.

In summary (player, regular, secondary):

Bob Lewis, 1st base, catcher
Chet Miller, 3rd base, pitcher
Eric Collins, shortstop, 2nd base
Jack Jordan, pitcher, right field
Mickey Nelson, left field, 1st base

LOGIC PROBLEM 40

One who likes tigers [trapeze artists (3)] isn't Billy (3) or one who likes popcorn (6); he's Louie (1). He doesn't like cotton candy (6); he likes hot dogs (6). One who likes lions [peanuts (3)] isn't Billy (3) or one who likes clowns [snow cones or candy apples (5)]; that one likes human cannonball (1). One who likes cotton candy isn't Billy or one who likes clowns (5); that one likes elephants (1). That one's favorite act isn't clowns (1), tightrope walkers (4), or acrobats (6); it's grand parade. That one isn't Billy, Joey (1), Carrie, or Emma (2); it's Nell. Carrie likes peanuts [cannonball, lions] (2). One who likes tightrope walkers doesn't like bears or horses (4); that one likes monkeys. That one doesn't like snow cones (4) or popcorn (6); that one likes candy apples, so is Billy (1). Joey doesn't like bears (4); Emma does. Joey likes horses, so doesn't like clowns (1); so likes acrobats. Emma likes clowns, so doesn't like popcorn (5); she likes snow cones. Joey likes popcorn.

In summary:

Billy, tightrope walkers, monkeys, candy apples
Carrie, human cannonball, lions, peanuts
Emma, clowns, bears, snow cones
Joey, acrobats, horses, popcorn
Louie, trapeze artists, tigers, hot dogs
Nell, grand parade, elephants, cotton candy

LOGIC PROBLEM 41

Black isn't Linda (1), Sandra, or Gina (3); she's Brenda or Maura. Black isn't Vicky [couldn't be Brenda or Maura (4), so couldn't be placed (above)], Mary (1), Lily, or Darcy (3); she's Ivy, so isn't Brenda (6), so is Maura (above). Lily [not Linda (2)] is either Maura or Brenda (1), but not Maura [Black] (2); she's Brenda [Rand (2)]. In (1), Rand [Brenda] isn't Maura [Maura's Ivy, and Rand's Vicky (7)], Brenda's in-law, or Linda's mom; she's Mary (1). The in-law of Darcy's daughter isn't Lily [Mary's daughter], Ivy (6), or Mary [Vicky's daughter (7)]; she's Vicky. Vicky isn't Maura's in-law [Ivy's daughter]; she's Linda's mom (1). Darcy is Maura's in-law (1). Mary Rand's in-law is Linda (7). Vicky's in-law isn't Gina (7); she's Sandra. Darcy's daughter is Sandra (above). Gina is Ivy's in-law and Lily's daughter. Vicky [in-law Sandra] isn't Smith (4) or Greer (5); she's Hall. Lily isn't Greer (2); Darcy is. Lily is Smith.

In summary (mom, daughter, daughter-in-law):
Darcy Greer, Sandra, Maura
Ivy Black, Maura, Gina
Lily Smith, Gina, Brenda

Mary Rand, Brenda, Linda
Vicky Hall, Linda, Sandra

LOGIC PROBLEM 42

First, set up a table with 1st nos. on the left side and second nos. and calculations across the top, and figure out the correct answers for each combination. One who gave right answer didn't subtract 7 or 14 (4), so only possible combinations for right answer are 21 + 13 = 34 and 27 + 16 = 43. One with right answer, Deb, and Alf added (above, 1). One who answered 19 added (5), but isn't one with right answer or Deb [gave answer Alf should have given (1), so answered 34 or 43 [only correct added answers among those given]]; he was Alf. He didn't add 9 [wouldn't result in any of the answers given, and Deb gave answer he should have given (1)], nor did one with right answer (above); Deb did. Alf [answered 19, should have answered 34 or 43] must have had either 21 + 13 or 27 + 16, but not 21 + 13 [his 1st no. was 4 less than Carol's (5), and 25 not a 1st no.]; he added 27 + 16 and should have answered 43, so Deb answered 43. One with right answer added 21 + 13 and answered 34. Carol's 1st no. was 4 more than Alf's [27] (5); it was 31. Alf's 2nd no. [16] was lower than Fred's (6); Fred's 2nd no. was 17 [only no. higher than 16]. Fred's 1st no. [2nd no. 17] wasn't 21 [2nd no. 13], 33 (2), or 23 [2nd no. lower than that of one with right answer [+ 13] (4), so + 9 or − 7]; it was 26. Fred's answer [26 − 17] wasn't 22 [lower answer than Carol [1st no. 31] (2), and 22 only lower than 34 [1st no. 21]] or 17 [− 17 highest 2nd no.] (3); it was 11. One who answered 17 had a lower 1st no. than one who answered 11 [26] (3); it was 23. Deb's 1st no. [answer 43] was 33 [only left]. Gil's 1st no. wasn't 23 [answer 17] (3); it was 21 [+ 13 = 34]. Lewis's 1st no. was 23 and answer was 17. Carol's answer was 22. Lewis's 2nd no. [answer 17] wasn't 14 [Gil's 2nd no. 13] (3); it was 7. Carol's 2nd no. was 14.
In summary:
Alf, 27 + 16 = 19
Carol, 31 − 14 = 22
Deb, 33 + 9 = 43
Fred, 26 − 17 = 11
Gil, 21 + 13 = 34, correct answer
Lewis, 23 − 7 = 17

LOGIC PROBLEM 43

Prices are $650, $750, $800, $1,000, and $1,200 (intro.). $1,200 isn't letter opener (3), emerald ring (4), or miniature portrait (5); it's brooch or gold coins, and isn't Cynthia [couldn't be coins (3) or brooch (8), so couldn't be placed (above)], Bridget (1), Ernest (4), or Myrtle (7), so is Rodney, and isn't brooch (6), so is coins (above). $1,000 [only less than Rodney] isn't portrait (2), opener [less than Cynthia (3)], or ring [less than Ernest (4)]; it's brooch. Bookcase [more than Ernest, who is more than ring (4)] isn't $1,200 [Rodney] or $1,000 [brooch] (6); it's $800, so Ernest's $750, and ring's $650 (4). Cynthia isn't $650 (3) or $1,000 [brooch] (8); she's $800, and isn't opener (3), so is portrait. Opener's $750. Cushion isn't Bridget (1), Myrtle, or Rodney [coins] (7); it's Ernest. Bridget isn't $1,000 [cushions $750] (1); Myrtle is. Bridget's $650. Myrtle's $1,000, so sofa's $1,200 (7). Myrtle [$1,000] isn't grandfather clock (2); Bridget is. Myrtle's wardrobe.
In summary:
Bridget, grandfather clock, $650, emerald ring
Cynthia, bookcase, $800, miniature portrait
Ernest, cushions, $750, letter opener
Myrtle, wardrobe, $1,000, brooch
Rodney, sofa, $1,200, gold coins

LOGIC PROBLEM 44

Bronc-riding scores are 25, 30, 40, 50, and 75, bull-riding scores are 40, 50, 60, 75, and 90, and calf-roping scores are 25, 30, 45, 50, and 60 (intro.). 75 bronc [highest] and 60 bull (6) isn't Tex [same bull as Joe bronc (1), so 40, 50, or 75 in bull (above)], Monty [no 65 in bull or calf] (3), Clyde (4), or Gabe (5); it's Joe. Tex is 75 bull (1); he's 30 calf (2). 90 bull isn't Monty (3) or Clyde [no 80 bronc] (4); it's Gabe. Clyde's 30 bronc [40 bull (4)] or 40 bronc [50 bull (4)] [only values left 10 pts. apart] (4). Tex [75 bull, 30 calf] isn't 30 bronc (3); his total is 130, 145, or 155 [25, 40, or 50 bronc, respectively]; Clyde's total is 100, 115, or 125 (4). If Clyde is 40 bronc, 50 bull [90 subtotal], his only possible value in calf roping is 25 (intro.) [115 total]. Tex's total would then be 145 (4), forcing his bronc value to be 40 as well [75 + 30 = 105], which isn't possible (intro.); Clyde is 30 bronc, 40 bull riding [70 subtotal], and his only possible value for calf roping is 45 [115 total] (intro., 4). Tex [145 total (4)] got 40 for bronc riding [75 + 30 + 40 = 145]. Monty didn't get 25 bronc riding (intro., 3); Gabe did. Gabe's 50 calf roping (5). Monty's 50 bronc and 50 bull; he's 60 calf (3). Joe's 25 calf. Champion [highest total (intro.)] isn't Joe [160 total], Monty [160 total], Tex [145 total (4)], or Clyde [4]; he's Gabe [165 total].
In summary (cowboy, bronc riding, bull riding, calf roping):
Clyde, 30, 40, 45
Gabe, 25, 90, 50, Champion

338

Joe, 75, 60, 25
Monty, 50, 50, 60
Tex, 40, 75, 30

LOGIC PROBLEM 45

Knife set [item 9823 (5)] is $34, $36, $38, or $39 [only amts. $2 less than another (intro.)] (5), but not $36 [jumpsuit (4)] or $39 [item 1705's $41 (3), and knife set $2 less than item 2700 (5)]; knife set is $34 or $38, and item 2700's $36 or $40 (5). Item 2700 was reduced by $2 more than cookware (5), so wasn't reduced by $5 [necklace reduced by $3 (2)]; it wasn't $40 [reduced $5 (1)]. Item 2700 cost $36 [jumpsuit] and the knife set $34 (above, 5). The necklace cost $3 less than item 6528 (2), so necklace cost $35 or $38 [only amts. left $3 less than another (intro.)], but not $38 [$38 + $3 = $41, cost of 1705]; the necklace cost $35 and item 6528 cost $38 (2). Item 2455 was reduced by $10 (4). The necklace [$35, reduced $3 [least]] isn't item 4507 (3), 1705 [$41], 6528 [$38], or 2455 [reduced $10]; it's item 2001. The $40 item [reduced $5] isn't 2455 [reduced $10], 6528 [$38], or 1705 [$41]; it's 4507. Item 2455 cost $39. The clock radio was reduced $4 [4507 reduced $5] [only amt. less than $5 left] (3). Item 2700 wasn't reduced by $6 [clock radio $4] or $9 [no item reduced by $7 (intro.)] (5); it was reduced by $8. The cookware was reduced by $6 (5). The knife set [9823] wasn't reduced by $5 [4507] or $10 [2455]; it was reduced by $9. Figurine wasn't reduced $5 (1); foot massager was. Figurine was reduced $10. Clock radio [reduced $4] isn't $41 [it would've been $45 before reduction, which isn't possible [foot massager $45 before reduction] (intro.)]; clock radio is $38. Cookware is $41.

In summary (item, no., paid, discount):
Capodimonte figurine, 2455, $39, $10
Clock radio, 6528, $38, $4
Cookware set, 1705, $41, $6
Foot massager, 4507, $40, $5
Knife set, 9823, $34, $9
Knit jumpsuit, 2700, $36, $8
Necklace, 2001, $35, $3

LOGIC PROBLEM 46

Sean isn't doctor [Matt (2)]; he's banker, and Hadley's doctor (4). Business manager isn't Karen (1) or Ron (5); she's Sylvia. Ron isn't publisher (4); Karen is. Ron's pilot. Sylvia [business manager] isn't Jones (1), Hansen [pilot (2)], or Collins (5); she's Blackburn. Karen isn't Jones (1); Sean is. Karen is Collins. Sylvia [business manager] isn't Spanish (1), Russian, German (3), or Italian (5); she's French. Karen isn't Russian, Spanish (1), or Italian (5); she's German. Sean Jones isn't Spanish or Italian (1); he's Russian. Ron isn't Italian (5); he's Spanish. Matt's Italian.

In summary:
Karen Collins, publisher, German
Matt Hadley, doctor, Italian
Ron Hansen, pilot, Spanish
Sean Jones, banker, Russian
Sylvia Blackburn, business manager, French

LOGIC PROBLEM 47

Catherine [played guitar (2)] isn't 1st, 5th [last] (2), 2nd (4), or 3rd [ventriloquism (5)]; she's 4th, so performed magic is 5th, and Beatrice's 3rd [only possible (2, above)]. Agnes isn't 1st or 5th [magic] (1); she's 2nd, so tap-danced is 1st (1). Sang is 2nd. Regina isn't 5th [last] (4); she's 1st. Evangeline's 5th, so Fortitude's 4th (5). Grace isn't 1st [tap-danced, so Hope (1)], 3rd, or 5th [Fortitude 4th] (3); it's 2nd. Charity isn't 3rd [Beatrice] (2); it's 5th. Faith's 3rd.

In summary:
1st, Regina, Sisters of Hope, tap-dance
2nd, Agnes, Sisters of Grace, sang
3rd, Beatrice, Sisters of Faith, ventriloquism
4th, Catherine, Sisters of Fortitude, played guitar
5th, Evangeline, Sisters of Charity, performed magic

LOGIC PROBLEM 48

Men are Aaron, Hugh, and Roy, and women are Charlene and Mandy (intro.). Stadium woman (2) isn't Charlene [furniture store (4)]; she's Mandy. Aaron ["Little Sister" (4)] isn't restaurant (2) or train depot [Roy (3)]; he's supermarket. Hugh's restaurant. Charlene [furniture store] isn't Bedford [restaurant (2)], Baker [supermarket (3)], Mandan, or Randolph (4); she's Hornell, so "Suspicious Minds" woman is Mandy (1). Mandy [stadium] isn't Randolph (2); she's Mandan. Roy's Randolph. "Love Me Tender" man isn't Hugh [restaurant] (1); he's Roy. Hugh [Bedford] isn't "Don't Be Cruel" (5); he's "Hound Dog." Charlene's "Don't Be Cruel."

In summary:
Aaron, Baker, supermarket, "Little Sister"
Charlene, Hornell, furniture store, "Don't Be Cruel"
Hugh, Bedford, restaurant, "Hound Dog"
Mandy, Mandan, stadium, "Suspicious Minds"
Roy, Randolph, train depot, "Love Me Tender"

LOGIC PROBLEM 49

Buckthorn woman (3) isn't Ms. Ferguson [plantain (5)]; she's Ms. Esterhaus [only woman left], so isn't Green Thumb, Bloomsday (2), Garden Variety (3), or Planter's Punch (6), so is Let It Grow. Ms. Ferguson [statue (5)] isn't Green [bench (2)], Bloomsday [pink flamingo (4)], or Planter's (6); she's Garden Variety. Planter's man isn't Mr. Katemsky or Mr. Thomerdahl (6); he's Mr. Stansfield. Esterhaus [Let It Grow] isn't bench [Green Thumb], pink flamingo [Bloomsday], or garden gnome (2); she's birdbath. Stansfield [Planter's] isn't bench [Green Thumb] or pink flamingo [Bloomsday]; he's garden gnome. Flamingo isn't foxtail (1) or chickweed (4); it's thistle, and isn't Katemsky (4), so is Thomerdahl. Katemsky's bench. Stansfield isn't foxtail (1); he's chickweed. Katemsky's foxtail.

In summary:

Ms. Esterhaus, buckthorn, Let It Grow, birdbath

Ms. Ferguson, plantain, Garden Variety, statue

Mr. Katemsky, foxtail, Green Thumb, bench

Mr. Stansfield, chickweed, Planter's Punch, garden gnome

Mr. Thomerdahl, thistle, Bloomsday, pink flamingo

LOGIC PROBLEM 50

Wisdom isn't Mr. Warren [man (3)] (1), Ms. Porthouser (2), Ms. Hill [fame (3)], or Mr. Fentress (4); it's Mr. Robinson. Riches [Hypatia (3)] isn't Warren (3) or Fentress [Ruella (4)]; it's Porthouser. Robinson [wisdom] isn't Waldemar (1) or Phoenicia (5); he's Fabian. Warren isn't Waldemar (1); Hill is. Warren is Phoenicia, so isn't preeminence (1); he's happiness. Fentress [Ruella] is preeminence, so isn't Falkner, Rhodes, Patmos (1), or Wrangel (2); he's Hispaniola. Robinson [Fabian, wisdom] isn't Rhodes, Falkner, or Wrangel (1); he's Patmos. Hill [Waldemar, fame] isn't Wrangel or Falkner (1); she's Rhodes. Warren isn't Wrangel (1); he's Falkner. Porthouser's Wrangel.

In summary:

Mr. Fentress, Hispaniola, Ruella, preeminence

Ms. Hill, Rhodes, Waldemar, fame

Ms. Porthouser, Wrangel, Hypatia, riches

Mr. Robinson, Patmos, Fabian, wisdom

Mr. Warren, Falkner, Phoenicia, happiness

LOGIC PROBLEM 51

Men are Adam, Byron, and Wilbur, and women are Margia and Rosalind (intro.). Ms. Maxwell [professor (3)] (3) isn't Margia [architect (1)]; she's Rosalind. Editor [defense attorney (5)] isn't Wilbur [plaintiff (1)] or Adam (2); he's Byron. Adam isn't engineer (2); he's research scientist. Wilbur's engineer. Rosalind Maxwell isn't witness (3) or judge [Dewitt (4)]; she's juror. Adam Knauss (2) isn't judge [Dewitt]; he's witness. Margia's judge. Byron [defense attorney] isn't Poff (5); he's Foxx. Wilbur's Poff.

In summary:

Adam Knauss, witness, research scientist

Byron Foxx, defense attorney, editor

Margia Dewitt, judge, architect

Rosalind Maxwell, juror, professor

Wilbur Poff, plaintiff, engineer

LOGIC PROBLEM 52

Worth [Palm Beach (1)] isn't NH (1), VT (2), CT [Tampa (3)], or MN [Moneypennys (6)]; it's NJ. VT isn't Orlando or Sarasota (2); it's Key West. Van Snoot isn't NH (1) or VT [Key West] (3); it's CT. Bigwig [Finland (5)] isn't VT [Key West, so Sweden (3)]; it's NH. Banks is VT. Bigwig isn't Orlando (5); it's Sarasota. Moneypenny [MN] is Orlando, and isn't Iceland [NJ (4)] or Denmark (6); it's Norway. Van Snoot is Denmark.

In summary:

Banks, VT, Key West, Sweden

Bigwig, NH, Sarasota, Finland

Moneypenny, MN, Orlando, Norway

Van Snoot, CT, Tampa, Denmark

Worth, NJ, Palm Beach, Iceland

LOGIC PROBLEM 53

Males are Fafnir, Gargouille, and Smaug, and females are Jormungand and Vermithrax (intro.). Mountain isn't 3rd, 4th, 5th [last] (1), or 1st [forest (5)]; it's 2nd. Topaz [male (3)] isn't 2nd [mountain [female (1)]]; it's 3rd (3). Emeralds isn't 1st, 2nd, or 5th [last] (2); it's 4th, so Jormungand's 2nd, and Gargouille's 5th [last] (2). 2nd [mountain] isn't diamonds or rubies (1); it's sapphires. Smaug isn't 3rd [mountain 2nd] or 4th (1); he's 1st. 3rd [topaz] is Fafnir [only male left] (3). Smaug isn't rubies (1); he's diamonds. Gargouille's rubies. Vermithrax is 4th, and isn't cave or island (4); she's lake. Topaz isn't cave (3); it's island. Rubies is cave.

In summary:

Fafnir, topaz, island, 3rd

Gargouille, rubies, cave, 5th

Jormungand, sapphires, mountain, 2nd

Smaug, diamonds, forest, 1st

Vermithrax, emeralds, lake, 4th

LOGIC PROBLEM 54

June isn't luxury sedan (2), minivan (4), utility vehicle, or sports car (6); she's station wagon. Beads isn't Wylie, June [station wagon] (3), Adele, or Cornelia (5); it's Rupert. Utility vehicle isn't Wylie, Rupert [beads] (3), or Cornelia (5); it's Adele. Sports car isn't Cornelia (2) or Rupert (6); it's Wylie. Rupert [beads] isn't Exotica, Suprema (1), Omaha (3), or Cygna [couldn't be minivan (1) or luxury sedan (4), so couldn't be placed (above)]; he's Camelot. Wylie [sports car] isn't Cygna (1), Omaha (3), or Suprema (6); he's Exotica. June [station wagon] isn't Omaha (3) or Cygna (6); she's Suprema. Rupert [Camelot] isn't minivan (6); he's sedan. Cornelia's minivan, so isn't Cygna (1); she's Omaha. Adele [utility vehicle] is Cygna, so isn't air freshener (1), crystal (5), or tassel (6); she's dice. Wylie [Exotica] isn't air freshener (4) or tassel (6); he's crystal. June isn't tassel (2); she's air freshener. Cornelia's tassel.

In summary:

Adele, Cygna, utility vehicle, dice
Cornelia, Omaha, minivan, tassel
June, Suprema, station wagon, air freshener
Rupert, Camelot, luxury sedan, beads
Wylie, Exotica, sports car, crystal

LOGIC PROBLEM 55

Boys are Calvin, Drake, and Eric, and girls are Michelle and Sophie (intro.). Hanson boy (1) isn't Blaine, Antoine (1), Shep (2), or Ace [Sophie (3)]; he's Birdy, so isn't Eric Miller (1) or Drake (5), so is Calvin. West boy (4) is Drake. Michelle isn't Whitney (5); she's Brooks. Sophie's Whitney. Shep boy (2) isn't Drake West [microwave oven (4)] (2); he's Eric. Drake [microwave] isn't Blaine [blender (1)]; he's Antoine. Michelle's Blaine. Dishwasher isn't Shep [Eric Miller] or Birdy [Hanson] (1); it's Ace. Birdy isn't pressure cooker (5); Shep is. Birdy's coffee maker.

In summary:

Calvin Hanson, coffee maker, Birdy
Drake West, microwave oven, Antoine
Eric Miller, pressure cooker, Shep
Michelle Brooks, blender, Blaine
Sophie Whitney, dishwasher, Ace

LOGIC PROBLEM 56

Yrs. are 1845, 1895, 1900, 1945, and 1995 (intro.). Brown isn't 1845 [1st], 1895 [no 1795], 1900 [no 1800] (4), or 1945 [Moreau (6)]; he's 1995, so dentist is 1895 (4). 1900 [sandwich dispenser (3)] isn't Quest [mechanical haberdasher (1)] or Brainard (3); it's Zarno. University isn't aquanaut's lunchbox, haberdasher [Quest], dispenser [1900, and no 1850] (2), or petite piano [duke (5)]; it's square fruit. 1845 [1st] isn't lunchbox, fruit [university] (2), or piano (5); it's haberdasher [Quest], so lunchbox is 1895, and university is 1945 (2). Piano's 1995. Brainard's lunchbox. Bridge club isn't Quest (1); it's Zarno. Quest's mother.

In summary:

Prof. Brainard, aquanaut's lunchbox, 1895, dentist
Dr. Brown, petite piano, 1995, duke
Dr. Moreau, square fruit, 1945, university
Dr. Quest, mechanical haberdasher, 1845, mother
Dr. Zarno, sandwich dispenser, 1900, bridge club

LOGIC PROBLEM 57

Weekdays are Mon.-Fri. (intro.). Fri. [last] isn't MacDougall (1), MacGregor (2), MacAllister, or MacLean (5); it's MacKenzie, so gutters are Thu., and haggis is Wed. (4). Fri. [last, MacKenzie] isn't salmon (1), shepherd's pie (2), or oatmeal [couldn't be hedges (3), so couldn't be placed (5)]; it's kippers. Shepherd's pie isn't Tue. [Thu. [gutters] would be gophers (2)] or Thu. [Fri. last] (2); it's Mon., so MacGregor's Tue., and gophers are Wed. (2). Fri. isn't herb garden or hedges (3); it's fountains. Hedges aren't Mon. [1st] (5); they're Tue., so MacAllister's Mon. (5). Oatmeal is hedges [MacAllister shepherd's pie] (5). Salmon's Thu., so isn't MacDougall (1); it's MacLean. MacDougall's Wed. Herb garden's Mon.

In summary:

Mon., MacAllister, herb garden, shepherd's pie
Tue., MacGregor, hedges, oatmeal
Wed., MacDougall, gophers, haggis
Thu., MacLean, gutters, salmon
Fri., MacKenzie, fountains, kippers

LOGIC PROBLEM 58

Mos. are Mar., June, July, Aug., and Oct., and profits. are $10,000, $15,000, $20,000, $30,000, and $35,000 (intro.). Bill isn't Oct. [Fred (2)], July (3), Mar. [no Apr.], or Aug. [no Sept.] (5); he's June, so ravioli's July (5). Quiche isn't Mar. [no Apr.], Aug. [no Sept.], or Oct. [last] (1); it's June, so Cameron's July (1), so isn't $10,000 [no $25,000], $30,000 [no $45,000], $35,000 [most] (2), or $15,000 [no $7,500] (3), so is $20,000, so Fred's $35,000 (2), and Bill's $10,000 (3). Dale isn't $15,000 (4); he's $30,000. Joe's $15,000, so isn't Mar. [1st] (4); he's Aug. Dale's Mar. Lollipop isn't Aug. [$15,000] or Oct. [last] (4); it's Mar. Chocolate-chip cookie isn't Oct. (6); it's Aug. Hot dog's Oct.

In summary:
Bill, quiche, June, $10,000
Cameron, ravioli, July, $20,000
Dale, lollipop, Mar., $30,000
Fred, hot dog, Oct., $35,000
Joe, chocolate-chip cookie, Aug., $15,000

LOGIC PROBLEM 59

Doberman pinscher [knocks down and licks face (5)] isn't Baby [runs in circles (3)] or Simpson (5); he's Porter [only possible in (1)], so isn't Baby (1), Curly (4), Elvis (6), or Dilly (7), so is Alfie. Dilly isn't poodle (2), collie, or bulldog (7); he's German shepherd, and isn't Simpson (8), so is blocks gate [only possible in (1)]. Curly isn't chases down block (9); he's chews on shoes, and isn't collie (4) or poodle (9), so is bulldog. Elvis is chases, so isn't poodle (2); he's collie. Baby [runs in circles] is poodle, so isn't Simpson (1), Billings (2), or Lettman (6); she's Jacobs. Elvis [chases] isn't Billings (2) or Lettman (6); he's Simpson. Dilly isn't Billings (2); he's Lettman. Curly is Billings.

In summary:
Billings, Curly, bulldog, chews on shoes
Jacobs, Baby, poodle, runs in circles
Lettman, Dilly, German shepherd, blocks gate
Porter, Alfie, Doberman pinscher, knocks down & licks face
Simpson, Elvis, collie, chases down block

LOGIC PROBLEM 60

Ages are 15-19 (intro.). Baxter [fiction (1)] isn't Lindsay (1), Jenny Garrison (2), Amy (3), or Dwight [news reporting (4)]; he's Frank. 15 yrs. [youngest] isn't Frank Baxter (1), Jenny (2), Amy (3), or Dwight (4); it's Lindsay, so Baxter's 16 yrs. (1). Lindsay [15 yrs.] isn't Robertson [Dwight would be 16 yrs. [Frank] (4)] or Martin [18 yrs. (5)]; she's Evans. Amy isn't Martin [18 yrs., so history would be 16 yrs. [fiction] (3)]; she's Robertson [17 yrs.], so history's 15 yrs. (3). Dwight is 16 yrs., so Robertson's 17 yrs. (4). Jenny's 19 yrs., so poetry's 17 yrs. (2). Jenny's biography.

In summary:
Amy Robertson, 17, poetry
Dwight Martin, 18, news reporting
Frank Baxter, 16, fiction
Jenny Garrison, 19, biography
Lindsay Evans, 15, history

LOGIC PROBLEM 61

Weekdays are Mon.-Fri., and holes are 6, 9, 12, 15, and 18 (intro.). Linden Hall [day before sand trap (4)] isn't hole 18 [Butler's (1)], 6 [1st], 9 [no hole 3] (4), or 12 [day before whiffed ball (5)]; it's hole 15, so Fri. is hole 9 (4). Schenley Park isn't hole 6 [1st] or 9 [no hole 3] (2); it's hole 12, so wrong hole is hole 6 (2). Schenley [hole 12] isn't Mon. (2), Thu., Fri., or Wed. [Butler [hole 18 [last]] would be Fri. (5)] (4); it's Tue., so wrong hole is Mon. (2), whiffed ball is Wed., and Butler's Thu. (5). Wed. is hole 15 [Linden], so sand is Thu. (4). Riverview isn't hole 9 [water hazard would be hole 15 [whiffed] (3)]; it's hole 6, so water's hole 12 (3). Willow Brook is rough and hole 9.

In summary:
Mon., Riverview, wrong hole, 6
Tue., Schenley Park, water hazard, 12
Wed., Linden Hall, whiffed ball, 15
Thu., Butler's, sand trap, 18
Fri., Willow Brook, rough, 9

LOGIC PROBLEM 62

Masterworks [invisible ink (3)] isn't Therrien (4), Dugdale, Ambrose (5), or Martin (6); it's Sawyer. Datatron isn't Ambrose (1), Therrien (3), or Dugdale (6); it's Martin. Troubador isn't Ambrose (1) or Therrien (6); it's Dugdale. Ambrose isn't Alliance (6); he's Productivity. Therrien is Alliance. Sawyer [Masterworks, invisible ink] isn't lentil (2), lima bean [moisturizer (2)], chickpea, or tamarind (3); he's navy bean. Martin [Datatron] isn't chickpea (3), lima bean, or lentil (4); he's tamarind. Ambrose [Productivity] isn't chickpea (1) or lima bean (2); he's lentil. Therrien isn't chickpea (3); he's lima bean. Dugdale is chickpea. Lighter fluid isn't Dugdale or Ambrose (5); it's Martin. Dugdale [chickpea] isn't milk substitute (1); he's scouring powder. Ambrose is milk.

In summary:
Dr. Ambrose, Productivity, lentil, milk substitute
Dr. Dugdale, Troubador, chickpea, scouring powder
Dr. Martin, Datatron, tamarind, lighter fluid
Dr. Sawyer, Masterworks, navy bean, invisible ink
Dr. Therrien, Alliance, lima bean, moisturizer

LOGIC PROBLEM 63

Boys are Bela, Duke, and Tor, girls are Joanna and Mona, and mins. are 15, 30, 45, 60, and 75 (intro.). Peanut butter [asleep 1st, so 15 min. (3)] isn't Bela, Duke (1), Joanna, or Mona (4); it's Tor. Mona isn't chocolate chip, pumpkinseed (1), or sugar (2); she's oatmeal. Joanna isn't chocolate chip or pumpkinseed

(1); she's sugar, so isn't witch (1), cat [Tor (1)], ghost, or jack-o'-lantern (2), so is spider. Duke isn't ghost (1) or jack-o'-lantern (3); he's witch. Bela isn't jack-o'-lantern (3); he's ghost. Mona's jack-o'-lantern. 45 min. boy (4) isn't Bela [ghost] (4); he's Duke, and isn't chocolate chip (4), so is pumpkinseed. Bela's chocolate chip. Joanna [spider] isn't 30 (3) or 75 min. [last] (4); she's 60 min. Mona isn't 75 min. [last] (4); she's 30 min. Bela's 75 min.

In summary:

Bela, chocolate chip, ghost, 75

Duke, pumpkinseed, witch, 45

Joanna, sugar, spider, 60

Mona, oatmeal, jack-o'-lantern, 30

Tor, peanut butter, cat, 15

LOGIC PROBLEM 64

Days are Mon.-Sat. (intro.). Madrid isn't Troy (1), Mike (3), Yvonne, Doreen (5), or Saul (6); it's Babs, so isn't Tue., Wed. (3), Thu., Sat. [last], or Mon. [1st] (7), so is Fri., so Saul is Sat. [last], and Rome is Thu. (7). Saul [Sat. [last]] isn't Moscow (6); he's Brussels (6). Paris isn't Tue. or Wed. (4); it's Mon. London isn't Tue. (4); it's Wed. Moscow's Tue. Mike isn't Mon. [Paris], Tue., or Wed. (3); he's Thu. Doreen isn't Mon. [1st] or Tue. [Moscow] (2); she's Wed. Troy's Mon., and Yvonne's Tue. (1).

In summary:

Babs, Madrid, Fri.

Doreen, London, Wed.

Mike, Rome, Thu.

Saul, Brussels, Sat.

Troy, Paris, Mon.

Yvonne, Moscow, Tue.

LOGIC PROBLEM 65

Yrs. are 1868, 1871, 1873, 1874, and 1876 (intro.). 2nd isn't 1868 (2), 1871 (3), 1876 [last] (5), or 1874 [South Pass City would be 1873, and railroad would be 1876 (5), but farming couldn't be 1876 [railroad] or 1874 [2nd] (1), so couldn't be placed in (6)]; it's 1873, so South Pass City is 1871, and railroad is 1874 (5). Farming isn't 1873 [2nd], 1868 [1st] (1), or 1871 [South Pass City] (6); it's 1876, so Medicine Bow is 1873 (1). Hadeyville isn't 1874 [railroad] or 1868 (2); it's 1876. 4th isn't railroad [South Pass City and 1868 couldn't both be placed (2)], farming [Hadeyville, so South Pass City and 1868 couldn't both be placed (2)], trading post (3), or gold mining [5th [last] (4)]; it's cattle ranching. 2nd isn't farming (1) or railroad (5); it's trading post, so Alden's Grove is 3rd, and 1871 is 4th (3). 3rd [Alden's] isn't farming

[Hadeyville]; it's railroad. 1st's farming. 5th's Fort Custer and 1868.

In summary:

1st, Hadeyville, 1876, farming

2nd, Medicine Bow, 1873, trading post

3rd, Alden's Grove, 1874, railroad

4th, South Pass City, 1871, cattle ranching

5th, Fort Custer, 1868, gold mining

LOGIC PROBLEM 66

Depths are 1,600, 2,600, 4,600, 6,600, and 7,600 ft. (intro.). 1,600 ft. [shallowest] isn't *Deep Rover* (1), *Nautile* [7,600 ft. [deepest] (3)], *Shinkai 6500* (4), or *Alvin* (5); it's *Deep Flight I*. *Shinkai 6500* isn't 2,600 [lower than only 1,600 ft.] or 4,600 ft. (4); it's 6,600 ft. *Alvin* is 4,600 ft., and *Deep Rover* [anglerfish (1)] is 2,600 ft. (5), so cranchiid squid is 1,600 ft. (1). 7,600 ft. [deepest, *Nautile*] isn't fangtooth (2) or gulper eel (3); it's deep-sea shrimp. Fangtooth [Pratt (2)] is 4,600 ft., and eel is 6,600 ft. (2). *Nautile* [7,600 ft., shrimp] isn't Baker (3), Dodd, or Abbott (4); it's Morgan. *Shinkai 6500* isn't Dodd or Abbott (4); it's Baker. *Deep Flight I* [1,600 ft. [shallowest]] isn't Abbott (4); it's Dodd. Abbott's *Deep Rover*.

In summary:

Abbott, *Deep Rover*, anglerfish, 2,600

Baker, *Shinkai 6500*, gulper eel, 6,600

Dodd, *Deep Flight I*, cranchiid squid, 1,600

Morgan, *Nautile*, deep-sea shrimp, 7,600

Pratt, *Alvin*, fangtooth, 4,600

LOGIC PROBLEM 67

Living room isn't bureau, chair, shelf [clock (5)] (1), or curtains (3); it's table, so isn't figurine (1), vase, or picture (3), so is plant. 5th [last, chair (4)] isn't clock [shelf], plant (2), figurine [1st (4)], or picture (5); it's vase. 1st [figurine] isn't table [plant], bureau (2), or shelf (5); it's curtains. Picture's bureau. 4th isn't plant [bureau would be 5th [chair] (2)] or picture [shelf would be 5th [chair] (5)]; it's clock. Bureau isn't 2nd (2); it's 3rd, so plant's 2nd, and kitchen's 1st (2). 5th [chair, vase] isn't bedroom (1) or dining room (3); it's bathroom. Bedroom isn't 3rd [bureau] (2); it's 4th. Dining room's 3rd.

In summary (order, room, furnishing, item):

1st, kitchen, curtains, figurine

2nd, living room, table, plant

3rd, dining room, bureau, picture

4th, bedroom, shelf, clock

5th, bathroom, chair, vase

LOGIC PROBLEM 68

Women are Alma Kern, Mae Morris, and Karla Olivet, and men are Horace Brown and Tony Boot (intro.). *Winner's Circle* isn't Mae Morris (2), Tony Boot, Karla Olivet, or Alma Kern (4); it's Horace Brown, so *Autumn Heat* is Tony Boot [only man left] (1). *Quarter Moon* isn't Mae Morris (2) or Alma Kern (5); it's Karla Olivet. *Last Dance* isn't Alma Kern (3); it's Mae Morris. *Lazy Dogs* is Alma Kern. Carly isn't Tony Boot [Adele Pogozowski (4)]; she's Horace Brown [only B surname left] (2). Sonya [unmarried (1)] isn't *Lazy Dogs* [Joan (3)] or *Last Dance* (3); she's *Quarter Moon*. Ann's *Last Dance*. Carly [*Winner's Circle*, Horace Brown [man]] isn't Reed (1), Wood [*Last Dance* (3)], or Booker [*Quarter Moon* (5)]; she's Young. Joan's Reed.

In summary:

Adele Pogozowski, *Autumn Heat*, Tony Boot
Ann Wood, *Last Dance*, Mae Morris
Carly Young, *Winner's Circle*, Horace Brown
Joan Reed, *Lazy Dogs*, Alma Kern
Sonya Booker, *Quarter Moon*, Karla Olivet

LOGIC PROBLEM 69

Women are Ann, June, and Sheila, and men are George and Les (intro.). Ann isn't alto (1), tenor (2), pianist (4), or flutist [man (4)]; she's soprano. June isn't flutist [man], tenor (2), or pianist (5); she's alto, so isn't not needed (1), left at work (2), dog ate [Berlioz (3)], or lost [man (5)], so is children scribbled. Ann isn't lost [man], dog [Berlioz], or work (2); she's not needed. Tenor isn't dog [Berlioz] or work (2); that one's lost, so is a man (above), so isn't Les (3), so is George [only man left]. Flutist is Les [only man left] (4). Sheila's pianist. Les isn't dog (3); he's work. Sheila's dog. June [children] isn't Verdi (3), Handel (4), or Schubert (5); she's Mozart. Ann [soprano] isn't Handel (4) or Schubert (5); she's Verdi. George [lost] isn't Schubert (5); he's Handel. Les is Schubert.

In summary:

Ann, soprano, Verdi, not needed
George, tenor, Handel, lost
June, alto, Mozart, children scribbled
Les, flutist, Schubert, left at work
Sheila, pianist, Berlioz, dog ate

LOGIC PROBLEM 70

Men are Jeff and Will, women are Pamela and Tanya, and amts. are $20, $21, $23, and $24 (intro.). 1st isn't Jeff, Will (1), or Pamela [4th [last] (3)]; it's Tanya. Jeff isn't $20, $24 (1), or $23 [couldn't be 2nd or 3rd (3), so couldn't be placed]; he's $21, so is 3rd [only possible in (3)]. Will's 2nd, and isn't $20 or $24 (1); he's $23. Slippery C. isn't $21 [Jeff], $23 [Will], or $24 [most] (4); it's $20. Delicious D. isn't $21 [Buster Move would be $20 [Slippery C., and no $22 (2)] or $24 [Pamela would be $21 [Jeff, and no $27 (2)]; it's $23, so Pamela's $20 [no $26], and Buster Move is $24 [no $22] (2). Tanya's $24. Ice Kream is $21.

In summary:

Jeff, Ice Kream, $21, 3rd
Pamela, Slippery C., $20, 4th
Tanya, Buster Move, $24, 1st
Will, Delicious D., $23, 2nd

LOGIC PROBLEM 71

Dr. Swami isn't vacation (5); he's birthday, and clear is vacation (2). Rita Sunshine [rain (3)] isn't WILL, WISH (5), or KELP or KNOW [couldn't be vacation [clear], so couldn't be placed in (5)]; she's WHEW, so isn't vacation [clear], crafts show (4), or fan club [Prognosticator (5)], so is agricultural fair. Wacky Waldo isn't crafts show (1); he's vacation, so isn't KNOW (1), so is KELP, and Dr. Swami is KNOW (5). Clint Isobar is crafts show, so isn't sleet or hail (4); he's snow. Prognosticator isn't sleet (5); he's hail. Dr. Swami is sleet. Clint Isobar [snow] isn't WILL (6); he's WISH. Prognosticator is WILL.

In summary:

Clint Isobar, WISH, snow, crafts show
Dr. Swami, KNOW, sleet, birthday
Prognosticator, WILL, hail, fan club
Rita Sunshine, WHEW, rain, agricultural fair
Wacky Waldo, KELP, clear, vacation

LOGIC PROBLEM 72

Exhibit nos., from left to right, are 101-106, and 1 is proto-Attic, 1 is proto-Corinthian, 2 are black figure, and 2 are red figure (intro.). Stamnos isn't proto-Corinthian [kylix (1)]; it's proto-Attic, and no. 105 is proto-Corinthian [kylix] (3), so hydria is no. 106 (1, above). No. 105 isn't Perseus saving Andromeda [no. 102 (2)], Leda and the Swan (3), Abduction of Helen [red-figure urns couldn't be placed (4)], Judgment of Paris, or Odysseus and the Sirens (5); it's Hercules and Cerberus. No. 102 is black figure (2), so other black figure [pithos (2)] isn't no. 106 [hydria], 101, or 103 (6); it's no. 104. No. 101 isn't red figure (4, illus.); it's proto-Attic. Nos. 103 and 106 are red figure [only left], so amphora is no. 102, and Abduction of Helen is no. 101 (4). Deinos is no. 103 [red], so isn't Judgment

344

of Paris or Odysseus and the Sirens (5); it's Leda and the Swan. Hydria [red] isn't Judgment of Paris (5); it's Odysseus and the Sirens. Pithos is Judgment of Paris.

In summary:

Amphora, 102, Perseus saving Andromeda, black figure

Deinos, 103, Leda and the Swan, red figure

Hydria, 106, Odysseus and the Sirens, red figure

Kylix, 105, Hercules and Cerberus, proto-Corinthian

Pithos, 104, Judgment of Paris, black figure

Stamnos, 101, Abduction of Helen, proto-Attic

LOGIC PROBLEM 73

Women are Angela and Jesse, men are Delbert, Skip, and Ty, rolls are 7-11, and cities are 25, 30, 35, 40, and 45 (intro.). 25 cities [least] isn't 10 (1), 7 [least], 8 [no 6 rolls] (2), or 11 rolls (4); it's 9 rolls, so Angela's 7 rolls (2). 35 cities [Iron Petticoats (3)] isn't 11 [most], 10 [no 12 rolls] (3), or 7 rolls [Jesse would be 9 rolls [25 cities, so man (2)] (3)]; it's 8 rolls, so Jesse's 10 rolls (3), and Watercoolers is 45 cities (5). 10 rolls isn't Starched Collars, Portentous Pilots, or Watercoolers [45 cities [most]] (1); it's Elbow Room. 25 cities [least, 9 rolls] isn't Elbow Room [10 rolls] or Portentous Pilots (1); it's Starched Collars. 30 cities isn't Portentous Pilots (1); it's Elbow Room [10 rolls], so Delbert's 25 cities (1). Portentous Pilots is 40 cities. Ty isn't 11 rolls (4); he's 8 rolls. Skip's 11 rolls. Angela isn't Portentous Pilots (2); she's Watercoolers. Skip's Portentous Pilots.

In summary (roadie, band, rolls, cities):

Angela, Watercoolers, 7, 45

Delbert, Starched Collars, 9, 25

Jesse, Elbow Room, 10, 30

Skip, Portentous Pilots, 11, 40

Ty, Iron Petticoats, 8, 35

LOGIC PROBLEM 74

Weeknights are Mon.-Fri. (intro.). Wife isn't Elvis [opera (3)], clown face, or Star Trek (2); she's Escher or Spiderman, so isn't Mon., Tue. (1), Fri. [last] (2), or Thu. [mother would be Fri. [last] (2), but then coworker couldn't be placed (4)], so is Wed., so mother's Thu. (2), and coworker's Fri. (4). Clown face isn't Wed. [wife], Tue. [Star Trek would be Wed. [wife] (5)] (2), Fri. [last] (5), or Thu. [Star Trek would be Fri. (5), and Escher couldn't be Mon. or Tue. (1), so Wed., but then Spiderman couldn't be Mon. or Tue. (1), so couldn't be placed]; it's Mon., so Star Trek's Tue. (5). Elvis [opera] isn't Wed. [wife]

(2) or Thu. [mother] (3); it's Fri. Spiderman isn't Thu. [mother] (2); it's Wed. Escher's Thu. Son isn't Star Trek (5); he's clown face. Aunt is Star Trek. Card game isn't Mon., Tue. (1), or Thu. [ball game would be Fri. [opera] (1)]; it's Wed., so ball game's Thu. (1). Movie isn't Tue. [Star Trek] (5); it's Mon. Fundraiser's Tue.

In summary:

Mon., clown face, son, movie

Tue., Star Trek, aunt, fundraiser

Wed., Spiderman, wife, card game

Thu., Escher, mother, ball game

Fri., Elvis, coworker, opera

LOGIC PROBLEM 75

Total no. of goals is 24, and each girl scored a different no. of goals (intro.). Uniform nos. are 6, 10, 12, 20, and 24 (intro.). Alice [most (1)] isn't score 24 [total no. of goals (above)], 20 [least possible total would be 30 goals [20 [most] + 1 + 2 + 3 + 4 = 30], but 24 goals total (above)], 6 [most possible total would be 20 goals [6 [most] + 5 + 4 + 3 + 2 = 20], but 24 goals total (above)], or 12 goals [Ellis would be 6 goals (1)] (1); she's 10 goals [only uniform no. left], so Ellis is 5 goals (1). Alice is 10 goals, Ellis is 5 goals, and Mary is 4 goals (4), so the other 2 girls scored a total of 5 goals [24 − 10 − 5 − 4 = 5], and aren't 0 and 5, or 1 and 4 goals [Mary 4 goals] (intro.); they're 2 and 3 goals, so goals are 2, 3, 4, 5, and 10 (above). Alice [10 goals [most]] isn't Ellis [5 goals], Loving (2), Jones [Audrey (3)], or Smith [Audrey Jones would be 5 goals [Ellis] (3)]; she's Holland. Audrey Jones isn't score 5 [Ellis] or 3 goals [no 6 goals] (3); she's 2 goals, so Smith's 4 goals (3). Loving's 3 goals. Beth isn't no. 12 [Mary would be no. 24 [highest] (4)] (2), 20 [no no. 40], 24 [no no. 48] (4), or 6 [Mary Smith would be no. 12 [Ellis (4)] (4)]; she's no. 10, so Mary is no. 20 (4), and Alice Holland's no. 24 [highest] (2). Audrey Jones isn't no. 12 [Ellis]; she's no. 6. Becca's no. 12. Beth is Loving.

In summary (1st & last names, uniform no., goals):

Alice Holland, 24, 10

Audrey Jones, 6, 2

Becca Ellis, 12, 5

Beth Loving, 10, 3

Mary Smith, 20, 4

LOGIC PROBLEM 76

4 are women, and 2 are men (intro.). Robin and Sydney are *Gazette* local news and sports, and were college local and sports, in some order (4), but col-

lege local isn't *Gazette* local (6); college local is *Gazette* sports, and college sports is *Gazette* local. College entertainment man (2) isn't *Gazette* op-ed [woman (1)], national news [college puzzles (2)], or entertainment (6); he's *Gazette* puzzles. College op-ed isn't *Gazette* op-ed (6); that one's *Gazette* entertainment. College national is *Gazette* op-ed. Nicky's college isn't op-ed [man would be *Gazette* op-ed [woman] (2)], entertainment [man would be *Gazette* entertainment [college op-ed, so woman (1)] (2)], national [man would be *Gazette* national [woman (1)] (2)], local, or sports (4); it's puzzles [*Gazette* national], so Tyler's college national (3). Drew's college isn't local, sports (4), or op-ed (5); it's entertainment. Blair's college isn't local or sports (4); it's op-ed. The 4 women's college are sports, op-ed, puzzles [*Gazette* national], and national [*Gazette* op-ed] (1), so the 2 men's college are entertainment and local [only left]. Robin's college [woman (5)] isn't local [man (above)]; it's sports. Sydney's college is local.

In summary (person, college, *Gazette*):

Blair, op-ed, entertainment; Drew, entertainment, puzzles; Nicky, puzzles, national news; Robin, sports, local news; Sydney, local news, sports; Tyler, national news, op-ed.

LOGIC PROBLEM 77

Mos. are Jan., Feb., Apr., May, and July, and dates are 3rd, 7th, 13th, 22nd, and 29th (intro.). Suzanne isn't 22nd, 3rd (1), 29th [Brad (2)], or 7th (4); she's 13th. Steffi isn't July [last] (4), February [no Mar.] (4), Apr. [Steffi [Abby or Roger (4)] couldn't be 13th [Suzanne], 29th [Brad], 22nd, 3rd (1), or 7th (4), so couldn't be placed], or May [Mary (5)]; she's Jan., so Suzanne's Feb. (4). Steffi [Jan. [1st]] isn't Abby (3); she's Roger (above). Miranda isn't Apr. or Feb. [Suzanne] (1); she's July, so isn't 22nd, 3rd (1), or 29th [Brad] (2), so is 7th. Apr. isn't 22nd or 3rd (1); it's 29th. May isn't 3rd (5); it's 22nd. Jan. is 3rd. Tasha isn't Apr. [Brad] (2); she's Feb. Amelia's Apr., so Abby's July pool (3). Ilse's May.

In summary (mo., mother, winner, date):

Jan., Steffi, Roger, 3rd

Feb., Tasha, Suzanne, 13th

Apr., Amelia, Brad, 29th

May, Mary, Ilse, 22nd

July, Miranda, Abby, 7th

LOGIC PROBLEM 78

Lbs. are 2, 4, 6, 8, and 10 (intro.). One was in Oakwoods Forest, 1 in Silent Woods (2), 2 in Tallpines Wood, and 1 in Darkwood Forest (3). Penelope isn't Oakwoods, Silent (2), or Tallpines (3); she's Darkwood, so isn't golden chanterelles (2), morels (3), oyster mushrooms [Theo (4)], or edible boletes (5), so is field mushrooms. Boletes isn't Silent or Tallpines (5); it's Oakwoods. Oyster [Theo] isn't Silent (1); it's Tallpines. Chanterelles aren't Silent (2); they're Tallpines [Ralph (3)]. Morels is Silent. 10 lbs. [most] isn't morels, field [Darkwood] (3), oyster [Theo [Tallpines], so Darkwood [field] would be 8 lbs. (3)] (1), or boletes (5); it's chanterelles. 2 lbs. [least] isn't Penelope [Darkwood] (3), Stacey, or Theo (4); it's Otto. 8 lbs. isn't Penelope [field] (1) or Stacey [Theo would be 10 lbs. [Ralph] (4)]; it's Theo [Tallpines], so Darkwood's 6 lbs., and morels is 4 lbs. (3). Stacey's 4 lbs. Otto's boletes.

In summary:

Otto, edible boletes, 2, Oakwoods Forest

Penelope, field mushrooms, 6, Darkwood Forest

Ralph, golden chanterelles, 10, Tallpines Wood

Stacey, morels, 4, Silent Woods

Theo, oyster mushrooms, 8, Tallpines Wood

LOGIC PROBLEM 79

Men are Dan Rainfeather, Joseph Red Crow, and Leroy Horsetamer, women are Kim Two Clouds and Wilma Little Bear, and yrs. are 1820, 1835, 1850, 1865, and 1880 (intro.). Moccasins man (2) isn't Leroy Horsetamer [shirt (2)] or Joseph Red Crow (5); he's Dan Rainfeather. Drum [30 yrs. older than bowl (1)] isn't Wilma Little Bear [30 yrs. older than Dan Rainfeather [moccasins] (3)] or Joseph Red Crow (5); it's Kim Two Clouds, so isn't 1880 [youngest], 1865 [no 1895] (1), 1820 [oldest] (3), or 1835 [Wilma Little Bear would be 1820, and Dan Rainfeather [moccasins] would be 1850 (3), but then Leroy Horsetamer couldn't be placed (2)], so is 1850, so bowl is 1880 (1), Wilma Little Bear is 1835, and Dan Rainfeather is 1865 (3). Leroy Horsetamer isn't 1880 [youngest] (2); he's 1820. Joseph Red Crow is 1880. Wilma Little Bear is pipe. Araphao isn't 1820 [oldest], 1880 [youngest], 1865 [no 1895], or 1835 [Pawnee would be 1820 [shirt] (4)] (4); it's 1850, so Comanche's 1880 (4). Pawnee isn't from 1820 [shirt] (4); it's 1835 [only other yr. before 1850 [Arapaho]] (4). Kiowa isn't 1865 [moccasins] (2); it's 1820. Osage is 1865.

In summary:

Bowl, Joseph Red Crow, Comanche, 1880

Drum, Kim Two Clouds, Arapaho, 1850

Moccasins, Dan Rainfeather, Osage, 1865

Pipe, Wilma Little Bear, Pawnee, 1835

Shirt, Leroy Horsetamer, Kiowa, 1820

LOGIC PROBLEM 80

Expert of Champion Cape Cod isn't Cape Cod (intro.), Colonial, Georgian (1), or ranch [Champion Georgian (4)]; it's Victorian. Expert of Champion ranch isn't Colonial or Georgian (1); it's Cape Cod. Expert of Champion Colonial isn't Colonial (intro.); it's Georgian. Expert of Champion Victorian is Colonial. Abe's Expert [Ace Colonial (3)] isn't Colonial, Georgian [Champion Colonial] (intro.), ranch, or Cape Cod [Champion ranch] (3); it's Victorian [Champion Cape Cod], so Nelson and Quinn are Ace Cape Cod and Expert Cape Cod, in some order [only Cape Cods left] (2). Rory's Expert isn't Cape Cod [Nelson or Quinn (above)], Georgian, or ranch [Champion Georgian] (2); it's Colonial, so Ace isn't Cape Cod [Nelson or Quinn (above)], Victorian (intro.), or Georgian (2), so is ranch. Expert of Ace Georgian isn't Georgian or ranch [Champion Georgian] (intro.); it's Cape Cod. Expert of Ace Victorian isn't Georgian (1); it's ranch. Expert of Ace Cape Cod is Georgian. Ace Victorian [Champion Georgian, Expert ranch] isn't Nelson or Quinn (2); it's Forrest. Quinn isn't Ace Georgian (5); Nelson is. Quinn's Ace Cape Cod.

In summary (man, Ace, Champion, Expert):

Abe, Colonial, Cape Cod, Victorian

Forrest, Victorian, Georgian, ranch

Nelson, Georgian, ranch, Cape Cod

Quinn, Cape Cod, Colonial, Georgian

Rory, ranch, Victorian, Colonial

LOGIC PROBLEM 81

Men are Brad, Kent, and Neil, and women are Leslie and Tara (intro.). Times left are 6:50, 6:55, 7:00, 7:05, and 7:10 a.m. (intro.). Each travel time was at least 2 hr. but fewer than 2 hr. 30 min., and each travel time was in multiples of 5 min. (intro.). Civic woman [history (2)] isn't Leslie [art (4)]; she's Tara. Mustang isn't Neil, Brad, or Leslie (4); it's Kent. Camaro isn't Neil or Brad (4); it's Leslie. Brad didn't leave at 7:10 [last, so Neil (2)], 6:50 [1st], 7:05 [before only 7:10 [Neil]] (3), or 7:00 [Kent couldn't have left at 6:50 [1st] or 7:05, so couldn't be placed in (3)]; he left at 6:55, so Leslie left at 6:50, and Kent didn't leave at 7:00 (3), so he left at 7:05. Tara left at 7:00. Leslie [left at 6:50] had same travel time as Tara [left at 7:00] (1), but not 2 hr. 25 min., 2 hr. [least, so would have same travel time as Neil (2), but then 3 would have same time] (1), 2 hr. 5 min. [Neil's travel time [least] couldn't be 2 hr. 5 min. [would be 3 with same travel time] (1) or 2 hr. [5 min. shorter than next longest travel time [2 hr. 5 min.]] (1), so couldn't be

placed], 2 hr. 20 min. [Tara [left at 7:00] would arrive at 9:20] (3), or 2 hr. 15 min. [Tara [left at 7:00] would arrive at 9:15] (4); it was 2 hr. 10 min., so Leslie arrived at 9:00, and Tara arrived at 9:10 (1). Neil's travel time [least, left at 7:00] was at least 10 min. shorter than 2 hr. 10 min. [Leslie] (1); it was 2 hr. [least possible], so he arrived at 9:10, and isn't Cherokee (4), so is Explorer. Brad's Cherokee. Arrived at 9:20 (3) isn't Brad [left at 6:55, so travel time would've been 2 hr. 25 min.] (1); he's Kent. Brad arrived at 9:15 (4).

In summary:

Brad, Cherokee, 6:55 a.m., 9:15 a.m.

Kent, Mustang, 7:05 a.m., 9:20 a.m.

Leslie, Camaro, 6:50 a.m., 9:00 a.m.

Neil, Explorer, 7:10 a.m., 9:10 a.m.

Tara, Civic, 7:00 a.m., 9:10 a.m.

LOGIC PROBLEM 82

Fleurs-de-lis [Beatnik Chicks (4)] isn't Theo [Worm Farm (2)] or Xavier [Crawdad (2)]; it's *Frankentomato* [only possible in (2)]. *Get to Work!* isn't snowmen, bananas [white V neck (1)] (1), or hearts [*Cotton* (4)]; it's drumsticks. *Superimplosion* isn't snowmen (3); it's bananas. *Ten Decibels* is snowmen. Drumsticks [*Work!*, Beatnik Chicks (2)] isn't white crew neck (1), gray V neck (2), or gray crew neck [Worm Farm (4)]; it's tank top, so isn't Uriah (1), Theo, Xavier (2), or Winona (3), so is Valerie. Fleurs-de-lis [*Frankentomato*, Beatnik Chicks] isn't gray crew neck [Worm Farm] or gray V neck (2); it's white crew neck, so isn't Uriah (1), Theo, or Xavier (2), so is Winona. Uriah isn't snowmen or bananas (1); he's hearts. Xavier [Crawdad (2)] isn't gray crew [Worm Farm] or gray V neck (2); he's white V neck. Theo's snowmen, and isn't gray V neck (2); he's gray crew neck. Uriah is gray V neck.

In summary:

Theo, snowmen, gray crew neck, *Ten Decibels*

Uriah, hearts, gray V neck, *Cotton*

Valerie, drumsticks, tank top, *Get to Work!*

Winona, fleurs-de-lis, white crew neck, *Frankentomato*

Xavier, bananas, white V neck, *Superimplosion*

LOGIC PROBLEM 83

Dates are 23rd, 24th, 25th, 26th, 29th, and 31st (intro.). Diana's new date isn't 31st [last], 29th [no 30th], 26th [no 27th], 23rd [Diana's original date would be 24th (5)] (5), or 24th [Kat's original date would be 24th (4), and Diana's original date would be 25th (5), so one originally scheduled for the 24th

347

would have new date of 25th (5), so Vinson's new date would be 24th [Diana's new date] (3)]; it's 25th, so Kat's original date is 25th (4), Diana's original date is 26th, the person whose new date is 26th is originally scheduled for 24th (5), and Vinson's new date is 26th (3). Zack's original date isn't 31st [last] (1) or 23rd [Zack's new date would be original date of one whose new date is 25th (1), so would be 26th [Vinson's new date] (above)]; it's 29th, so the original date of one whose new date is 31st is Zack's new date (1). One whose new date is 31st isn't originally scheduled for 31st (intro.), 29th [Zack's original date 29th] (1), or 25th [Zack's new date would be 25th [Diana's new date] (1, above)]; it's 23rd, so Zack's new date is 23rd (1). Kat's new date [original date 25th] isn't 31st [original date 23rd] or 24th [George's new date would be 23rd [1st, Zack's new date] (2)]; it's 29th. George's new date isn't 31st [last] (2); it's 24th. Layla's new date is 31st. George's original date is 31st.

In summary (person, original date, new date):
Diana, 26th, 25th
George, 31st, 24th
Kat, 25th, 29th
Layla, 23rd, 31st
Vinson, 24th, 26th
Zack, 29th, 23rd

LOGIC PROBLEM 84

Times are at quarter past [:15], half past [:30], quarter of [:45], or on the hour [:00] (intro.). Earliest possible time is 10:30 a.m. (intro.), and last is 2:00 p.m. (4). Boardwalk isn't 10:45 a.m. [penny would be 1:45 p.m., and ring would be 2:00 p.m. [silver dollar (4)] (1)] or 11:00 a.m. or later [penny would be at least 2:00 p.m. [last], so ring couldn't be placed (1)]; it's 10:30 a.m., so penny is 1:30 p.m., and ring is 1:45 p.m. (1). Necklace isn't 10:45 (2), 10:30 [1st, so spoon couldn't be placed (2)], or 11:15 or later [last [2:00] would be 2:15 or later (2)]; it's 11:00, so rocks is 2:00 (2). Dunes is 12:15 (3), so 6 times are 10:30, 11:00, 12:15, 1:30, 1:45, and 2:00 (above), and pier is 11:00 [only time left before 12:15 (above)] (3). Spoon is 10:30 [boardwalk, necklace 11:00] (2, above), so aluminum foil is dunes [12:15]. Tin can is 11:00 [2nd (above)] (4). Key chain is 1:45 (above). Playground isn't 1:30 p.m. [penny] (5); it's 1:45 p.m. Beach is 1:30 p.m. Medallion is 10:30 a.m., wristwatch is 12:15 p.m., and gold doubloon is 1:30 p.m. (6).
In summary:
10:30 a.m., boardwalk, medallion, spoon

348

11:00 a.m., pier, necklace, tin can
12:15 p.m., dunes, wristwatch, aluminum foil
1:30 p.m., beach, gold doubloon, penny
1:45 p.m., playground, ring, key chain
2:00 p.m., rocks, silver dollar, bottle cap

LOGIC PROBLEM 85

Sec. are 4, 5, 6, 7, 9, and 10, bull's-eyes are 3, 4, 6, 7, 8, and 9, and boomerangs are 2, 3, 4, 6, 7, and 8 (intro.). 2 boomerangs [least] isn't 7 (1), 9 (3), 10 [4 bull's-eyes would be 9 sec. (5), which isn't possible [no 5 bull's-eyes] (3)], 6 (4), or 4 sec. [least] (5); it's 5 sec., so 4 bull's-eyes is 4 sec. (5). 6 sec. isn't 7, 3 [no 5 bull's-eyes], 8 [no 10 bull's-eyes], or 9 bull's-eyes [most] (4); it's 6 bull's-eyes, so 2 boomerangs is 8 bull's-eyes (4). Cameron is 4 sec. [only time faster than 5 sec. [8 bull's-eyes] (above)] (2). 7 sec. isn't 3 [Gillian would be 4 bull's-eyes [Cameron] (1)] or 9 bull's-eyes [most] (1); it's 7 bull's-eyes, so Gillian is 8 bull's-eyes (1). 9 sec. isn't 9 bull's-eyes [most] (3); it's 3 bull's-eyes, so 7 boomerangs is 4 bull's-eyes (3), and Robin's 8 boomerangs [most] (5). 10 sec. is 9 bull's-eyes. 3 boomerangs [1 sec. slower than Max [8 bull's-eyes is 2 boomerangs] (2)] isn't 9 [no 8 sec.] (2), 7 [7 bull's-eyes, and no 1 boomerang], or 6 sec. [no 5 boomerangs] (4); it's 10 sec., so Max is 9 sec. [8 bull's-eyes is 2 boomerangs, and 3 boomerangs is 10 sec.] (2). 8 boomerangs [most, Robin] isn't 9 [Max] or 6 sec. [no 10 boomerangs] (4); it's 7 sec. [7 bull's-eyes], so 6 sec. is 6 boomerangs (4). 9 sec. is 4 boomerangs. William isn't 6 boomerangs [9 sec. is 4 boomerangs] (3); Kroc is. William's 3 boomerangs.
In summary (contestant, sec., bull's-eyes, boomerangs):
Cameron, 4, 4, 7
Gillian, 5, 8, 2
Kroc, 6, 6, 6
Max, 9, 3, 4
Robin, 7, 7, 8
William, 10, 9, 3

LOGIC PROBLEM 86

5th [last] isn't Pittsburgh (1), Chicago (2), Memphis (3), or Houston (4); it's Cincinnati. Houston isn't 3rd, 4th (4), or 2nd [Brooklyn would be 4th, and Rex would be 5th (4), but then Gwynne couldn't be 1st, 4th [Brooklyn] (1), 3rd [Pittsburgh couldn't be 1st or 2nd (5), so couldn't be placed (1)], or 2nd [Pittsburgh would be 1st (1)] (5), so couldn't be placed]; it's 1st, so Brooklyn's 3rd (4). Bronx isn't 1st, 5th [last] (5), or 4th [Pittsburgh would be 5th [Cincinnati] (5)]; it's 2nd, so Isabel's 1st (5). 2nd [Houston 1st] isn't

Gwynne (1), Vinnie (3), or Rex (4); it's Thelma. 3rd isn't Rex (4) or Gwynne [Pittsburgh would be 2nd [Bronx] (1)] (5); it's Vinnie, so Memphis is 2nd [Houston 1st] (3). Manhattan isn't Isabel or Rex (3); it's Gwynne. Isabel [1st] isn't Staten Island (2); Rex is. Isabel's Queens. Rex isn't Pittsburgh or Chicago (2); he's Cincinnati. Gwynne's 4th, so Pittsburgh's 3rd (1). Chicago's 4th.

In summary:
1st, Isabel, Houston, Queens
2nd, Thelma, Memphis, Bronx
3rd, Vinnie, Pittsburgh, Brooklyn
4th, Gwynne, Chicago, Manhattan
5th, Rex, Cincinnati, Staten Island

LOGIC PROBLEM 87

Days are Sun., Mon., Tue., Thu., Fri., and Sat., cardinals are 5, 6, 7, 8, 10, and 11, and chickadees are 6, 7, 8, 9, 11, and 12 (intro.). 7 cardinals isn't 11 [Sat. [last] would be 8 cardinals, which isn't possible (1)], 6 [least], 7 [no 5 chickadees], 8, or 12 chickadees [no 10 chickadees] (4); it's 9 chickadees, so Sat. is 7 chickadees (4). 11 chickadees isn't 8 [no 9 cardinals], 11 [most] (1), 10 [no 10 chickadees] (3), or 6 cardinals [Sat. would be 7 cardinals (1)] (4); it's 5 cardinals, so Sat. is 6 cardinals (1). Ryder is 5 cardinals [only no. less than 6 cardinals [7 chickadees]] (2). 8 cardinals isn't 6 [least] (1) or 12 chickadees [Tina would be 11 chickadees [Ryder] (1)]; it's 8 chickadees, so Tina is 7 chickadees (1). 10 cardinals isn't 6 chickadees [least] (3); it's 12 chickadees, so Mon. is 11 chickadees (3). 11 cardinals is 6 chickadees. Henry's Sun. [only day before Mon. [11 chickadees]] (1). Fri. isn't 10 [Max would be Sat. [last, Tina] (3)], 7 [no Wed.], or 8 cardinals [8 chickadees, and Sat. last] (4); it's 11 cardinals [most], so Carol's 10 cardinals [Sat. 7 chickadees] (2). Henry [Sun. [1st]] isn't 11 [Fri.] or 7 cardinals (4); he's 8 cardinals [8 chickadees], so Tue. is 7 cardinals (4). 10 cardinals is Thu., so Max is Fri. (3). Jean is Thu.

In summary (day, person, cardinals, chickadees):
Sun., Henry, 8, 8
Mon., Ryder, 5, 11
Tue., Jean, 7, 9
Thu., Carol, 10, 12
Fri., Max, 11, 6
Sat., Tina, 6, 7

LOGIC PROBLEM 88

No one uses the same machine on more than one day (intro.). Phyllis's Fri. [treadmill Wed. (2)] isn't treadmill (intro.), Lifecycle (2), NordicTrack [Lifecycle Wed. (6)], or rowing machine [Phyllis's Mon. couldn't be treadmill, rowing machine (intro.), Lifecycle (2), StairMaster [Malcolm (4)], or NordicTrack [Phyllis would be NordicTrack [Mon.], treadmill [Wed.], and rowing machine [Fri.], so Malcolm would be 2 of these machines (2), but Malcolm couldn't be treadmill Fri. (2), and he couldn't be rowing machine Wed. [NordicTrack would be Fri. [Lifecycle Wed.] (2)], so couldn't have 2 machines in common with Phyllis], so couldn't be placed]; it's StairMaster, so is the rowing machine Mon. (5). Phyllis is rowing machine [Mon.], treadmill [Wed.], and StairMaster [Fri.], and Malcolm is StairMaster Mon., so is rowing machine or treadmill (2), but isn't treadmill Fri. (2) or rowing machine Wed. [Wed. machine for one who uses Lifecycle, treadmill, and rowing machine, in some order (1) couldn't be Lifecycle [NordicTrack Fri.], treadmill [StairMaster Fri.], or rowing machine [StairMaster Mon.], so couldn't be placed]; he's the rowing machine Fri. Malcolm's Wed. [StairMaster Mon., rowing machine Fri.] isn't Lifecycle [NordicTrack Fri.], StairMaster, or rowing machine (intro.); it's NordicTrack. Zara's Wed. isn't rowing machine [Woodrow's Fri. would be rowing machine [Malcolm] (3)] or StairMaster [Woodrow's Fri. would be StairMaster [Phyllis] (3)]; it's Lifecycle, so Woodrow's Fri. is Lifecycle. Rhoda's Fri. is treadmill. Zara's Mon. [Lifecycle Wed., NordicTrack Fri.] isn't Lifecycle or NordicTrack (intro.); it's treadmill. Woodrow's Mon. [Lifecycle Fri.] isn't Lifecycle (intro.); it's NordicTrack. Rhoda's Mon. [treadmill Fri.] is Lifecycle, so Wed. is rowing machine [only way to get one person to work out on Lifecycle, treadmill, and rowing machine, in some order] (1). Woodrow's Wed. is StairMaster.

In summary (person, Mon., Wed., Fri.):
Malcolm, StairMaster, NordicTrack, rowing machine
Phyllis, rowing machine, treadmill, StairMaster
Rhoda, Lifecycle, rowing machine, treadmill
Woodrow, NordicTrack, StairMaster, Lifecycle
Zara, treadmill, Lifecycle, NordicTrack

LOGIC PROBLEM 89

Men are Dane and Peter, and women are Erica and Heather (intro.). There are 5 concerts (intro.), and only 1 person conducted twice (2); each of the other 3 conducted once. Only 1 park held 2 concerts (5); each of the other 3 held 1 concert. Dane isn't Tuchman (2), Ms. Gresham (5), or Zucker [Heather couldn't be Waters (2) or Tuchman (4), so Gresham, so Handel couldn't be Heather Gresham, Waters, Dane Zucker, or Tuchman (2), so couldn't be placed];

349

he's Waters. Heather isn't Handel (2) or Tuchman (4); she conducted 2 concerts [only possible in (2)]. Mozart isn't Heather [2 concerts (above)] or Tuchman (4); it's Dane [only possible in (2)]. Heather [2 concerts] isn't Mozart concert [Dane], so Bach and Mozart aren't the same person (1); they're the same park (1), so Peter and Ms. Gresham are Haydn and Handel, in some order [only possible in (5)]. Heather [2 concerts (above)] isn't Handel (2), and she's only 1 of Beethoven and Haydn (3); she's Bach, and either Beethoven or Haydn (above). Erica isn't Zucker [couldn't be Handel [Peter or Ms. Gresham (above)] or 2 concerts [Heather (above)], so couldn't be placed in (2)]; she's Veterans Park (4). Bach [Heather] and Mozart [Dane] [same park (above)] isn't Veterans Park [Erica], Farmer's Park (1), or Park in the Green [only 1 concert (3)]; it's Seaside Park. Heather [Beethoven or Haydn (above)] isn't Park in the Green (3); she's Farmer's Park. Peter's Park in the Green [only left], so isn't Haydn (3); he's Handel, so Ms. Gresham's Haydn (above). Tuchman isn't Peter [Handel] or Heather [2 concerts (above)] (2); she's Erica. Heather's Ms. Gresham [only woman left]. Peter's Zucker. Erica's Beethoven concert.

In summary:

Bach, Heather Gresham, Seaside Park
Beethoven, Erica Tuchman, Veterans Park
Handel, Peter Zucker, Park in the Green
Haydn, Heather Gresham, Farmer's Park
Mozart, Dane Waters, Seaside Park

LOGIC PROBLEM 90

Each woman rooms with 1 of the other 5 (intro.). Irene is MI or VA, and her roommate is MI or VA (3), so her roommate isn't Kim [DE couldn't be Irene or Irene's roommate [MI and VA, in some order (above)], so couldn't be placed (1)], Samantha (3), Rachel [FL (3)], or Jane [WA couldn't be Irene or Irene's roommate [MI and VA, in some order (above)], so couldn't be placed (4)]; she's Lizabeth, so Irene and Lizabeth are Eiffel Tower and surfing, in some order (3). Eiffel isn't Lizabeth [Rachel's roommate would be lying in a field (5), so would be OH [only possible in (2)], but couldn't be Kim (1), Samantha (2), or Jane (4), so couldn't be placed]; it's Irene, so Lizabeth's surfing (above), and Jane's roommate is lying in a field (5), so Jane's convertible, and her roommate's WA (4). Jane's roommate [WA, lying in field] isn't Rachel [FL] or Kim [Rachel's roommate couldn't be Rachel (intro.) or Samantha (2), so couldn't be placed]; she's Samantha, so Jane

[convertible] is OH, and Rachel's roommate is playing guitar (2). Rachel's roommate [playing guitar] is Kim [only left], so Kim is from DE, and Rachel is Oscars (1). Irene [Eiffel] isn't VA (5); Lizabeth is. Irene's MI.

In summary (young woman, roommate, state, poster):

Irene, Lizabeth, MI, Eiffel Tower
Jane, Samantha, OH, convertible
Kim, Rachel, DE, playing guitar
Lizabeth, Irene, VA, surfing
Rachel, Kim, FL, Oscars
Samantha, Jane, WA, lying in a field

LOGIC PROBLEM 91

Least isn't Summers (1), Little (4), Steging (6), or Khalil [couldn't be Jeanne (1), Gage (2), Eleanor (5), Kay (6), or Marcus (8), so couldn't be placed]; that one's Mooney, so isn't Jeanne (1), Gage (2), Eleanor (5), or Kay (6), so is Marcus. Kay [twice as much as strawberries Romanoff (6)] isn't Summers [twice as much as chocolate soufflé (1)], Steging (6), or Khalil (8); she's Little [twice as much as Marcus (4)], so Marcus is strawberries (above). Kay Little [half as much as Steging (6)] isn't chocolate soufflé [half as much as Summers (1)], orange-chiffon cake (3) or Bavarian cream (4); she's cherry torte. Chocolate soufflé isn't Summers (1) or Steging (9); it's Khalil, so isn't Jeanne (1) or Gage (2), so is Eleanor. Jeanne isn't Summers (1); Gage is. Jeanne's Steging, so isn't Bavarian cream [would be $2.00 more than Kay Little (4) and twice as much as Kay Little (6), so would be $4.00, and Kay would be $2.00 [only possible for Jeanne to be both $2.00 more than Kay and twice as much as Kay], Summers would be $3.00 (1), chocolate soufflé would be $1.50 (1), and strawberries would be $1.00 (6), so total would be $11.50 [$4.00 [Jeanne] + $3.00 [Summers] + $2.00 [Kay] + $1.50 [chocolate soufflé] + $1.00 [strawberries] = $11.50] (above)] (7); she's orange-chiffon cake. Gage's Bavarian cream. Jeanne Steging is $1.00 more than Gage Summers [Bavarian cream] (1), who is $2.00 more than Kay Little (4), so Jeanne Steging [twice as much as Kay (6)] is $3.00 more than Kay; Jeanne's $6.00, and Kay's $3.00 [only possible for Jeanne to be both $3.00 more than Kay and twice as much as Kay], so Gage Summers is $5.00 (1), Eleanor [chocolate soufflé] is $2.50 (1), and Marcus [strawberries] is $1.50 (6).

In summary:

Eleanor Khalil, chocolate soufflé, $2.50
Gage Summers, Bavarian cream, $5.00

Jeanne Steging, orange-chiffon cake, $6.00
Kay Little, cherry torte, $3.00
Marcus Mooney, strawberries Romanoff, $1.50

LOGIC PROBLEM 92 & 93

Clues from part 1 are designated as I and clues from part 2 as II. Expenses are $30, $70, $120, $160, $210, and $250 (I,intro.). Settings are 5:00, 6:00, 7:00, 9:00, 10:00, and 11:00, and days are Mon., Tue., Wed., Thu., Fri., and Sat. (II,intro). Vhorishkova isn't $70 [Fyodor (I,1)], $30 [least], $120 [no $80], $210 [no $170], or $250 (I,2); she's $160, so Riga's $120 (I,2). Odessa [Luvaduvsky (I,3)] isn't $70 [Fyodor], $160 [Vhorishkova], $30 [least], or $250 [no $200] (I,4); it's $210, so Moscow [red wine (I,4) is $160 (I,4). Kinski [glass (II,5)] isn't Riga [ice (I,2)], St. Petersburg (II,1), or Kiev (II,5); she's Vilnius, so isn't $120 [Riga] or $30 [least] (II,5), so is $250. Kiev [10:00 (II,5)] isn't $30 [least] (II,5); it's $70, so Mon. is $30 [only amt. less than $70] (II,5). St. Petersburg's $30 [Mon.], so Kinski's Tue. (II,1). Bulgakov isn't $30 [Mon.] (II,3); he's $120. Goodnik's $30 [Mon.]. Rock candy isn't Bulgakov [Riga, so ice], Luvaduvsky [Odessa] (I,3), Goodnik, or Vhorishkova [$160] (II,2); it's Fyodor. 6:00 isn't Fyodor [Kiev, so 10:00], Vhorishkova [$250 [Kinski] would be 10:00 [Fyodor] (I,2)], Kinski [$250 [no 2:00]] (I,2), Goodnik [St. Petersburg [no 8:00]] (II,1), or Bulgakov [no 4:00] (II,3); it's Luvaduvsky. 5:00 [1st] isn't Kinski [$250] (I,2), Goodnik [St. Petersburg [Kinski [$250] would be 7:00 (II,1), so Vhorishkova would be 3:00 (I,2)]], or Bulgakov (II,3); it's Vhorishkova, so Kinski [$250] is 9:00 (I,2), so St. Petersburg [Goodnik] is 7:00 (II,1). Bulgakov's 11:00, so silly hat's 9:00 [Kinski, Tue.] (II,3), so Bulgakov's Thu. (II,3). Fyodor [rock candy] isn't Fri. or Sat. (I,3); he's Wed., so Odessa [Luvaduvsky] is Fri. (I,3). Vhorishkova's Sat. Quartz [hotel booked (I,1)] isn't Vhorishkova [red wine] or Luvaduvsky [Fri.] (I,1); it's Goodnik. Plastic isn't Vhorishkova [Moscow] (I,4); it's Luvaduvsky. Vhorishkova's Hoopla. Flat tire isn't Fyodor [Wed., so martini stirred would be on Tue. [Kinski, so silly hat] (II,4)] or Bulgakov [11:00 [last]] (II,4); it's Luvaduvsky [Fri.], so martini's Thu. [Bulgakov] (II,4). Fyodor's stained cuff.

In summary, Logic Problem 92:
Bulgakov, Riga, $120, martini stirred
Fyodor, Kiev, $70, stained cuff
Goodnik, St. Petersburg, $30, hotel booked
Kinski, Vilnius, $250, silly hat
Luvaduvsky, Odessa, $210, flat tire
Vhorishkova, Moscow, $160, red wine

In summary, Logic Problem 93:
Bulgakov, ice, 11:00, Thu.
Fyodor, rock candy, 10:00, Wed.
Goodnik, quartz, 7:00, Mon.
Kinski, glass, 9:00, Tue.
Luvaduvsky, plastic, 6:00, Fri.
Vhorishkova, Hoopla, 5:00, Sat.

LOGIC PROBLEM 94

Men are Andrew and John, women are Diane, Katie, and Sally, hiking is 8:45 a.m.-1:00 p.m. [4 hr. 15 min.], 9:00 a.m.-12:45 p.m. [3 hr. 45 min.], 9:15 a.m.-12:30 p.m. [3 hr. 15 min.], 9:30 a.m.-1:30 p.m. [4 hr.], and 9:45 a.m.-12:30 p.m. [2 hr. 45 min.], and swimming is 2:15-4:15 p.m. [2 hr.], 2:45-4:00 p.m. [1 hr. 15 min.], 2:45-4:30 p. m. [1 hr. 45 min.], 3:15-4:45 p.m. [1 hr. 30 min.], and 3:45-5:00 p.m. [1 hr. 15 min.] (intro.). Book reader is either hiking 9:45-12:30 and swimming 2:45-4:00 or 3:45-5:00, or hiking 9:15-12:30 and swimming 2:45-4:30 [only hiking times 90 min. more than swimming times (above)] (3), so that one's hike ended at 12:30; that one's Diane [only possible in (4)], so she's hiking 9:45-12:30 and swimming 2:45-4:00 [only possible in (4)]. Swam 3:15-4:45 [90 min.] hiking 9:15-12:30 (4, above). Jigsaw puzzle is swimming 3:45-5:00 [75 min., same as book reader (above)] (2, above). Katie isn't drive (1), crossword [man (5)], or jigsaw [swimming 3:45-5:00, so stopped swimming last (above)] (6); she's movie. Katie isn't hike 8:45-1:00 [none hiking until 1:15 (above)] or 9:30-1:30 [none hiking until 1:45 (above)] (1); either Katie [movie] is hiking 9:00-12:45, and drive is hiking 8:45-1:00, or Katie is hiking 9:15-12:30, and drive is hiking 9:00-12:45 (1), so hiking 9:00-12:45 is either drive or movie. Jigsaw [swimming 3:45-5:00] isn't hike 9:15-12:30 [swimming 3:15-4:45], 9:00-12:45 [drive or movie (above)], or 9:30-1:30 [ended hike last (above)] (2); it's hiking 8:45-1:00, so Andrew is hiking 9:30-1:30 [only hiking time that ended after 1:00] (2). Drive [hiking 8:45-1:00 or 9:00-12:45 (above)] is hiking 9:00-12:45, so Katie is hiking 9:15-12:30, so is swimming 3:15-4:45 (above), so Sally is swimming 3:45-5:00 [only swimming time that ended after 4:45 (above)] (6). John is hiking 9:00-12:45. Andrew is crossword, so is swimming 2:15-4:15 [2 hr.], and John is swimming 2:45-4:30 [1 hr. 45 min.] (5).

In summary (person, hiking, swimming, activity):
Andrew, 9:30-1:30, 2:15-4:15, crossword puzzles
Diane, 9:45-12:30, 2:45-4:00, book

John, 9:00-12:45, 2:45-4:30, drive
Katie, 9:15-12:30, 3:15-4:45, movie
Sally, 8:45-1:00, 3:45-5:00, jigsaw puzzle

LOGIC PROBLEM 95

Times are 1:00, 1:15, 1:30, 1:45, 2:00, and 2:15 p.m., men are Adam, Bill, and Marc, and women are Dina, Faye, and Jane (intro.). The three men are the dancer (2), the singer (4), and the comedian (8); the three women are the public speaker (intro.), the pianist (1), and the magician (3). TX [man, 1:15 [1:00 1st] (7)] isn't Marc (3) or Adam [1st (6), so 1:00]; he's Bill [only man left]. Adam [1:00 [1st]] isn't singer [UT would be 1:15 [TX] (4)] or comedian [OH would be 1:15 [TX] (8)]; he's dancer [only left for a man] (above), so isn't IA (2), HI (3), UT (4), or OH (8), so is ME. Dina [just after UT (4)] isn't UT, HI [would be magician [only possible in (3)]] (4), or OH [just after comedian (8), so comedian [man (above)] would be UT (above), so would be Marc [only man with state unplaced], so singer [man (above)] would be Bill [1:15, only man left], but then Marc [UT] would be 1:30 (4), which isn't possible [1:00 1st] (3)]; she's IA. Marc isn't UT [just before Dina [IA], but then couldn't be singer (4) or comedian [just before OH (8)], so couldn't be placed (above)] or OH [comedian [man (above)] couldn't be Marc [OH] (8), so would be Bill [1:15, only man left], but then Marc [OH] would be 1:30 (8), which isn't possible [1:00 1st] (3)]; he's HI, so magician [woman (above)] is winner (3), so isn't Faye (1) or Dina (4), so is Jane, so Faye and Dina [only women left] performed consecutively (5). 1:30 [1:00 1st] isn't Marc, Jane [magician] (3), or Dina [UT would be 1:15 [TX] (4)]; it's Faye, so Dina's 1:45 [Bill 1:15] (above), so singer is 1:15 and UT is 1:30 (4). Marc's comedian [only left for a man] (above), so isn't 2:15 [last] (8); he's 2:00, so OH is 2:15 (8). Jane's 2:15. Faye isn't pianist (1); she's public speaker. Dina's pianist.
In summary:
1:00, Adam, dancing, ME
1:15, Bill, singing, TX
1:30, Faye, public speaking, UT
1:45, Dina, piano playing, IA
2:00, Marc, comedy, HI
2:15, Jane, magician, OH, winner

LOGIC PROBLEM 96

Nos. are 11, 14, 17, 20, and 23, and mos. are Mar., May, July, Sept., and Nov. (intro.). Greenway [2 mos. after pine (3)] isn't no. 20 [2 mos. after stainless steel (2)], 11 [lowest] (5), 17 [pine would be no. 14 (5), but then Fir couldn't be no. 20, 23 [highest] (1), 11 [cherry would be no. 14 [pine] (1)], or 14 [May would be no. 20 (1), which isn't possible [no Jan.] (2)], so couldn't be placed], or 23 [pine would be no. 20 (5), but then May [after only Mar.] couldn't be no. 11 [lowest], 14 (1), 20, 23 [Greenway, so pine [no. 20] would be Mar. [1st] (3)] (2), or 17 [cherry would be no. 14, and Fir would be no. 11 (1), so Dayton [2 mos. after no. 23 [Greenway] (4)] couldn't be no. 17 [May, so Greenway would be Mar. [1st] (above)] (3) or 20 [pine [2 mos. before Greenway (3)], so would be no. 14, but then Rover couldn't be no. 20 (2) or 17 [May, so no. 20 [pine] would be Sept. (2), but then Greenway [no. 23] would be Nov. [last] (3)] (4), so couldn't be placed], so couldn't be placed]]; Greenway's no. 14, so pine's no. 11 (5). Fir isn't no. 20, 23 [highest] (1), or 17 [May would be no. 23 (1), so Dayton would be July (4), but then Rover couldn't be no. 20 (2), 11 [pine, but then couldn't be May [no. 23], Sept., Nov. [last] (2), or Mar. [Greenway [no. 14] would be May [no. 23] (3)], so couldn't be placed], or 23 [May, so no. 20 would be Sept. (2), but then Greenway [no. 14] couldn't be Sept. [no. 20], Mar. [1st] (3), or Nov. [pine [no. 11] would be Sept. [no. 20] (3)], so couldn't be placed], so couldn't be placed]; Fir's no. 11, so May's no. 17, and cherry's no. 14 (1). Greenway [cherry, no. 14] isn't May [no. 17], Mar. [1st] (3), July [pine [no. 11] would be May [no. 17] (3)], or Sept. [pine would be July (3), but then Rover couldn't be Nov. [last] (2), Mar. [no. 20 would be July [pine [no. 11]] (2)], May [no. 20 would be Sept. [no. 14] (2)], or July [pine [Fir] (3)], so couldn't be placed]; it's Nov., so pine's Sept. (3). Rover isn't May [no. 20 would be Sept. [no. 11] (2)] or July [no. 20 would be Nov. [no. 14] (2)]; it's Mar., so steel's May, and no. 20 is July (2). Mar. is no. 23, so Dayton is May (4). Carver's July. No. 23 isn't Formica (4); it's birch. No. 20 is Formica.
In summary:
Birch, 23 Rover St., Mar.
Cherry, 14 Greenway St., Nov.
Formica, 20 Carver Way, July
Pine, 11 Fir St., Sept.
Stainless steel, 17 Dayton St., May

LOGIC PROBLEM 97

Man whose 1st-name initial matches animal initial (1) isn't Mitch [couldn't be mule (1), so couldn't be placed], Chet [couldn't be camel (1), so couldn't be placed], Evan [couldn't be elephant (2), so couldn't be placed], or Drake [couldn't be donkey (3), so couldn't be placed]; he's Bill or Zeke, so is buffalo or zebra (1). Man whose animal initial matches town initial (1) isn't Mortville [couldn't be mule (1), so couldn't be placed], Chadwick [couldn't be camel (1), so couldn't be placed], Dixon [couldn't be donkey (3), so couldn't be placed], or Edgehill (5); he's Brockton or Zalestown, so is buffalo or zebra (1), so either Bill rode buffalo and one from Zalestown rode zebra, or Zeke rode zebra and one from Brockton rode buffalo [only possible]. Hotel isn't buffalo, zebra, camel, mule (1, above), or elephant (2); it's donkey, so isn't Zalestown (3), so is Zeke, and Zalestown is bank (4). Zebra isn't Zeke [donkey]; it's Zalestown, so is Chet (6), so buffalo's Bill (above), and judge is Mortville (6). Elephant is man whose initial is the same as town [only left in (1, above)], so isn't Evan (2) or Drake (3); it's Mitch, so is Mortville [judge], so Evan's sheriff (2), so isn't camel [would be Edgehill (5), which isn't possible [Mitch's Mortville] (1)], so is mule. Drake is camel, so isn't Edgehill (3); he's lawyer, so buffalo's Edgehill (5). Bill's dentist. Drake [camel] isn't Chadwick [zebra's Zalestown] (1); he's Brockton, and donkey is Chadwick (3). Evan is Dixon.

In summary:

Bill, Edgehill, buffalo, dentist

Chet, Zalestown, zebra, bank

Drake, Brockton, camel, lawyer

Evan, Dixon, mule, sheriff

Mitch, Mortville, elephant, judge

Zeke, Chadwick, donkey, hotel

LOGIC PROBLEM 98

Each wrote a different no. of letters (intro.), and each wrote at least 6 letters for a total of 51 letters (3). Al didn't write 11 or more [Jack would be at least 22 letters (2), so would be at least 54 letters total [11 [Al] + 22 [Jack] + 6 [least possible] + 7 + 8 = 54], but 51 letters total (above)], 10 [Jack would be 20 letters (2), so the 3 remaining would total 21 letters [51 − 10 − 20 = 21], so would be 6, 7, and 8 letters [only possible (above)], so the 5 nos. would be 6, 7, 8, 10, and 20 letters, but then Christmas tree and reindeer couldn't be placed in (2)], 9 [Jack would be 18 letters (2), and someone would be 10 letters (2), so the 2 remaining would total 14 letters [51 − 9 − 10 − 18 = 14], so would be 6 and 8 [only possible (above)], so the 5 nos. would be 6, 8, 9, 10, and 18 letters, but then Christmas tree and reindeer couldn't be placed in (2)], 8 [Jack would be 16 letters (2), and someone would be 10 letters (2), so the 2 remaining would total 17 letters [51 − 8 − 10 − 16 = 17], but couldn't be 7 and 10, 8 and 9 (above), or 6 and 11 letters [the 5 nos. would be 7, 8 [Al], 10, 11, and 16 letters

[Jack], but then Virgil couldn't be 7 [least], 11 [no 9 letters] (1), or 10 letters (2), so couldn't be placed], or 7 letters [Jack would be 14 letters (2), and someone would be 10 letters (2), so the 2 remaining would total 20 [51 − 7 − 10 − 14 = 20], but couldn't be 6 and 14, 7 and 13 (above), 8 and 12 [the 5 nos. would be 7 [Al], 8, 10, 12, and 14 letters [Jack], so Virgil couldn't be 8 [no 6 letters] (1) or 10 letters (2), so would be 12 letters, but then reindeer couldn't be 7 [least], 8 [no 3 letters], 10 [no 5 letters], 14 [no 9 letters], or 12 letters [Virgil] (2), so couldn't be placed], or 9 and 11 letters [the 5 nos. would be 7 [Al], 9, 10, 11, and 14 letters [Jack], so reindeer couldn't be 7 [lowest], 9 [no 4 letters], 10 [no 5 letters], or 11 letters [no 6 letters] (2), so would be 14 letters, so Christmas trees would be 9 letters (2), but then Virgil couldn't be 10 [no 8 letters] (1), 9 [Christmas trees] (2), or 11 letters [Stover would be 9 letters [Christmas trees] (1)] (4), so couldn't be placed]; Al's 6 letters, so Jack's 12 letters (2). Al's 6 letters, Jack's 12 letters, and someone's 10 letters (2), so the 2 remaining total 23 [51 − 6 − 10 − 12 = 23], but aren't 6 and 17, 10 and 13, 11 and 12 (above), 7 and 16 [the 5 nos. would be 6 [Al], 7, 10, 12 [Jack], and 16 letters, but then Virgil couldn't be 7 [no 5 letters], 16 [no 14 letters] (1), or 10 letters (2), so couldn't be placed], or 9 and 14 letters [the 5 nos. would be 6 [Al], 9, 10, 12 [Jack], and 14 letters, so reindeer couldn't be 6 [least], 9 [no 4 letters], 10 [no 5 letters], or 12 [no 7 letters] (2), so would be 14 letters, but then Virgil couldn't be 9 [no 7 letters] (1), 14 [reindeer], or 10 letters (2), so couldn't be placed]; the 2 remaining are 8 and 15, so the 5 nos. are 6 [Al], 8, 10, 12 [Jack], and 15 letters. Virgil isn't 15 [no 13 letters] (1) or 10 letters (2); he's 8 letters, so Stover's 6 letters (1). Reindeer isn't 6 [least], 8 [no 3 letters], 10 [no 5 letters], or 12 letters [no 7 letters] (2); it's 15 letters, so Christmas tree is 10 letters (2). 15 letters [most, reindeer] isn't Miller, Hupp (3), or Flint (6); it's Orndorff, so isn't Becky (1), so is Hayley. Becky's 10 letters, so isn't Flint (1) or Miller (3); she's Hupp. Virgil isn't Miller (6); Jack is. Virgil's Flint. Al isn't hot cocoa (4) or stockings (5); he's snowmen. Virgil isn't stockings (1); Jack is. Virgil's hot cocoa.

In summary:

Al Stover, snowmen, 6

Becky Hupp, Christmas trees, 10

Hayley Orndorff, reindeer, 15

Jack Miller, stockings, 12

Virgil Flint, hot cocoa, 8

LOGIC PROBLEM 99

Trees aren't Flopsy (1), Cottontail [green (5)] (2), Mopsy, or Hoppy (3); they're Fluffy. Windowsills aren't

Mopsy, Hoppy (3), or Cottontail (5); they're Flopsy. Cottontail [green] isn't porches (2) or mailboxes (5); it's bushes. Red isn't Flopsy, Hoppy (1), or Mopsy (2); it's Fluffy. Pink isn't Flopsy or Hoppy (1); it's Mopsy. AL isn't Mopsy, Hoppy (3), Flopsy [windowsills] (4), or Fluffy [TX (5)]; it's Cottontail. PA isn't Flopsy (1) or Hoppy (3); it's Mopsy. Yellow isn't ME (4); it's VA. ME is purple. Porches aren't ME or PA (4); they're VA. Flopsy [windowsills] isn't VA [porches]; that one's ME. Hoppy's VA. Mopsy's mailboxes.

In summary:

Cottontail, green, AL, bushes
Flopsy, purple, ME, windowsills
Fluffy, red, TX, trees
Hoppy, yellow, VA, porches
Mopsy, pink, PA, mailboxes

LOGIC PROBLEM 100

Norma [Family Celebration (3)] isn't Charleston (1), Jelcanodir (3), Mermaid [Important Arrival (3)], or Fragrant Cloud (4); she's Mascotte. Maisie [Mother's Joy (2)] isn't Mermaid [Important], Charleston, or Jelcanodir [figurine (3)] (2); she's Fragrant Cloud. Agnes [balloon (4)] isn't Jelcanodir [figurine] or Charleston [stuffed animal (1)]; she's Mermaid. Nadine isn't Charleston (1); she's Jelcanodir. Carol is Charleston [stuffed animal [last alphabetically]], so isn't It's a Girl (3); she's New Addition. Nadine [figurine] is It's a Girl!, so Norma is mug [only left alphabetically after figurine] (3). Maisie is basket.

In summary:

Agnes, Important Arrival, Mermaid, balloon
Carol, New Addition, Charleston, stuffed animal
Maisie, Mother's Joy, Fragrant Cloud, basket
Nadine, It's a Girl!, Jelcanodir, figurine
Norma, Family Celebration, Mascotte, mug

LOGIC PROBLEM 101

Son [Sawtooth (2)] isn't Nathan [Bridger-Teton (1)], Rita (2), Hannah [Flathead (2)], or Quinn [brother (4)]; he's Frank. Sister [cross-country skiing (3)] isn't Nathan (1) or Rita [biking (2)]; she's Hannah. Spouse [snowshoeing (4)] isn't Rita [biking]; she's Nathan. Daughter is Rita. Rita [biking] isn't Mount Hood [hiking (3)]; she's Colville. Quinn is Mount Hood. Frank is fishing.

In summary:

Frank, Sawtooth, fishing, son
Hannah, Flathead, cross-country skiing, sister
Nathan, Bridger-Teton, snowshoeing, spouse
Quinn, Mount Hood, hiking, brother
Rita, Colville, biking, daughter

LOGIC PROBLEM 102

Labrador [digs holes (2)] doesn't belong to Todd [chases tail (1)], Sarah [Doberman (1)], Jennifer (2), or Craig (3); that one belongs to Simon [Arthur (3)]. Scottish terrier doesn't belong to Craig or Jennifer (3); that one belongs to Todd. Todd's dog [Scottish terrier, chases tail] isn't Guenevere [barks at doorbell (1)], Percival [collie (1)], or Lancelot (3); he's Gawain. Lancelot isn't the Chihuahua (3); Guenevere is. Lancelot's the Doberman [Sarah], so he doesn't fetch (2); he chews on sticks. Percival fetches, so he isn't Jennifer's (2); he's Craig's. Guenevere's Jennifer's.

In summary:

Craig, Percival, collie, fetches
Jennifer, Guenevere, Chihuahua, barks at doorbell
Sarah, Lancelot, Doberman, chews on sticks
Simon, Arthur, Labrador, digs holes
Todd, Gawain, Scottish terrier, chases tail

LOGIC PROBLM 103

Amts. are $100, $125, $150, $175, and $200 (intro.). Craps isn't $150, $175, $200 [most] (1), or $100 (2); it's $125, so roulette's $150, and slot machines is $175 [$200 is most] (1). Blackjack isn't $200 (4); it's $100. Video poker's $200. Veronica isn't Wayne Newton (2); she's Tom Jones, and Steve's Newton (5). $200 [most] isn't Siegfried & Roy (3); it's David Copperfield, and Eldon's Siegfried (4). Nancy isn't Copperfield (3); Beth is. Nancy's Elvis Presley impersonator. Veronica [Jones] isn't $100 [least] (2), $175 [less than only $200 [Copperfield]] (3), or $125 [craps] (5); she's $150, so Steve [Newton] isn't $125 [craps] (5), so is $100 [only left less than $150] (2), and Nancy [Elvis] is $175 (3). Eldon's $125.

In summary:

Beth, video poker, $200, David Copperfield
Eldon, craps, $125, Siegfried & Roy
Nancy, slot machines, $175, Elvis Presley impersonator
Steve, blackjack, $100, Wayne Newton
Veronica, roulette, $150, Tom Jones

LOGIC PROBLEM 104

Weekdays are Mon.-Fri. (intro.). Eunice [Landmark (3)] isn't comma [Pitman (1)], dash [Dwight (2)], apostrophe, or semicolon (3); she's question mark [Fri. (2)]. Clifford isn't comma or apostrophe (1); he's semicolon. Pearl isn't apostrophe (4); Mae is. Pearl's comma. Tue. isn't Dwight [dash], Clifford [semi-colon] (3), or Mae [Thu. (4)]; she's Pearl. Dwight isn't Mon. (2); Clifford is. Dwight's Wed. Alphabet isn't Dwight or Clifford [Mon.] (2); she's

Mae. Dwight [Wed.] isn't Gregg (4); he's Speed-writing. Clifford's Gregg.

In summary:

Clifford, Mon., Gregg, semicolon
Dwight, Wed., Speedwriting, dash
Eunice, Fri., Landmark, question mark
Mae, Thu., Alphabet, apostrophe
Pearl, Tue., Pitman, comma

LOGIC PROBLEM 105

Ms. Jerrin isn't smooth (1); she's rectangle [only possible in (6)]. Ms. Gentry's smooth [only possible in (6)]. Mr. Keyes [11:30 (4)] isn't triangle [11:00 (3)]; Mr. Ingels is (3). Square [11:45 (4)] isn't Mr. Keyes [11:30] or Ms. Gentry [11:00 (3)]; it's Ms. Hope. Mr. Keyes isn't circle (1); Ms. Gentry is. Mr. Keyes is oval. Apple isn't Mr. Keyes [oval] (1); it's Mr. Ingels (1). Book [11:30 (4)] isn't Ms. Gentry [11:00], Ms. Hope [square [11:45]], or Mr. Keyes (4); it's Ms. Jerrin. Mr. Keyes [spongy (2)] isn't leaf (2) or pencil (5); he's hand. Ms. Gentry isn't leaf [most students (2)] (3); she's pencil. Ms. Hope's leaf. Sandy isn't Mr. Ingels [apple] or Ms. Jerrin (1); it's Ms. Hope. Mr. Ingels [triangle] isn't wrinkly (3); it's fuzzy. Ms. Jerrin's wrinkly.

In summary:

Ms. Gentry, circle, smooth, pencil
Ms. Hope, square, sandy, leaf
Mr. Ingels, triangle, fuzzy, apple
Ms. Jerrin, rectangle, wrinkly, book
Mr. Keyes, oval, spongy, hand

LOGIC PROBLEM 106

Yig [clarinet (3)] isn't rattlesnake (1), taipan (3), anaconda [Satha (3)], or black mamba [piccolo (4)]; it's cobra. Acrylic isn't Ouroboros [nylon (1)], Yig [cobra], Kaa (2), or Satha (3); it's Monty. Black mamba [piccolo] isn't Monty [acrylic], or Kaa (2); it's Ouroboros. Taipan isn't concert flute (1) or recorder (3); it's bass flute. Taipan [bass flute] isn't Kaa [couldn't be wool (2), jute (3), or cotton (4), so couldn't be placed]; it's Monty. Kaa's rattlesnake, so isn't in wool (2) or cotton (4); it's jute. Kaa [jute] isn't recorder (3); it's concert flute. Satha's recorder, so isn't cotton (4); it's wool. Yig's cotton.

In summary:

Kaa, rattlesnake, jute, concert flute
Monty, taipan, acrylic, bass flute
Ouroboros, black mamba, nylon, piccolo
Satha, anaconda, wool, recorder
Yig, cobra, cotton, clarinet

LOGIC PROBLEM 107

Ramon's starting [electronic equipment (2)] isn't Des Moines [Will (1)], Duluth [Luther (1)], Los Angeles [aircraft parts (2)], or Raleigh [kitchen cabinets (3)]; it's Denver. Tullis's starting isn't Los Angeles (2); it's Raleigh. Mack's starting is Los Angeles. Luther's cargo isn't farm machinery (3); it's metal roofing. Will's cargo is farm machinery, so destination isn't Phoenix [Luther (1)], Houston [Ramon (2)], Portland (3), or Topeka [Mack (4)]; it's Fresno. Tullis's destination is Portland.

In summary (driver, starting, destination, cargo):

Luther, Duluth, Phoenix, metal roofing
Mack, Los Angeles, Topeka, aircraft parts
Ramon, Denver, Houston, electronic equipment
Tullis, Raleigh, Portland, kitchen cabinets
Will, Des Moines, Fresno, farm machinery

LOGIC PROBLM 108

Men are Anthony, Louis, and Vincenzo, women are Marissa and Roberta, and corners are 8th, 9th, 10th, 12th, and 13th (intro.). Pat's Steaks woman (2) isn't Roberta [Le Bec-Fin (4)]; she's Marissa. 13th [highest] isn't Dock St. Brewery (1), Pat's Steaks (2), Dave & Buster's (3), or Le Bec-Fin [Roberta] (4); it's Bookbinder's. 12th isn't Dock St. Brewery [no 15th] (1), Pat's Steaks (2), or Le Bec-Fin [Roberta] (4); it's Dave & Buster's. Anthony isn't Dave & Buster's or Bookbinder's [13th] (3); he's Dock St. Brewery. Vincenzo isn't Dave & Buster's [12th, and no 11th] (5); he's Bookbinder's [13th], so Reading Terminal is 12th (5). Louis is Dave & Buster's [12th], so Dock St. is 9th (1). Chinatown man isn't Anthony (4); he's Vincenzo. Museum of Art man (2) is Anthony. South Street isn't Marissa (3); she's Roberta. Marissa's Independence Hall, so isn't 10th (5); she's 8th. Roberta's 10th.

In summary:

Anthony, Museum of Art, Dock St. Brewery, 9th
Louis, Reading Terminal, Dave & Buster's, 12th
Marissa, Independence Hall, Pat's Steaks, 8th
Roberta, South St., Le Bec-Fin, 10th
Vincenzo, Chinatown, Bookbinder's, 13th

LOGIC PROBLEM 109

Dallas's father isn't Brady, Slate (4), Dylan, or Arley (5); he's Pierce. 1st isn't Arley (1), Dylan (2), Brady (3), or Pierce [Dallas] (4); he's Slate, so Dallas's 2nd (4). Quinn isn't 5th [last], 4th (2), 1st, or 2nd [Dallas] (5); she's 3rd, so Madison is 4th and Dylan 5th (2). 1st [Slate] isn't Hyatt (3) or Montana (4); he's Carlyle. 2nd [Pierce, Dallas] isn't Julia, Greta (1), or Randy (3); she's Tabitha. 1st [Slate] isn't Greta (3) or Julia (4); she's Randy. Montana's mother [MT college (4)] isn't Greta [U. of VA (1)] or Quinn (5); she's Julia. Julia [Montana] isn't 4th [Madison]; she's 5th. Greta's 4th. Hyatt's 3rd. Arley [engaged in NJ (1)] isn't Madison's father [engaged in NY (2)]; Brady is. Arley is Hyatt's father.

In summary (order, husband, wife, baby):
1st, Slate, Randy, Carlyle
2nd, Pierce, Tabitha, Dallas
3rd, Arley, Quinn, Hyatt
4th, Brady, Greta, Madison
5th, Dylan, Julia, Montana

LOGIC PROBLEM 110

Boys are Carl and Lenny, and girls are Gina, Lainie, and Martha (intro.). Sunleaf Ct. isn't Kings (1), Sellers [Highland Dr. (2)], Parkers, or Florentines (3); it's Benedicts, so is Martha, and Lowell Ln. is "very mature" (4). "Terrific" girl isn't Lainie or Martha [Sunleaf (3)]; she's Gina. "Terrific" isn't Oak Dr. ["1st rate" (1)], Sunleaf (3), or Highland (5); it's Platte Dr. "Dependable" isn't Highland (2); it's Sunleaf. "Wonderful" is Highland. "Terrific" [Gina] isn't Parkers (3) or Florentines (5); it's Kings, so Carl's Oak (1). Parkers' girl (3) is Lainie, so she isn't "wonderful" [Sellers]; she's "very mature." Lenny's "wonderful." Carl's Florentines.

In summary:
Carl, "first rate," Oak Dr., Florentines
Gina, "terrific," Platte Dr., Kings
Lainie, "very mature," Lowell Ln., Parkers
Lenny, "wonderful," Highland Dr., Sellers
Martha, "dependable," Sunleaf Ct., Benedicts

LOGIC PROBLEM 111

Yvette isn't wicker basket (1), houseplant [Gail (3)], magazine rack, or gardening tools (5); she's wind chimes, so Sonia's gardening tools, and Jerry's wind chimes (4). Judy isn't wicker basket (1); she's magazine rack. Olivia's wicker basket, so isn't Tschida (1), Fernandez, Janello (2), or Locklear (3); she's Stoller. Jerry [Yvette] isn't Stoller [Olivia], Tschida (1), Fernandez, or Janello (2); he's Locklear. Barry isn't Fernandez, Janello, or Stoller [wicker basket] (2); he's Tschida. Kurt isn't Janello (2) or Stoller [Olivia] (3); he's Fernandez. Adam isn't Stoller [wicker basket] (5); Wayne is. Adam's Janello, so isn't Judy (1) or Gail (3); he's Sonia. Barry Tschida isn't Judy (1); he's Gail. Kurt's Judy.

In summary:
Adam & Sonia Janello, gardening tools
Barry & Gail Tschida, houseplant
Jerry & Yvette Locklear, wind chimes
Kurt & Judy Fernandez, magazine rack
Wayne & Olivia Stoller, wicker basket

LOGIC PROBLEM 112

Mins. are 10, 20, 25, 40, and 50 (intro.). Traffic isn't 25 min. [5th [last] would be 50 min. (4)] (1), 10 [least], 40 [no 80 min.], or 50 [most] (4); it's 20 min., so 5th is 40 min., and crop-dusting is 10 min. [least] (4). Volcanoes isn't 40 [no 80 min.] or 50 min. [most] (2); it's 25 min., so Zephyrus is 50 min. (2). Construction site [Aeolus (3)] isn't 50 min. [Zephyrus]; it's 40 min. Deliver cargo is 50 min. [Zephyrus], so isn't 4th [no 6th] (1), 3rd [dusting would be 5th [construction site] (1)], or 1st (5); it's 2nd, so Xanthus is 3rd, dusting is 4th [construction site 5th] (1), and 20 min. is 1st (5). Volcanoes is 3rd. Leto isn't traffic (4); Typhon is. Leto's dusting.

In summary:
1st, Typhon, traffic, 20
2nd, Zephyrus, deliver cargo, 50
3rd, Xanthus, volcanoes, 25
4th, Leto, crop-dusting, 10
5th, Aeolus, construction site, 40

LOGIC PROBLEM 113

Prices are $14, $16, $18, $20, and $22 (intro.). Anne [4th (3)] isn't $14 [least] or $22 [most] (3); she's Salvado [only possible in (5)]. 3rd isn't Salvado [4th], $22 [most], or Stan (4); it's $14 [only possible in (5)], so 1st is $18 (4). 4th isn't $20 or $22 [most] (3); it's $16, so Olimpico is $14 [least] (3). 2nd isn't $22 (5); 5th is. 2nd is $20. Stan isn't 2nd, 3rd [$14], or 5th [$22] (5); he's 1st. Pasillo isn't $20 [2nd] or $22 [most] (1); it's $18. Alianza isn't $22 [most] (2); Jirafa is. Alianza is $20, so Fran's $22 [most] (2). Dan isn't $14 [least] (1); Jan is. Dan's $20.

In summary:
1st, Stan, Pasillo, $18
2nd, Dan, Alianza, $20
3rd, Jan, Olimpico, $14
4th, Anne, Salvado, $16
5th, Fran, Jirafa, $22

LOGIC PROBLEM 114

Doors are 3-7 (intro.). Sea captain isn't 4th, 5th [last] (2), 1st [one who enters 4 would be 2nd [enters 5 (3)] (2)], or 3rd [policeman (3)]; he's 2nd, so one who enters 4 is 3rd, and one who exits 5 is 4th (2). One who enters 7 isn't 1st or 5th [last] (4); that one's 4th, so one who exits 6 is 3rd, and cook's 5th (4). Scientist [exits 7 (1)] isn't 4th [exits 5]; he's 1st. Bank robber's 4th. One who exits 4 [enters 3 (1)] isn't 2nd

356

[enters 5]; he's 5th. One who enters 6 is 1st. One who exits 3 is 2nd.

In summary (order, character, enters, exits):
1st, scientist, 6, 7
2nd, sea captain, 5, 3
3rd, policeman, 4, 6
4th, bank robber, 7, 5
5th, cook, 3, 4

LOGIC PROBLEM 115

Yrs. are 1954, 1955, 1957, 1958, and 1959 (intro.). Relatives are Simon [5 letters] (intro.), Theo [4 letters], Bertha [6 letters], Fred [4 letters] (1), and Agnes [5 letters] (3). Funky Funnel isn't Bertha, Fred (1), Theo [Wacky Whangee (1)], or Agnes [couldn't be 1954 [1st], 1955 [no 1951], 1957 [no 1953] (2), 1958 [no 1961], or 1959 [last] (3), so couldn't be placed]; it's Simon. Zany Zither isn't Bertha or Fred (4); it's Agnes. Fred [4 letters [least]] isn't Kooky Klaxon (2); he's Silly Siphon. Bertha [6 letters] is Kooky Klaxon, so *Talent Scouts* is Agnes or Simon [only 5-letter names], but not Simon [Funnel] (2), so Agnes. Agnes [Zither, *Talent Scouts*] isn't 1957 [no 1961], 1958 [no 1962], 1959 [last] (2), or 1955 [no 1956] (4); she's 1954, so Funnel's 1958 (2), *Art Linkley's Talent Time* is 1957 (3), and Bertha's 1955 (4). Theo isn't 1959 [last] (1); Fred is. Theo's 1957, so *Talk of the Town* is 1958 (1). Bertha isn't *Amateur Hour* (4); Fred is. Bertha's *Funny People*.

In summary:
1954, Agnes, Zany Zither, *Talent Scouts*
1955, Bertha, Kooky Klaxon, *Funny People*
1957, Theo, Wacky Whangee, *Art Linkley's Talent Time*
1958, Simon, Funky Funnel, *Talk of the Town*
1959, Fred, Silly Siphon, *Amateur Hour*

LOGIC PROBLEM 116

Times are 9:00 a.m., 10:00 a.m., 1:00 p.m., 2:00 p.m., and 4:00 p.m., and refunds are $66, $135, $792, $810, and $1,555 (intro.). 9:00 couple [1st, smallest (1), so $66] isn't Jussims (1), Shearers [4:00 (1)], Mohrs [2:00 (2)], or Burkes (4); it's Tafts. Jussims are 10:00, and Burkes are 1:00 (4). Child-Care-Credit couple isn't Mohrs [Moving Expenses (2)], Tafts [$66 [smallest]] (3), Jussims [Mortgage Interest (4)], or Burkes (5); it's Shearers. Tafts aren't Charitable Contributions (5); Burkes are. Tafts are IRA. Child Care is $810 [only amt. 6 times another], so Moving is $135 [$810 [Child Care] ÷ 6 = $135] (3). Jussims [10:00] aren't $1,555 [largest] (1); they're $792. Burkes are $1,555.

In summary:
9:00 a.m., Tafts, IRA, $66
10:00 a.m., Jussims, Mortgage Interest, $792
1:00 p.m., Burkes, Charitable Contributions, $1,555
2:00 p.m., Mohrs, Moving Expense, $135
4:00 p.m., Shearers, Child Care Credit, $810

LOGIC PROBLEM 117

Aves., from east to west, are 5th, 6th, 7th, 8th, and 9th, and sts., from south to north, are 42nd, 43rd, 44th, 45th, and 46th (intro.). SoHo isn't lederhosen, boomerang (4), tea cozy, or duck decoy (5); it's sextant. 46th St. [northernmost] isn't Greenwich Village (1), Little Italy, Chinatown (2), or SoHo (5); it's Tribeca. Tribeca [46th St. [northernmost]] isn't lederhosen, boomerang (4), or tea cozy (5); it's duck decoy, so SoHo's 45th, 5th Ave. is 44th, and tea cozy's 43rd St. (5). Tribeca [duck] isn't 5th [easternmost], 9th [westernmost], 6th [no 4th], or 7th Ave. (5); it's 8th, so SoHo's 9th, and Little Italy is 6th Ave. (3). Boomerang isn't 42nd St. [southernmost] (1); it's 44th St., so Greenwich is 43rd, and 6th Ave. is 42nd St. (1). Chinatown's 44th St. Greenwich is 7th Ave. Little Italy is lederhosen.

In summary (picked up, avenue & street, item):
Chinatown, 5th & 44th, boomerang
Greenwich Village, 7th & 43rd, tea cozy
Little Italy, 6th & 42nd, lederhosen
SoHo, 9th & 45th, sextant
Tribeca, 8th & 46th, duck decoy

LOGIC PROBLEM 118

5th [last] isn't King St. (2), Boyne St. (3), Victoria St. (4), or Hancey Ct. (6); it's Beatty Ave. 1st isn't King (2), Victoria (4), or Hancey (6); it's Boyne. 3rd [May (3)] isn't King [Irwin (2)] or Hancey [Irwin (5)]; it's Victoria, so group of 1 is 2nd, and winterization is 4th (4). Hancey isn't 4th [winterization] (6); it's 2nd, so group of 2 is 1st (6). King is 4th. Oil change [May (3)] isn't 2nd [Irwin], 3rd, or 1st (3); it's 5th. Transmission overhaul isn't 2nd [Hancey] or 1st (5); it's 3rd. New muffler isn't 1st (5); it's 2nd. Tire rotation is 1st. Total of 12 were picked up, and no group has more than 3 (1). 1st is 2 people, and 2nd is 1 person, so 3rd, 4th, and 5th must each be 3 people [only possible to total 12].

In summary:
1st, Boyne St., 2, tire rotation
2nd, Hancey Ct., 1, new muffler
3rd, Victoria St., 3, transmission overhaul
4th, King St., 3, winterization
5th, Beatty Ave., 3, oil change

LOGIC PROBLEM 119

Men are Alvin, Chip, and Donald, women are Dale and Minnie, yesterday was 14, 16, 18, 22, and 24 mi., and previous bests were 10, 12, 14, 16, and 18 mi. (intro.). Yesterday of one who's previous 16 isn't 14, 16 [no increase] (intro.), 22, or 24 [most] (2); it's 18, so Waitz yesterday is 22 mi., and Dale yesterday is 24 mi. (2). Previous 16 [yesterday 18] isn't Dale, Minnie, Donald (2), or Chip [no yesterday 20] (4); he's Alvin. Alvin [previous 16, yesterday 18] is increase of 2 mi., so Salazar and one with previous 12 are also increase of 2 mi. (3), so previous 12 is yesterday 14, and Salazar is previous 14 and yesterday 16 [only possible]. Yesterday 16 [Salazar] isn't Chip or Donald (1); it's Minnie, so Dale [yesterday 24] is largest increase (1), so her previous isn't 12 [yesterday 14] or 18 [would be increase of 6 [24 − 18 = 6], but then previous 10 would be yesterday 22 [only left], so would be increase of 12 [22 − 10 = 12]], so it's 10. Previous 18 is yesterday 22 [only left]. Yesterday 14 isn't Chip [Kuscsik would be yesterday 16 [Salazar] (4)]; it's Donald. Chip is yesterday 22, so Kuscsik is yesterday 24 (4). Alvin isn't Fleming (3); he's Rogers. Donald's Fleming.

In summary (member, st., yesterday, previous best):
Alvin, Rogers, 18, 16
Chip, Waitz, 22, 18
Dale, Kuscsik, 24, 10
Donald, Fleming, 14, 12
Minnie, Salazar, 16, 14

LOGIC PROBLEM 120

Bacall isn't ice cream (4), pizza, chocolate (5), or oatmeal [couldn't be Sadie [ice cream or pizza (1)], Diane, Joey (2), Bill, or Mona (4), so couldn't be placed]; that one's popcorn. Janssen isn't ice cream (6), oatmeal (7), or chocolate [couldn't be Sadie [ice cream or pizza], Diane [Bacall or Wilde (2)], Joey (3), Mona (6), or Bill (7), so couldn't be placed]; that one's pizza. Geary isn't oatmeal or chocolate (5); that one's ice cream. Geary [ice cream] isn't traffic jam (4), lost game (5), washing machine (6), or unproductive day [couldn't be Diane [Bacall or Wilde], Joey (3), Bill (4), Mona (6), or Sadie (7), so couldn't be placed]; that one's bad haircut. Janssen [pizza] isn't unproductive day, lost game (5), or washing machine (6); that one's traffic jam. One with unproductive day isn't Bacall [popcorn] (1) or Wilde (3); that one's Summerville. Summerville [unproductive day] isn't Diane [Bacall or Wilde], Joey (3), Mona (6), or Sadie (7); he's Bill. Janssen [traffic jam] isn't Diane [Bacall or Wilde], Sadie (1), or Joey (3); she's Mona, so

Sadie [ice cream or pizza] is ice cream. Joey isn't Wilde (3); he's Bacall. Diane's Wilde, and isn't oatmeal (2); Bill is. Diane's chocolate, so isn't lost softball game (7); she's washing machine. Joey's lost softball game.

In summary:
Bill Summerville, oatmeal, unproductive day
Diane Wilde, chocolate, washing machine
Joey Bacall, popcorn, lost softball game
Mona Janssen, pizza, traffic jam
Sadie Geary, ice cream, bad haircut

LOGIC PROBLEM 121

Series nos. are 300, 450, 600, 750, and 900 (intro.). Artie Deco [Domesticron or Radicon (3)] isn't 900 [couldn't be Domesticron or Radicon (2)], 300 [lowest], 450 [no 225], or 750 [no 375] (3); he's 600, so gardener's 300 (3). Sprockets isn't 750 [Domesticron would be 900 (4)] (2), 300 [lowest], or 900 [highest] (4); he's 450, so Robbie's 300 [lowest] (4). Tintype isn't 750 [chauffeur' would be 600 [Artie] (1)] (1); she's 900, so chauffeur's 750 (1). Rusty's 750. Artie [Domesticron or Radicon] isn't maid or valet (2); he's chef. Tintype isn't valet (4); Sprockets is. Tintype's maid. Sprockets [valet] isn't Domesticron, Radicon (2), Lectroman [Tintype (4)], or Technotron (7); he's Handibyte. Robbie [300, gardener] isn't Domesticron (4) or Radicon (5); he's Technotron. Rusty isn't Radicon (5); Artie is. Rusty's Domesticron.

In summary:
Artie Deco, Radicon 600, chef
Robbie, Technotron 300, gardener
Rusty, Domesticron 750, chauffeur
Sprockets, Handibyte 450, valet
Tintype, Lectroman 900, maid

LOGIC PROBLEM 122

Mos. hosted and mos. won are Aug., Sept., Oct., Nov., and Dec. (intro.). Aug. host [1st, won mo. after red dog (3)] isn't Virginia [won mo. after catch the ten (1)], Peggy (2), Mona (3), or Faith (5); she's Karen. One who won in Aug. [1st] isn't Virginia (1), Karen [hosted Aug.], Mona (3), or Faith (5); she's Peggy. Nov. host [won 2 mos. after catch the ten (1)] isn't Peggy [won in Aug. [1st]], Virginia (1), or Mona [won 2 mos. after red dog (3)]; she's Faith, so one who hosted Michigan won in Nov. (4). Red dog host [won mo. before Aug. host (3)] isn't Virginia [won mo. before Nov. host (1)], Peggy (2), Karen [Aug. host], or Mona (3); she's Faith. Faith [red dog, Nov. host] didn't win in Nov. [Michigan], Sept. [no July] (1), or Dec. [last] (3); she won in Oct., so Virginia won in Sept., catch-the-ten host won in Aug. (1), Aug. host won in Nov., and Mona won in Dec. (3). Mona [won in Dec.] didn't host in Sept. (3) or Dec. (5); she hosted in Oct. Virginia [won in Sept.] didn't host in Sept. (5); Peggy did. Virginia hosted in Dec. Virginia didn't host spoilfive (1); Mona did. Virginia hosted napoleon.

In summary (hostess, mo. hosted, game, mo. won):

Faith, Nov., red dog, Oct.

Karen, Aug., Michigan, Nov.

Mona, Oct., spoilfive, Dec.

Peggy, Sept., catch the ten, Aug.

Virginia, Dec., napoleon, Sept.

LOGIC PROBLEM 123

The co-host of a critic was one of the other 4 critics, and no more than 2 critics are on any 1 show (intro.). "Thumbs up!" [no TV show (4)] isn't Leeza (2), Roger (3), Eugene (4), or Leonard (5); he's Michael. Michael [no co-host, "Thumbs up!"] isn't *Open 24 Hours* (1), *Piece of the Action 3* ["Nonstop action!" (3)], *No Quarter* ["Riveting!" (3)], or *Extreme Measures* [Eugene or his co-host (4)]; he's *Ophidiophobia*. *Open* isn't "I laughed! I cried!" (1); it's "A tour de force!" [*Globe* (5)]. *Extreme* is "I laughed!" Michael [no co-host, *Ophidiophobia*] isn't *Globe* [*Open*], *Inquirer* (1), *Chronicle* [Leeza (2)], or *Sun* [Eugene or his co-host (4)]; he's *Times*. *Extreme* isn't *Chronicle* [Leeza] (2) or *Sun* (4); that one's *Inquirer*. Roger isn't *Piece*, *No Quarter* (3), or *Extreme* [*Inquirer*] (5); he's *Open*. Eugene's co-host [*Extreme* [*Inquirer*] or *Sun* (4)] isn't Roger [*Globe*] or Leeza [*Chronicle*]; he's Leonard, so Leeza's co-host is Roger (intro., above). Eugene [Leonard's co-host] isn't *Extreme* (5); he's *Sun*, and Leonard's *Extreme* (4). *No Quarter* isn't Leeza [Roger's co-host] (3); it's Eugene. Leeza's *Piece*.

In summary:

Eugene, "Riveting!," *Sun*, *No Quarter*

Leeza, "Nonstop action!," *Chronicle*, *Piece of the Action 3*

Leonard, "I laughed! I cried!," *Inquirer*, *Extreme Measures*

Michael, "Thumbs up!," *Times*, *Ophidiophobia*

Roger, "A tour de force!," *Globe*, *Open 24 Hours*

LOGIC PROBLEM 124

Mos. are March [5 letters], May [3 letters], June [4 letters], August [6 letters], September [9 letters], and December [8 letters] (intro.). Students are Carla [5 letters], Margarite [9 letters], Paul [4 letters] (intro.), Amy [3 letters] (1), Benjamin [8 let-

ters] (2), and Quentin [7 letters] (3). States are California [10 letters], Indiana [7 letters], Ohio [4 letters] (intro.), Maine [5 letters] (1), Tennessee [9 letters] (2), and Kentucky [8 letters] (3). Mar. [5 letters] isn't Paul [4 letters, but no 6-letter name], Benjamin [8 letters, but no 10-letter name], Margarite [9 letters [most]], Amy [ME [5 letters] would be June [4 letters] (1), but no 3-letter state], or Carla [5 letters, so KY would be Quentin [7 letters] (3)] (3); it's Quentin [7 letters], so KY is Margarite [9 letters] (3). Mar. [Quentin] isn't KY [Margarite], OH [4 letters, but no 6-letter state], TN [9 letters, but no 11-letter state], CA [10 letters [most]] (3), or ME [Amy [3 letters [shortest]] would be in Aug. [4 letters] (1), which isn't possible (5)]; it's IN [7 letters, so June is TN [9 letters] (3), so computer science is May [3 letters, only shorter than June [4 letters]] (4). ME isn't Aug. [6 letters, and no 7-letter mo.], Sept. [9 letters [most]] (1), or Dec. [8 letters, so Amy [3 letters [shortest]] would be Sept. [9 letters] (1), which isn't possible (2)]; it's May [3 letters, computer], so Amy is June [4 letters] (1), and history is OH [4 letters, only less than ME [5 letters]] (4). Sept. isn't CA [10 letters [most]] (2) or KY [8 letters, so Benjamin would be TN [9 letters, Amy] (2)]; it's OH [4 letters], so Benjamin's ME [5 letters] (2), so mathematics is Margarite [9 letters, only longer than Benjamin [8 letters]] (1). Aug. isn't CA [10 letters [most]] (5); it's KY. Dec. is CA. Paul [4 letters] isn't Sept. [physics would be Amy [3 letters [shortest]], TN (2)] (4); he's Dec. Carla [5 letters] is Sept., so physics is Amy [3 letters] or Paul [4 letters], but not Amy [TN] (2), so Paul. Aug. is KY [8 letters], so political science is TN [9 letters, only left longer than KY] (5). Quentin's theater arts.

In summary:

Amy, June, political science, TN

Benjamin, May, computer science, ME

Carla, Sept., history, OH

Margarite, Aug., mathematics, KY

Paul, Dec., physics, CA

Quentin, Mar., theater arts, IN

LOGIC PROBLEM 125

Philip brought woodcarving (1); he took compact disc (2), so Jeremy brought compact disc (1). One who took sand sculpture isn't Tessa [brought sand sculpture (3)] (intro.), Jeremy [Elise would have brought sand sculpture [Tessa] (1)], Kim (5), or Elise [Kim would have brought sand sculpture [Tessa] (5)]; he's Albert. One who took woodcarving [brought scarf (2)] isn't Jeremy [brought compact disc], Tessa [brought sand sculpture], or Elise [Kim would have brought woodcarving [Philip] (5)]; she's Kim, so Elise took scarf (5). Elise [took scarf] didn't bring gift certificate (4); she brought teddy bear, so Jeremy took teddy bear (1). Tessa took gift certificate. Albert brought gift certificate.

In summary (employee, brought, took home):
Albert, gift certificate, sand sculpture
Elise, teddy bear, scarf
Jeremy, compact disc, teddy bear
Kim, scarf, woodcarving
Philip, woodcarving, compact disc
Tessa, sand sculpture, gift certificate

LOGIC PROBLEM 126

Periods are Early Dynastic, Old, Middle, New, and Late, and mastabas are 10, 13, 15, 20, and 25 (intro.). Absinthes isn't 15 [New would be 20 (5), which isn't possible (4)], 13 [no 18], 25 [most] (5), or 20 [couldn't be pyramid [no 30], obelisk, sphinx (3), temple (4), or colossus (5), so couldn't be placed]; he's 10, so New's 15 (5). Late [last] isn't 20 (4), 10 [least], or 13 (5); it's 25. Absinthes [10 mastabas [least]] isn't obelisk, sphinx (3), colossus (5), or temple [couldn't be New [15 mastabas], Late [25 mastabas], Early [1st], Old (4), or Middle (5), so couldn't be placed]; it's pyramid, so obelisk's 20 (3). 25 [Late [last]] isn't colossus (2) or sphinx (4); it's temple. 15 [New] isn't colossus [Late is temple] (3); it's sphinx. Colossus is 13. 15 [New, sphinx] isn't Cleophatra (1), Ramalamaten [colossus would be Late (2), which isn't possible (2)], or Porphorpot (4); it's Opprobrias, so Porphorpot's Late (1). Middle isn't Ramalamaten [colossus couldn't be New [sphinx] or Late [temple], so couldn't be placed (2)] or Absinthes [10 mastabas [least]] (5); it's Cleophatra. Absinthes isn't Old [Cleophatra is Middle] (1); it's Early. Ramalamaten's Old, so colossus is Middle (2). Obelisk is Old.

In summary:
Early Dynastic, Absinthes, pyramid, 10
Old, Ramalamaten, obelisk, 20
Middle, Cleophatra, colossus, 13
New, Opprobrias, sphinx, 15
Late, Porphorpot, temple, 25

LOGIC PROBLEM 127

Nos. of *Bugle* articles are 1, 2, 3, 4, 5, and 6, nos. of *Gazette* articles are 1, 2, 3, 4, 5, and 6, and nos. of *Tribune* articles are 1, 2, 3, 5, 6, and 7 (intro.). 1 *Bugle* [least] isn't election (1), centennial, football (2), freeway, or park (3); it's poll tax, so park is 2

Bugle (3). 1 *Gazette* [least] isn't centennial (1), football (2), poll tax, park (3), or election (4); it's freeway. *Tribune* for freeway [1 *Gazette*] isn't 1 [no 4 *Tribune*], 5 [no 8 *Tribune*], 6 [no 9 *Tribune*], 7 [most] (1), or 2 [no 4 *Tribune*] (3); it's 3, so 1 *Bugle* [poll tax] is 6 *Tribune* (1), so park is 7 *Tribune* [most] (3). *Tribune* for football isn't 1 [least] or 2 (2); *Tribune*. 6 *Gazette* [most] isn't poll tax [1 *Bugle*] (1), centennial (2), football [5 *It's* s, which is 2 more than freeway [3 *Tribune*]] (3), or election [one with 1 fewer *Gazette* than election would have 5 *Gazette*, which isn't possible (4)]; it's park, so 3 *Bugle* is with 5 *Gazette* (3). *Tribune* with 5 *Gazette* [3 *Bugle*] isn't 6 [1 *Bugle*], 5 [2 more *Tribune* than freeway [3 *Tribune*], so freeway would be 6 *Gazette* [park] (3)], or 1 [least] (4); it's 2, so one with 1 *Tribune* has 1 fewer *Gazette* than election (4). Election isn't 1 *Tribune* (above); it's 2 *Tribune* [5 *Gazette*], so 1 *Tribune* is 4 *Gazette* (above), so 1 *Bugle* is 3 *Gazette* (1). 1 *Tribune* is centennial. Football is 2 *Gazette*. Football is 5 *Tribune*, so is 1 more *Bugle* than one with 2 *Tribune* [3 *Bugle*] (2), so football is 4 *Bugle*. Centennial isn't 6 *Bugle* [most] (1); freeway is. Centennial's 5 *Bugle*.

In summary (story, *Bugle*, *Gazette*, *Tribune*):
Centennial, 5, 4, 1
Election, 3, 5, 2
Football, 4, 2, 5
Freeway, 6, 1, 3
Park, 2, 6, 7
Poll tax, 1, 3, 6

LOGIC PROBLEM 128

Costumes are hearts/rainbows, hearts/stars, lightning bolts/spirals, lightning bolts/stars, and rainbows/spirals (intro.). Rainbows/spirals costume didn't have the rainbow nose (1); that one used seltzer bottle, and lightning bolts/spirals costume had rainbow nose (1). Heart nose isn't hearts/rainbow, hearts/stars (1), or lightning bolts/stars (6); it's rainbows/spirals. Star nose isn't hearts/stars or lightning bolts/stars (1); it's hearts/rainbows. Lightning-bolt nose isn't lightning bolts/stars (1); it's hearts/stars. Spiral nose is lightning bolts/stars. Cappy isn't spiral nose [lightning bolts/stars would have poodle prop (4), which isn't possible (6)]; she is rainbow nose (4). Zippy's nose isn't heart, star [hearts/rainbow], or spiral [lightning bolts/stars] (6); it's lightning bolt. Buster's nose isn't spiral or heart [rainbows/spirals] (3); it's star. Hearts/stars [Zippy] isn't big shoes, cream pie (2), or horn (6); it's poodle. Horn costume isn't hearts/rainbows or lightning bolts/stars (6); it's

360

lightning bolts/spirals. Cream pie isn't lightning bolts/stars [Giggles couldn't be lightning bolts/stars [cream pie] or rainbow/spirals (5), so couldn't be placed]; it's hearts/rainbows, so Giggles is rainbows/spirals [only left with hearts or rainbows] (5). Chuckles had spiral nose and big shoes.

In summary (clown, nose, costume, prop):
Buster, star, hearts/rainbows, cream pie
Cappy, rainbow, lightning bolts/spirals, horn
Chuckles, spiral, lightning bolts/stars, big shoes
Giggles, heart, rainbows/spirals, seltzer bottle
Zippy, lightning bolt, hearts/stars, poodle

LOGIC PROBLEM 129

Answers are 7-12 (intro.). 11 answers [lower than only 12, china place setting (5)] isn't blanket (1), beach hat [glassware (2)], bikini (4), suntan lotions (5), or beach towels (6); it's sandals. Towels isn't 9 [no 13], 10 [no 14], or 12 answers [most] (6); it's 7 or 8, and blanket is 7 or 8 (1), so blanket and towels are 7 and 8 answers, in some order. Bikini isn't 7 or 8 [blanket and towels, in some order (above)], 9 (4), or 12 answers [cappuccino maker would be 11 [china] (4)]; it's 10, so cappuccino maker is 9 (4). Towels isn't 7 answers [pasta-bowl set would be 9 [cappuccino] (6)]; it's 8, so blanket's 7 (above), pasta bowl is 10, and Tia's 12 (6). Glassware [hat] isn't 7 [blanket] or 8 [towels]; it's 12, so Stephanie's 11 (2). Lotions is 9. Maggie isn't 7, 8 (1), or 10 answers [pasta bowl] (3); she's 9. Shannon isn't 7 or 8 (1); she's 10. Raleigh isn't 8 [beach towels] (6); Brianna is. Raleigh's 7. Brianna isn't skillet (3); Raleigh is. Brianna's toaster.

In summary:
Brianna, 8, toaster, beach towels
Maggie, 9, cappuccino maker, suntan lotions
Raleigh, 7, skillet, blanket
Shannon, 10, pasta-bowl set, bikini
Stephanie, 11, china place setting, sandals
Tia, 12, glassware, beach hat

LOGIC PROBLEM 130 & 131

Clues from part 1 are designated as I and clues from part 2 as II. Days are Mon.-Sat., postcards are 5, 7, 10, 12, 15, and 17, and T-shirts are 2, 3, 4, 6, 7, and 8 (II, intro.). Hugo isn't 7 [no 9], 12 [no 14], 17 [most], 5 (I,3), or 15 postcards [Tatum (II,2)]; he's 10 postcards, so Carlos V [ensalada valenciana (I,3)] is 12 (I,3). Leon [Regente (I,2)] isn't 12 [Carlos V], 5 [no 8], or 17 postcards [most] (I,2); he's 7, so Plaza [Velásquez (I,2)] is 10 (I,2). Nora [gazpacho (I,1)] isn't 12 [ensalada] or 17 postcards (I,1); she's 5. Nora

[5 postcards] isn't 3 [no 5], 7 [no 9], 8 [most] (I,1), 6 [no 10] (I,3), or 2 T-shirts [Hugo would be 6 T-shirts (I,3), but then Robin couldn't be 3 [no 5], 7 [no 9], 8 [most] (II,5), or 4 T-shirts [Ribera would be 6 [Velásquez] (II,5)], so couldn't be placed]; she's 4 T-shirts, so Victoria bought 6 (I,1) and Hugo 8 (I,3). Robin isn't 3 [no 5], 7 [no 9] (II,5), or 6 T-shirts [Ribera would be 8 [Velásquez] (II,5)]; she's 2 T-shirts, so Ribera's 4 (II,5). Hugo [Plaza, Velásquez, 10 postcards, 8 T-shirts [most]] isn't ensalada [Carlos V], huevos alla flamenco (I,2), arroz con pollo [El Greco (II,1)], or paella (II,2); he's empanadas, so Mon. is 6 T-shirts (II,3). Nora [Ribera] is Tue. [Victoria's Mon. [1st]] (I,1), so Robin is Thu. [Mon. 1st] (II,5). Leon [Regente] isn't 6 [Victoria] or 3 T-shirts (I,2); he's 7. He isn't ensalada [Carlos V], paella (I,2), or arroz [no 5 or 9 T-shirts] (II,1); he's huevos. He isn't Mon. [6 T-shirts], Sat. [last] (II,1), or Wed. [Thu. 2 shirts [fewest], so arroz would be 4 T-shirts [gazpacho] (II,1)]; he's Fri., so paella's Wed. (I,2). Paella [Wed.] isn't Robin [Thu.] or Sylvester (II,2); it's Tatum. Mon. [6 T-shirts] isn't Hugo [8 T-shirts]; it's Sylvester. Hugo's Sat. Tatum's 3 T-shirts. Sylvester [Victoria] isn't ensalada [Carlos V]; Robin is. Sylvester's arroz. Nora isn't Internacional (I,1); Tatum is. Nora's Moderno. Sylvester's 17 postcards. Goya isn't Thu. [2 T-shirts] (II,4) or Wed. [Murillo would be Tue. [Ribera] (II,4)]; he's Fri., so Murillo's Thu. (II,4). Titian's Wed.

In summary, Logic Problem 130 (person, hotel, artist, dish):
Hugo, Plaza, Velásquez, empanadas
Leon, Regente, Goya, huevos alla flamenco
Nora, Moderno, Ribera, gazpacho
Robin, Carlos V, Murillo, ensalada valenciana
Sylvester, Victoria, El Greco, arroz con pollo
Tatum, Internacional, Titian, paella

In summary, Logic Problem 131 (person, day, postcards, T-shirts):
Hugo, Sat., 10, 8
Leon, Fri., 7, 7
Nora, Tue., 5, 4
Robin, Thu., 12, 2
Sylvester, Mon., 17, 6
Tatum, Wed., 15, 3

LOGIC PROBLEM 132

Addresses are 100 Patterway, 200 Patterway, 300 Fultonview, 400 Fultonview, and 500 Tresser, and bricks are 100, 200, 300, 400, and 500 (intro.). 3 are men and 2 are women (intro.). Fultonview is

100 bricks and 500 Tresser is 200 bricks [only possible to have 2 addresses with house nos. at least 300 higher than no. of bricks] (1). 1 woman is at 100 Patterway (4), and other woman isn't at either 200 Patterway [men would be at 300 Fultonview, 400 Fultonview, and 500 Tresser [only left], which isn't possible (5)] or at 500 Tresser [men would be at 200 Patterway, 300 Fultonview, and 400 Fultonview [only left], which isn't possible (5)]; 200 Patterway and 500 Tresser are both men. Grill isn't at 300 Fultonview (1), 100 Patterway [lowest] (3), or 400 Fultonview [100 bricks, so Val would be 200 bricks [500 Tresser [highest]], which isn't possible (3)]; it's at 200 Patterway or 500 Tresser, so is a man (above), so Val is a woman (3). 2 women are Val (above) and Dana (5), so 3 men are Jordan, Lane, and Sam. Val [woman, 100 bricks more than grill (3)] isn't at 200 Patterway, 500 Tresser [both men (above)], 400 Fultonview [100 bricks [least]] (3), or 300 Fultonview [100 bricks more than front walk (4)]; she's at 100 Patterway. Man at 500 Tresser [200 bricks] (above) isn't Lane [no other Tresser address] (2) or Jordan [100 Patterway [Val] would be 100 bricks [least] (4), which isn't possible (3)]; he's Sam. Grill man [fewer bricks than Val [100 Patterway] (3)] (above) isn't Lane [chimney (2)] or Jordan [more bricks than 100 Patterway (4)]; he's Sam [200 bricks], so Val is 300 bricks (3). Fireplace man (5) is Jordan [only man left (above)]. Front walk is Dana or Val [only left], so is a woman (above), so isn't at 200 Patterway [man (above)], 300 Fultonview (4), or 400 Fultonview [100 bricks, so 300 Fultonview would be 200 bricks [500 Tresser] (4)]; it's at 100 Patterway [300 bricks], so 300 Fultonview is 400 bricks (4). 200 Patterway is 500 bricks. Dana's patio, so isn't at 200 Patterway [man (above)] or 400 Fultonview [Lane would be at 300 Fultonview [400 bricks], which isn't possible (2)]; she's at 300 Fultonview, so Lane's at 400 Fultonview (2). Jordan's at 200 Patterway.

In summary:

Dana, 300 Fultonview, patio, 400

Jordan, 200 Patterway, fireplace, 500

Lane, 400 Fultonview, chimney, 100

Sam, 500 Tresser, grill, 200

Val, 100 Patterway, front walk, 300

LOGIC PROBLEM 133

Battering rams are 2, 3, 4, 5, and 6, guillotines are 2, 4, 5, 6, and 7, and octopi are 2, 3, 4, 5, and 7 (intro.). Rug cleaner [13 items (3)] isn't 6 guillotines (3); it's 2 octopi [only possible in (5)]. 4 octopi [total of 7 rams and guillotines (1), so 11 items total [4 + 7 = 11]] isn't can opener [12 items total (5)] or one with 6 guillotines [5 rams (5), so would have 0 octopi [5 + 6 = 11]]; it's dog walker [only possible in (5)]. Dog walker's rams [4 octopi] isn't 4 [would have 3 guillotines [4 + 3 = 7] (1), but no 3 guillotines], 6 [would be 1 guillotine [6 + 1 = 7] (1), but no 1 guillotine], 3, or 5 (5); it's 2, so 5 guillotines [2 + 5 = 7] (1). Rug cleaner's rams [13 total, 2 octopi] isn't 3 [would be 8 guillotines [2 + 8 + 3 = 13], but no 8 guillotines], 6 [would be 5 guillotines [2 + 6 + 5 = 13], but dog walker's 5 guillotines], or 5 (5); it's 4, so 7 guillotines [2 + 4 + 7 = 13]. 6 guillotines [5 rams] isn't dishwasher [dog walker is 5 guillotines] (2) or can opener (5); it's coffee grinder, so dishwasher is 15 items [only unplaced in (5)]. Dishwasher's rams [15 total] isn't 3 [guillotines couldn't be 2 [would have 10 octopi [3 + 2 + 10 = 15], but no 10 octopi] or 4 [would be 8 octopi [3 + 4 + 8 = 15], but no 8 octopi], so couldn't be placed]; it's 6. Dishwasher's guillotines [15 total, 6 rams] isn't 4 [would be 5 octopi [6 + 4 + 5 = 15], which isn't possible (4)]; it's 2, so 7 octopi [6 + 2 + 7 = 15]. Can opener [12 total] is 3 rams and 4 guillotines, so 5 octopi [3 + 4 + 5 = 12]. Coffee grinder's 3 octopi.

In summary (device, battering rams, guillotines, octopi):

Can opener, 3, 4, 5

Coffee grinder, 5, 6, 3

Dishwasher, 6, 2, 7

Dog walker, 2, 5, 4

Rug cleaner, 4, 7, 2

LOGIC PROBLEM 134

Women are Arletty, Vandalay, and Zuleika, and men are Orestes and Stedman (intro.). Only 2-word albums are *Frequent Flier* (intro.) and *Chattering Class* (4), so both are women (1). Karaoke [2-word album (4)] is woman in (1), so bungee [only possible in (1)]. Karaoke woman [bungee] (above) isn't Arletty [romance (3)] or Vandalay (4); she's Zuleika. Karaoke [Zuleika] isn't *Chattering* (4); it's *Frequent*, so talent show is *Chattering* (1, above). Open-mike woman [*Bad Hair Day* (2)] isn't Vandalay (2); she's Arletty. Talent-show woman (1) is Vandalay. Stedman isn't *Arabesque* (2); Orestes is. Stedman's *Mondegreen* [billboard (3)]. Vandalay [*Chattering*] isn't queen (4); she's rooftop concert. Orestes is queen, so isn't birthday (5); he's state fair. Stedman's birthday.

In summary:

Arletty, open-mike night, *Bad Hair Day*, romance with athlete

Orestes, state fair, *Arabesque*, descendant of queen

Stedman, birthday party, *Mondegreen*, billboard

Vandalay, talent show, *Chattering Class*, rooftop concert

Zuleika, karaoke bar, *Frequent Flier*, bungee jump

LOGIC PROBLEM 135

Maps are 7, 8, 9, 10, and 11, photos are 11, 12, 14, 15, and 16, and sketches are 9, 10, 12, 13, and 14 (intro.). 14 sketches [most, 1 photo less than Virgin Islands (4)] isn't Bahamas, Cayman Islands (1), Jamaica (2), or Virgin (4); it's Trinidad & Tobago [1 photo less than book with 9 maps (3)], so Virgin has 9 maps (above), so 14 sketches has 8 maps (4), and Jamaica has 13 sketches (2). 11 maps [most] isn't Bahamas (1) or Jamaica (2); it's Cayman. Trinidad [14 sketches, most] isn't 16 [most], 12 [no 13 photos] (3), 14 (5), or 11 photos [Virgin [9 maps] would have 12 photos (3), so Jamaica would have 7 maps [only map no. under 9 left] (2), so 15 photos wouldn't be Bahamas or Jamaica [7 maps, least] (1), so Cayman, so sketches in Cayman [15 photos] wouldn't be 9 or 10 [no 11] (1), so 12, but book with 13 sketches [1 more than Cayman] has 7 maps, and Cayman has 11 maps] (1); Trinidad [8 maps] has 15 photos, so Virgin [9 maps] has 16 photos (3), and Bahamas has 7 maps [only no. under 8] (1). Jamaica [13 sketches] has 10 maps, so Cayman [11 maps, most] has 12 sketches (1) and 12 photos (2). Jamaica [13 sketches [14 most]] isn't 14 photos (5); it's 11. Bahamas has 14 photos, so Bahamas sketches isn't 9 [least] (5); it's 10. Virgin has 9 sketches.

In summary (book, maps, photographs, sketches):

Bahamas, 7, 14, 10

Cayman Islands, 11, 12, 12

Jamaica, 10, 11, 13

Trinidad & Tobago, 8, 15, 14

Virgin Islands, 9, 16, 9

LOGIC PROBLEM 136

Men are Clifford and Rufus, and women are Faith, Hedda, and Priscilla (intro.). Woman with marshmallow sandwich ["Goose" or "Nature" (3)] (3) isn't Faith (3) or Hedda ["Wit" or "Superior" (4)]; she's Priscilla. Priscilla [marshmallow, day after Napoleon flying plane (2)] isn't "Nature" [day after dinosaur with binoculars (1)]; she's "Goose," and Faith is "Nature" (3). Faith ["Nature" [day before president climbing maple (1)]] isn't dinosaur, president (1), or Napoleon [day before Priscilla, so Priscilla [marshmallow] would be president (2, above)]; she's teacup. Fri. one [last] isn't dinosaur, teacup ["Nature"] (1), marshmallow [Priscilla], or Napoleon (2); that one's

president, so "Nature" one is Thu., and dinosaur one's Wed. (1). Marshmallow one [Priscilla] isn't Mon. [1st] (2); Napoleon one is, so Priscilla's Tue., and "Wit" one is Wed. (2). Napoleon one isn't "Hubbard" (4); president one is. Napoleon one's "Superior." Hedda ["Wit" or "Superior" (above)] isn't Fri. ["Hubbard"] or Mon. [Napoleon] (4); she's Wed. Cliff isn't "Superior" (4); Rufus is. Clifford's "Hubbard."

In summary:

Mon., Rufus, Napoleon flying plane, "Superior"

Tue., Priscilla, marshmallow sandwich, "Goose"

Wed., Hedda, dinosaur with binoculars, "Wit"

Thu., Faith, teacup on Mt. Everest, "Nature"

Fri., Clifford, President climbing maple, "Hubbard"

LOGIC PROBLEM 137

Lanes are 1, 2, 3, 4, and 5, and laps are 10, 20, 30, 40, and 50 (intro.). Greg isn't 20 [10 laps [least] couldn't be Esther [Burt would be 20 [Greg] (4)], Burt [Esther would be 20 [Greg] (4)], Audrey [Janet would be 20 [Greg] (6)], or Janet [Audrey would be 20 [Greg] (6)], so couldn't be placed], 40 [50 laps [most] couldn't be Esther [Burt would be 40 [Greg] (4)], Burt [Esther would be 40 [Greg] (4)], Audrey [Janet would be 40 [Greg] (6)], or Janet [Audrey would be 40 [Greg] (6)], so couldn't be placed], 10 [least], or 50 laps [most] (7); he's 30 laps, so lane 1 is 40 laps (7). Greg [30 laps] isn't lane 1 [40 laps], 3 (2), 2 [lane 1 [lowest] couldn't be Burt [Janet would be 2 [Greg] (4)], Janet [Burt would be 2 [Greg] (4)], Esther [Audrey would be 2 [Greg] (6)], or Audrey [Esther would be 2 [Greg] (6)], so couldn't be placed], or 4 [lane 5 [highest] couldn't be Burt [Janet would be 4 [Greg] (4)], Janet [Burt would be 4 [Greg] (4)], Esther [Audrey would be 4 [Greg] (6)], or Audrey [Esther would be 4 [Greg] (6)], so couldn't be placed]; he's lane 5. Greg [lane 5 [highest], 30 laps] isn't sidestroke (1), backstroke (2), or butterfly (7); he's breaststroke or front crawl, so lane 4 is also breaststroke or front crawl (5). Backstroke isn't lane 4 or 5 [breaststroke and front crawl, in some order (above)], 2 [butterfly and sidestroke would be lanes 1 and 3, in some order [only lanes left (above)], which isn't possible (1)], or 3 (2); it's lane 1. 50 laps [most] isn't breaststroke [sidestroke would be 40 laps [backstroke] (5)], sidestroke [breaststroke would be 40 laps [backstroke] (5)], or butterfly (7); it's front crawl. Front crawl [50 laps] isn't lane 5 [30 laps]; it's lane 4, and breaststroke is lane 5 [30 laps], so sidestroke is 20 laps [backstroke 40 laps] (5, above). Butterfly is 10

363

laps, and isn't lane 3 [front crawl lane 4] (3); it's lane 2. Sidestroke is lane 3. Audrey isn't lane 4 [50 laps [most], so Janet would be 40 laps [backstroke] (6)] (2), 2 [butterfly], or 3 [front crawl lane 4] (3); she's lane 1 [40 laps], so Esther's lane 2, and Janet's 50 laps [Greg 30 laps] (6). Burt's 20 laps.

In summary (lane, swimmer, stroke, laps):

1, Audrey, backstroke, 40
2, Esther, butterfly, 10
3, Burt, sidestroke, 20
4, Janet, front crawl, 50
5, Greg, breaststroke, 30

LOGIC PROBLEM 138

Alexis [4 boards less than leotard (3)] isn't San Juan, Kaanapali (1), Miami [4 boards less than energy bar (3)], or Santa Barbara [Tricia (4)]; she's Sedona. Sedona is 1 less than Russ, which is 1 less than mineral water (2), and Sedona [Alexis] is also 4 less than leotard (3), so the 5 locales are Sedona, Russ, water, leotard, and one other, called X. 7 boards (1) isn't Russ, Sedona [Alexis] (1), leotard [Sedona [Alexis] would be 3 boards (3), so Russ would be 4 boards [Cliff (4)] (2)], or water [Russ would be 6 and Sedona [Alexis] 5 boards (2), so leotard would be 9 (3), so the 5 nos. would be 4 [Cliff], 5 [Sedona], 6 [Russ], 7 [water], and 9 [leotard], but then Miami couldn't be 4 [no 8], 6 [no 10], 7 [no 11], or 9 [most] (3), so couldn't be placed]; 7 boards is X [only left (above)]. 4 boards [Cliff] isn't Sedona [Alexis], Russ, X [7 boards], or leotard [Alexis would be 0 boards (3)]; it's water [only left (above)], so Russ is 3, Sedona [Alexis] is 2 (2), and leotard's 6 (3). The 5 nos. are 2 [Sedona], 3 [Russ], 4 [water], 6 [leotard], and 7 [X] (above), so Miami isn't 4 [no 8], 6 [no 10], or 7 [most] (3); it's 3, so energy bar's 7 (3). 2 boards [fewest] isn't barbells (4); it's sneakers. Barbells are 3 boards. San Juan isn't Cliff (1); Kaanapali is. San Juan is Shaniqua, and it isn't 7 boards (1); it's 6. Santa Barbara's 7 boards.

In summary:

Kaanapali, mineral water, Cliff, 4
Miami, barbells, Russ, 3
San Juan, leotard, Shaniqua, 6
Santa Barbara, energy bar, Tricia, 7
Sedona, sneakers, Alexis, 2

LOGIC PROBLEM 139

Women are Etta, Gloria, Rochelle, and Theresa, and men are Kurt and Nate (intro.). Nos. of leaves are at least 15 and at most 50 (1). Men are reniform (5) and deltoid (7), and there are 2 men, so women are cor-

date, orbicular, peltate, and spatulate [only left]. Man with cinder block (6) is at most 25 [if at least 26, peltate would be at least 52 (6), but 50 highest], so isn't reniform [reniform would be at most 25, so bag of flour would be at most 10 (5), but 15 lowest]; he's deltoid [only man's leaf left]. Man with deltoid [cinder block] is at most 25 (above), and man with reniform is at least 30 [if 29 or less, bag of flour would be 14 or less (5), but 15 lowest], so deltoid man is lower than reniform man, so deltoid man is Nate and reniform man is Kurt (4). One with fewest isn't deltoid [Nate], reniform [Kurt], spatulate (4), peltate (6), or cordate (7); that one's orbicular. Woman with 35 leaves isn't Gloria (2), Theresa [bag of flour would be 10 (5), but 15 lowest], or Etta [Nate [deltoid] would be at least 36 (4), so cordate at least 51 (7), but 50 highest]; she's Rochelle. Rochelle [35 leaves] isn't cordate (2), peltate [cinder block would be $17\frac{1}{2}$ (6), but not whole no.], or orbicular [least, so deltoid would be at least 36, and cordate at least 72 (7), but 50 highest]; she's spatulate. Theresa isn't orbicular [least] (5) or peltate (6); she's cordate. Theresa [cordate] is at least 40 [if 39 or less, bag of flour would be 14 or less (5), but 15 lowest] and at most 40 [if 41 or more, deltoid [cinder block] would be 26 or more (7), so peltate would be 52 or more (6), but 50 highest]; Theresa [cordate] is 40 leaves, so reniform is 30, bag of flour 15 (5), deltoid [cinder block] 25 (7), and peltate 50 (6). Etta isn't 50 [Nate 25] (4); Gloria is. Etta's 15, and orbicular. Theresa [cordate] isn't dictionary, clay bricks (3), or Shakespeare (7); she's typewriter. Rochelle [spatulate] isn't dictionary or clay bricks (3); she's Shakespeare. Gloria [50 leaves [most]] isn't dictionary (3); she's clay bricks. Kurt's dictionary.

In summary:

Etta, orbicular, 15, bag of flour
Gloria, peltate, 50, clay bricks
Kurt, reniform, 30, dictionary
Nate, deltoid, 25, cinder block
Rochelle, spatulate, 35, Shakespeare
Theresa, cordate, 40, typewriter

LOGIC PROBLEM 140

Wives are Ali, Carly, Dee, Estelle, Fern, and Shelley, and husbands and surnames are Allen, Franklin, Owen, Thomas, Trent, and Wilbur (intro.). Each woman's surname is the same as that of another woman's husband's 1st name (intro.). The 2 women in (6) whose 1st-name initials, last-name initials, and husbands' initials are the same 3 letters aren't Carly [no other initial C], Dee [no other initial D], Estelle [no other initial E], or Shelley [no other initial S]; they're Ali and Fern. Ali's husband isn't Franklin (5); Ali's surname is Franklin [only name left with initial F left to share with initial F in Fern] (6, above). Fern must have initial A to share with Ali (6, above), so either her surname or her husband's 1st name is Allen [only other name with initial A]. Fern's surname isn't Allen [to share all 3 initials, Ali Franklin and Fern Allen would have to have husbands with the same 1st-name initials (6, above), so their husbands would be Thomas and Trent, in some order [only husbands with same 1st-name initials], but then Carly's husband couldn't be Thomas or Trent [Ali and Fern, in some order (above)], Wilbur (4), Franklin, or Allen (5), so Owen, but then Shelley's husband couldn't be Thomas or Trent [Ali and Fern, in some order (above)], Wilbur, Allen (3), or Franklin (5), so couldn't be placed]; Fern's husband's 1st name is Allen (above). Ali Franklin's husband isn't Franklin, Owen [Fern's surname would be Owen [only name with initial O] (6, above), which isn't possible] or Wilbur [Fern's surname would be Wilbur [only name with initial W] (6, above), which isn't possible] (6, above); he's Thomas or Trent, so Fern's last name is Thomas or Trent (6, above). Rm. 130 [highest] isn't Dee [no rm. 127] (1), Ali Franklin (2), Shelley, Fern [Allen's wife] (3), or Carly (4); she's Estelle. Wilbur's wife isn't Ali [husband Thomas or Trent (above)], Shelley, Estelle [rm. 130 [highest]] (3), or Carly (4); she's Dee. Dee & Wilbur weren't in rm. 121 [lowest], 123 [no rm. 120] (1), 124 [no rm. 127], or 129 [no rm. 132] (3); they were in rm. 126. Rm. 129 [lower than only rm. 130] isn't Fern [husband Allen], Shelley (3), or Carly (4); she's Ali Franklin, so Ms. Owen was in rm. 130 (2). Rm. 124 [no rm. 127] isn't Fern [Allen's wife] or Shelley (3); she's Carly. Franklin's wife isn't Carly, Ali, or Shelley (5); she's Estelle. Ms. Wilbur wasn't in rm. 121 [lowest], 123 [no rm. 120], or 126 [Dee] (1); she was in rm. 124. Owen's wife isn't Ali [husband Thomas or Trent (above)] or Carly Wilbur (2); she's Shelley. Ms. Trent isn't Dee or Shelley [husband Owen] (2); she's Fern, so Ali Franklin's husband isn't Trent, so he's Thomas (6, above). Carly's married to Trent. Owen shares a name with Ali or Fern (6, above), but not with Ali [rm. 129 [lower than only rm. 130 [husband Franklin]]] (6), so with Fern Trent [husband Allen], so Owen's surname is Allen [only possible]. Fern's rm. no. was 121, and Shelley's [husband Owen] was 123 (6, above). Dee's surname is Thomas.

In summary (wife & husband, surname, rm. no.):

Ali & Thomas Franklin, 129

Carly & Trent Wilbur, 124

Dee & Wilbur Thomas, 126

Estelle & Franklin Owen, 130

Fern & Allen Trent, 121

Shelley & Owen Allen, 123

LOGIC PROBLEM 141

Two did absorption, 2 contraposition, and 1 constructive dilemma (intro.). Two used chalk, 2 pencil, and 1 fountain pen (intro.). Two used absorption, and there are 5 people, so 3 didn't use absorption, and they are the 2 women (1) and the man with statistics (2), so the man with geometry (3) used absorption. He isn't Mr. Wentworth or Mr. Sternhagen [pencil (2)] (3); he's Mr. Pankhurst. Man with statistics [chalk (2)] isn't Mr. Sternhagen [pencil]; he's Mr. Wentworth. Probability isn't Ms. Sawyer (1) or Mr. Sternhagen (2); she's Ms. Chalmers. Woman with calculus is Ms. Sawyer (2). Mr. Sternhagen's algebra. Fountain pen isn't Ms. Chalmers or Ms. Sawyer (1); he's Mr. Pankhurst. Ms. Sawyer [calculus] isn't chalk (2); she's pencil. Ms. Chalmers is chalk. One with absorption isn't Ms. Chalmers, Ms. Sawyer (1), or Mr. Wentworth [statistics] (2); he's Mr. Sternhagen. Mr. Wentworth isn't constructive dilemma [Ms. Chalmers and Ms. Sawyer would both be contraposition [only left], which isn't possible (4)]; he's contraposition. Ms. Chalmers [chalk] isn't contraposition [Mr. Wentworth's contraposition and chalk] (4); she's constructive dilemma. Ms. Sawyer's contraposition.

In summary:

Ms. Chalmers, probability, constructive dilemma, chalk

Mr. Pankhurst, geometry, absorption, fountain pen

Ms. Sawyer, calculus, contraposition, pencil

Mr. Sternhagen, algebra, absorption, pencil

Mr. Wentworth, statistics, contraposition, chalk

LOGIC PROBLEM 142

Women are Carola, Emma, and Kathryn, men are Jeffrey, Leopold, and Tyson, pretzel rods are 1-6, red die nos. are 1-6, and black die nos. are 1-6 (intro.). No one rolled the same no. on both dice (intro.). No. of rods bet by man with 5 black (2) isn't 4 [woman (1)], 1 [lowest], 2 (2), 3 [woman (3)], or 5 (4); it's 6, so Kathryn bet 4 rods (2). No. of rods bet by man with 5 red (1) isn't 3, 4 [both women], 6 [highest] (1), or 5 [Carola would've bet 6 rods [man] (1)]; it's either 1 or 2. If man with 5 red bet 1 rod, Carola would've bet 2 rods (1), and woman who bet 3 rods would be Emma [only left]. Emma's red [3 rods] wouldn't be 5 [1 rod], 4 [no 7 red], 6 [highest] (2), 1 [lowest] (3), or

3 [Tyson would be 2 red [woman (3)] (3)]; it would be 2, so 4 black would be 5 red (2), and Tyson would be 1 red (3). Emma's black [3 rods, 2 red] wouldn't be 4 [5 red], 5 [6 rods], 1 [lowest], 2 (3), or 3 (4); it would be 6, so Leopold would be 4 black (3). 2 black couldn't be Jeffrey (1), Kathryn [4 rods, so Jeffrey would be 4 black [Leopold] (1)], or Carola [2 rods] (4); it would be Tyson. Man with 5 black is Jeffrey [only left], so 4 rods would be 3 black (1). Jeffrey's red [6 rods, 5 black] couldn't be 3 [total would be 8, but Emma's total is 8 [2 [red] + 6 [black] = 8]], 4 [total would be 9, but Leopold's total is 9 [5 [red] + 4 [black] = 9]], or 6 (4), so couldn't be placed; man with 5 red didn't bet 1 rod, so he bet 2 rods (above), so Carola bet 3 rods (1). Emma's red wasn't 1 [4 black would be 4 red (2)] (intro.), 4 [no 7 red], 5 [no 8 red], or 6 [highest] (2); it was 2 or 3. If it was 3 red, 4 black would be 6 red (2). Tyson's red wouldn't be 6 [highest] (3), 4 [Carola [3 rods] would be 5 red [2 rods] (3)], 5 [Carola [3 rods] would be 6 red [4 black [man (2)]] (3)], or 2 [Carola [3 rods] would be 3 red [Emma] (3)]; it would be 1, so Carola [3 rods] would be 2 red (3). Carola's black [3 rods, 2 red] couldn't be 4, 5 [both men], 1 [lowest], 2 (3), or 3 (4); it would be 6, so Leopold would be 4 black (3). Man with 5 red would be Jeffrey [only left], but then his black couldn't be 5 (intro.), 1 [lowest], 2 (1), or 3 [total would be 8, but Carola's total would also be 8 [2 [red] + 6 [black] = 8]] (4), so couldn't be placed; Emma's red wasn't 3, so it was 2 (above), and 4 black was 5 red (2). Leopold's black wasn't 5 [no 7 black], 6 [highest] (3), 2 [2 red would be 4 black [5 red] (3)] or 3 [2 red [Emma] would be 5 black [man] (3)]; it was 1 or 4. If Leopold's black was 4, 2 red would be 6 black (3). Tyson's red wouldn't be 5 [4 black [Leopold]], 6 [highest] (3), 1 [3 rods [Carola] would be 2 red [Emma] (3)], or 4 [3 rods would be 5 red [2 rods] (3)]; it would be 3, so 3 rods would be 4 red (3). Man with 5 black wouldn't be Tyson [his total would be 8 [3 [red] + 5 [black] = 8], but Emma's total is 8 [2 [red] + 6 [black] = 8]] (4), so would be Jeffrey [only left], so 4 rods would be 3 black (1). Red with 3 black [Kathryn] wouldn't be 4 [Carola], 3 [Tyson], or 6 [would have total of 9, but Leopold has 5 red and 4 black, for total of 9] (4); it would be 1. Tyson's black [3 red] couldn't be 1 [total would be 4, but Kathryn's total is 4 [1 [red] + 3 [black] = 4]] (4) or 2 [total would be 5, and Carola's black [4 red] would be 1 [only left], so her total would be 5, which isn't possible (4)]; Leopold's black isn't 4, so it's 1 (above), and 2 red is 3 black (3). Jeffrey's black isn't 2 (1), 5 [4 rods [Kathryn] would be 3 black [Emma]

(1)], or 6 [4 rods would be 4 black [2 rods] (1)]; it's 4, so 4 rods is 2 black (1). 6 rods [5 black] isn't Emma [3 black] or Leopold [1 black]; he's Tyson. Leopold [1 black] isn't 1 rod (4); Emma is. Leopold is 5 rods. Carola is 6 black. Tyson's red [5 black] isn't 6 [highest] (3), 1 [3 rods would be 2 red [1 rod] (3)], or 4 [total would be 9, but Jeffrey's total is 9 [5 [red] + 4 [black] = 9]] (4); it's 3, so 3 rods is 4 red (3). Leopold [1 black] isn't 1 red (intro.); Kathryn is. Leopold is 6 red.

In summary (coworker, pretzel rods, red die, black die):
Carola, 3, 4, 6
Emma, 1, 2, 3
Jeffrey, 2, 5, 4
Kathryn, 4, 1, 2
Leopold, 5, 6, 1
Tyson, 6, 3, 5

LOGIC PROBLEM 143

Coffee mug isn't lilies (1), daisies (2), gardenias, or tulips (4); it's carnations. Candy jar isn't lilies (1), daisies (2), or tulips (4); it's gardenias. Norma isn't lilies [Virginia (1)], daisies, gardenias [candy] (2), or carnations [coffee] (4); she's tulips. Carl isn't gardenias or carnations [coffee] (3); he's daisies. Alan isn't carnations (4); he's gardenias. Dennis is carnations. Daisies [Carl] aren't flowerpot (3); they're glass vase (2), so lilies are basket (1). Tulips are flowerpot.

In summary:
Alan, gardenias, candy jar
Carl, daisies, glass vase
Dennis, carnations, coffee mug
Norma, tulips, flowerpot
Virginia, lilies, basket

LOGIC PROBLEM 144

Men are Carl, Mario, and Tom, and women are Kathryn and Rita (intro.). Wristwatch man isn't Mario (2) or Carl (4); he's Tom. Tom [wristwatch] isn't ice cream (1), hot dog [mug (1)], hamburger [Mario (2)], or pretzel (3); he's bratwurst. Carl isn't hot dog or ice cream (1); he's pretzel. Raspberry isn't Tom or Carl [pretzel] (3); it's Mario. Mario [hamburger, raspberry] isn't mug [hot dog], poster [jalapeño (2)], or baseball cap (4); he's T-shirt. Carl [pretzel] isn't mug [hot dog] or baseball cap (4); he's poster. Ice cream is baseball cap, and isn't rosemary garlic or red pepper (5); it's orange honey. Rosemary garlic isn't Tom (3) or Rita (5); it's Kathryn. Tom [bratwurst] isn't orange honey

366

[ice cream]; he's red pepper. Rita's orange honey. Kathryn's hot dog.

In summary:

Carl, pretzel, jalapeño, poster
Kathryn, hot dog, rosemary garlic, mug
Mario, hamburger, raspberry, T-shirt
Rita, ice cream, orange honey, baseball cap
Tom, bratwurst, red pepper, wristwatch

LOGIC PROBLEM 145

Cross [1st alphabetically] isn't trousers (3), dress (4), vest, or jacket (5); it's skirt [jersey (2)]. Aries isn't cross [skirt], feather (2), Gobelin [last alphabetically], or eyelethole (4); it's diamond. Aries [diamond] isn't crepe (1), jersey, rayon (2), or twill (4); it's velvet. Velvet [Aries, diamond] isn't dress (4), vest, or jacket (5); it's trousers, so Virgo is cross [1st alphabetically] (3). Rayon isn't Scorpio (2) or Gemini (3); it's Capricorn. Rayon [Capricorn] isn't vest (1) or jacket (5); it's dress. Twill isn't jacket (4); it's vest. Crepe is jacket. Rayon [Capricorn] isn't feather (1) or Gobelin (3); it's eyelethole. Crepe isn't Gobelin (1); it's feather. Twill is Gobelin, and isn't Gemini (3); it's Scorpio. Crepe is Gemini.

In summary:

Crepe jacket, Gemini, feather
Jersey skirt, Virgo, cross
Rayon dress, Capricorn, eyelethole
Twill vest, Scorpio, Gobelin
Velvet trousers, Aries, diamond

LOGIC PROBLEM 146

Speeds are 125, 130, 135, 140, and 150 mph, and uniform nos. are 7, 19, 23, 42, and 84 (intro.). 125 [slowest] isn't Lopez (1), Iriondo (2), Garcia (3), or Badiola (5); it's Zabala. 130 [faster than only 125] isn't Iriondo (2), Lopez [no. 7 would be 125 (1), which isn't possible (3)], or Badiola (5); it's Garcia. No. 7 isn't 140, 150 [fastest] (1), 130 [Garcia], or 125 (3); it's 135, so Lopez is 140, and Alberto's 150 [fastest] (1). Miguel isn't 125, 130, or 140 [Lopez] (4); he's 135. 135 [Miguel] isn't Badiola (4); it's Iriondo, so no. 23 is 130, and Jorge's 125 (2). Badiola's 150. Raul isn't Garcia (3); he's Lopez. Luis is Garcia. No. 19 isn't 140 or 150 [fastest] (5); it's 125. No. 84 isn't 150 [Alberto] (1); it's 140. No. 42 is 150.

In summary:

125 mph, Jorge Zabala, 19
130 mph, Luis Garcia, 23
135 mph, Miguel Iriondo, 7
140 mph, Raul Lopez, 84
150 mph, Alberto Badiola, 42

LOGIC PROBLEM 147

Jurors are #3, #4, #6, #9, and #11 (intro.). Reginald isn't #3 (1), #4, #9, or #6 (5); he's #11. Cyrano de Bergerac [debut (3)] isn't #9 (2), #11 [Reginald [Broadway veteran (5)]], #6 [Broadway veteran (5)], or #3 (6); he's #4. Juror #6 [Broadway veteran] isn't Richard III [debut (3)], Tartuffe (4), or Oedipus (6); he's Willy Loman. Juror #11 [Broadway veteran] isn't Richard III [debut] or Tartuffe (1); he's Oedipus. Terence [London veteran (3)] isn't Richard III [debut], Cyrano [debut], or Willy Loman [Broadway veteran (3)]; he's Tartuffe. Tartuffe [Terence] isn't #9 (3); he's #3. Richard III is #9. Lines cut isn't Cyrano [debut], Richard III [debut], Willy Loman [Juror #6], or Tartuffe (4); it's Oedipus. Costume too tight isn't Richard III (3), Cyrano, or Willy Loman [Juror #6] (6); it's Tartuffe. Cyrano [Juror #4] isn't broken lock (1) or top billing (2); he's unflattering photo. Wanted top billing isn't #6 (5); it's #9. Broken lock is #6. Bernard isn't #6 [broken lock] or #4 (1); he's #9. Morris isn't #6 (4); he's #4. Dexter is #6.

In summary:

Bernard, wanted top billing, #9, Richard III
Dexter, broken lock, #6, Willy Loman
Morris, unflattering photo, #4, Cyrano de Bergerac
Reginald, lines cut, #11, Oedipus
Terence, costume too tight, #3, Tartuffe

LOGIC PROBLEM 148

Prizes, from highest to lowest, are gold, silver, bronze, trophy, and hon. mention (intro.). Toby isn't hearts or hon. mention (2); he's fired decorating [only possible in (1)]. Copper-wheel-engraving man isn't Ian (3); he's Donald, and isn't hon. mention (3), so is hearts (1). Ian is hon. mention (1). Rebecca isn't cutting or sandblasting (2); she's etching. Vanessa isn't cutting (4); she's sandblasting. Ian is cutting. Vanessa [sandblasting] isn't musical notes (4), garden, or geese (5); she's fountain. Ian [hon. mention] isn't garden (3) or geese (5); he's musical. Toby [fired] isn't garden (2); he's geese. Rebecca is garden. Vanessa [sandblasting] isn't bronze (4), gold [1st], or trophy [hon. mention is lowest] (5); she's silver, so copper-wheel is gold [1st] (5). Rebecca isn't trophy [hon. mention is lowest] (2); she's bronze. Toby's trophy.

In summary:

Donald, gold, copper-wheel engraving, hearts
Ian, hon. mention, cutting, musical notes
Rebecca, bronze, etching, garden
Toby, trophy, fired decorating, geese
Vanessa, silver, sandblasting, fountain

LOGIC PROBLEM 149

Gains are 2%, 4%, 6%, 8%, and 10% (intro.). Plates aren't 2% [least], 4% (1), 6% [Ms. Allen would be 2% (1)] (3), or 10% [most] (5); they're 8%, so Allen's 4% (1), and Mr. Kennon's 10% [most] (5). Tissues [Ms. Hurley or Mr. Watson (3)] aren't 4% [Allen], 10% [Kennon], or 2% (3); they're 6%. Towels aren't 2% [least] or 4% (4); they're 10%, so Lansing's 8%, and Hurley is 6% [tissues] (4), so Watson's 2% (3). Mr. Cadieux is 8%. Pierre isn't 2% (3), 6% [tissues], or 10% [most] (6); it's 4%, so is cups, so 2% is Olympia (2). Napkins are 2%. Kennon isn't Jackson (5); Hurley is. Kennon's Montpelier.

In summary:

Cups, Ms. Allen, Pierre, 4%
Napkins, Mr. Watson, Olympia, 2%
Plates, Mr. Cadieux, Lansing, 8%
Tissues, Ms. Hurley, Jackson, 6%
Towels, Mr. Kennon, Montpelier, 10%

LOGIC PROBLEM 150

Taxi isn't Tower of London or National Gallery (5); it's Globe Theatre (2). Riverbus isn't Buckingham Palace or Westminster Abbey (4); it's National Gallery or Globe [only left], and isn't Atkinson (4), so is Sherlock Holmes [only left in (2)]. Freemason's Arms isn't double-decker bus (1), tube (3), or taxi (5); it's carriage. Carriage [Freemason's] isn't Buckingham (1), Westminster (3), or Tower (6); it's National Gallery, so Riverbus is Tower (above). Atkinson isn't Globe [taxi] or Tower [Sherlock] (2); it's National Gallery (2). Buckingham Palace isn't double-decker (1); it's tube. Westminster is double-decker, and isn't Moore (1), Palin (2), or Cook (3); it's Grant. Riverbus [Sherlock] isn't Cook or Moore (2); it's Palin. Tube isn't Moore (4); it's Cook. Taxi is Moore, so isn't Black Friar (4) or Rose and Crown (5); it's The Lamb. Tube isn't Black Friar (4); it's Rose and Crown. Double-decker is Black Friar.

In summary:

Atkinson, National Gallery, Freemason's Arms, carriage
Cook, Buckingham Palace, Rose and Crown, tube
Grant, Westminster Abbey, Black Friar, double-decker bus
Moore, Globe Theatre, The Lamb, taxi
Palin, Tower of London, Sherlock Holmes, Riverbus

LOGIC PROBLEM 151

Geoff isn't Nugent [would be 1-handed [woman (2)] (5)]; he's chain saws, and Robert is Nugent (2), so Geoff's Woodhall (5). Kristin isn't Byron (1) or Cal- loway (3); she's Riley. Kristin Riley isn't 1-handed [Calloway (1)] or blindfolded (3); she's swords [only left in (2)]. Byron isn't chairs (1) or fish bowls (3); that one's bowling balls. Calloway isn't chairs (4); that one's bowls. Robert Nugent's chairs, so Amy's balls (3). Nicole's bowls [1-handed], so Amy's blindfolded [Kristin swords, so only woman unplaced in (2)]. Skateboarding isn't saws or chairs (4); it's swords. Behind back isn't Woodhall (5); it's Nugent. Standing on head is Woodhall.

In summary:

Amy Byron, bowling balls, blindfolded
Geoff Woodhall, chain saws, standing on head
Kristin Riley, swords, skateboarding
Nicole Calloway, fish bowls, one-handed
Robert Nugent, chairs, behind back

LOGIC PROBLEM 152

Sizes, from smallest to largest, are 5″×7″, 8″×10″, 9″×12″, 16″×20″, and 24″×36″ (intro.). 5″×7″ [smallest] isn't garage (1), tag sale (2), attic [9″×12″ (3)], or antique shop (4); it's farmhouse. 24″×36″ [largest] isn't tag sale (2) or antique shop (4); it's garage. Coins isn't farmhouse [5″×7″] (1), tag sale, garage [24″ × 36″] (2), or antique shop (4); it's attic [9″ × 12″], so antique shop is 8″ × 10″, and picnic is 5″×7″ [smallest] (4). Tag sale is 16″ x 20″. Broken glass isn't 5″×7″, 24″×36″ [garage] (1), or 8″×10″ (4); it's 16″×20″. Garage [24″×36″, largest] isn't English cottage (1), covered bridge (2), or rocking horse (5); it's kittens, so isn't wood chips (3) or dried flowers (5), so is straw. Wood chips is 5″ x 7″, and dried flowers is 8″×10″ [only left] (3). Attic [coins] isn't covered bridge (2) or rocking horse (3); it's English cottage. Rocking horse isn't dried flowers (5); it's broken glass. Covered bridge is dried flowers.

In summary:

Covered bridge, dried flowers, 8″×10″, antique shop
English cottage, coins, 9″×12″, attic
Kittens, straw, 24″×36″, garage
Picnic, wood chips, 5″×7″, farmhouse
Rocking horse, broken glass, 16″×20″, tag sale

LOGIC PROBLEM 153

Hrs. are 2-6 (intro.). Abandoned building [3 hrs. (5)] isn't werewolf (5); it's *The Visitor* [only possible in (4)]. Farmhouse isn't 5 [no 7 hrs.], 6 [most] (1), or 2 hrs. (4); it's 4 hrs., so mummy is 5 hrs., and *Terror By Moonlight* is 6 hrs. [most] (1). Werewolf isn't 3 [*The Visitor*], 4 [farmhouse], or 2 hrs. (4); it's 6 hrs. Were- wolf [6 hrs.] isn't abandoned building [3 hrs.], farm- house [4 hrs.], train station (2), or Victorian mansion

(4); it's subway tunnel. Victorian mansion isn't 2 hrs. (4); it's 5 hrs. Train station is 2 hrs. Farmhouse [4 hrs.] isn't goblin (1) or sea monster [*Don't Open the Door!* would be 6 hrs. [*Terror by Moonlight*] (3)]; it's zombie. Sea monster isn't 3 hrs. [*The Visitor*] (3); goblin is. Sea monster is 2 hrs., so *Don't Open the Door!* is 4 hrs. (3). Mummy isn't *It's Alive* (1); it's *Nothing to Fear*. Sea monster is *It's Alive*.
In summary:
Goblin, *The Visitor*, abandoned building, 3
Mummy, *Nothing to Fear*, Victorian mansion, 5
Sea monster, *It's Alive*, train station, 2
Werewolf, *Terror by Moonlight*, subway tunnel, 6
Zombie, *Don't Open the Door!*, farmhouse, 4

LOGIC PROBLEM 154

Gals. are 30, 40, 60, 70, and 100, and hrs. are 3-7 (intro.). 30 gals. isn't 7 hrs. [most] (1); it's 3 hrs. [least], and Yeardon is 7 hrs. [most] (4). 40 gal. isn't 4 hrs. [no 10 gal.] (2), 6, or 7 hrs. [most] (4); it's 5 hrs., so Walnut St. is 4 hrs. (3), Sunny Ln. is 6 hrs., and 70 gal. is 7 hrs. [most] (4). Hickory Hill Rd. isn't 7 hrs. [most] (2) or 5 hrs. [Fontaine would be 7 hrs. [Yeardon] (2)]; it's 3 hrs. [30 gal.], so 4 hrs. is 60 gal., and Fontaine is 5 hrs. (2). 100 gals. is 6 hrs. Baldwin St. isn't 5 hrs. [Fontaine] (2); it's 7 hrs. Mason Ave. is 5 hrs., so Hathaway is 4 hrs. (1). 30 gal. isn't Mitchell (1); it's Green. 100 gal. is Mitchell.
In summary (family, street, gals., hrs.):
Fontaine, Mason Ave., 40, 5
Green, Hickory Hill Rd., 30, 3
Hathaway, Walnut St., 60, 4
Mitchell, Sunny Ln., 100, 6
Yeardon, Baldwin St., 70, 7

LOGIC PROBLEM 155

Oberton isn't feather or wombat [Dina and Mary, in some order (3)], or Barbra Streisand or eyelash [couldn't be cement or handcuffs (2), so couldn't be placed in (7)]; he's milk. Sal isn't feather or wombat [Dina and Mary, in some order (3)], or Streisand (6); he's eyelash. Joe isn't feather or wombat [Dina and Mary, in some order (3)]; he's Streisand. Sal [eyelash] isn't handcuffs [couldn't be baseball bat (1), book (2), taffy, zucchini (5), or rose (6), so couldn't be placed]; he's cement, and Joe [Streisand] is handcuffs (7). Mary isn't salt or telephone (4); she's gold. Baseball bat isn't Oberton [milk], Dina, Sal [cement], or Joe [handcuffs] (1); it's Mary, so isn't feather (1), so is wombat. Dina's feather. Rose isn't Oberton (2), Sal, or Joe [Streisand] (6); it's Dina, so isn't salt (6), so is telephone. Oberton's salt. Sal [eye-lash] isn't taffy or zucchini (5); he's book. Joe isn't taffy (5); he's zucchini. Oberton's taffy.
In summary (person, animal, vegetable, mineral):
Dina, feather, rose, telephone
Joe, Barbra Streisand, zucchini, handcuffs
Mary, wombat, baseball bat, gold
Oberton, milk, taffy, salt
Sal, eyelash, book, cement

LOGIC PROBLEM 156

Apts. are 1A, 2B, 3C, 4D, and 5E (intro.). Jean-Luc [used back entrance (1)] doesn't live in 2B [distracted by Muzak (5)]; he entered 2B and lives in 1A (1). One who lives in 5E [Simone (2)] entered 4D (2); one who lives in 2B entered 5E (6). One who lives in 3C didn't enter 3C (3); that one entered 1A [armful of groceries (4)]. One who lives in 4D [Angelique (4)] entered 3C, so talked to neighbor, so Mimi lives in 3C (3). Pierre lives in 2B. Simone's new coat of paint.
In summary (person, reason, lives, entered):
Angelique, talked to neighbor, 4D, 3C
Jean-Luc, used back entrance, 1A, 2B
Mimi, armful of groceries, 3C, 1A
Pierre, distracted by Muzak, 2B, 5E
Simone, new coat of paint, 5E, 4D

LOGIC PROBLEM 157

Ruby [Dizzy Dupree (2)] isn't *Disorder in the Court*, *Monkey Business* (1), *Toon in Tomorrow* (2), or *Week Daze* (4); she's *Mouseterpiece Theatre*. Kelly isn't Egbert (2), Nemo, or Peabody (3); she's Mr. Muggs. *Week Daze* isn't Zoe (3), Kelly [Mr. Muggs], or Gina (4); it's Faye, so isn't Egbert or Peabody (3), so is Nemo. Gina isn't Peabody (2); she's Egbert. Zoe's Peabody. Faye [Nemo, *Week Daze*] isn't Moe (1), Ozzie, Drew (3), or Art (4); she's Knox. Kelly [Mr. Muggs] isn't Ozzie (1), Moe (2), or Art (4); she's Drew. Ozzie isn't Ruby [*Mouseterpiece*] (3) or Zoe (4); he's Gina. Ozzie isn't *Toon* (1) or *Monkey* (4); he's *Disorder*. Zoe isn't *Monkey* (4); she's *Toon*, so isn't Moe (1), so is Art. Kelly's *Monkey*. Ruby's Moe.
In summary:
Art & Zoe, Peabody, *Toon in Tomorrow*
Drew & Kelly, Mr. Muggs, *Monkey Business*
Knox & Faye, Nemo, *Week Daze*
Moe & Ruby, Dizzy Dupree, *Mouseterpiece Theatre*
Ozzie & Gina, Egbert, *Disorder in the Court*

LOGIC PROBLEM 158

Yrs. are 2012, 2013, 2013, 2014, and 2014 (intro.). Son isn't 2014 [latest] (1) or 2013 [both women (2)];

he's 2012, so isn't *Carousel*, so daughter is (3). *Brigadoon* [seat 8F (2)] isn't son [seat 5A (1)], husband [*Bye Bye Birdie* (1)], or sister [seat 1A (3)]; it's mother. *Oklahoma!* isn't son [woman (2)]; *Show Boat* is. *Oklahoma!* is sister, so daughter and mother [only other women] are both 2013 (2). Husband and sister are both 2014 [only left]. Husband isn't seat 4C (1); he's seat 6D. Daughter is seat 4C.

In summary:

Brigadoon, 2013, mother, 8F
Bye Bye Birdie, 2014, husband, 6D
Carousel, 2013, daughter, 4C
Oklahoma!, 2014, sister, 1A
Show Boat, 2012, son, 5A

LOGIC PROBLEM 159

Years are 1500 B.C., 1400 B.C., 1250 B.C., 1100 B.C., and 1000 B.C., and ranks, in order from lowest to highest, are hunter, warrior, medicine man, oracle, and chief (intro.). Medicine man isn't 1500 B.C. [1st], 1400 B.C. [no 1550 B.C.], 1000 B.C. [no 1150 B.C.] (5), or 1100 B.C. [bark would be 1250 B.C. (5), but then grass couldn't be 1500 B.C. [1st], 1400 B.C. [no 1550 B.C.], 1000 B.C. [no 1150 B.C.] (4), or 1100 B.C. [ocean shell would be 1250 B.C. [bark]] (4), so couldn't be placed]; it's 1250 B.C., so bark's 1400 B.C. (5). Grass isn't 1500 B.C. [1st], 1000 B.C. [no 1150 B.C.] (4), or 1250 B.C. [shell would be 1400 B.C. [bark] (4)]; it's 1100 B.C., so shell's 1250 B.C. (4). Grass [1100 B.C.] isn't medicine man [1250 B.C.], hunter, oracle, or chief [highest] (3); it's warrior. 1500 B.C. isn't oracle or chief (4); it's hunter. Wooden beads aren't chief, oracle, medicine man [shell], or hunter [1500 B.C.] (4); they're warrior. Chief isn't feathers (1), colored sand (2), or stone beads (3); it's terra cotta. Terra cotta [chief, feasts (1)] isn't shell [medicine man], leather [ceremonial (2)], or clay (5); it's bark [1400 B.C.], so stone beads are oracle (3). Oracle [stone beads] isn't leather (2); hunter is. Oracle's clay, and 1000 B.C. Hunter [leather] isn't sand (2); medicine man is. Hunter's feathers.

In summary:

1500 B.C., leather, feathers, hunter
1400 B.C., bark, terra cotta, chief
1250 B.C., ocean shell, colored sand, medicine man
1100 B.C., grass, wooden beads, warrior
1000 B.C., clay, stone beads, oracle

LOGIC PROBLEM 160

Victorian isn't cherry (3), oak (4), mahogany, or birch (5); it's maple. Queen Anne isn't mahogany (3), oak, or cherry (4); it's birch. Tudor isn't oak (4) or cherry [couldn't be mother, daughter (1), wife (2), cousin, or aunt (3), so couldn't be placed]; it's mahogany. Gothic isn't cherry (5); it's oak, so Georgian's gargoyle (4), so is wife, so maple is parquet floors [only possible in (2)]. Georgian's cherry. Queen Anne [birch] isn't cupola (4) or flying buttress (5); it's skylight. Tudor [mahogany] isn't mother, daughter (1), or aunt (3); it's cousin, so is buttress [only possible in (5)]. Gothic's cupola. Queen Anne [birch, skylight] isn't daughter (1) or aunt (3); it's mother, so aunt's Victorian [cousin buttress, so only possible in (5)]. Gothic's daughter.

In summary:

Georgian, cherry, gargoyle, wife
Gothic, oak, cupola, daughter
Queen Anne, birch, skylight, mother
Tudor, mahogany, flying buttress, cousin
Victorian, maple, parquet floors, aunt

LOGIC PROBLEM 161

Nos. of slides are 30, 40, 50, 60, and 70 (intro.). Gus isn't 50 [no 80], 60 [no 90], 70 [most] (4), or 40 [Jessup [Indian (4)] would be 70 (4), but then Bates couldn't be 30, 40 [Gus], 50 (1), or 60 [white would be 70 [most, Indian] (1)], so couldn't be placed]; he's 30, so Jessup's 60 (4). Bates isn't 30 [Gus], 40, or 70 [most] (1); Bates is 50, so white's 70 [only left more than 50] (1). Gruber isn't 30 [least] or 40 (3); Gruber's 70. Wilkins isn't 30 [Gus] (4); Childs is. Wilkins is 40, so isn't Queenie [no 20] (2); Wilkins is Lucky (4). 70 [most, white] isn't Cupid (1) or Flo (3); it's Queenie, so Sumatran's 50 (2). Flo isn't 60 [Javan would be 50 [Sumatran] (3)]; she's 50, so Javan's 40 (3). Cupid's 60. Black's 30.

In summary:

Bates, Sumatran, Flo, 50
Childs, black, Gus, 30
Gruber, white, Queenie, 70
Jessup, Indian, Cupid, 60
Wilkins, Javan, Lucky, 40

LOGIC PROBLEM 162

$550 [most] isn't Wonder World (1), Gleeco, Pennywhistle (2), or Funtastic (3); it's Playtime. Playtime [$550] isn't 1962 (1), 1963 (2), 1959 [Pennywhistle (2)], or 1960 (3); it's 1961. Playtime [1961, $550] isn't Wrestling Robots (1), Magic Phone (3), Lights Fantastic, or Sgt. Steve Starcruiser (4); it's Treasure Island Play Set. $350 [least] isn't Sgt. Steve (2), Magic Phone (3), or Lights (5); it's Robots. Robots [$350] isn't Wonder World (1), Funtastic, or Gleeco

(5); it's Pennywhistle. Gleeco isn't 1963 (2) or 1960 (5); it's 1962. Lights isn't 1960 [$400 would be 1959 [1st, $350] (4)] or 1963 (5); it's 1962, so $400 is 1960 [only left before 1962 [Lights]] (4). 1960 [$400] isn't Magic Phone [Funtastic would be $350 [Pennywhistle] (3)]; it's Sgt. Steve. 1963 is Magic Phone, so isn't Funtastic (3); Sgt. Steve is. Magic Phone is Wonder World, so isn't $450 (5); it's $500. Gleeco's $450.

In summary:

Funtastic, Sgt. Steve Starcruiser, 1960, $400
Gleeco, Lights Fantastic, 1962, $450
Pennywhistle, Wrestling Robots, 1959, $350
Playtime, Treasure Island Play Set, 1961, $550
Wonder World, Magic Phone, 1963, $500

LOGIC PROBLEM 163

Mary [last, thistle (5)] isn't soil (1), seeds, fertilizer (2), or plant food (5); she's mulch. Mary [last, mulch] isn't "Weeds are our friends" (3), "Stop the weed whacking!," "Save the weeds!" (4), or "No more Weed-B-Gone!" (5); she's "Weeds: We're plants too!" 4th isn't Neil [ragweed would be 5th [last, thistle] (1)], Sheila [cattail would be 5th [thistle] (3)], or Alan [1st (4)]; it's Donald. Donald [4th, and no 6th] isn't soil (1), fertilizer (2), or seeds ["Save!" would be 5th [last, "We're plants too!"] (2)]; he's plant food. Neil [just before ragweed, just after soil (1)] isn't soil (1) or seeds [just after fertilizer (2)]; he's fertilizer [just before seeds (2)], so ragweed is seeds (above). Alan [1st] isn't seeds [ragweed] (1); he's soil. Sheila [just after "Weeds are our friends" (3)] is seeds [ragweed, so just after Neil (1)], so Neil is "Weeds are our friends" (above). Alan [1st] isn't cattail (3) or dandelion (4); he's wild carrot. Neil ["Weeds are our friends"] isn't cattail (3); he's dandelion. Donald's cattail. Alan [1st] isn't "Save!" (2) or "Stop!" (4); he's "No more!" Sheila [seeds] isn't "Save!" (2); she's "Stop!" Donald's "Save!"

In summary:

Alan, wild carrot, "No more Weed-B-Gone!" soil
Donald, cattail, "Save the weeds!" plant food
Mary, thistle, "Weeds: We're plants too!" mulch
Neil, dandelion, "Weeds are our friends," fertilizer
Sheila, ragweed, "Stop the weed whacking!" seeds

LOGIC PROBLEM 164

Months are Mar.-July (intro.). Bronze [fewer hrs. than Fire (2)] isn't July [last] (1), Mar. [1st], Apr. (3), or June [wood would be May, and Water would be Apr. (3), but then Mar. [1st] couldn't be Earth, Fire [more hrs. than bronze (2)], Life [more hrs. than Air

(3)] (1), or Air [Earth would be Apr. [Water] (1)], so couldn't be placed]; it's May, so wood's Apr., and Water's Mar. (3). Clay [fewer hrs. than bronze, which is fewer hrs. than Fire (2)] isn't June or July [last] (1); it's Mar. 125 hrs. (1) isn't Earth, Air (1), Water [Mar. [1st], so 125 hrs. would be fewest (1), but wood's 50 hrs. (3)], or Life [Air would be 25 hrs. [125 [Life] ÷ 5 = 25] (3), so would be earlier than Apr. [50 hrs.] (1), but Mar. [1st] is Water]; it's Fire, so bronze is 75 hrs., and clay's 25 hrs. (2). Apr. [50 hrs.] isn't Fire [125 hrs.], Earth [Air would be Mar. [Water] (1)], or Life [Air [fewer hrs. than Life (3)] would be Mar. [1st, Water] (1)]; it's Air, so Earth's May, Fire [125 hrs.] is June (1), and Life's 250 hrs. [50 [Air × 5 = 250]] (3). Life's July, and isn't alabaster [Fire (2)]; it's marble.

In summary:

Air, wood, 50, Apr.
Earth, bronze, 75, May
Fire, alabaster, 125, June
Life, marble, 250, July
Water, clay, 25, Mar.

LOGIC PROBLEM 165

Least no. of objects is 5, and most is 12 (3). Clyde isn't 5 [least] (2) or more than 6 objects [gravy boats would be more than 12 objects [most] (4)]; he's 6 objects, so gravy boats is 12 (4), and Lucy's 5 (2), so paint rollers is 10, so Arp is 8 (1). 6 objects [Clyde] isn't cheese graters or shoehorns (2); it's snorkels. 5 objects [Lucy] isn't cheese graters (1); it's shoehorns. 8 objects is cheese graters. Lucy [shoehorns] isn't Arp [cheese graters], Tzara (2), Ball, or Ernst (4); she's Duchamp. Darla isn't Ernst, Tzara, or Ball (3); she's Arp [8 objects], so Ball is 6 objects [Duchamp 5 objects] (3). Wilma isn't Ernst (3); she's Tzara. Uriah's Ernst. Uriah's 10 objects, and Wilma's 12 objects [only left] (3).

In summary:

Clyde Ball, 6 snorkels
Darla Arp, 8 cheese graters
Lucy Duchamp, 5 shoehorns
Uriah Ernst, 10 paint rollers
Wilma Tzara, 12 gravy boats

LOGIC PROBLEM 166

"Surf Master" [6 wipeouts (1)] isn't Slade [7 highest] (5); it's 360 (1), so is Sandi, "Hawaiian Tropic" is 3 wipeouts (3), and "Boogie Board" is 5 wipeouts (5), so is Larue, and "Big Kahuna" is turn-around (2). Hobie isn't roller coaster [reverse take-off would be 5 [Larue] (4)] (2); he's crossover, and reverse take-off is 4 (4). "Kahuna" [turn-around] isn't 4 wipeouts [reverse take-off]; it's 7. Crossover [Hobie] isn't "Boogie" [Larue]; it's "Hawaiian." Roller coaster is "Boogie." Slade isn't 7 [most] (5); Gidget is. Slade's 4.

In summary:

Gidget, "Big Kahuna," turn-around, 7
Hobie, "Hawaiian Tropic," crossover, 3
Larue, "Boogie Board," roller coaster, 5
Sandi, "Surf Master," 360, 6
Slade, "Moon Doggie," reverse take-off, 4

LOGIC PROBLEM 167

Rents are $450, $550, $650, $700, and $800 (intro.). Chosen apt. isn't $650 (1), $700, $800 (2), or $550 (4); it's $450, so isn't doorman (1), fireplace (2), garden (3), or dishwasher (5), so is public transportation, so isn't Lager (1), Rutherford (3), Palm (4), or Benson (6), so is Arbor, and isn't no pets (1), too far from work (2), no window (4), or basement [dishwasher (5)], so is walk-up. Dishwasher [basement] isn't chosen apt. [$450], no pets, or $650 (5); it's Lager [only possible in (1)]. $550 isn't chosen apt. [$450], Lager [dishwasher] (5), or no pets (6); it's doorman [only possible in (1)], so isn't no pets (1) or no window (4), so is too far. $650 isn't no pets (1) or basement (5); it's no window. Palm isn't $800, $650 [no window], or $550 (4); it's $700, so isn't basement [Lager], so is no pets. $800 is basement. $700 isn't garden (3); it's fireplace. $650 is garden. $550 isn't Benson (6); it's Rutherford. $650 is Benson.

In summary:

Arbor Pl., $450, public transportation, 5th-floor walk-up, chosen apt.
Benson Rd., $650, garden, no window in bedroom
Lager St., $800, dishwasher, basement apt.
Palm Blvd., $700, fireplace, no pets
Rutherford Ave., $550, doorman, too far from work

LOGIC PROBLEM 168

Males are Fafnir, Gargouille, and Smaug, females are Jormungand and Vermithrax, and ornaments are 5, 10, 15, 20, and 25 (intro.). Scale shiner [5 less than Vermithrax (3)] isn't Gargouille [5 less than cave-door opener (2), so Vermithrax would be opener, which isn't possible (2)], Vermithrax (3), Jormungand [couldn't be 5 [least], 10, 15 (1), 20 [no 30], or 25 [most] (3), so couldn't be placed], or Smaug [5 fewer than "Fiery the Snowman" [male (4)] (4)]; it's Fafnir. 25 [most] isn't Gargouille (2), Vermithrax, Fafnir [scale shiner] (3), or Smaug (4); it's Jormungand, so claw sharpener's 10 (1). 5 [least] isn't Smaug ["Fiery"

would be 10 [sharpener] (4)] (1), Gargouille [opener would be 10 [sharpener] (2)], or Vermithrax (3); it's Fafnir [scale shiner], so Vermithrax is 10, and "Here Comes Santa Claws" is 15 (3). Smaug isn't 20 ["Fiery" [male] would be 25 [Jormungand] (4)]; he's 15, so "Fiery" is 20 (4). Gargouille's 20, so opener is 25 (2). 15 ["Here Comes"] isn't wing brush (3); it's place mats. 20 is wing brush. "Silent Knight" isn't 25 [most] (2) or 10 ["O Lizard Town of Bethlehem" would be 15 ["Here Comes"] (2)]; it's 5, so "O Lizard" is 10 (2). "All I Want for Christmas" is 25.

In summary:

5, Fafnir, scale shiner, "Silent Knight"
10, Vermithrax, claw sharpener, "O Lizard Town of Bethlehem"
15, Smaug, place mats, "Here Comes Santa Claws"
20, Gargouille, wing brush, "Fiery the Snowman"
25, Jormungand, cave-door opener, "All I Want for Christmas"

LOGIC PROBLEM 169

Grades, from highest to lowest, are fine, very fine, extremely fine, uncirculated, and proof (intro.). 1966 isn't penny (2); it's nickel, and penny is grade lower than pouch and grade higher than dime (1). Nickel [1966] isn't album, pouch (1), jar [no 1968], or envelope (3); it's cabinet. Nickel [1966, cabinet] isn't extremely fine (1), proof [highest], uncirculated (2), or very fine [no 1968] (3); it's fine [lowest], so jar is 1964 (3). Penny isn't extremely fine, proof [highest] (1, above), or very fine [dime would be fine [nickel] (1, above)]; it's uncirculated, so dime is extremely fine, and pouch is proof (1, above). Half dollar isn't proof [highest] (2); it's very fine. Quarter is proof. Quarter [pouch] is 1969 [only possible in (1)]. Half dollar is album [only left in (1)]. Penny isn't jar [1964] (2); it's envelope. Dime is jar. Envelope is 1967, and very fine is 1965 (3).

In summary:

Dime, extremely fine, 1964, jar
Half dollar, very fine, 1965, album
Nickel, fine, 1966, cabinet
Penny, uncirculated, 1967, envelope
Quarter, proof, 1969, pouch

LOGIC PROBLEM 170

Mos. are 8, 10, 14, 16 and 20 (intro.). 8 mos. [shortest] isn't Mr. Weaver (1), Mr. Glover (2), Mr. Smith, or Mr. Carver (3); it's Mr. Mason, so Giles is 14 mos. (3). 10 mos. isn't Mr. Glover [Mr. Weaver would be 8 mos. [shortest, Mr. Mason] (2)], Mr. Smith [no 4 mos.], or Mr. Carver [no 5 mos.] (3); it's

Mr. Weaver. Mr. Carver isn't Orville (2), Giles [14 mos., and no 7 mos.] (3), Dunston [couldn't be 16 [no 22 months] or 20 mos. [most] (3), so couldn't be placed], or Terrence (4); he's Wallace [stonemason (4)], so Mr. Mason is glovemaker (2). Mr. Carver isn't 14 [no 7 mos.] (3) or 16 mos. [woodcarver would be 8 mos. [glovemaker] (3)]; he's 20 mos., so woodcarver is 10 mos. [Mr. Weaver] (3), and Giles is weaver (1). Blacksmith is 16 mos., and isn't Mr. Smith (intro.); he's Mr. Glover. Mr. Smith is 14 mos., so Dunston is 8 mos. (3). Terrence isn't Mr. Glover [Dunston Mason is glovemaker] (4); Orville is. Terrence is Mr. Weaver.

In summary:

Dunston Mason, glovemaker, 8
Giles Smith, weaver, 14
Orville Glover, blacksmith, 16
Terrence Weaver, woodcarver, 10
Wallace Carver, stonemason, 20

LOGIC PROBLEM 171

Brad isn't 4 [least] or 6 settings [no 2 settings] (1); he's 8 settings, so Nadine is 4 (1), so Seurat is 4 (2). Alex isn't 8 [Brad, only 1 (2)] or 4 settings [least] (4); he's 6 settings, so Degas is 4 (4). Brad [only 8 settings] isn't Nadine [4 settings], Monica (2), Elaine, or Suzanna (3); he's Alicia. Brad [only 8 settings [most]] isn't Degas [4 settings], Seurat [4 settings], Monet (1), or Renoir (3); he's Pisarro. Alex [6 settings] isn't Nadine [4 settings] or Seurat [4 settings]; he's Monica [only possible in (2)], so Stewart's 6 settings (2). 1 couple is 8 settings, Monica and Stewart are both 6 settings, and Nadine and Seurat are both 4 settings (above), so 1 couple is 8 settings, 2 are 6 settings, and 2 are 4 settings, so Degas [4 settings] is Nadine (above). Suzanna isn't Renoir (3) or Seurat [4 settings, so Nadine [only other 4 settings, Degas] would be Renoir (3)]; she's Monet. Monica [6 settings] isn't Seurat [4 settings]; she's Renoir. Elaine's Seurat [4 settings], so Greg's 4 settings, so is Degas [only other 4 settings] (3). Stewart [6 settings] isn't Elaine [4 settings]; he's Suzanna. Jake's Elaine.

In summary:

Alex & Monica, Renoir, 6
Brad & Alicia, Pisarro, 8
Greg & Nadine, Degas, 4
Jake & Elaine, Seurat, 4
Stewart & Suzanna, Monet, 6

LOGIC PROBLEM 172

Yrs. are 2009, 2010, 2011, 2013, and 2014 (intro.). *Carmen* isn't 2013 [*Madama Butterfly* (4)], 2009 [1st],

2011 [no 2012], or 2014 [last] (5); it's 2010, so France is 2011, and *The Marriage of Figaro* is 2009 [1st] (5), so Argentina is Lucretia (3). 2009 [1st] isn't Italy [*Otello* would be 2010 [*Carmen*] (1)], Austria (2), or Argentina [Lucretia] (5); it's Spain. Arabella isn't 2014 [last] (5); she's Spain (3). Josephine isn't 2011 [no 2012], 2014 [last] (1), or 2013 [Maria would be 2014 (1), but then Lucretia [Argentina] couldn't be 2011 [France] or 2010 [2009 is 1st] (5), so couldn't be placed]; she's 2010, so Maria's 2011 (1). Volante is 2013, and Lucretia's 2014 (5). Lucretia [2014, Argentina] isn't *Don Giovanni* (2); she's *Otello*, so Italy's 2013 (1). Austria's 2010. *Don Giovanni*'s 2011.

In summary:

2009, Arabella, *The Marriage of Figaro*, Spain
2010, Josephine, *Carmen*, Austria
2011, Maria, *Don Giovanni*, France
2013, Volante, *Madama Butterfly*, Italy
2014, Lucretia, *Otello*, Argentina

LOGIC PROBLEM 173

Channels are 2, 4, 5, 7, and 9 (intro.). *Beginner's Luck* isn't Gwen Hart, Whit Masterson, Veronica Starr [next higher or lower than Whit Masterson (5)] (3), or Jack Gates (5); it's Bruce Warner [daytime (4)], so isn't $50,000 (1), Hawaiian vacation (2), computer (4), or entertainment center [Jack Gates (5)], so is Porsche. *On a Roll* isn't Jack Gates, Veronica Starr, or Whit Masterson (5); it's Gwen Hart. *Bet the Bank* isn't Veronica Starr or Whit Masterson (5); it's Jack Gates. Channel 9 [highest] isn't Gwen Hart [*On a Roll*] (1), Jack Gates [*Bet the Bank*], Whit Masterson (3), or Veronica Starr [Whit Masterson would be channel 7 (5), which isn't possible [*Beginner's Luck* couldn't be placed (3)]]; it's Bruce Warner. Channel 7 [channel 9 highest] isn't Gwen Hart [*On a Roll*, but Porsche channel 9] (1), Jack Gates [*Bet the Bank*], or Whit Masterson [*Beginner's Luck* channel 9] (3); it's Veronica Starr, so Whit Masterson's channel 5 [Bruce Warner channel 9] (5). Veronica Starr [channel 7] isn't *Anyone's Guess* [Porsche channel 9] (3); Whit Masterson is. Veronica Starr [channel 7] is *The Quiet Game*, so computer is channel 5 (4). Gwen Hart isn't $50,000 (1); she's vacation. Veronica Starr's $50,000. *On a Roll* isn't channel 2 [Jack Gates [*Bet the Bank*] would be channel 4 [only left, next higher than *On a Roll* [channel 2]]] (1); it's channel 4. *Bet the Bank* is channel 2.

In summary:

2, *Bet the Bank*, Jack Gates, entertainment center

LOGIC PROBLEM 174

Days are Wed.-Fri. (intro.). Kay [Wed. (1)] isn't Peterson & Porter (1), Pucket & Prentice, Pepper & Pickney (3), or Pippin & Prosky (4); she's Pilsner & Patton. Kay [Pilsner & Patton, Wed.] isn't florist [same day as Pepper & Pickney (5), but then Pepper & Pickney couldn't be placed in (1)], publishing (3), construction (4), or dentist (5); she's law. Antoinette [only wrong no. of day (2)] isn't dentist (2), publishing [couldn't be Pippin & Prosky (2), so couldn't be placed in (4)], or florist (5); she's construction, so Basil's Pippin & Prosky (4). Publishing isn't Tracy or Basil [Pippin & Prosky] (2); it's Leo. Pepper & Pickney isn't Leo [publishing] (3) or Antoinette [only call of day] (5); it's Tracy. Tracy [Pepper & Pickney] isn't florist (5); she's dentist. Basil's florist. Antoinette [only call of day] isn't Peterson & Porter [Wed. (1)] (1); Leo is. Antoinette's Pucket & Prentice. Tracy [Pepper & Pickney, dentist] isn't Wed. [both already placed (1)] or Fri. [last] (2); she's Thu., so Antoinette's Fri. [last] (2), and Basil [florist] is Thu. (5).

In summary:

Antoinette, Pucket & Prentice, construction, Fri.
Basil, Pippin & Prosky, florist, Thu.
Kay, Pilsner & Patton, law, Wed.
Leo, Peterson & Porter, publishing, Wed.
Tracy, Pepper & Pickney, dentist, Thu.

LOGIC PROBLEM 175

Ludificasaurus isn't Oscar (2), Aaron (3), Sara [couldn't be stick (1), fishing rod, antenna (2), handlebars, or trowel (3), so couldn't be placed], or Lola (4); it's Heidi, so isn't femur (2), fibula, mandible (3), or ulna (4), so it's humerus. Fishing rod isn't *vagaridactyl*, *ludificasaurus* (2), *peccarosaurus* [couldn't be Aaron (1), Oscar (2), Sara (3), or Lola (4), so couldn't be placed], or *improbusaurus* [couldn't be femur, ulna (4), mandible (5), or fibula [couldn't be Oscar (2), Aaron (3), Lola (4), or Sara (5), so couldn't be placed], so couldn't be placed]; it's *mendacedon*. Oscar isn't *mendacedon* [fishing rod] (2), *improbusaurus* (4), or *vagaridactyl* (5); he's *peccarosaurus*. Trowel isn't *improbusaurus* (4), *vagaridactyl*, or *peccarosaurus* [Oscar] (5); it's *ludificasaurus*. Handlebars isn't *peccarosaurus* (1) or *vagaridactyl* (2); it's *improbusaurus*, so isn't mandible (3), femur, or ulna (4), so it's fibula. *improbusaurus* [fibula] isn't Aaron (3) or Sara (5); it's

Lola. Oscar [*peccarosaurus*] isn't ulna (1) or femur (4); he's mandible. Aaron isn't ulna (1); he's femur. Sara's ulna. Stick isn't Sara or Oscar [mandible] (1); it's Aaron. Fishing rod isn't Oscar (2); it's Sara. Oscar's antenna. Aaron's *vagaridactyl*.

In summary:

Aaron, femur, *vagaridactyl*, stick
Heidi, humerus, *ludificasaurus*, trowel
Lola, fibula, *improbusaurus*, handlebars
Oscar, mandible, *peccarosaurus*, antenna
Sara, ulna, *mendacedon*, fishing rod

LOGIC PROBLEM 176

Pages are 121, 222, 323, 424, and 525, men are Bob and Otto, and women are Eve, Hannah, and Lil (intro.). Bob isn't 121 [shortest], 525 [longest] (1), 323 [Kinnik would be 424 (1), and Otto couldn't be 222 [121 is shortest, so Drassard would be 424 [Kinnik] (4)], so he'd be 424, and Drassard would be 222 [525 is longest] (4), but then Ms. Seles couldn't be 121 [shortest], 525 [longest], or 323 [Bob] (2), so couldn't be placed], or 424 [Kinnik would be 525 (1), and Otto couldn't be 525 [longest, so Drassard would be 323 (4), but then Lil couldn't be 121 [shortest], 222 (2), or 323 [Drassard] (4), so couldn't be placed], so he'd be 323, and Drassard would be 121 [Kinnik 525] (4), and Lil couldn't be 121 [shortest] or 222 (2), so she'd be 525, and Ms. Seles couldn't be 323 [Otto] or 424 [Bob], so she'd be 222, and *Martini Tram* would be 121 [shortest] (2), but then Eve [*Sail On, Olias* (5)] couldn't be 121 [*Martini*] or 222 (5), so couldn't be placed]; Bob's 222, so *Yo, Banana Boy!* is 121 [shortest], and Kinnik is 323 (1). Ms. Seles isn't 121 [shortest], 525 [longest], or 222 [Bob] (2); she's 424, so Lil's 525 [longest], and *Martini* is 323 (2). Eve [*Olias*] isn't 121 [*Banana*] or 323 [*Martini*]; she's 424. Otto isn't 121 [shortest, so Drassard would be 323 [Kinnik] (4)]; Hannah is. Otto's 323, and Drassard isn't 525 [Lil] (4); she's 121 (4). Trebert isn't 525 [longest] (3); Emufume is. Trebert's 222, so *L.A. Usual* is 525 [only left longer than 222 [Trebert]] (3). *Tess, a Basset* is 222.

In summary:

Bob Trebert, *Tess, a Basset*, 222
Eve Seles, *Sail On, Olias*, 424
Hannah Drassard, *Yo, Banana Boy!* 121
Lil Emufume, *L.A. Usual*, 525
Otto Kinnik, *Martini Tram*, 323

LOGIC PROBLEM 177

Original prices are $6, $7, $8, $9, and $10, and reduced prices are $2, $3, $3, $4, and $5 (intro.).

Original price of item Flora bought is $8 (3), so original price of item Arnie sold was $6 (2). Reduced price of item Arnie sold [original $6] isn't $2 [no original $4] (3), $4, or $5 [most] (4); it's $3, so reduced price of item Arnie bought is $5 (4). Seller of original $7 isn't Guiseppe [no original $4] (1), Lester (2), or Valeria [original price of item Valeria bought would be $8 [original price of item Flora bought] (4)]; it's Flora. Valeria didn't buy Flora's item [original $7, so original price of item Valeria sold would be $6 [original price of item Arnie sold] (4)]; item Flora bought [original $8] was sold by Valeria (5), so original price of item Valeria bought is $9 (4). Seller of original $9 [bought by Valeria] isn't Guiseppe (5); it's Lester. Seller of original $10 is Guiseppe, so Guiseppe bought original $7 (1). Buyer of original $6 [sold by Arnie] isn't Arnie (intro.); it's Lester, so original $8 is reduced $2 (3). Original $10 [sold by Guiseppe] was bought by Arnie [reduced $5], so Guiseppe bought reduced $3 (1). Valeria bought reduced $4.

In summary (buyer, seller, original price, reduced price):
Arnie, Guiseppe, $10, $5
Flora, Valeria, $8, $2
Guiseppe, Flora, $7, $3
Lester, Arnie, $6, $3
Valeria, Lester, $9, $4

LOGIC PROBLEM 178

Ball 15 [highest, Elsie (3)] isn't The Master [Lita (1)], Big Sneaky (2), Ziparoo (3), Through the Woods [Johnette or Mark (4)], or Bongo's Revenge (5); it's Levitation. Ball 14 isn't Big Sneaky [cowboy would be ball 15 [Elsie, so Mr. and Mrs. (3)] (2), Bongo's [ball 15 highest] (5), The Master [Lita, but Elsie ball 15] (6), or Woods [line-up would be ball 13 (4), and Johnette couldn't be ball 14 [Elsie ball 15] (6), so she'd be 13, and Mark would be 14 (4), but then ball 12 couldn't be Big Sneaky [cowboy would be ball 13 [line-up] (2)], Bongo's [eight ball would be ball 13 [line-up] (5)], or The Master [Lita, but Johnette ball 13] (6), so it would be Ziparoo, so eight ball would be ball 11, and Bongo's would be 10 (5), but then Lita [The Master] couldn't be ball 10 [Bongo's], 11 [eight ball] (1), or 12 [Johnette ball 13] (6), so couldn't be placed]; ball 14 is Ziparoo, so eight ball is ball 13, and Bongo's is ball 12 (5). Woods isn't ball 10 [lowest] (4) or 11 [line-up would be ball 10 (4), so balls 10 and 11 would be Johnette and Mark, in some order (4), but then The Master [Lita] couldn't be

ball 10 [Johnette or Mark (above)] or 13 [eight ball] (1), so couldn't be placed]; it's ball 13, so line-up is ball 12 (4). Big Sneaky isn't ball 11 [cowboy would be ball 12 [line-up] (2)]; it's ball 10, so cowboy's ball 11 (2), and is The Master [only left]. Johnette isn't line-up [ball 12, but Lita ball 11] (6); she's Woods, and Mark's line-up (4). Nat isn't ball 10 [Big Sneaky] (2); he's ball 14. Anthony's ball 10, and isn't rotation (1); he's forty-one. Nat's rotation. In summary:
Anthony, forty-one, Big Sneaky, 10
Elsie, Mr. and Mrs., Levitation, 15
Johnette, eight ball, Through the Woods, 13
Lita, cowboy, The Master, 11
Mark, line-up, Bongo's Revenge, 12
Nat, rotation, Ziparoo, 14

LOGIC PROBLEM 179

Ages are 13, 15, 17, 19, and 21, and 2013 and 2014 heights are 6′1″, 6′2″, 6′3″, 6′4″, and 6′5″ (intro.). One 2 yrs. younger than Benjamin [taller 2014 than 2013 (4)] isn't Will [taller 2013 than 2014 (2)], Salvatore [2 yrs. younger than Will (2)], Benjamin (4), or Matthew [21-yr.-old [oldest] couldn't be Ivan (1), Salvatore (2), Will [Salvatore [2014 19 shorter than Matthew's 2013 (3)] would be 19 [same 2014 as Matthew's 2013 (3)] (2)], Benjamin [Matthew would be 19 (4, above)] (3), or Matthew (4, above), so couldn't be placed]; he's Ivan [2014 6′3″ (1)], so Benjamin's 2013 6′3″ (1, above). Same both years (4) isn't Benjamin [6′3″ 2013, and Ivan's 6′3″ 2014], Ivan [6′3″ 2014, and Benjamin's 6′3″ 2013], Will (2), or Matthew (3); it's Salvatore. Matthew's 2013 isn't 6′1″ [least] (3), 6′4″ [Salvatore's 2014 would be 6′3″ [Ivan] (3)], or 6′2″ [Salvatore would be 6′1″ [shortest] 2013 and 2014 (3, above), but then Ivan [shorter 2013 than 2014 [6′3″] (4, above)] couldn't be placed]; Matthew's 2013 is 6′5″, so Salvatore's 2013 and 2014 are both 6′4″, and 19-yr.-old's 2014 is 6′5″ (3, above). Will's 2013 isn't 6′1″ [shortest] (2); it's 6′2″, so his 2014's 6′1″ [shortest] (2). Ivan's 2013 is 6′1″. Matthew [2013 6′5″] isn't 2014 6′5″ (3); he's 2014 6′2″. Benjamin's 2014 6′5″ [19-yr.-old], so Ivan's 17 (4, above). Will isn't 13 [youngest] (2) or 21 yrs. [Salvatore would be 19 yrs. [Benjamin] (2)]; he's 15, so Salvatore's 13 (2). Matthew's 21.

In summary (son, age, 2013 height, 2014 height):
Benjamin, 19, 6′3″, 6′5″
Ivan, 17, 6′1″, 6′3″
Matthew, 21, 6′5″, 6′2″
Salvatore, 13, 6′4″, 6′4″
Will, 15, 6′2″, 6′1″

LOGIC PROBLEM 180

Dates are 1st-5th, predicted is boy, boy, girl, twin girls, and twins boy/girl, and actual is boy, girl, triplet boys, twin boys, and twins boy/girl (intro.). The 2 single boys weren't predicted 2nd, 3rd (2), or 1st (4); they were predicted 4th and 5th [only left]. 5th [single boy, Sasha or Kayla (1)] could only actually have girls (1), so is actual single girl [only possible], so is Kayla, and Sasha's 1st (1). The 2 predicted single boys are 4th and 5th, so Jacqui and one with 2 predicted babies are 3rd and 4th, in some order (4), but one with 2 predicted babies isn't 4th [predicted single boy], so is 3rd, and Jacqui's 4th. 3rd [2 predicted babies] isn't Erin (4, above); it's Mandy. 2nd is Erin. Prediction for one with actual twins boy/girl wasn't twins boy/girl, twin girls [Kayla [predicted single boy] is only 1 with same predicted and actual (1)], or single boy [would be Jacqui [only left with predicted single boy], so Jacqui [4th] and Kayla [5th, actual single girl] would have actual total of 1 boy, so Sasha [1st] and Erin [2nd] would have actual total of 1 boy (3), which isn't possible [each of the only actual births left contains at least 1 boy]]; it was single girl. Prediction for one with actual twin boys wasn't twins boy/girl or twin girls [Kayla [predicted single boy] is only 1 with same predicted and actual (1)]; it was single boy, so Jacqui [only predicted single boy left]. One with predicted single girl [actual twins boy/girl] isn't Mandy [predicted 2 babies (above)] or Sasha (1); she's Erin. 4th is actual twin boys, and 5th is actual single girl, so 4th and 5th have actual total of 2 boys, and 2nd is actual twins boy/girl, so is actual 1 boy, so 1st must be actual 1 boy (3), so is single boy [only possible]. Mandy's actual triplet boys. Sasha [actual single boy] isn't predicted twins boy/girl (1); she's predicted twin girls. Mandy's predicted twins boy/girl.

In summary (woman, date, predicted, actual):

Erin, 2nd, girl, twins boy/girl
Jacqui, 4th, boy, twin boys
Kayla, 5th, boy, girl
Mandy, 3rd, twins boy/girl, triplet boys
Sasha, 1st, twin girls, boy

LOGIC PROBLEM 181

Spain isn't bicycle tour or $25 [least (1)] (4); it's bellhop [only possible in (1)]. France isn't bellhop [Spain] or $25 [least] (5); it's bicycle [only possible in (1)]. Waiter isn't Italy (2), bicycle, or $25 [least] (4); it's Argentina [only possible in (1)]. Beach isn't Italy (2), Argentina [waiter], or Spain (3); it's Aus-

tralia, so isn't bellhop [Spain], so is $25 [only possible in (1)]. Australia [beach] isn't doorman or barber (2); it's cab driver. $75 [most (1)] (1) isn't bicycle, shopping (4), or relatives (5); it's museums. Argentina [waiter] isn't museums [$75 [most]] (3) or shopping (4); it's relatives. Beach [$25 [least]] is less than waiter (3), so Spain must be more than waiter [otherwise, Spain would be beach [Australia] (3)], so isn't shopping [less than waiter (4)]; it's museums [$75], so waiter [relatives] is $50 [beach $25, so only possible] (3), so France is $60 (5). Italy is shopping, so isn't barber (5); it's doorman. France is barber. Italy is $40 [$250 [total (6)] − $25 [Australia] − $50 [Argentina] − $60 [France] − $75 [Spain] = $40].

In summary:

Argentina, relatives, waiter, $50
Australia, beach, cab driver, $25
France, bicycle tour, barber, $60
Italy, shopping, doorman, $40
Spain, museums, bellhop, $75

LOGIC PROBLEM 182

Ranks, from lowest to highest, are tiger, bobcat, wolf, bear, lion, and webelo (intro.). Billy isn't lion, webelo [highest] (5), tiger [couldn't be safety (1), so would be Parsons [only possible in (3)], and swimming would be bobcat, but couldn't be Gino (5), so couldn't be placed in (3)], bobcat [couldn't be safety (1), so would be Parsons [only possible in (3)], and swimming would be wolf, but couldn't be Gino (5), so couldn't be placed in (3)], or bear [swimming would be lion, and Cortez would be webelo (5), but then Bergman couldn't be lion [swimming] or bear [Billy] (1), so couldn't be placed in (4)]; Billy's wolf, so swimming is bear, and Cortez is lion (5). Wolf [Billy] isn't safety (1); it's Parsons [only possible in (3)]. Bear [swimming] isn't Bergman (1); it's Dennis, so lion [Cortez] is hiking [only possible in (4)]. Webelo [highest] is Bergman [only unplaced in (4)]. Witt isn't tiger [lowest] or bear [Dennis] (2); she's bobcat, so camping's tiger [lowest] (2), so is Gino [only possible in (3)]. Safety's bobcat [only unplaced in (3)]. Vane isn't tiger [lowest] (2); she's bear, so Julio's bobcat [only left lower than bear] (2). Shaw's tiger. Marcus isn't Bergman (1); he's Cortez. Raphael's Bergman, and isn't fitness (1); he's leadership. Billy's fitness.

In summary:

Billy, wolf, Mr. Parsons, fitness
Dennis, bear, Ms. Vane, swimming
Gino, tiger, Mr. Shaw, camping
Julio, bobcat, Ms. Witt, safety

Marcus, lion, Ms. Cortez, hiking
Raphael, webelo, Mr. Bergman, leadership

LOGIC PROBLEM 183

Cheese isn't 4th [freestyle (2)] (2), 1st, 2nd, or 3rd
(4); it's 5th, so pepperoni's 3rd (4). Mushroom isn't
1st or 2nd (1); it's 4th, so Harry's 5th [last], and backstroke's 2nd (1). Onion isn't 1st (5); it's 2nd, so
breaststroke's 1st, and Helen's 3rd (5). Deluxe is 1st.
5th [last] isn't butterfly (3); it's relay. 3rd's butterfly,
so Amanda's 2nd (3). Joy isn't 1st (3); she's 4th.
Tom's 1st.

In summary:

Amanda, backstroke, 2nd, onion
Harry, relay, 5th, cheese
Helen, butterfly, 3rd, pepperoni
Joy, freestyle, 4th, mushroom
Tom, breaststroke, 1st, deluxe

LOGIC PROBLEM 184 & 185

Clues from part 1 are designated as I and from part
2 as II. Times are 7:30, 8:00, 8:30, 9:00, and 9:30 (I,
intro.), and weights are 7, 8, 10, 11, and 13 lbs. (II,
intro.). "Zany" isn't 11 [9:30 [last] (II,4)] (I,2), 7 [no
9], 10 [no 12], or 13 lbs. [most] (II,1); she's 8 lbs.,
so toast butterer is 10 lbs. (II,1). 7:30 [1st] isn't same
train tickets ["crusty" (I,2)] (I,2), golf balls switched
(I,3), or spilled soup (II,3); it's fender bender or taxi
ride. 8:00 [after only 7:30] isn't train ["crusty"] (I,2),
golf balls (I,3), or soup (II,3); it's fender or taxi, so
7:30 and 8:00 are fender and taxi, in some order
(above). 9:30 [last] isn't "screwy" (I,1), "zany" (I,2),
"eccentric" [fender [7:30 or 8:00 (above)] would be
8:30 (II,2)], or "madcap" (II,4); it's "wacky."
"Wacky" [9:30 [last], 11 lbs.] isn't toast [10 lbs.],
spaghetti twirler [taxi (I,4)] (I,4), banana peeler
["eccentric" (II,2)], or pancake flipper (II,3); she's
ketchup squirter. "Zany" [8 lbs., 30 mins. before
"crusty" (I,2)] isn't toast [10 lbs.] or spaghetti [taxi
[30 mins. before "irascible" (I,4)]]; she's pancake.
7:30 [1st] isn't "screwy" (I,1), "zany" ["crusty"
[train] would be 8:00 [fender bender or taxi (above)]
(I,2)], or "eccentric" (II,2); it's "madcap." 9:00 isn't
"screwy" [7 lbs. would be 9:30 [last, 11 lbs.] (I,1)]
or "zany" [pancake, but no 10:00] (II,3); it's "eccentric," so fender is 8:00 (II,2), so taxi is 7:30 (above),
so "irascible" is 8:00 (I,4). 9:30 [last] isn't "wisecracking" (I,3), "sardonic" (I,4), or "crusty" ["zany"
[pancake] would be 9:00 (I,2), but no 10:00] (II,3);
it's "gruff." 7:30 [1st] isn't "crusty" (I,2) or "wisecracking" (I,3); it's "sardonic." "Zany" [pancake, 30
mins. before "crusty" [train] (I,2)] isn't with

"crusty" (I,2) or "wisecracking" [30 mins. before
golf balls (I,3)]; she's with "irascible" [8:00], so
"crusty" is 8:30 (I,2), and spilled soup is 9:00 (II,3).
"Wisecracking" is 9:00, so golf balls are 9:30, and
Cuddles is 8:30 (I,3). "Screwy" is 8:30 and toast. 7
lbs. isn't "madcap" [7:30 [1st]] (I,1); it's "eccentric."
13 lbs. is "madcap." Pancake is 8 lbs., so Binky is 7
[least] (II,3). Nugget isn't "zany" [fender, so Poopsie
(II,2)] or "wacky" [Snookums (II,4)]; she's
"madcap."

In summary, Logic Problem 184 (heiress, reporter,
time, met):
"Eccentric," "wisecracking," 9:00, spilled soup
"Madcap," "sardonic," 7:30, taxi ride
"Screwy," "crusty," 8:30, same train tickets
"Wacky," "gruff," 9:30, golf balls switched
"Zany," "irascible," 8:00, fender bender

In summary, Logic Problem 185 (heiress, weight,
baby, appliance):
"Eccentric," 7, Binky, banana peeler
"Madcap," 13, Nugget, spaghetti twirler
"Screwy," 10, Cuddles, toast butterer
"Wacky," 11, Snookums, ketchup squirter
"Zany," 8, Poopsie, pancake flipper

LOGIC PROBLEM 186

Sept. isn't $20 [June (1)], $10 [least], $18 [no $8], or
$36 [most] (3); it's $28, so May's $36, and Aug. is
$18 (3). July's $10. Balmorals aren't July [stogies
(1)], Sept. [wingtips (1)], May [1st], Sept. [last] (2),
or Aug. [brogans would be Sept. [last, wingtips (2)];
they're June, so brogans are Aug. [only left after
June] (2). Oxfords are May. Henry Ford isn't May
[J.P. Morgan (1)], Aug. [Andrew Carnegie (1)], Sept.
(3), or July [stogies] (4); he's June. H.L. Hunt isn't
July [stogies] (4); he's Sept. John D. Rockefeller's
July.

In summary:

May, J.P. Morgan, oxfords, $36
June, Henry Ford, balmorals, $20
July, John D. Rockefeller, stogies, $10
Aug., Andrew Carnegie, brogans, $18
Sept., H.L. Hunt, wingtips, $28

LOGIC PROBLEM 187

Bids are $70, $80, $90, $100, and $110 (intro.). $80
[Brad (5)] isn't Tammy [$100, Josh (1)], Lisa [Adam
(3)], Anna [$110 (4)], or Erica (5); it's Holly. $70
[Seafood Shanty (3)] isn't Lisa (3); it's Erica, so she
isn't Trent [Manor House (2)], so Steve. Lisa's $90.
Anna's Trent. Tammy isn't Donetto's or Town Fare (1);

she's Clarissa's. Lisa isn't Town Fare (3); she's Donetto's. Holly's Town Fare.

In summary:

Anna & Trent, Manor House, $110
Erica & Steve, Seafood Shanty, $70
Holly & Brad, Town Fare, $80
Lisa & Adam, Donetto's, $90
Tammy & Josh, Clarissa's, $100

LOGIC PROBLEM 188

Movie star [The Shoe Shack (5)] isn't Robert Craig (1), Chloe Wofford (4), Susan Tomaling (5), or Allen Konigsberg [talk-show host (6)]; he's Howard O'Brien. Sportscaster isn't Chloe Wofford or Susan Tomaling (4); he's Robert Craig, so Chloe Wofford's "Now that's a great deal!" (3). News anchor isn't Susan Tomaling (2); she's Chloe Wofford. Sitcom star is Susan Tomaling. Allen Konigsberg [talk-show host] isn't Mattress Planet [Susan Tomaling (3)], Wonder Weeder (5), or Atomic Cola (6); he's Viking Burger. Chloe Wofford [news anchor] isn't Atomic Cola (2); she's Wonder Weeder. Robert Craig's Atomic Cola. Howard O'Brien isn't "Who wants to limbo?" [Robert Craig (1)], "Don't miss the party!" (2), or "To pay more would be a crime" [Susan Tomaling (5)]; he's "Save us, Value Man!" Allen Konigsberg is "Don't miss the party!"

In summary:

Allen Konigsberg, talk-show host, Viking Burger, "Don't miss the party!"
Chloe Wofford, news anchor, Wonder Weeder, "Now that's a great deal!"
Howard O'Brien, movie star, The Shoe Shack, "Save us, Value Man!"
Robert Craig, sportscaster, Atomic Cola, "Who wants to limbo?"
Susan Tomaling, sitcom star, Mattress Planet, "To pay more would be a crime"

LOGIC PROBLEM 189

Flight nos. are 181, 281, 381, 481, and 581, and departure times are 1:00, 1:30, 2:00, 3:00, and 3:30 a.m. (intro.). 3:30 [last] isn't Carla, Stephanie (2), Mallory, or Lenny (5); it's Jasper. 1:00 [1st] isn't Carla, Lenny, or Mallory (2); it's Stephanie. 1:30 [1:00 1st] isn't Lenny or Mallory (2); it's Carla. Mallory's 3:00, and Lenny's 2:00 (5). Carla [1:30 [LAX (3)]] isn't no. 181 [Kennedy (1)], 381 (2), 481, or 581 [highest] (4); she's no. 281, so Mallory's no. 381, and Jasper's no. 481 (4). Lenny's no. 581, and Stephanie's no. 181 (5). Heathrow isn't Lenny or

Jasper [no. 481] (1); it's Mallory. Ronald Reagan isn't Jasper (3); it's Lenny. O'Hare's Jasper.

In summary:

Carla, LAX, 281, 1:30
Jasper, O'Hare, 481, 3:30
Lenny, Ronald Reagan, 581, 2:00
Mallory, Heathrow, 381, 3:00
Stephanie, Kennedy, 181, 1:00

LOGIC PROBLEM 190

4th [turned wand to roses (2)] isn't statue [sawed woman in half (1)], motorcycle (2), tree [1st (4)], or birdcage (5); it's panther, so Enchantra is 3rd or 5th (3), but not 3rd (1), so 5th [last] (above), so isn't turned doves to butterflies (1), levitated assistant (3), or pulled items from suitcase (5), so is sawed woman. 4th [turned wand, panther] isn't Mephisto (2), Carnack (3), or Raven (5); it's Merlin. Turned doves isn't 3rd (1) or 1st (4); it's 2nd. Raven isn't tree [1st] (4) or motorcycle (5); she's birdcage. Mephisto isn't motorcycle (2); he's tree. Carnack's motorcycle, and isn't 2nd (1); he's 3rd, and isn't pulled items from suitcase (2), so is levitated assistant. Raven's 2nd. Pulled items is 1st.

In summary:

1st, Mephisto, pulled items from suitcase, tree
2nd, Raven, turned doves to butterflies, birdcage
3rd, Carnack, levitated assistant, motorcycle
4th, Merlin, turned wand to roses, panther
5th, Enchantra, sawed woman in half, statue

LOGIC PROBLEM 191

Yrs. are 1929, 1933, 1937, 1941, and 1945 (intro.). 1929 [oldest] isn't Studebaker (3), Nash (4), Hudson, or Oldsmobile (5); it's DeSoto, so isn't Ms. Bell (1), Mr. Francis (3), Ms. Ford (4), or Mr. Barker [Hudson (5)], so is Mr. Robinson. 1933 [newer than only 1929] isn't Studebaker (3), Nash (4), or Oldsmobile (5); it's Hudson, so Oldsmobile is 1937 (5). 1945 isn't Nash (2); it's Studebaker. 1941 is Nash. 1945 [newest] isn't Mr. Francis (3) or Ms. Ford (4); it's Ms. Bell. Ms. Ford isn't 1941 [Nash] (4); she's 1937. Mr. Francis is 1941, so engine is 1937 (3). 1945 [newest] isn't headlights (1), wheel design (2), or interior (4); it's grille. 1941 [Nash] isn't wheel design (2) or interior (4); it's headlights. 1929 [Mr. Robinson] isn't wheel design (2); it's interior. 1933 is wheel design.

In Summary:

Mr. Barker, Hudson, 1933, wheel design
Ms. Bell, Studebaker, 1945, grille
Ms. Ford, Oldsmobile, 1937, engine

Mr. Francis, Nash, 1941, headlights
Mr. Robinson, DeSoto, 1929, interior

LOGIC PROBLEM 192

Women are Ingrid, Loretta, and Norma, men are Orville and Rodney, fruit blends are banana-kiwi, papaya-strawberry, and plum-tangerine, and vegetable blends are asparagus-spinach and broccoli-carrot (intro.). "Pungent!" isn't broccoli-carrot (1); it's asparagus-spinach, so "savory!" is broccoli-carrot (2). Ingrid [fruit (1)] isn't "flavorful!" (1), "savory!," "pungent!" (2), or "delicious!" [Norma (2)]; she's "yummy!" Loretta [only woman left] is "pungent!" (3). Rodney isn't "flavorful!" (1); he's "savory!" Orville is "flavorful!" Strawberry-papaya [cinnamon (4)] isn't Orville or Norma (4); it's Ingrid. Norma isn't allspice (2), ginger, or anise (4); she's nutmeg, so isn't plum-tangerine (3), so is banana-kiwi. Orville is plum-tangerine. Rodney [broccoli-carrot [vegetable]] isn't ginger (3) or anise (4); he's allspice. Loretta [asparagus-spinach [vegetable]] isn't ginger (3); Orville is. Loretta is anise.

In summary:
Ingrid, papaya-strawberry, cinnamon, "yummy!"
Loretta, asparagus-spinach, anise, "pungent!"
Norma, banana-kiwi, nutmeg, "delicious!"
Orville, plum-tangerine, ginger, "flavorful!"
Rodney, broccoli-carrot, allspice, "savory!"

LOGIC PROBLEM 193

Ranks are 2nd, 3rd, 5th, 7th, 9th, and 10th, and secs. are 55, 58, 59, 62, 64, and 65 (intro.). Heather isn't 55 [no 56 sec.], 59 [no 60 sec.], 62 [no 63 sec.], 65 [longest] (4), or 64 sec. [65 sec. [slalom (4)] would be downhill (4)]; she's 58 sec., so 59 sec. is downhill (4). Zoe isn't 55 [no 56 sec.], 59 [no 60 sec.], 62 [no 63 sec.], or 65 sec. [longest] (6); she's 64 sec., so snowplow's 65 sec. (6). Zoe [64 sec.] isn't 9th, 10th [lowest] (4), 2nd, 3rd, or 7th [no 4th] (6); she's 5th, so tempo is 7th (4), and snowplow [65 sec.] is 2nd (6), so christie is 62 sec. (2). Christie [62 sec.] isn't 5th [64 sec.], 3rd [no 1st], or 10th [no 8th] (2); it's 9th, so 55 sec. is 7th (2). 58 sec. [more than only 55 sec. [shortest]] isn't stem (1) or jump (5); it's Telemark. 64 sec. [Zoe, 5th] isn't jump (5); it's stem, so Heather's 10th [only left lower than stem] (1). 59 sec. is jump and 3rd. Kate [slalom (5)] isn't 3rd [59 sec. [downhill (above)]], 7th [Zoe's 5th] (5), or 9th [downhill (5)]; she's 2nd. Donovan isn't 3rd or 7th [tempo] (3); he's 9th. 55 sec. [shortest] isn't Linus (1); it's Owen. 59 sec. is Linus.

In summary:
Donovan, 9th, christie, 62
Heather, 10th, Telemark, 58
Kate, 2nd, snowplow, 65
Linus, 3rd, jump, 59
Owen, 7th, tempo, 55
Zoe, 5th, stem, 64

LOGIC PROBLEM 194

Nuts are biscotti, cannoli, and spumoni (intro.). Ms. Cannoli [nuts] is biscotti (3), so Louisa Biscotti [nuts] (3) isn't cannoli [nuts], spumoni [nuts] (1), or zeppoli [Sally (2)]; she's zabaglione, so Ms. Spumoni [nuts] isn't cannoli [nuts] or spumoni [nuts] (1), so she's zeppoli. Ms. Zeppoli [decaf. cappuccino (2)] isn't spumoni [cappuccino (4)]; she's cannoli. Ms. Zabaglione's spumoni. Doreen [hazelnut (4)] isn't Ms. Zabaglione [cappuccino] or Ms. Zeppoli [decaf. cappuccino]; she's Ms. Cannoli. Ms. Spumoni [zeppoli] isn't espresso (3); she's latte, so Theresa's Ms. Zeppoli (2). Marie's Ms. Zabaglione. Louisa's espresso.

In summary (1st & last names, coffee, dessert):
Doreen Cannoli, hazelnut, biscotti
Louisa Biscotti, espresso, zabaglione
Marie Zabaglione, cappuccino, spumoni
Sally Spumoni, latte, zeppoli
Theresa Zeppoli, decaf. cappuccino, cannoli

LOGIC PROBLEM 195

Rounds are 1-5 (intro.). He-Man isn't round 4 [round 5 last] (3); it's Reid (5). Whitney isn't G.I. Joe [Kevin (2)], Mr. Spock (4), or Darth Vader [He-Man Reid] (5); she's Batman. Ashley isn't Darth Vader (1); she's Mr. Spock. Margaret's Darth Vader. Reid [He-Man] isn't round 3, 4, 5 [last] (3), or 1 [queen would be round 2 (1), and knight would be round 4 (3), so Whitney would be round 3 (4), but then Kevin couldn't be round 2, 5 [last] (2), or 4 [rook would be round 2 [queen] (2)], so couldn't be placed]; Reid's round 2, so queen is round 3 (1), and knight is round 5 (3), so Whitney [Batman] is round 4 (4), and bishop's round 2 (3). Rook isn't round 4 [round 5 last] (2); it's round 1, so Kevin's round 3 (2). King is round 4. Round 5 [last] isn't Ashley (1); it's Margaret. Ashley's round 1.

In summary:
1, Ashley, Mr. Spock, rook
2, Reid, He-Man, bishop
3, Kevin, G.I. Joe, queen
4, Whitney, Batman, king
5, Margaret, Darth Vader, knight

LOGIC PROBLEM 196

Boys are Arthur, Greg, and Owen, girls are Felicia and Rhonda, and planets, from closest to farthest from sun, are Mars, Jupiter, Saturn, Uranus, and Neptune (intro.). Rhonda isn't Neptune [boy (1)], Mars [closest], Jupiter [Mars closest] (5), or Uranus [orbit [boy (5)] would be Saturn (5), but then Felicia couldn't be placed (4, above)]; she's Saturn, so Felicia's Uranus (4), orbit's Jupiter, and Arthur's Mars [closest] (5). Rhonda [Saturn] is surface features, and Felicia [Uranus] is orange [only possible in (2)]. Owen isn't Neptune [grapefruit would be Uranus [orange] (3)]; he's Jupiter [orbit], so grapefruit's Mars [closest] (3). Greg's Neptune. Felicia isn't atmosphere (1) or rotation (4); she's satellites. Greg [Neptune] isn't atmosphere (1); he's rotation, so isn't baseball (1) or beachball (4), so he's volleyball. Arthur's atmosphere. Rhonda isn't baseball (1); she's beachball. Owen's baseball.

In summary:

Arthur, Mars, atmosphere, grapefruit
Felicia, Uranus, satellites, orange
Greg, Neptune, rotation, volleyball
Owen, Jupiter, orbit, baseball
Rhonda, Saturn, surface features, beachball

LOGIC PROBLEM 197

Stops are 1-5 (intro.). Grace isn't 1 [least] (1), 3 [no 0 or 6 stops] (3), 4, or 5 stops [most] (5); she's 2 stops, so Sherlyn's 1 stop [least] (1), and Casey's 5 stops (3). Toys isn't Sherlyn [fresh produce (1)], Travis, Casey [5 stops [most]], or Michael (6); it's Grace [2 stops], so Knoxville is 1 stop [least] (6), so Lexington's 4 stops (2). Chattanooga isn't 5 [most] or 3 stops [lumber would be 5 stops [Casey] (4)] (4); it's 2 stops, so lumber is 4 stops (4). Travis isn't furniture or clothing (5); he's lumber [4 stops], so clothing is 5 stops [most] (5). Michael is furniture and 3 stops. Memphis isn't clothing (5); it's furniture. Louisville is clothing.

In summary:

Casey, clothing, 5, Louisville
Grace, toys, 2, Chattanooga
Michael, furniture, 3, Memphis
Sherlyn, fresh produce, 1, Knoxville
Travis, lumber, 4, Lexington

LOGIC PROBLEM 198

Times are 10:30 a.m., 12:00 p.m., 1:45 p.m., 3:00 p.m., and 4:30 p.m. (intro.). 4:30 p.m. [last] isn't Upper West Side [3:00 p.m. (1)], Greenwich Village (2), Chelsea (3), or Midtown (4); it's Murray Hill

[ballet (3)], so isn't Martha Robbins (1), Twyla Graham (2), E.M. Duncan [Chelsea (3)], or Jerome Tharp (4), so is Isadora Pavlova. Music video isn't 3:00 p.m. (1), 10:30 a.m. [1st], or 12:00 p.m. (4); it's 1:45 p.m., so film is 12:00 p.m., and Midtown is 10:30 a.m. [1st] (4), so isn't dance company (3); it's musical. Dance is 3:00 p.m. 12:00 p.m. [film] isn't Greenwich Village (2); it's Chelsea. 1:45 p.m. is Greenwich Village. Twyla Graham isn't 10:30 a.m. (2) or 3:00 p.m. (3); she's 1:45 p.m. Jerome Tharp isn't 10:30 a.m. [1st] (1); he's 3:00 p.m. Martha Robbins is 10:30 a.m.

In summary:

10:30 a.m., Martha Robbins, Midtown, musical
12:00 p.m., E.M. Duncan, Chelsea, film
1:45 p.m., Twyla Graham, Greenwich Village, music video
3:00 p.m., Jerome Tharp, Upper West Side, dance company
4:30 p.m., Isadora Pavlova, Murray Hill, ballet

LOGIC PROBLEM 199

Suzanne [pastry brush (3)] isn't mother (2), grandmother [wooden spoon (2)], sister (3), or aunt [Rosemary (5)]; she's cousin, and isn't Bundt [whisk (4)], so is muffin (1). Aunt Rosemary isn't whisk [Bundt] or spatula (5); she's corkscrew, so isn't jelly roll [mother (2)] or omelet (3), so is paella, so Terry's omelet (1). Mother [jelly roll] isn't whisk [Bundt]; she's spatula. Sister's whisk. Terry [omelet] isn't sister [Bundt] or mother [jelly roll]; she's grandmother. Lindsey isn't sister (4); she's mother. Nora's sister.

In summary:

Lindsey, mother, jelly roll, spatula
Nora, sister, Bundt, whisk
Rosemary, aunt, paella, corkscrew
Suzanne, cousin, muffin, pastry brush
Terry, grandmother, omelet, wooden spoon

LOGIC PROBLEM 200

Oz. are 2-6 (intro.). Body wash [quince (1)] isn't 2, 6 [philodendron (4)] (1), 4 [papaya (2)], or 5 oz. [bubble bath (2)]; it's 3 oz., so isn't eryngo (3), so is calendula (1). Avocado isn't 6 [most] (3) or 5 oz. [eryngo would be 6 oz. [most, philodendron] (3)]; it's 2 oz. Facial mask isn't 2 [avocado] or 6 oz. [most] (3); it's 4 oz., so eryngo's 5 oz. [only left more than facial mask] (3). Lespedeza [shampoo (3)] isn't 4 oz. [facial mask]; it's 2 oz. Fraxinella's 4 oz. Hand lotion's 6 oz., so isn't coconut (4); it's mango. 5 oz. is coconut.

In summary:
Body wash, 3, quince, calendula
Bubble bath, 5, coconut, eryngo
Facial mask, 4, papaya, fraxinella
Hand lotion, 6, mango, philodendron
Shampoo, 2, avocado, lespedeza

LOGIC PROBLEM 201

Men are Baxter, Jim, and Teddy, women are Marilyn and Shirley, and fingers, from lowest to highest, are pinkie, ring, middle, index, and thumb (intro.). Baxter isn't doorknob [Marilyn (2)], window (3), cabinet, or nightstand (5); he's glass. Shirley isn't cabinet or nightstand (5); she's window. Teddy [thumb (2)] isn't nightstand (4); he's cabinet. Jim's nightstand. Pinkie [lowest, woman (1)] isn't Shirley [window] (3); it's Marilyn. Ring [pinkie lowest] isn't Shirley [window] (3) or Jim [nightstand] (4); it's ring, so Shirley [window] isn't middle [whorl couldn't be placed in (3)], so she's index, and whorl is middle [Baxter ring] (3). Jim [nightstand] is middle, so tented arch is pinkie [lowest] (4). Double loop isn't Baxter [glass] or Shirley (1); it's Teddy. Arch isn't Shirley [index] (2); it's Baxter. Ulnar loop is Shirley.
In summary:
Baxter, glass, ring, arch
Jim, nightstand, middle, whorl
Marilyn, doorknob, pinkie, tented arch
Shirley, window, index, ulnar loop
Teddy, cabinet, thumb, double loop

LOGIC PROBLEM 202

Beeps are 2-6 (intro.). 2 beeps [least, rechargeable (2)] isn't Maritochi [6 beeps (2)], Cyber Friend (3), Robo Pet, or Spot 6.0 (4); it's Virtual Vinnie. Robo isn't 3 [no 1 beep] or 4 beeps [wanted to play would be 2 beeps [rechargeable (above)] (4)] (4); it's 5 beeps, so play is 3 beeps (4). Spot isn't 3 beeps [play] (4); it's 4 beeps. Cyber is 3 beeps, so Carl's 2 beeps [least], and hungry's 4 beeps (3). Maritochi [6 beeps [most]] isn't Rachel (1), Barbara [rechargeable (2)] (2), or Tad (3); it's Gina, so isn't needed walk or sick (1), so is stuck in tree. Virtual isn't sick (1); it's needed walk. Robo is sick. Spot isn't Rachel (1) or Barbara [rechargeable (above)] (4); it's Tad. Barbara [rechargeable (above)] isn't play (4); she's sick. Rachel's play.
In summary:
Cyber Friend, Rachel, 3, wanted to play
Maritochi, Gina, 6, stuck in tree
Robo Pet, Barbara, 5, sick

Spot 6.0, Tad, 4, hungry
Virtual Vinnie, Carl, 2, needed walk

LOGIC PROBLEM 203

Times are 9:45-10:15 a.m. [30 min.], 10:20-10:40 a.m. [20 min.], 10:50-11:40 a.m. [50 min.], 12:10-12:50 p.m. [40 min.], and 1:00-2:00 p.m. [60 min.], and rings are 2-6 (intro.). 6 rings [most] isn't Julie (1), Mary, Winnie (2), or Alonzo (4); it's Grant. 5 rings isn't Julie [no 10 rings] (1), Winnie [6 rings most] (2), or Alonzo [no 10 rings] (4); it's Mary, so won lottery is 6 rings [most] (2), so Alonzo is 3 rings (4). 4 rings isn't Julie [no 8 rings] (1); it's Winnie. Julie's 2 rings, so moving is 4 rings (1). Julie isn't 10:20-10:40 [20 min. [shortest (above)]], 9:45-10:15 [30 min., but no 15 min. (above)], 10:50-11:40 [50 min., but no 25 min. (above)], or 1:00-2:00 [60 min. [longest (above)]] (1); she's 12:10-12:50 [40 min.], so 5 rings is 10:20-10:40 [20 min.] (1). 9:45-10:15 [1st] isn't 4 (3) or 6 rings [won lottery] (4); it's 3 rings. Mary [Dubuque (2)] isn't job promotion (3) or engaged (5); she's baby. 4 rings isn't 10:50-11:40 [job promotion would be 10:20-10:40 [baby] (3)]; it's 1:00-2:00, so promotion is 12:10-12:50 (3). 10:50-11:40 is 6 rings. Engaged is 3 rings.
In summary:
9:45-10:15 a.m., Alonzo, 3, engaged
10:20-10:40 a.m., Mary, 5, baby
10:50-11:40 a.m., Grant, 6, won lottery
12:10-12:50 p.m., Julie, 2, job promotion
1:00-2:00 p.m., Winnie, 4, moving

LOGIC PROBLEM 204

Tracks are 6, 8, 11, 13, and 16 (intro.). Sum of Drake and Wichita is at least 14 [6 [lowest] + 8 [2nd lowest] = 14]; knapsack is track 16 [highest], so Drake and Wichita are tracks 6 and 8, in some order [only possible (4, above)]. Track 6 [lowest] isn't duffel bag (2), footlocker (3), or portmanteau (5); it's wardrobe trunk, so isn't Drake (2), so is Wichita, and Drake is track 8 (above). Knapsack [track 16 [highest]] isn't Erin (3); it's Morgan, so Erin's 5 lower than Chicago (1). Drake [track 8] isn't wardrobe [track 6], duffel (2), or portmanteau [duffel would be track 6 [lowest, wardrobe] (5)]; he's footlocker, so Erin's track 6 (3), so Chicago's track 11 (above). Duffel isn't track 13 [portmanteau would be track 16 [highest, knapsack] (5)]; it's track 11. Portmanteau is track 13. Dallas isn't track 16 [highest] or 8 [Drake] (2); it's track 13, so isn't Olivia (3), so is Gary, and St. Louis is track 16 [highest] (2). Olivia's track 11. Cincinnati's track 8.

In summary:
Drake, Cincinnati, 8, footlocker
Erin, Wichita, 6, wardrobe trunk
Gary, Dallas, 13, portmanteau
Morgan, St. Louis, 16, knapsack
Olivia, Chicago, 11, duffel bag

LOGIC PROBLEM 205

Animals are *Cat on a Hot Tin Roof*, and *The Night of the Iguana*, non-animals are *The Glass Menagerie*, *The Rose Tattoo*, and *A Streetcar Named Desire*, and grades, from highest to lowest, are A–, B+, B, B–, and C+ (intro.). Blanche [Tenn. Waltz (6)] isn't *Cat* or *Iguana* [couldn't be placed in (1)], *Menagerie* (2), or *Streetcar* [Tenn. warbler (3)]; she's *Tattoo*. Tenn. Ernie Ford isn't *Cat* or *Iguana* (4); that one's *Menagerie*, so isn't Stanley (1), Maggie (4), or Brick (7), so is Stella [B (5)]. Tenn. Red peanut isn't Stanley (1) or Brick (7); it's Maggie. Tenn. warbler [*Streetcar*] isn't Stanley (1); it's Brick. Stanley is Tenn. Tuxedo. *Iguana* is B– (2), so isn't Maggie [Tenn. Ernie Ford grade B] (4); it's Stanley. Maggie's *Cat*, so isn't C+ [lowest] (4) or B+ (5); she's A–. Blanche isn't C+ [lowest] (6); she's B+. Brick is C+.
In summary:
Blanche, *The Rose Tattoo*, B+, Tenn. Waltz
Brick, *A Streetcar Named Desire*, C+, Tenn. warbler
Maggie, *Cat on a Hot Tin Roof*, A–, Tenn. Red peanut
Stanley, *The Night of the Iguana*, B–, Tenn. Tuxedo
Stella, *The Glass Menagerie*, B, Tenn. Ernie Ford

LOGIC PROBLEM 206

Tips are $100, $150, $175, $225, and $250 (intro.). Ricky Nelson isn't $100 [least], $175 [no $125], $250 [no $200] (2), or $225 [Jerry Lee Lewis (3)]; he's $150, so Bobby Darin's $100 (2). Buddy Holly isn't $250 [most] (4); Elvis Presley is. Buddy Holly's $175, so "Johnny B. Goode" isn't $225 [Jerry Lee Lewis] (3), so is $250 [most] (4). "Volare" isn't $100 [least], $225 [lunch (3)] (1), or $150 [Harold would be $100 [least, Philip (3)] (1)]; it's $175, so Harold's $150 (1). Eric isn't Elvis Presley [Ira (1)] or Jerry Lee Lewis [lunch (3)] (2); he's Buddy Holly. Stan is Jerry Lee Lewis, but isn't "Chantilly Lace" [Harold (1)] or "Summertime Blues" (4); he's "Rock Around the Clock." Philip's "Summertime."
In summary:
Eric, Buddy Holly, "Volare," $175
Harold, Ricky Nelson, "Chantilly Lace," $150
Ira, Elvis Presley, "Johnny B. Goode," $250
Philip, Bobby Darin, "Summertime Blues," $100

Stan, Jerry Lee Lewis, "Rock Around the Clock," $225

LOGIC PROBLEM 207

King Tux [group discount (6)] isn't peak (5) or Perry Ellis (6); it's Southbridge [only possible in (1)], so Dress for Less is peak (3). Bill Blass isn't $20 off, peak, or Southbridge [group discount] (5); it's Tuxedo Junction [only left in (1)]. Ralph Lauren [shawl (2)] is $20 off [only possible in (1)], so isn't Fiesta Formal (2); it's Mr. Tuxedo [only unplaced in (1)]. Fiesta Formal is Perry Ellis [only left in (1)]. Oscar de la Renta isn't Dress for Less (3); it's King Tux. Christian Dior is Dress for Less, so isn't two-evening rental or free cuff links (4); it's 15% off. Perry Ellis isn't two-evening (1); it's cuff links, so isn't cutaway (4), so is notch. Bill Blass is cutaway and two-evening.

In summary:

Dress for Less, Christian Dior, peak, 15% off

Fiesta Formal, Perry Ellis, notch, free cuff links

King Tux, Oscar de la Renta, Southbridge, group discount

Mr. Tuxedo, Ralph Lauren, shawl, $20 off

Tuxedo Junction, Bill Blass, cutaway, two-evening rental

LOGIC PROBLEM 208

Hrs. asleep are 5-9 (intro.). 9 hrs. [most] isn't swam across ocean (1), played golf on moon (3), met president (4), or sky-dived with sheep (5); it's became baseball star. 8 hrs. [9 hrs. most] isn't swam (1), president, or sky-dived [refreshed would be 9 hrs. [most] (5)] (4); it's golf. 5 hrs. [least] isn't sky-dived (5) or president [refreshed would be 6 hrs. (4), which isn't possible [5 hrs. least] (5)]; it's swam, so Gilbert is 6 hrs., and tranquil is 7 hrs. (1). President isn't 6 hrs. [refreshed would be 7 hrs. [tranquil] (4)]; it's 7 hrs., so refreshed is 8 hrs., and Amos is 9 hrs. [most] (4). Sky-dived is 6 hrs., so Preston is 5 hrs. [least] (5). Rita isn't 8 hrs. [confident would be 7 hrs. [tranquil] (2)]; she's 7 hrs., so confident is 6 hrs. (2). Dottie's 8 hrs. Exhilarated isn't 5 hrs. [least] (2); it's 9 hrs. Cheerful is 5 hrs.

In summary:

Amos, 9, became baseball star, exhilarated

Dottie, 8, played golf on moon, refreshed

Gilbert, 6, sky-dived with sheep, confident

Preston, 5, swam across ocean, cheerful

Rita, 7, met president, tranquil

LOGIC PROBLEM 209

Women are Constance and Rosalind, men are Dudley, Irwin, and Norman, and days are 1-4 (intro.). Repair drawbridge [woman, 2 days (4)] isn't Rosalind (6); it's Constance [only woman left], so isn't horse [decorate courtyard (1)], so is vacation, so secure the keep is 1 day [least] (2). Decorate courtyard [horse] isn't Irwin (1), Dudley [refill moat (3)], or Norman [family dinner (3)]; it's Rosalind. Secure keep isn't Norman (3); it's Irwin, so isn't attend ball (2), so is raise. Norman is clean ballroom. Dudley is attend ball. Dudley [refill moat, attend ball] is fewer days than Norman [family dinner] (5) but more days than Rosalind [horse] (6); Dudley's 3 days, Norman's 4 days, and Rosalind's 2 days [Irwin only 1 day (5, above)].

In summary:

Constance, repair drawbridge, 2, vacation

Dudley, refill moat, 3, attend ball

Irwin, secure the keep, 1, raise

Norman, clean ballroom, 4, family dinner

Rosalind, decorate courtyard, 2, horse

LOGIC PROBLEM 210

Weekdays are Mon.-Fri. (intro.). Letter to Caroline isn't Fri. [last] (3), Mon. [1st], Tue., or Wed. (5); it's Thu., so from moving is Fri. [last] (3), and from Lauren is Mon., so to visiting is Wed. (5). From Lauren [Mon. [1st]] isn't moving [Fri.], engagement (2), promotion (4), or baby [Maggie (4)]; it's visiting, so recipient of Lauren's letter sent one on Wed. (above). From Maggie [baby] isn't Fri. [moving], Wed. [recipient of Lauren's letter [sent Mon.] (above)] (1), or Thu. [from promotion would be Fri. [last, from moving] (4)]; it's Tue. Mon. [1st, from Lauren] isn't to Lauren (intro.), Maggie (1), or Morton [from engagement would be Tue. [from baby] (2)]; it's to Jerry, so from Jerry is Wed. (above), so to Maggie is Fri. [only left after from Jerry [Wed.]] (1). From Caroline isn't Thu. [to Caroline] (intro.); it's Fri. From Morton is Thu. [Fri. last], so to Morton is Tue., and from engagement is Wed. (2). Wed. is to Lauren. Thu. is from promotion.

In summary (weekday, sender, news, recipient):

Mon., Lauren, visiting, Jerry

Tue., Maggie, baby, Morton

Wed., Jerry, engaged, Lauren

Thu., Morton, promotion, Caroline

Fri., Caroline, moving, Maggie

LOGIC PROBLEM 211

Yrs. are 2010-2014 (intro.). Luis isn't 2012, 2013, 2014 [last] (5), or 2011 [Marcel would be 2013 (5), but then Jaime couldn't be 2014 [last] or 2010 [1st], so would be 2012, so Braga would be 2013 (2), but then Pablo couldn't be 2010 [1st] (3) or 2014 [Tiant would be 2013 [Braga] (3)], so couldn't be placed]; he's 2010, so Marcel's 2012, and Colombia's 2013 (5). Jaime isn't 2014 [last] (2) or 2013 [Pablo couldn't be 2011 [2010 1st] or 2014 [Tiant would be 2013 [Jaime] (3)] (2), so couldn't be placed]; he's 2011, so Braga's 2012, and Allende's 2010 [1st] (2). Pablo isn't 2013 [Tiant would be 2012 [Braga] (3)]; he's 2014, so Tiant's 2013, and Argentina's 2012 (3). Guillermo's 2013. Uruguay isn't 2010 [Allende] or 2014 [last] (1); it's 2011, and isn't Lopez (1), so is Cruz. Lopez is 2014 [last], so isn't Chile (4); he's Peru. Luis is Chile.

In summary:

Guillermo Tiant, Colombia, 2013

Jaime Cruz, Uruguay, 2011

Luis Allende, Chile, 2010

Marcel Braga, Argentina, 2012

Pablo Lopez, Peru, 2014

LOGIC PROBLEM 212

Total no. of snowballs is 100 (1). Most snowballs must be a multiple of 12 [only possible to be exactly divisible by 2, 3, 4, and 6 (1)], but not 48 or higher [one would be at least 24, one would be at least 16, one would be at least 12, and fewest would be at least 8 (1), for a total of at least 108 [48 + 24 + 16 + 12 + 8 = 108], but 100 total (above)], 12 [one would be 6, one would be 4, one would be 3, and fewest would be 2 (1), for a total of 27 [12 + 6 + 4 + 3 + 1 = 27], so one would be 73 [100 [total] − 27 = 73], but 12 most (above)], or 24 snowballs [one would be 12, one would be 8, one would be 6, and fewest would be 4 (1), for a total of 54 [24 + 12 + 8 + 6 + 4 = 54], so one would be 46 [100 [total] − 54 = 46], but 24 most (above)]; it's 36 [only multiple of 12 left] (above), so one is 18, one is 12, one is 9, and fewest is 6 snowballs (1), so one is 19 [100 [total] − 36 − 18 − 12 − 9 − 6 = 19], so snowballs are 6, 9, 12, 18, 19, and 36 (above). Helen isn't 6 [fewest], 9 [no 4¹/₂], 19 [no 9¹/₂], 36 [most] (2), or 18 snowballs [3rd most (above), so Glenn (3)]; she's 12 snowballs, so Olivia is 6 snowballs (2). Larry isn't 9 [no 4¹/₂] or 19 snowballs [no 9¹/₂] (5); he's 36 snowballs. Rebecca isn't 9 snowballs [5th most, so mocha (3)] (4); Eliot is. Rebecca's 19 snowballs, so is cinnamon [only odd no. of snowballs left] (2). Helen [12 snowballs] isn't

383

vanilla [Glenn (3)], Irish cream [fewest (4), so 6 snowballs (above)], or butterscotch [most (4), so 36 snowballs (above)]; she's raspberry, so isn't ice skate [cinnamon (2)], snowman [mocha (3)], pine tree, snowflake (4), or icicle [no 24 snowballs (above)] (5), so is sled, so icicle's 6 snowballs (5). Larry isn't pine tree (5); Glenn is. Larry's snowflake.

In summary:

Eliot, snowman, 9, mocha
Glenn, pine tree, 18, vanilla
Helen, sled, 12, raspberry
Larry, snowflake, 36, butterscotch
Olivia, icicle, 6, Irish cream
Rebecca, ice skate, 19, cinnamon

LOGIC PROBLEM 213

Days are Wed.-Sun. (intro.). Sun. [last] isn't Donald Duck (1), Pluto (3), or Minnie Mouse [Wed. (5)]; it's Goofy or Mickey Mouse. Sat. [before only Sun.] isn't Donald Duck (1) or Pluto (3); it's Goofy or Mickey Mouse, so Sat. and Sun. are Goofy and Mickey Mouse, in some order (above). Wed. [1st] isn't Adventureland (1), Frontierland [Goofy Sat. or Sun. [last] (above)] (2), Fantasyland (3), or Tomorrowland (4); it's Liberty Square. Thu. [after only Wed. [Minnie Mouse]] isn't Adventureland (1), Fantasyland (3), or Tomorrowland (4); it's Frontierland, so Goofy is Sat. (2), and Mickey Mouse is Sun. (above). Donald Duck [Morocco (1)] isn't Fri. [Pluto would be Thu., so Japan would be Sat. (3), so Germany would be Sun. [only left after Morocco] (1), and France couldn't be Wed. (5), so would be Thu., so Tomorrowland would be Sat. (4), but then Adventureland couldn't be Fri. [Morocco] or Sun. [Germany] (1), so couldn't be placed]; he's Thu. Pluto's Fri., so Fantasyland's Sat., and Japan's Sun. (3). France isn't Sat. (4) or Wed. (5); it's Fri., so Tomorrowland's Sun. (4). Adventureland's Fri. Germany isn't Wed. [1st] (1); it's Fri. Norway's Wed.

In summary:

Wed., Minnie Mouse, Liberty Square, Norway
Thu., Donald Duck, Frontierland, Morocco
Fri., Pluto, Adventureland, France
Sat., Goofy, Fantasyland, Germany
Sun., Mickey Mouse, Tomorrowland, Japan

LOGIC PROBLEM 214

No. of toys are 2,000, 2,500, 3,000, 3,500, and 4,000 (intro.). 2,000 [least] isn't Blip, Herbie (1), Mitzi, or Pixel (2); it's Clarice. 2,500 [2,000 least] isn't Blip (1), Pixel (2), or Mitzi [trains would be 2,000 [Clarice] (2)] (3); it's Herbie, so set of tools is 2,000

[least, Clarice] (1), so isn't dolls, trains (3), cars, or soldiers (4), so is airplanes. Soldiers isn't ride in sleigh (3), vacation to South Pole, or new snowsuit [4,000 (5)] (4); it's extra cookies, so isn't 3,500 [4,000 most] (2), so is 3,000 (4), so Pixel's 4,000 [most] (2). Trains isn't 4,000 [most] (2) or 3,500 [Mitzi would be 4,000 [Pixel] (2)]; it's 2,500, so Mitzi's 3,000 (2). Blip's 3,500. Cars isn't 4,000 [most] (4); it's 3,500, so isn't vacation (4), so is sleigh. Herbie's vacation. Pixel's dolls.

In summary:

Blip, 3,500 cars, ride in sleigh
Clarice, 2,000 airplanes, set of tools
Herbie, 2,500 trains, vacation to South Pole
Mitzi, 3,000 soldiers, extra cookies
Pixel, 4,000 dolls, new snowsuit

LOGIC PROBLEM 215

Lights are 2-6, and ornaments are 45, 50, 55, 60, and 65 (intro.). 5 lights [6 lights most] isn't Girl Scouts [2 lights (1)], 4-H Club (3), Rotary Club, or Boy Scouts [no 2½ lights] (4); it's Humane Society, so 4-H is 3 lights [only left at least 2 fewer than Humane Society] (3). 4-H [3 lights] isn't 65 [most], 55 [Girl Scouts would be at least 65 ornaments [most] (1)] (1), 60 [Girl Scouts would be at least 70 ornaments (1), but 65 most], or 45 ornaments [blue spruce (2), but no 1½ lights] (2); it's 50 ornaments, so Girl Scouts isn't 55 or 65 ornaments [most] (1), so it's 60 ornaments, and Douglas fir is 65 ornaments [most] (1). 50 ornaments [4-H, 3 lights] isn't Fraser fir (2) or Scotch pine (3); it's balsam fir, so Boy Scouts is 6 lights (4). Rotary Club is 4 lights. Fraser fir isn't 4 [no 8 lights], 5 [no 10 lights], or 6 lights [most] (2); it's 2 lights, so blue spruce is 4 lights (2). Humane Society isn't Scotch pine (3); it's Douglas fir. Boy Scouts is Scotch pine and 55 ornaments.

In summary (group, tree, lights, ornaments):

Boy Scouts, Scotch pine, 6, 55
4-H Club, balsam fir, 3, 50
Girl Scouts, Fraser fir, 2, 60
Humane Society, Douglas fir, 5, 65
Rotary Club, blue spruce, 4, 45

LOGIC PROBLEM 216

1st isn't Celia (1), Jerry (3), Lydia, or Marjorie (5); it's Tim. 5th isn't Celia (1), Jerry (3), or Lydia (5); it's Marjorie, so isn't camping (1), safari (3), circus, or picnic (5), so is time travel. 4th isn't camping (1), safari (3), or picnic (5); it's circus. Celia [immediately before thematic continuity (2)] isn't camping, safari [immediately before Jerry (3)] (1), or circus

(6); she's picnic. Jerry [immediately before descriptive fillers (3)] isn't safari (3) or camping [immediately before Celia (1)] (6); he's circus [4th], so safari's 3rd, and fillers is 5th (3). Tim [1st] isn't safari [3rd]; he's camping, so Celia's 2nd, and continuity's 3rd (1). Lydia's 3rd. Voice modulation isn't 2nd [Celia] (2) or 4th (4); it's 1st. Plot development isn't 4th (4); it's 2nd. Gesturing's 4th.

In summary:
1st, Tim, camping, voice modulation
2nd, Celia, picnic, plot development
3rd, Lydia, safari, thematic continuity
4th, Jerry, circus, gesturing
5th, Marjorie, time travel, descriptive fillers

LOGIC PROBLEM 217

Days are Mon., Tue., Thu., Fri., and Sat., and prices are $50, $100, $200, $250, and $300 (intro.). Fri. isn't $300 [most], $100 [no $150] (3), $250 [armoire would be $300 [most] (3)] (2), or $50 [armoire would be $100 (3), which isn't possible [no $150] (2)]; it's $200, so armoire is $250 (3), so Sat. is $300 (2). Mon. [1st, roll-top desk (1)] isn't $250 [no $500] (1) or $50 (4); it's $100, so daybed's $200, so $300 [most] is more letters than $250 (1). Tue. isn't $50 [Mon. 1st] (4); it's $250 [armoire], so Angela's Mon. [1st] (2). Thu. is $50, so Drew [4 letters] is Tue. [armoire, $250] (4), so $300 is Patsy [5 letters, only left with more letters than $250 [Drew 4 letters]]] (above), and Lyn [3 letters [fewest]] is Fri. (3). Kirk is $50, so isn't davenport (4); he's ottoman. Patsy's davenport.

In summary:
Mon., Angela, roll-top desk, $100
Tue., Drew, armoire, $250
Thu., Kirk, ottoman, $50
Fri., Lyn, daybed, $200
Sat., Patsy, davenport, $300

LOGIC PROBLEM 218

Nights are 997th-1,001st, Baghdad are Abdul, Jafar, and Sharif, and Tabriz are Hamal and Kasim (intro.). Flying carpet [Baghdad (1)] isn't 998th [Tabriz (3)], 999th [eternal life (4)], 1,000th, or 1,001st [last] (5); it's 997th. Sultan's palace isn't 1,000th or 1,001st [last] (6); it's 998th [Tabriz (above)], so isn't Jafar [Baghdad], so is bottle (2). Jafar [Baghdad] isn't bottle [Tabriz (above)], mirror (4), jar [Sharif (7)], or ring [Tabriz (7)]; he's lantern. Abdul [Baghdad] isn't ring [Tabriz (above)] or bottle [Tabriz (above)]; he's mirror, so isn't untold wealth (3), carpet [997th [1st]], palace, or eternal life [999th, but palace 998th] (6), so is swift Arabian stallion, so Sharif's 997th (7).

Lantern [Jafar] isn't 1,001st [last] (1) or 999th (2); it's 1,000th, and Hamal [Tabriz] isn't 1,001st [last, so Baghdad (1)], so he's 999th (8), so 998th [Tabriz] is Kasim [only unplaced from Tabriz]. Abdul's 1,001st. Ring's 999th. Untold wealth is 1,000th.

In summary:
997th, Sharif, jar, flying carpet
998th, Kasim, bottle, sultan's palace
999th, Hamal, ring, eternal life
1,000th, Jafar, lantern, untold wealth
1,001st, Abdul, mirror, swift Arabian stallion

LOGIC PROBLEM 219

1st isn't Cleveland Dr. (2), Garden Dr. (4), or Poplar St. (5); it's Countryside Dr. or Monroe Terr. 5th [last] isn't Cleveland (2), Garden (4), or Poplar (5); it's Countryside or Monroe, so 1st and 5th are Countryside and Monroe, in some order (above), so Poplar is 2nd or 4th, and Duffy is 3rd (5). 5th [last] isn't Washington Pl. (1), Kellogg Ave. [Jeb would be 3rd [Duffy] (2)], Forrest St. (3), or Sunset Rd. [Ruby would be 3rd [Duffy] (5)]; it's 26th Ave. 4th [5th last] isn't Washington, Sunset [Ruby would be 2nd (4)] (1), or Forrest (3); it's Kellogg, so Cleveland's 3rd, and Jeb's 2nd (2). 1st isn't Ruby (1) or Sophie (3); it's Sydney, so isn't Washington (1) or Sunset [Ruby would be 3rd [Duffy] (4)], so is Forrest. Sunset isn't 2nd [Garden would be 3rd [Cleveland] (4)]; it's 3rd, so Garden's 4th, and Ruby's 5th [Sydney 1st] (4), so Poplar's 2nd (above), so Monroe's 1st [Duffy 3rd] (5). Sophie's 4th. Countryside's 5th. Washington's 2nd.

In summary (pos., person, old address, new address):
1st, Sydney, Monroe Terr., Forrest St.
2nd, Jeb, Poplar St., Washington Pl.
3rd, Duffy, Cleveland Dr., Sunset Rd.
4th, Sophie, Garden Dr., Kellogg Ave.
5th, Ruby, Countryside Dr., 26th Ave.

LOGIC PROBLEM 220

Bonus pts. are 15, 20, 25, 30, and 35, and final pts. are 150, 170, 190, 210, and 230 (intro.). Bonus 35 pts. [most] isn't final 210 (3), 150 [least] (5), 170, or 190 pts. [Percolator would be final 170 pts. (5)] (6); it's final 230 pts., so Percolator's final 210 pts. (5). Bonus 30 pts. [bonus 35 pts. most] isn't final 150 [lowest], 170 (1), or 210 [Percolator] (2); it's final 190 pts., so Country Club's final 150 pts. [lowest] (1). Final 210 pts. [Percolator] isn't Stuart (2), Lisa [no final 250 pts.] (4), Jodie (5), or Klaus [couldn't be bonus 15 [lowest], 20, or 25 pts. (6), so couldn't be placed]; it's Cliff. Final 170 pts. isn't Jodie [no

385

final 130 pts.] (4), Lisa [Jodie would be final 210 pts. [Cliff] (4)], or Klaus (6); it's Stuart. Final 150 pts. [least] isn't Jodie (4) or Klaus [couldn't be bonus 15 [least], 20, or 25 pts. (6), so couldn't be placed]; it's Lisa, so Jodie's final 190 pts. (4). Klaus is final 230 pts. [bonus 35 pts.], so final 170 pts. [Stuart] is bonus 20 pts. (6), so Percolator [final 210 pts.] is bonus 15 pts. [least] (2), so Kablinkee's bonus 20 pts. (3). Lisa's bonus 25 pts. Maestro bonus isn't 30 pts. (3); it's 35 pts. Arugula bonus is 30 pts.

In summary (player, roll, bonus pts., final score):
Cliff, Percolator, 15, 210
Jodie, Arugula, 30, 190
Klaus, Maestro, 35, 230
Lisa, Country Club, 25, 150
Stuart, Kablinkee, 20, 170

LOGIC PROBLEM 221

A answers are 10, 11, 12, 14, and 15, B answers are 12, 13, 15, 16, and 17, and C answers are 14, 15, 16, 17, and 18 (intro.). 17 B answers [most, 1 A answer more than Kathleen (2)] isn't Franz (1), Kathleen (2), Beth (4), or Tara (5); it's Sidney, so Kathleen is 16 C answers (3), so Sidney [17 B answers] is 15 C answers (2), and Tara's 16 B answers (5). Sidney A answers [17 B answers, 15 C answers] isn't 12 [Kathleen 16 C answers] (2), 10 [least], 14 [no 13 A answers], or 15 (3); he's 11 A answers, so Franz is 14 C answers [least] (1), and Kathleen's 10 A answers (2). Tara isn't 18 C answers [most] (5); she's 17 C answers, so 14 A answers is 18 C answers [most] (5). Beth is 18 C answers, so is 15 B answers [17 C answers is 16 B answers] (4). Franz [14 C answers] isn't 15 A answers [Sidney 15 C answers] (3); Tara is. Franz is 12 A answers, so isn't 12 B answers [no 13 A answers] (1); he's 13 B answers. Kathleen's 12 B answers.

In summary (person, A answers, B answers, C answers):
Beth, 14, 15, 18
Franz, 12, 13, 14
Kathleen, 10, 12, 16
Sidney, 11, 17, 15
Tara, 15, 16, 17

LOGIC PROBLEM 222

Nos. are 11, 16, 28, 37, and 44 (intro.). Fewest isn't 10 or more tickets [2nd fewest would be at least 13 tickets (1), so most would be at least 26 tickets (3), but 24 tickets most possible (1)]; it's 9 tickets [fewest possible (1)], so 2nd most is 18 tickets (3). 2nd fewest [9 tickets fewest (above)] isn't 10, 11 (1), or 13 or more tickets [most would be at least 26 tickets

(3), but 24 tickets most possible (above)]; it's 12 tickets, so most is 24 tickets (3). 3rd fewest [2nd fewest 12 tickets, 2nd most 18 tickets] is 15 tickets [only possible in (1)], so tickets are 9 [fewest], 12, 15, 18, and 24 [most] (above). 24 tickets [most (above)] isn't Country Grocer (2), Walt's Mart (4), SuperShop, or Dairy Market (5); it's Quik Stop. No. 44 [highest] isn't SuperShop (1), Quik [24 tickets [most (above)]], Country, or Dairy (2); it's Walt's. No. 16 isn't Country (2), SuperShop, or Dairy (5); it's Quik. 9 tickets [fewest (above)] isn't Walt's [no. 44 [highest]] (2), Country (4), or SuperShop (5); it's Dairy, so isn't no. 11 [lowest] (2) or 28 (3), so is no. 37, so Erica's no. 44 [highest] (2). No. 28 isn't Country (2); it's SuperShop. No. 11 is Country. Dairy [no. 37, 9 tickets [fewest (above)]] isn't Melinda (1), Jolene (4), or Thomas (5); it's William. SuperShop isn't Melinda or Jolene (1); it's Thomas. Country isn't Jolene (4); it's Melinda. Quik is Jolene. Walt's [no. 44] isn't 12 [Country would be 9 tickets [fewest (above), Dairy] (2)] or 18 tickets [2nd most (above)] (3); it's 15 tickets, so Country is 12 tickets [only left less than no. 44 [15 tickets] (2)]. SuperShop is 18 tickets.

In summary (friend, no., store, tickets):
Erica, 44, Walt's Mart, 15
Jolene, 16, Quik Stop, 24
Melinda, 11, Country Grocer, 12
Thomas, 28, SuperShop, 18
William, 37, Dairy Market, 9

LOGIC PROBLEM 223

Metal are chain link, wire mesh, and wrought iron, wooden are split rail and white picket, addresses are 125 Chestnut St., 140 Camden Ln., 155 Lexington Ct., 230 Fields Rd., and 260 Water Shadow Pl., and ft. are 10, 12, 15, 20, and 25 (intro.). Wrought iron isn't Tue. [1st] (2), Wed. [wooden would be Tue. [metal (4)] (2)], or Thu. (3); it's Fri., so wooden is Thu. (2), so is white picket [only possible in (3)], so 260 Water Shadow Pl. is split rail [only wooden left] (2), and 125 Chestnut St. is wire mesh (3). Split rail [260 Water Shadow Pl.] isn't Tue. (4); it's Wed., and isn't 20, 25 [most] (2), 15 [white picket [Thu., and wrought iron Fri.] would be 25 ft. [most] (2)] (3), or 12 ft. [no 17 ft.] (4); it's 10 ft., so white picket [Thu., and wrought iron Fri.] is 20 ft. (2), and Tue. is 15 ft. (4), so 155 Lexington Ct. is 25 ft. (3). Fri. isn't 12 ft. [Wed. (1)]; it's 25 ft. 230 Fields Rd. isn't Wed. [12 ft.] (1) or Tue. (4); it's Thu. 140 Camden Ln. is chain link, and isn't 15 ft. [20 ft. 230 Fields] (5); it's 12 ft. 125 Chestnut is 15 ft.

In summary:
Tue., wire mesh, 125 Chestnut St., 15
Wed., chain link, 140 Camden Ln., 12
Wed., split rail, 260 Water Shadow Pl., 10
Thu., white picket, 230 Fields Rd., 20
Fri., wrought iron, 155 Lexington Ct., 25

LOGIC PROBLEM 224

Legal pads are 30, 40, 50, 70, 80, and 90, manila envelopes are 20, 30, 50, 60, 70, and 80, and red pens are 40, 50, 60, 70, 90, and 100 (intro.). Pens ordered with 60 envelopes isn't 60, 90 [90 pads [most] would be 50 envelopes (2)] (1), 40 [least], 50 [no 30 pens], or 100 [no 80 pens] (5); it's 70 pens, so 90 pads is 50 pens (5). Pens ordered with 40 pads isn't 40 (1), 70 [no 80 pens], 100 [most] (4), or 60 [30 envelopes would be 70 pens [60 envelopes] (4)]; it's 90 pens, so marketing is 30 pads [least] (2), and 30 envelopes is 100 pens (4). Pens ordered with 50 envelopes isn't 40 [least], 50, or 90 [no 80 pens] (1); it's 60 pens, so public relations is 50 pens (1). Envelopes ordered with 50 pens [90 pads] isn't 80 [most] (2) or 20 [90 pens would be 30 envelopes [100 pens] (2)]; it's 70 envelopes, so 90 pens is 80 envelopes (2), so art is 80 envelopes [most], and personnel is 100 pens [most] (3). 40 pens is 20 envelopes. Pads ordered with 60 envelopes [70 pens] isn't 70 (1), 30 [least], or 80 [no 60 pads] (5); it's 50 pads, so 60 pens is 30 pads (5). 30 envelopes isn't 80 pads [accounting would be 90 pads [most, public relations] (4)]; it's 70 pads, so accounting is 80 pads [only left more than 30 envelopes] (4). 20 envelopes is 80 pads. Computer is 50 pads.
In summary (dept., legal pads, manila envelopes, red pens):
Accounting, 80, 20, 40
Art, 40, 80, 90
Computer, 50, 60, 70
Marketing, 30, 50, 60
Personnel, 70, 30, 100
Public Relations, 90, 70, 50

LOGIC PROBLEM 225

"Handsome" isn't silk (4), polyester (5), or cashmere [couldn't be Paolo Ferrari (1), Donna Vitali (2), Calvin Phelps (3), Yves St. Denis, or Rory Bean (5), so couldn't be placed]; it's cotton or satin. Cotton isn't Vitali (2), Bean (3), or Denis (4); it's Phelps or Ferrari. Cocktail dresses aren't "splendid" (2), "lovely" (3), "elegant" (5), or "handsome" [couldn't be satin (2) or cotton [couldn't be Phelps (3) or Ferrari (4), so couldn't be placed (above)], so couldn't be placed

(above)]; they're "eye-pleasing." Tailored suits aren't "elegant" (1), "splendid" (6), or "handsome" [couldn't be St. Denis (1), Phelps (3), Ferrari (4), Bean (5), or Vitali (6); so couldn't be placed]; they're "lovely." Evening gowns aren't "handsome" (3) or "elegant" (5); they're "splendid." Jackets aren't "handsome" (1); they're "elegant." Leisure wear is "handsome," so isn't satin (6); it's cotton (above), but isn't Phelps (3), so is Ferrari (above). Jackets ["elegant"] aren't Bean (3), St. Denis (4), or Vitali (6); they're Phelps. Tailored suits aren't St. Denis (1) or Vitali (6); they're Bean. Evening gowns aren't Vitali (2); cocktail dresses are. Evening gowns ["splendid"] are St. Denis, so aren't silk (1), cashmere (5), or polyester (6); they're satin. Bean ["lovely"] isn't silk (3) or polyester (5); he's cashmere. Phelps isn't silk (4); he's polyester. Vitali's silk.
In summary:
Calvin Phelps, jackets, polyester, "elegant"
Donna Vitali, cocktail dresses, silk, "eye-pleasing"
Paolo Ferrari, leisure wear, cotton, "handsome"
Rory Bean, tailored suits, cashmere, "lovely"
Yves St. Denis, evening gowns, satin, "splendid"

LOGIC PROBLEMS 226 & 227

Clues from part 1 are designated as I, and clues from part 2 are designated as II. Wks. are 4, 5, 7, 8, 9, and 10, mos. are June-Nov. (I,intro.), and lines are 1, 2, 4, 5, 6, and 7 (II,intro.). 4 wks. [least, Loopy Larry, 1 line more than Journalist (II,4)] isn't June (I,2), Nov. [Jiggly Jalopy (I,4)], Oct. (II,1), Aug. [1 line more than Bus Driver (II,2)], or July (II,5); it's Sept. [1 line more than Loony Goon (I,1)], so Loony Goon is Journalist (above), and Troubled Teen is 5 wks. (I,1). 7 wks. [no 6 wks.] isn't Nov. (I,4), Oct. (II,1), Aug. (II,2), or July (II,5); it's June, so 4 wks. [least, Loopy Larry] is *Law & Order*, and Margie Muffen [1 line more than Plumber (I,2)] is 5 wks. [Troubled Teen [1 line more than Mr. Goop (I,1)]] (I,2), so Mr. Goop is Plumber (above). 10 wks. [most] isn't Oct. (II,1), Aug. (II,2), or July (II,5); it's Nov. [Jiggly Jalopy], so *Party of Five* is 9 wks. (I,4). Oct. [*Touched by an Angel* (II,1)] isn't 9 wks. [*Party of Five*] or 5 wks. [Slappy Frog would be 4 wks. [Loopy Larry] (II,1)]; it's 8 wks., so Slappy Frog is 7 wks. (II,1). 8 wks. [*Touched by an Angel*] isn't Loony Goon (II,1); it's Mr. Goop. 9 wks. *Party of Five* is Loony Goon [Journalist], so 4 lines is 10 wks. [most, Jiggly Jalopy] (II,4). 5 wks. [Margie Muffen, 1 line more than Plumber (I,2)] isn't Aug. [1 line more than Bus Driver (II,2)]; it's July [*Jekyll & Hyde* (II,5)]. 9 wks. is Aug., so Bus Driver is 10 wks. [most, Jiggly Jalopy [4 lines]], so Loony Goon [Aug.] is 5 lines (II,2), so

387

Loopy Larry [Sept.] is 6 lines (I,1). Loopy Larry [4 wks. [least], 6 lines] isn't Concerned Parent (II,5); he's Cashier #3 [*Sunset Boulevard* (II,3)], so *Miss Saigon* is 7 lines [most] (II,3). Mr. Goop [Plumber] isn't 2 [no 3 lines] or 7 lines [most] (I,2); he's 1 line, so Margie Muffen is 2 lines (I,2). Slappy Frog [7 wks.] is Concerned Parent and 7 lines [*Miss Saigon*], so *ER* is 10 wks. [Jiggly Jalopy, only left more than 7 wks.] (II,3). *NYPD Blue* isn't 2 lines [no 0 lines] (I,3); it's 7 lines, so *Evita* is 5 lines [Loony Goon] (I,3). *The X-Files* is 2 lines. Mr. Goop [Oct.] isn't *The Phantom of the Opera* (II,1); he's *Les Misérables*. Jiggly Jalopy is *The Phantom of the Opera*.

In summary, Logic Problem 226:
Jiggly Jalopy, *The Phantom of the Opera*, Nov., 10
Loony Goon, *Evita*, Aug., 9
Loopy Larry, *Sunset Boulevard*, Sept., 4
Margie Muffen, *Jekyll & Hyde*, July, 5
Mr. Goop, *Les Misérables*, Oct., 8
Slappy Frog, *Miss Saigon*, June, 7

In summary, Logic Problem 227:
Jiggly Jalopy, Bus Driver, *ER*, 4
Loony Goon, Journalist, *Party of Five*, 5
Loopy Larry, Cashier #3, *Law & Order*, 6
Margie Muffen, Troubled Teen, *The X-Files*, 2
Mr. Goop, Plumber, *Touched by an Angel*, 1
Slappy Frog, Concerned Parent, *NYPD Blue*, 7

LOGIC PROBLEM 228

Parent [guest on Jasmine French series (4)] isn't Cedric Howe (2), Victor Walsh [guest on Cedric Howe series (2)], Peter Santos (4), or Jasmine French [guest on parent series (4)]; she's Laura Pontz, so her guest appearance isn't *Practice Makes Perfect* [detective guest star (1)], *Losing Patients* [*Family Business* star (3)] (3), *Overboard* [star would be Jasmine French (4)] (4), or *Family Business* [star would be Jasmine French (4), so Jasmine French's guest appearance would be *Losing Patients* (3), so *Losing Patients* [psychiatrist (1)] would be lawyer (4)], so is On the Job, so Jasmine French's series is On the Job (4). Laura Pontz [parent] series isn't *Losing Patients* [psychiatrist] or *Family Business* (3); it's *Overboard* or *Practice*. Jasmine French [On the Job series, lawyer guest (4)] guest appearance isn't *Losing Patients* [psychiatrist] or *Family Business* (5); it's *Overboard* or *Practice*, so *Overboard* and *Practice* are parent and lawyer, in some order (above). *Family Business* [*Losing Patients* guest] isn't parent or lawyer [*Overboard* and *Practice*, in some order (above)], or detective [*Practice* guest (above)]; it's

traffic cop. Jasmine French [On the Job series] isn't psychiatrist [*Losing Patients*], traffic cop [*Family Business*], or lawyer (4); she's detective [*Practice* guest (above)], so *Practice* is lawyer (4), and *Practice* guest is *Family* star (5). *Overboard* is parent. Cedric Howe series [Victor Walsh guest (2)] isn't lawyer [Jasmine French guest (above)] or traffic cop (2); he's psychiatrist [*Losing Patients*], so Victor Walsh is *Losing Patients* guest (above). Peter Santos is lawyer. Cedric Howe's guest appearance is *Overboard*.

In summary (star, role, series, guest):

Cedric Howe, psychiatrist, *Losing Patients*, *Overboard*

Jasmine French, detective, *On the Job*, *Practice Makes Perfect*

Laura Pontz, parent, *Overboard*, *On the Job*

Peter Santos, lawyer, *Practice Makes Perfect*, *Family Business*

Victor Walsh, traffic cop, *Family Business*, *Losing Patients*

LOGIC PROBLEM 229

Pennant and Eddie Armstrong [same day (2)] are 2nd [only day with 2 players (4)], so pennant's left fielder, and Eddie Armstrong's autograph book [only possible in (4)]. Lenny Ayala [1st (1)] isn't pennant [2nd (above)], bat [Roger Merrick (1)], or baseball [4th (2)]; he's photograph. Alan Dykstra isn't baseball (2); he's pennant. Jackson Butler's baseball. Lenny Ayala [1st (above)] isn't catcher (1), shortstop [3rd (3)], or pitcher [4th (3)]; he's first baseman. Eddie Armstrong [2nd (above)] isn't shortstop [3rd (above)] or pitcher [4th (above)]; he's catcher. Jackson Butler [4th (above)] isn't shortstop [3rd (above)]; he's pitcher. Roger Merrick [bat] is shortstop, so isn't Oswego Ospreys (1), Wichita Redwings (2), Kansas City Suns (3), or Topeka Flyers [1st (3), so Lenny Ayala (4, above)]; he's Pratt Penguins. Jackson Butler [baseball] isn't Ospreys (1) or Redwings (2); he's Suns. Alan Dykstra isn't Redwings (2); he's Ospreys. Eddie Armstrong is Redwings.

In summary:

Alan Dykstra, Oswego Ospreys, left fielder, pennant

Eddie Armstrong, Wichita Redwings, catcher, autograph book

Jackson Butler, Kansas City Suns, pitcher, baseball

Lenny Ayala, Topeka Flyers, first baseman, photograph

Roger Merrick, Pratt Penguins, shortstop, bat

LOGIC PROBLEM 230

Girls are Cindy, Elise, Lana, and Millie, boys are Joseph and Vince, and mins. are 25, 35, 45, 55, 65, and 75 (intro.). Mother isn't 45 min. or more [Cindy would be at least 90 min. (2), but 75 min. most] or 35 min. (3); that one's 25 min. Father isn't 45 min. or more [Cindy would be at least 90 min. (2), but 75 min. most]; that one's 35 min., so Cindy is at least 70 min. (2), so is 75 min. [only possible]. Brother isn't Millie (3) or Cindy [75 min. [most]] (5); it's Lana [only girl unplaced in (1)], and isn't 10 min. more than Joseph (1), so is 10 min. more than Vince [only boy left] (5). Vince isn't 25 min. [brother would be 35 min. [father] (above)] or 45 min. or more [cousin would be at least 90 min. (4), but 75 min. most]; he's 35 min., so brother is 45 min. (above), and cousin is at least 70 min. (4), so is 75 min. [only possible]. Joseph isn't 25 [Vince is 35 min.] (1) or 55 min. [brother is 45 min.] (5); he's 65 min., and Cindy's 75 min., so Millie's sandbox [only girl unplaced in (1)], so isn't 25 min. [mother] (3), so is 55 min. Elise is 25 min. Friend isn't 65 min. [2 seesaws would total 130 min. [65 + 65 = 130] (5), but couldn't include 25 [no 105 min.], 35 [no 95 min.], 45 [no 85 min.], 65 [only one 65 min.], or 75 min. [55 min. is sandbox], so couldn't be placed]; it's 55 min. [Millie], so sister is slide [only unplaced in (3)]. Sister's 65 min. 2 seesaws total 110 min. [55 [friend] + 55 = 110] (5), but don't include 25 [no 95 min.] or 45 min. [65 min. is slide], so are 35 and 75 min. (above). Swings is 25 min., and jungle gym is 45 min. (4).

In summary:
Cindy, cousin, seesaw, 75
Elise, mother, swings, 25
Joseph, sister, slide, 65
Lana, brother, jungle gym, 45
Millie, friend, sandbox, 55
Vince, father, seesaw, 35

LOGIC PROBLEM 231

Nos. are 626, 930, 1218, 1453, 1687, and 2750, spirit types are poltergeist, specter, and wraith, and bedrooms (BR) are 4, 5, and 6 (intro.). 2 are 4 BR (2), and 1 is 6 BR [most] (4), so 3 are 5 BR [only possible to total 6], so no. 1687 and Mason Rd. are 4 BR [only possible in (1, above)], so Mason Rd. is Jed, and no. 1687 is Wingate Cir. (2, above), so cold drafts, Horace, and Greenwood Way are 5 BR [only possible in (3, above)]. 2 are wraiths, 1 is specter, 3 are poltergeists (5), so no. 1687 isn't specter [only no. 626 [lowest] (5, above)]; it's poltergeist, so Mason Rd. is specter [only no. 626 (above)] (1).

Petra [6 BR [most] (4)] isn't Wingate Cir. [4 BR (above)], Greenwood Way [5 BR (above)], Park Ln., or Oak Terr. [wraith (5)] (4); she's Silver St., so isn't specter [only Mason Rd. (above)] or wraith (4), so is poltergeist. Cold drafts [5 BR (above)] isn't Mason Rd. [4 BR (above)], Wingate Cir. [4 BR (above)], Silver St. [6 BR (above)], Greenwood Way, or Oak Terr. [wraith (above)] (3); it's Park Ln. [1218 (4)], so isn't specter [only Mason Rd. (above)] or wraith (3), so is poltergeist, so is Marvin [only possible in (5, above)]. 1687 Wingate Cir. [poltergeist (above)] is loose floorboards [only possible in (5, above)]. Silver St. [poltergeist (above)] is no. 2750 [only unplaced in (5, above)]. Wingate Cir. [4 BR [least] (above)] isn't Horace [5 BR (above)] or Danica (2); it's Ileana. Greenwood Way [5 BR (above)] isn't Horace (3); it's Danica, so isn't no. 930 (6), so is no. 1453, so creaking staircase is 4 BR [least] (2), so is Jed [only unplaced in (2)]. Horace is 930 Oak Terrace. Petra isn't banging shutters or attic [wraith (5)] (4); she's revolving bookcase. Oak Terr. isn't attic (5); it's shutters. Danica's attic.

In summary:
Danica, 1453 Greenwood Way, attic
Horace, 930 Oak Terr., banging shutters
Ileana, 1687 Wingate Cir., loose floorboards
Jed, 626 Mason Rd., creaking staircase
Marvin, 1218 Park Ln., cold drafts
Petra, 2750 Silver St., revolving bookcase

LOGIC PROBLEM 232

Mos. are May-Oct. (intro.). Kirk isn't May [1st], June, July (4), Oct. [Bent Knee Cave would be July (4), and Kim couldn't be July [Boer's Cavern would be May (6)] (3), May [1st], June (6), or Sept. [Boer's would be July [Bent Knee] (6)], so would be Aug., so stalactites would be July, and Boer's would be June (6), but then Sheila couldn't be May [1st] (2), June [gypsum flowers would be July [stalactites] (2)], July [Destiny's Cavern would be June [Boer's] (2)], or Sept. [gypsum would be Oct. (2)] (5), so couldn't be placed], or Aug. [Bent Knee would be May (4), and Destiny's couldn't be Sept., Oct. [last] (2), July [Sheila would be Aug. [Kirk] (2)], or Aug. [gypsum would be Oct. (2)] (5), so would be June, so Sheila would be July, and gypsum would be Aug. (2), but then Dennis couldn't be June [Symmes Ridge Cave would be Aug. [gypsum] (7)] (5), Sept., Oct. [last], or May [Symmes would be July [Sheila] (7)] (7), so couldn't be placed]; he's Sept., so Bent Knee is June (4). Kim isn't July [Boer's would be May (6)] (3),

May [1st], June (6), or Aug. [Boer's would be June [Bent Knee] (6)]; she's Oct., so stalactites is Sept., and Boer's is Aug. (6). Sheila isn't May [1st] (2), July [Destiny's would be June [Bent Knee] (2)], or Aug. [gypsum would be Sept. [stalactites] (2)]; she's June, so gypsum is July, and Destiny's is May (2). Dennis isn't May [Symmes would be July [gypsum] (7)] (5) or Aug. [helictites would be Sept. [stalactites] (7)]; he's July, so helictites is Aug., and Symmes is Sept. (7). Bo isn't Aug. [Boer's] (3); he's May. Enid is Aug, Linoch Falls Cave isn't Oct. [flowstone would be Sept. [stalactites] (1)]; it's July, so flowstone is June (1). Tom Thumb Cavern is Oct. Bo isn't drapery (3); he's stalagmites. Kim's drapery.

In summary:

May, Bo, Destiny's Cavern, stalagmites
June, Sheila, Bent Knee Cave, flowstone
July, Dennis, Linoch Falls Cave, gypsum flowers
Aug., Enid, Boer's Cavern, helictites
Sept., Kirk, Symmes Ridge Cave, stalactites
Oct., Kim, Tom Thumb Cavern, drapery

LOGIC PROBLEM 233

Possible yrs. are 1301-1399 (intro.). Each visit is a whole no. of mos. (intro.), and 4 of the 5 mos. are 5 (1), 3 (2), 7 (4), and 4 (6). 1384 (3) isn't 1 [fewest possible (above)], 3 [no 1½ mo.], 5 [no 2½ mos.], 7 [no 3½ mos.] (3, above), 2 [Ireland would be 1 mo. [fewest possible (above)] (3), so would be 6 visits [1, 2, 3, 4, 5, and 7 mos.] (above)], 8 or more [the 5 visits would be 3, 4, 5, 7, and 8 or more mos. (above), so 1384 would be longest (above), so 3 mos. [fewest (above)] would be 1386 (7), so dragonflies would be 1409 (2), but 1399 latest possible], or 6 mos. [the 5 visits would be 3, 4, 5, 6, and 7 mos. (above), so Ireland would be 3 mos. (3), but then Cuba couldn't be 5 [no 8 mos. (above)], 6 [no 9 mos. (above)], or 7 mos. [longest (above)] (5), so would be 4 mos. (above), so jellyfish would be 7 mos. (5), but then latest couldn't be 3 (2), 7 (4), 5 [6 mos. [1384] would be earliest (7), but 1 yr. 1323 (1)], or 6 mos. [7 mos. [longest (above)] would be earliest (7), so latest possible yr. for 7 mos. would be 1323 (above), so latest possible yr. for 3 mos. [fewest (above)] would be 1325 (7), so latest possible yr. for dragonflies would be 1348 (2), but then 6 mos. [1384, latest (above)] couldn't be Maui (4) or Borneo (6), so would be Sri Lanka, but then Maui couldn't be 7 mos. (4), so would be 5 mos., and Borneo would be 7 mos., but then 6 mos. [Sri Lanka, 1384 [latest (above)]] couldn't be dragonflies [1348 latest possible yr. (above)], radishes (1), or orchids (6), so would be bats, so Maui would be at least 1361 [1384 [bats] −

1323 or earlier [7 mos.] = at least 1361] (4), so dragonflies [1348 latest possible yr. (above)] couldn't be 5 [at least 1361 (above)] or 3 mos. (2), so would be 4 mos., and Borneo [7 mos. [longest]] would be 2 yrs. earlier than 3 mos. [shortest] (7), which is 23 yrs. earlier than 4 mos. [dragonflies] (2), so Borneo would be 25 yrs. earlier than 4 mos., so orchids would be 1325 (6), and wouldn't be Maui [at least 1361 (above)], so would be Ireland [3 mos.], so dragonflies [Cuba] would be 1348 (2), which isn't possible (5)], so 4 mos. would be latest, so 5 mos. would be earliest (7), but then 1323 couldn't be 4 [latest, but 1 yr. 1384 (above)], 7 [longest (above), so 3 mos. [fewest (above)] would be 1325 (7), so dragonflies would be 1348 (2), but couldn't be 3 [1325], 6 [1384], 4 [latest, but 1 yr. 1384 (above)], or 5 mos. [earliest, but 1 yr. 1323 (above)], so couldn't be placed], 3 [shortest (above), so dragonflies would be 1346 (2), and 7 mos. [longest (above)] would be 1321 (7), but then 1346 couldn't be 4 [latest, but 1 yr. 1384 (above)] or 5 mos. [earliest, but 1 yr. 1323 (above)], so couldn't be placed], or 5 mos. [earliest (above), so 6 mos. [1384] couldn't be Maui [latest possible yr. for 7 mos. would be 1315 [1399 [latest possible (above)] − 1384 [Maui] = 1315] (4), but 1323 earliest yr. (above)] or Borneo [latest possible for orchids would be 1315 [1399 [latest possible yr. (above)] − 1384 [Borneo] = 1315] (6), but 1323 earliest yr. (above)], so would be Sri Lanka, but then 7 mos. couldn't be Maui (4), so would be Borneo, so 5 mos. would be Maui, but then 6 mos. [1384, Sri Lanka] couldn't be radishes (1), dragonflies [3 mos. [shortest (above)] would be 1361 (2), so 7 mos. [Borneo, longest (above)] would be 1359 (7), so bats would be 1382 [1323 [Maui] + 1359 [7 mos.] = 1382] (4), but couldn't be 4 mos. [latest, but 1 yr. 1384 (above)], so couldn't be placed], orchids [latest possible yr. for Borneo would be 1315 [1399 [latest possible yr. (above)] − 1384 [orchids] = 1315] (6), but 1323 earliest (above)], or bats [7 mos. [longest (above)] would be 1361 [1384 [bats] − 1323 [Maui] = 1361] (4), so 3 mos. [shortest (above)] would be 1363 (7), so dragonflies would be 1386 (2), so would be 4 mos. [only left], so orchids would be 1325 [1386, [4 mos.] − 1361 [Borneo] = 1325] (6), so couldn't be placed [would be 6 visits [1323, 1325, 1361, 1363, 1384, and 1386 (above)]], so couldn't be placed], so couldn't be placed]; 1384 is 4 mos., so Ireland's 2 mos. (3), so the 5 visits are 2, 3, 4, 5, and 7 mos. (above). Cuba isn't 3 [no 6 mos.], 5 [no 8 mos.], or 7 mos. [longest] (5); it's 4 mos., so jellyfish's 7 mos. (5). Maui isn't 3 (2) or 7 mos. (4); it's 5 mos. Latest isn't 3 (2), 5 [no 6 mos.], 7 [longest] (7), or 2 mos. [would be at least 1385 [4 mos. 1384], so 7 mos. [longest (above)] would be at least 1383 (7), so Maui [5 mos.] would be at most 1316 [1399 [latest possible (above)] − 1383 [earliest possible for 7 mos. (above)] = 1316] (4), but then 1323 couldn't be 2 [at least 1383 (above)], 5 [at most 1316 (above)], 7 [at least 1385 (above)], or 3 mos. [dragonflies would be 1346 (2), but couldn't be 2 [at least 1385 (above)], 4 [1384], 5 [at most 1316 (above)], or 3 mos. (2), so couldn't be placed]]; latest is 4 mos., so earliest is 5 mos. (7). Dragonflies isn't 3, 5 [earliest (above)] (2), or 2 mos. [shortest (above), so would be 23 yrs. later than 3 mos. (2), and 2 yrs. later than 7 mos. [longest (above)] (7), so the 5 visits, in order from earliest to latest, would be 5, 3, 7, 2, and 4 mos. (above), and bats couldn't be 7, 5, or 3 mos. (4, above), so would be 4 mos., but then 1323 couldn't be 2 [dragonflies, and no 1300] (2), 3 [dragonflies [2 mos. [shortest (above)]] would be 1346 (2), and 7 mos. [longest (above)] would be 1344 (7), so 5 mos. [Maui, earliest (above)] would be 1340 [1384 [bats] − 1344 [7 mos.] = 1340] (4), which isn't possible [1 yr. 1323]], 5 [Maui, so 7 mos. [longest (above)] would be 1361 [1384 [bats] − 1323 [Maui] = 1361] (4), so 2 mos. [dragonflies, shortest (above)] would be 1363 (7), so 3 mos. would be 1340 (2), but then Borneo couldn't be 3 [1340, so orchids would be 1344 [1384 [4 mos.] − 1340 [Borneo] = 1344] (6), which isn't possible [would be 6 visits [1323, 1340, 1344, 1361, 1363, and 1384 (above)]]]] or 7 mos. [1361, so orchids would be 1323 [1384 [4 mos.] − 1361 [Borneo] = 1323 [5 mos.]] (6), so 3 mos. would be Sri Lanka and radishes [only left], which isn't possible (1), so couldn't be placed], or 7 mos. [Maui [5 mos. [earliest (above)]] would be 1361 [1384 [bats] − 1323 [7 mos.] = 1361] (4), which isn't possible [1 yr. 1323]], so couldn't be placed]; dragonflies is 4 mos. [1384], so 3 mos. is 1361 (2). Bats isn't 5 [Maui] (4) or 3 mos. [1323 couldn't be 7 [Maui [5 mos. [earliest (above)]] would be 1338 [1361 [bats] − 1321 [7 mos.] = 1338] (4), which isn't possible [1 yr. 1323]], 2 [shortest (above), so 7 mos. [longest (above)] would be 1321 (7), so Maui [earliest (above)] would be 1340 [1361 [bats] − 1321 [7 mos.] = 1340] (4), which isn't possible [1 yr. 1323]], or 5 mos. [Maui, so 7 mos. [longest (above)] would be 1338 [1361 [bats] − 1323 [Maui] = 1338] (4), so 2 mos. [shortest (above)] would be 1340 (7)] (3), so couldn't be placed]; bats is 2 mos. [shortest (above), so 2 yrs. longer than 7 mos. [longest] (7)], so Maui's 1302 [only possible in (4, above)]. Borneo isn't 3 mos. [1361, so orchids would be 1323 [1384 [4 mos.] − 1361 [Borneo] = 1323] (6), but then couldn't be 3 [1361] or 5 mos. [1302], so couldn't be placed]; it's 7

mos. Sri Lanka's 3 mos. [1361], and isn't radishes (1); it's orchids, so Borneo [7 mos. [longest (above)]] is 1323 [1384 [4 mos.] − 1361 [orchids] = 1323] (6), so 2 mos. [shortest (above)] is 1325 (7). 5 mos. is radishes.

In summary:

1302, radishes, Maui, 5
1323, jellyfish, Borneo, 7
1325, bats, Ireland, 2
1361, orchids, Sri Lanka, 3
1384, dragonflies, Cuba, 4

LOGIC PROBLEM 234

The Embrace [action (1)] isn't love potion (1), candy hearts (2), chocolates [*Love on the Nile* (3)], or silk roses (4); it's love poems. *Chance Encounter* [Lacey Arrow (4)] isn't love potion [Anita Beakist (1)] or roses (4); it's candy hearts, so isn't horror, mystery, or suspense (2), so is Western. Roses isn't Ed Schmaltz or Lily Valentine (4); it's Lottie Hart, so isn't mystery or suspense (2), so is horror, so isn't *Forever Paradise* (1), so is *Kiss of an Angel*. Love potion is *Paradise*, and isn't mystery (1); it's suspense. Love is mystery. Ed Schmaltz isn't poems (4); he's chocolates. Lily Valentine's poems.

In summary:

Anita Beakist, *Forever Paradise*, suspense, love potion
Ed Schmaltz, *Love on the Nile*, mystery, chocolates
Lacey Arrow, *Chance Encounter*, Western, candy hearts
Lily Valentine, *The Embrace*, action, love poems
Lottie Hart, *Kiss of an Angel*, horror, silk roses

LOGIC PROBLEM 235

Giant squirrel isn't Lionel [ape-man (1)], Alice, Curtis (2), or Trudy [river griffin (5)]; it's Joanita [singing camp songs (4)], so isn't flashlight [campfire spook (1)], bug spray [picking flowers (3)], flaming marshmallows (4), or soda pop [Lionel (4)], so is camera flash. Tree brute isn't Alice (6); it's Curtis, so isn't marshmallows (4), so is bug spray. Spook is Alice. Trudy [griffin] is marshmallows, so isn't whispering (5) or hiking [Lionel (6)]; she's gathering firewood. Alice is whispering.

In summary:

Alice, campfire spook, whispering, flashlight
Curtis, tree brute, picking flowers, bug spray
Joanita, giant squirrel, singing camp songs, camera flash
Lionel, ape-man, hiking, soda pop

Trudy, river griffin, gathering firewood, flaming marshmallows

LOGIC PROBLEM 236

Weekdays are Mon.-Fri. (intro.). Mon. [stock shelves (1)] isn't Sam, Hilda, Cheryl, or Tim (1); it's Marie. Tue. [veterinarian (2)] isn't Sam, Hilda (1), or Cheryl (2); it's Tim. Thu. [car trouble (3), cash register (4)] isn't Sam (3) or Cheryl (4); it's Hilda. Wed. isn't Sam (3); it's Cheryl. Fri. is Sam, so isn't dentist or house hunting (1); it's airport. Wed. [unload trucks (3)] isn't dentist (3); it's house hunting. Mon. is dentist. Tim isn't customer service (4); he's display produce. Sam's customer service.

In summary:

Mon., Marie, stock shelves, dentist
Tue., Tim, display produce, veterinarian
Wed., Cheryl, unload trucks, house hunting
Thu., Hilda, cash register, car trouble
Fri., Sam, customer service, airport

LOGIC PROBLEM 237

Wks. are 6, 8, 10, 12, and 14 (intro.). Will isn't 6 [least], 14 [most] (1), 8 [Jon (3)], or 10 wks. [Gina (4)]; he's 12 wks., so attorney's 14 wks. [most] (1), so isn't Maxwell [advertising executive (2)], so is Heather. Maxwell's 6 weeks. Will [12 wks.] isn't air-traffic controller (3) or stockbroker [Gina (4)]; he's surgeon. Jon's air-traffic. Gina [stockbroker, 10 wks.] isn't karma [attorney (1)], hatha [Maxwell (2)], raja [12 wks. (3)], or bhakti (4); she's jnana. Jon's bhakti.

In summary:

Gina, stockbroker, jnana, 10
Heather, attorney, karma, 14
Jon, air-traffic controller, bhakti, 8
Maxwell advertising executive, hatha, 6
Will, surgeon, raja, 12

LOGIC PROBLEM 238

RAM is 16, 28, 32, 64, and 128 GB (intro.). Packard [scanner (1)] isn't Macroletter 3.0, Notetaker 4.0 (1), LetterWriter 2000 [DVD-ROM (2)], or Office Keeper 4.1 [Omega (3)]; it's Writer's Workshop 2.0. Notetaker isn't zip drive or camera (1); it's sub woofer [64 GB (2)], so isn't Orange (2) or Matrix [32 GB (3)], so is Harvard. Orange isn't Macroletter (1); it's LetterWriter. Matrix is Macroletter, and isn't zip drive (3); it's camera. Omega [Office Keeper] is zip drive, and isn't 16 [Writer's Workshop (2)] or 128 GB (3); it's 28 GB. Orange is 128 GB.

In summary:

Harvard, Notetaker 4.0, sub woofer, 64

Matrix, Macroletter 3.0, camera, 32
Omega, Office Keeper 4.1, zip drive, 28
Orange, LetterWriter 2000, DVD-ROM, 128
Packard, Writer's Workshop 2.0, scanner, 16

LOGIC PROBLEM 239

Clothing is Arcadia, Fashion Exchange, and Threads (intro.). Papadamaki [Fashion Exchange (1)] isn't U.S. Unlimited (1); she's Apostolia [only possible in (5)]. Gentle [clothing (3)] is U.S. Unlimited [only unplaced in (5)]. Supercard isn't Zelinski, Papadamaki [Fashion Exchange [clothing]], or Ozeri [clothing (5)] (2); it's Santangelo. Thomas isn't Santangelo [Supercard], Ozeri [clothing (above)], or Gentle [U.S. Unlimited [clothing (5)] (2); he's Zelinski. Beth [CreditPlus (3)] isn't Gentle [U.S. Unlimited] or Santangelo [Supercard]; she's Ozeri [clothing (above)], and isn't Threads (3), so is Arcadia [only clothing left]. U.S. Unlimited [clothing (above)] is Threads [only clothing left], and isn't Georgette (1); it's Franklin. Georgette's Santangelo. Visions isn't Apostolia [Fashion Exchange] (4); it's Thomas, and isn't Purley Discount (4), so is Array of Appliances. Apostolia's Passway. Georgette's Purley Discount.

In summary (1st & last names, credit card, catalog):

Apostolia Papadamaki, Passway, Fashion Exchange
Beth Ozeri, CreditPlus, Arcadia
Franklin Gentle, U.S. Unlimited, Threads
Georgette Santangelo, Supercard, Purley Discount
Thomas Zelinski, Visions, Array of Appliances

LOGIC PROBLEM 240

Pens are 3-7, and piglets are 4, 6, 8, 10, and 12 (intro.). Berkshire isn't pen 6 [no pen 8], 7 [highest] (2), 5 [fish would be pen 7 [bananas (1)] (2)], or 3 [lowest] (4); she's pen 4, so fish is pen 6 (2), and apples is pen 3 [lowest] (4). 4 piglets is pen 3 [only pen no. less than 4 piglets] (5). 6 piglets isn't pen 4 [Berkshire] (2); it's pen 5 [only pen no. left less than 6 piglets] (5). 12 piglets isn't pen 4 [Berkshire] or 7 [bananas] (1); it's pen 6. 8 piglets isn't pen 7 [highest] (3); it's pen 4. 10 piglets is pen 7. Tomatoes isn't 6 piglets [Hampshire would be 4 piglets [least, Berkshire] (5)]; it's 8 piglets, so Hampshire is 6 piglets [only piglets left less than 8 piglets [tomatoes]] (5). Sweet corn is 6 piglets. Poland China isn't 10 or 4 piglets [apples] (4); she's 12 piglets. Chester White isn't 4 piglets [least] (2); she's 10 piglets. Duroc's 4 piglets.

In summary (breed, pen, piglets, treat):

Berkshire, 4, 8, tomatoes

392

Chester White, 7, 10, bananas
Duroc, 3, 4, apples
Hampshire, 5, 6, sweet corn
Poland China, 6, 12, fish

LOGIC PROBLEM 241

Rms. are 101, 102, 104, 105, and 106 (intro.). Rm. 106 [highest] isn't philosophy building (3), gymnasium (4), cafeteria (5), or main quadrangle (6); it's library. Rm. 101 [lowest] isn't gymnasium [no rm. 103] (4), cafeteria (5), or philosophy (6); it's main quad., so provost is rm. 102 (6). Rm. 105 isn't cafeteria (2) or gymnasium [no rm. 107] (4); it's philosophy, so admissions director is rm. 106 [highest] (3). Dean isn't rm. 101 [lowest] or 105 [no rm. 103] (4); it's rm. 104, so gymnasium's rm. 102 (4). Cafeteria's rm. 104. Fortescue isn't rm. 101, 102, 106 [library] (1), or 104 [cafeteria] (5); he's rm. 105. Sanders isn't rm. 106 [admissions], 102 [provost], or 101 (3); she's rm. 104. Rathburn isn't rm. 101 or 102 [provost] (6); he's rm. 106. Henkels isn't rm. 101 [main quad.] (2); he's rm. 102. McGee's rm. 101, but isn't football coach (5); she's president. Fortescue's football coach.

In summary:

101, Ms. McGee, president, main quadrangle
102, Mr. Henkels, provost, gymnasium
104, Ms. Sanders, dean, cafeteria
105, Mr. Fortescue, football coach, philosophy building
106, Mr. Rathbum, admissions director, library

LOGIC PROBLEM 242

Boys are Buddy, Holden, and Seymour, girls are Franny and Phoebe, months are Jan.-May, and days are 3-7 (intro.). Seymour isn't Mayor 7 days [most] (1); he's science [only possible in (2)]. Buddy isn't May [last] (4); he's 7 days, and Holden is May [only left in (2)]. Buddy [7 days] isn't history (3), geography (4), or music [5 days (4)]; he's literature. Geography isn't Phoebe or Holden (5); it's Franny. 3 days [least] isn't science [Seymour] (1) or geography (5); it's history, so isn't Holden (5), so is Phoebe. Holden's music [5 days], so geography's 4 days, and Mar. is 3 days [least] (5). Seymour's 6 days, so Jan. is 7 days [most] (1). Franny [4 days] isn't Apr. (3); she's Feb. Seymour's Apr.

In summary:

Buddy, Jan., 7, literature
Franny, Feb., 4, geography
Holden, May, 5, music
Phoebe, Mar., 3, history
Seymour, Apr., 6, science

LOGIC PROBLEM 243

Shelves are 1-5 (intro.). Shelf 2 [ceramic turtles (2)] isn't Becky [shelf 1 (1)], Robyn [paperweights (3)], Trish (4), or Paige [thimbles (5)]; it's Marcia. Shelf 5 isn't Trish (4) or Paige (5); it's Robyn. Shelf 4 [lace (2)] isn't Paige [rayon (5)]; it's Trish, and isn't seashells (4), so is crystals. Becky's seashells. Shelf 3 is Paige. Silk isn't Marcia [cotton (1)] or Robyn (3); it's Becky. Velveteen is Robyn.

In summary:

1, Becky, seashells, silk
2, Marcia, ceramic turtles, cotton
3, Paige, thimbles, rayon
4, Trish, crystals, lace
5, Robyn, paperweights, velveteen

LOGIC PROBLEM 244

Rings are 1-5 (intro.). Ashley Fowler [sitcom (4)] isn't *Law of Averages* or *Life Lines* [both dramas (1)], *Baker's Dozen* (2), or *Shop Talk* [lower ring than Greg Benz (1)] (4); she's *Odd Jobs* [1 ring higher than *Life* (5)], so isn't human cannonball, lion taming (2), hot-coal walker [1 ring higher than *Law* (3)], or trapeze (4), so is tightrope, and isn't ring 3 [Greg would be ring 1 [lowest] (4)] (1), 1 [lowest], 2 (4), or 5 [*Life* would be ring 4 (above), but then *Baker's* would be ring 5 [highest, *Odd*] (5)], so is ring 4, so *Life* is ring 3 (above), so *Baker's* is ring 5 [only left higher than ring 3 [*Life*]] (5). Greg isn't ring 1 [lowest] (1), 3, or 5 [Ashley ring 4] (4); he's ring 2, so *Shop* is ring 1 [lowest] (1), so isn't Hank Rialto (1) or Dylan McCrae (2), so is Whitney Marks. *Law* is ring 2, so hot-coal walker is ring 3 (3). Trapeze [sitcom (4)] isn't *Law* [drama (above)] or *Baker's* (4); it's *Shop*. Lion taming isn't ring 5 [highest] (2); it's ring 2. Human cannonball is ring 5, and isn't Dylan (2); it's Hank. Hot-coal walker is Dylan.

In summary:

1, trapeze, Whitney Marks, *Shop Talk*
2, lion taming, Greg Benz, *Law of Averages*
3, walk on hot coals, Dylan McCrae, *Life Lines*
4, tightrope, Ashley Fowler, *Odd Jobs*
5, human cannonball, Hank Rialto, *Baker's Dozen*

LOGIC PROBLEM 245

Candles are 2-6 (intro.). Kaars isn't 2 [Kerze would be 4 candles (5), so Vela would be 2 candles [least, Kaars] (3)], 3 [Candela (4)], 5, or 6 candles [most] (5); that one's 4 candles, so lavender's 5 candles, and Kerze's 6 candles (5), so Stefan's 5 candles, and Vela's 2 candles [only left less than 5 candles [Stefan]] (3). Bougie's 5 candles, so Walter's 4 candles, and bayberry's 3 candles (2). Louisa's 6 candles [only left more than jasmine [4 candles (4)]] (3). Dominique isn't Candela (1); she's Vela, and isn't sandalwood (1), so is patchouli. Victor's Candela. Louisa's sandalwood.

In summary:

Dominique Vela, 2, patchouli
Louisa Kerze, 6, sandalwood
Stefan Bougie, 5, lavender
Victor Candela, 3, bayberry
Walter Kaars, 4, jasmine

LOGIC PROBLEM 246

Dates are 11th-15th (intro.). Mario Puzo isn't 11th earliest], 15th [latest] (2), 13th [Mario Van Peebles (3)], or 12th [Mario Cuomo would be 13th [Mario Van Peebles] (2)]; he's 14th, so Mario Cuomo's 15th (2). Mario Lanza [Ramirez (1)] isn't 11th [1st] (1); he's 12th, so Ortega's 11th [1st] (1). Mario Andretti's 11th. Movie isn't 11th [Ortega [day off (1)]] or 12th (2); it's 13th [only left before Mario Puzo [14th]] (2). Dinner isn't 12th [Ramirez] or 15th [last] (4); it's 14th, so Scarano's 15th [last], so isn't present (4), so is party. Present is 12th. Hellman isn't Puzo (2); he's Van Peebles. Bumoni's Puzo.

In summary (surname, namesake, event, date):

Bumoni, Mario Puzo, dinner, 14th
Hellman, Mario Van Peebles, movie, 13th
Ortega, Mario Andretti, day off, 11th
Ramirez, Mario Lanza, present, 12th
Scarano, Mario Cuomo, party, 15th

LOGIC PROBLEM 247

Pieces are 144, 167, 190, 213, and 236 (intro.). Basement isn't 144 (2), 190, 213, or 236 pieces [most] (3); it's 167 pieces, so Gail's 190 pieces, Jed's 213 pieces, and Omar's 236 pieces [most] (3), so living room's 213 pieces, and Rodan's 236 pieces [most] (1). Randy isn't 144 pieces [least] (2); he's 167 pieces. Pearl's 144 pieces [least], so isn't office (2) or kitchen (3), so is bedroom, so isn't King Kong (1), Freddy Krueger, or Gill-Man (2), so is alien. Randy isn't King Kong or Freddy Krueger (2); he's Gill-Man. Freddy Krueger's 190 pieces, and King Kong's 213 pieces (1). Kitchen isn't 236 pieces (3); it's 190 pieces. Office is 236 pieces.

In summary:

Gail, Freddy Krueger, 190, kitchen
Jed, King Kong, 213, living room
Omar, Rodan, 236, office
Pearl, alien, 144, bedroom
Randy, Gill-Man, 167, basement

LOGIC PROBLEM 248

Chromium & iron isn't lightweight (1), strong [malgamite (2)] (2), low melting pt. (3), or high electrical resistance [combinal [bismuth (4)] (4)]; it's does not rust. Blendium isn't rust [chromium & iron] or melting (3); it's lightweight, so isn't bismuth & chromium (1), bismuth & iron, or iron & tin (3), so is magnesium & tin. Melting isn't bismuth & iron or iron & tin (3); it's bismuth & chromium. Electrical [combinal] is bismuth & iron [only bismuth left] (4). Strong is iron & tin. Electrical [bismuth & iron, combinal] isn't Axis (1), McNeal (2), Vittorio (4), or Zeemu [emixion (5)]; it's Pushkin. Vittorio is bismuth & chromium [only bismuth left] (4). McNeal isn't iron & tin [malgamite] (2); he's magnesium & tin [only tin left] (2). Bismuth & chromium [Vittorio] isn't emixion [Zeemu]; it's additon. Chromium & iron is emixion. Axis is malgamite.

In summary:

Dr. Axis, iron & tin, malgamite, strong
Dr. McNeal, magnesium & tin, blendium, lightweight
Dr. Pushkin, bismuth & iron, combinal, high electrical resistance
Dr. Vittorio, bismuth & chromium, additon, low melting point
Dr. Zeemu, chromium & iron, emixion, does not rust

LOGIC PROBLEM 249

Rowley isn't Bittina (1); that one's Eugene (3). Gloria ["Mikey's Tale" (2)] isn't Ganison (2); she's WYJM [only possible in (1)]. "Five Days in Cleveland" isn't KRYX, KNTP [Bittina (4)] (1), or WBQO ["Knockin' on My Door" (3)]; it's WUNH, so isn't Rodney (4), so is Pam [only unplaced in (1)]. Rodney's Ganison [only left in (1)]. "Let's Play Cricket" isn't KRYX (3); it's KTNP. "Have Some Cake" is KRYX, and isn't Eugene (4); it's Rodney. "Knockin'" is Eugene. Bittina ["Cricket"] isn't Barran (2) or Persaud (3); she's Esopo. Pam isn't Persaud (2); she's Barran. Gloria's Persaud.

In summary:

Bittina Esopo, "Let's Play Cricket," KNTP
Eugene Rowley, "Knockin' on My Door," WBQO
Gloria Persaud, "Mikey's Tale," WYJM
Pam Barran, "Five Days in Cleveland," WUNH
Rodney Ganison, "Have Some Cake," KRYX

LOGIC PROBLEM 250

Sizes, from smallest to largest, are monarch, statement, crescent, executive, letter, and legal (intro.). Résumé isn't crescent, executive, letter, legal [largest] (3), or statement [invitation (3)]; it's monarch, so green [Nora (3)] is letter (3). Legal [largest] isn't yellow, orange (1), red (2), or blue (4); it's gray, and isn't Arte (1), Freida, Glenn (2), or Moe (4), so is Holly. Monarch [smallest] isn't Moe (1), Freida, or Glenn (2); it's Arte. Blue [1 size smaller than program (4)] isn't Freida [1 size smaller than newsletter (2)], Moe, or Arte [monarch [smallest]] (4); it's Glenn. Red [2 sizes smaller than newsletter (2)] isn't Freida (2) or Moe [2 sizes smaller than program (4)]; it's Arte [monarch], so Freida's statement, and newsletter's crescent (2). Moe isn't executive [blue would be letter [green] (4)]; he's crescent, so blue is executive, and program is letter (4). Glenn isn't poster (2); he's flyer. Holly's poster. Invitation isn't orange (3); it's yellow. Newsletter's orange.

In summary:

Arte, résumé, monarch, red
Freida, invitation, statement, yellow
Glenn, flyer, executive, blue
Holly, poster, legal, gray
Moe, newsletter, crescent, orange
Nora, program, letter, green

LOGIC PROBLEM 251

Episodes are 1-4 (intro.). Nilda isn't episode 1 [1st], 4 [last] (1), or 3 [couldn't be Xenakis (1), Heredia [episode 4 last] (2), Robos (3), or Zados (4), so couldn't be placed]; she's episode 2, so servant is episode 1 [1st], and Xenakis is episode 3 (1). Guard isn't episode 4 [last] (2) or 2 [Nilda, so Heredia would be episode 1 [1st, servant] (2), but then Zados couldn't be guard [Nilda], messenger, or street vendor (4), so couldn't be placed]; that one's episode 3, so Troy's episode 4 [last] (2). Episode 3 isn't Sondra (3); it's Leo. Episode 1 is Sondra. Zados isn't street vendor or messenger (4); that one's servant. Robos isn't street vendor (3); that one's messenger. Heredia is street vendor, and isn't episode 4 [last] (2); that one's episode 2. Robos is episode 4.

In summary:

1, Sondra, Zados, servant
2, Nilda, Heredia, street vendor
3, Leo, Xenakis, guard
4, Troy, Robos, messenger

LOGIC PROBLEM 252

Kings are Cedric and Rufus, queens are Imogene, Wilhemina, and Xanthe, and nos. are I-V (intro.). Sild [king (3)] isn't Cedric [couldn't be I [lowest], II, III (2), V [highest] (3), or IV [king would be V [highest] (3), but couldn't be Rufus (4), so couldn't

be placed], so couldn't be placed]; it's Rufus [only king left], so is 1 less than Cedric [only king left] (3). Cedric isn't I [lowest], II, III (2), or V [Rufus would be IV (above), but V highest] (4); he's IV, so Rufus is III (above), so clock tower is IV, and Fyrement Cathedral is V [highest] (4). Cabrini Castle isn't I [lowest] or II (2); it's III, so ringa's II, and Wilhemina's I [lowest] (2). Arenque isn't I [lowest] or V [highest] (1); it's IV, so Xanthe's V [highest] (1), and isn't nishin (3), so is dagmeluach. Nishin's I. Imogene's II [ringa], so isn't Donago Monument (3); she's House of Parliament. Wilhemina's Donago.

In summary:

Arenque, Cedric IV, clock tower
Dagmeluach, Xanthe V, Fyrement Cathedral
Nishin, Wilhemina I, Donago Monument
Ringa, Imogene II, House of Parliament
Sild, Rufus III, Cabrini Castle

LOGIC PROBLEM 253

Votes are 2, 4, 5, 6, and 8 (intro.). Off-magenta isn't 5 [no 3 or 7 votes] (1), 2 [no 3 votes], 6 [no 7 votes], or 8 votes [most] (3); it's 4 votes, so Holly's 5 votes (3). Chutney isn't 2 [least], 5 [no 2½ votes], or 6 votes [no 3 votes] (2); it's 8 votes, so calligraphic tip is 4 votes [off-magenta] (2), so scented is crustacean (1). Carmine isn't 2 [no 3 votes], 6 [no 7 votes], or 8 votes [most] (2); he's 4 votes, so glow-in-the-dark is 5 votes (2). Ginger isn't erasable (3) or glitter (4); she's scented [crustacean], so isn't 8 [chutney] or 6 votes [Amber couldn't be 2 [least] or 8 votes (4), so couldn't be placed], so is 2 votes. I-can't-believe-it's-not-butter isn't 5 votes [Holly] (4); it's 6 votes, so Amber isn't 8 votes (4), so is 6 votes. Electric turtle's 5 votes. Merle's 8 votes, and isn't erasable (3); he's glitter. Amber's erasable.

In summary:

Amber, I-can't-believe-it's-not-butter, erasable, 6
Carmine, off-magenta, calligraphic tip, 4
Ginger, crustacean, scented, 2
Holly, electric turtle, glow-in-the-dark, 5
Merle, chutney, glitter, 8

LOGIC PROBLEM 254

Centuries are 15th-19th (intro.). Errol [18th (1)] isn't first bowling alley, grew giant radish (1), named dog "Rover" [19th latest] (4), or domesticated the peacock [Sheba (5)]; he's shrubbery stakes, so Ashley di Ponte is 19th [latest] (2). "Rover" isn't 15th [earliest], 19th [latest] (4), or 17th [Basset Basile couldn't be 19th [Ashley di Ponte], so couldn't be placed] (4)]; it's 16th, so Rachel's 15th [earliest], and Basset Basile's 18th [only possible in (4)]. 16th ["Rover"] isn't Sheba [peacock] or Bobbie (4); it's Oswald, so bowling alley is 15th [earliest] (3). Sheba isn't 17th (5); she's 19th. 17th is Bobbie and giant radish. Efemera Equerrius isn't 15th [earliest] or 17th [giant radish] (6); she's 16th, so Victor Stavinere's 15th [earliest] (6). Pallida de Muse is 17th.

In summary:

Bobbie, Pallida de Muse, grew giant radish, 17th

Errol, Basset Basile, shrubbery stakes, 18th

Oswald, Efemera Equerrius, named dog "Rover," 16th

Rachel, Victor Stavinere, first bowling alley, 15th

Sheba, Ashley di Ponte, domesticated the peacock, 19th

LOGIC PROBLEM 255

Experience levels, from lowest to highest, are pussywillow, kitten, catechumen, cub, and dewclaw, and lives are 5-9 (intro.). Claudia isn't 7, 9 [ocelot hunter would be 8 lives, and kitten [higher than only pussywillow] would be 7 lives (5)] (2), 5 [least], or 6 lives (5); she's 8 lives, so ocelot hunter is 7 lives, and kitten is 6 lives (5). Purvis isn't 9 [caracal meowtlaw would be 8 lives [Claudia] (3)] (2), 5 [least], or 6 lives (3); he's 7 lives, so caracal meowtlaw is 6 lives [kitten], and cub is 5 lives [least] (3), so Claudia's pussywillow [lowest] (2). Lynx catalyst isn't 8 [pussywillow [lowest]] or 9 lives (1); it's 5 lives [cub], so 9 lives is dewclaw [highest] (1). 7 lives is catechumen. Puma purrtector isn't 8 lives [Claudia] (5); it's 9 lives. Serval caterwauler is 8 lives. Puma purrtector isn't Christopher or Lionel (4); it's Kitty. Caracal meowtlaw isn't Christopher (3); it's Lionel. Lynx catalyst is Christopher.

In summary:

Christopher, lynx catalyst, cub, 5

Claudia, serval caterwauler, pussywillow, 8

Kitty, puma purrtector, dewclaw, 9

Lionel, caracal meowtlaw, kitten, 6

Purvis, ocelot hunter, catechumen, 7

LOGIC PROBLEM 256

Men are Apu, Naji, and Sanjay, and women are Arothana and Manjula (intro.). Apu isn't "Prince Five-Weapons and Sticky-Hair" or meditation (6); he's mango [only left in (1)], and isn't karma [woman (5)], so is "King Goodness the Great" [only possible in (5)]. Karma [woman (above)] is "The Bull Called Delightful" [only possible in (2)]. Bodhi isn't Arothana, Sanjay (3), or Naji (5); it's Manjula, and

isn't "Bull" [karma] (5), so is nirvana, and Arothana is "Bull" (2). Sanjay is cycad [only unplaced in (5)], so isn't "Prince Five-Weapons" (6); he's meditation [only left in (1)]. Naji is "Prince Five-Weapons" [only unplaced in (1)]. "The Shovel Wise Man" isn't Sanjay [meditation] (6); it's Manjula, so deodar is Naji [only man with tree unplaced], and isn't marriage (4), so is discipline. Apu is marriage. Arothana is banyan. Sanjay is "Fear Maker and Little Archer."

In summary:

Apu, marriage, mango, "King Goodness the Great"

Arothana, karma, banyan, "The Bull Called Delightful"

Manjula, nirvana, bodhi, "The Shovel Wise Man"

Naji, discipline, deodar, "Prince Five-Weapons and Sticky-Hair"

Sanjay, meditation, cycad, "Fear Maker and Little Archer"

LOGIC PROBLEM 257

Men are Carmine, Kelly, and Lincoln, and women are Fawn, Hazel, and Scarlet (intro.). *Marooned* isn't 1st (3), 3rd [*The Caller at Midnight* (3)], 5th, 6th [last] (4), or 2nd [Kelly would be 4th [Carmine (5)] (4)]; it's 4th, so insurance appraiser's 5th, and Kelly's 6th (4). 6th [last, Kelly] isn't police officer [*Clean Slate* would be 4th [*Marooned*] (1)], artist, psychic (2), or landscaper [Scarlet (5)]; it's laboratory technician. 4th [Carmine] isn't landscaper [Scarlet], psychic (2), or artist [psychic couldn't be placed in (2)]; it's police officer, so Hazel's 3rd, and *Slate*'s 2nd (1). *The Canary's Cage* [artist (2)] isn't 5th [appraiser] or 6th [last] (2); it's 1st. Landscaper [Scarlet] isn't 3rd [Hazel]; it's 2nd. Psychic's 3rd. Fawn [*The Jade Monkey* (5)] isn't 1st [*Canary's*]; she's 5th. Lincoln's 1st. *The Lady in the Mink Coat* is 6th.

In summary:

1st, *The Canary's Cage*, Lincoln, artist

2nd, *Clean Slate*, Scarlet, landscaper

3rd, *The Caller at Midnight*, Hazel, psychic

4th, *Marooned*, Carmine, police officer

5th, *The Jade Monkey*, Fawn, insurance appraiser

6th, *The Lady in the Mink Coat*, Kelly, laboratory technician

LOGIC PROBLEM 258

Times are 9:00 a.m., 10:00 a.m., 12:00 p.m., 2:00 p.m., and 3:00 p.m. (intro.). Elgin Veritas isn't 2:00 [Waltham William Emery (1)], 10:00 [no 11:00], 12:00 [no 1:00], or 3:00 [last] (2); it's 9:00, so Lewiston is 10:00 (2). Hamilton 992E is 10:00, Bunn Special 60-Hour is 12:00, and Longines 15J is

3:00 (3). Merrick isn't 12:00 [no 1:00], 3:00 [last] (2), or 9:00 [1st] (4); that one's 2:00. Victoria Embers isn't 3:00 [Merrick 2:00] (2) or 12:00 (4); she's 9:00. Devlin isn't 3:00 [Longines] (3); that one's 12:00. Allen's 3:00. Nancy isn't 2:00 [Waltham] (1), 10:00 [Fanny (1)], or 12:00 [Bunn] (3); she's 3:00. Chuck isn't 2:00 [Merrick] (4); he's 12:00. Quinn's 2:00.

In summary:

9:00 a.m., Victoria Embers, Elgin Veritas
10:00 a.m., Fanny Lewiston, Hamilton 992E
12:00 p.m., Chuck Devlin, Bunn Special 60-Hour
2:00 p.m., Quinn Merrick, Waltham William Emery
3:00 p.m., Nancy Allen, Longines 15J

LOGIC PROBLEM 259

1st wks. are Jan. 1, Jan. 8, Jan. 15, Jan. 29, Feb. 5, and Feb. 12, and 2nd wks. are Oct. 1, Oct. 8, Oct. 15, Oct. 22, Oct. 29, and Nov. 5 (intro.). Oct. 1 [earliest 2nd wk.] isn't Scott (1), Jake (2), Michele, Tiffany (3), or Harry (4); it's Dorothy, so Scott 2nd wk. is Oct. 8 (1). Michele 2nd wk. isn't Oct. 15 [1st wk. Jan. 8 would be 2nd wk. Oct. 8 (3)] (1), Nov. 5 [last 2nd wk.] (3), or Oct. 22 (5); it's Oct. 29, so 1st wk. Jan. 8 is 2nd wk. Oct. 22, Tiffany 2nd wk. is Nov. 5 [latest 2nd wk.] (3), and Michele 1st wk. is Jan. 1 [earliest 1st wk.] (5). Jake 2nd wk. isn't Oct. 22 [1st wk. Jan. 8, so Harry 1st wk. would be Jan. 1 [earliest 1st wk., Michele] (4)]; it's Oct. 15, so 1st wk. Feb. 12 is 2nd wk. Oct. 8 (2). Harry 2nd wk. is Oct. 22 [1st wk. Jan. 8], so 1st wk. Jan. 15 isn't 2nd wk. Oct. 15 (1) or Nov. 5 [last 2nd wk.] (4); it's Oct. 1. Tiffany 1st wk. [2nd wk. Nov. 5] isn't Feb. 5 (1); it's Jan. 29. Jake 1st wk. is Feb. 5.

In summary (employee, 1st wk., 2nd wk.):

Dorothy, Jan. 15, Oct. 1
Harry, Jan. 8, Oct. 22
Jake, Feb. 5, Oct. 15
Michele, Jan. 1, Oct. 29
Scott, Feb. 12, Oct. 8
Tiffany, Jan. 29, Nov. 5

LOGIC PROBLEM 260

Amts. are $10 million, $11 million, $12 million, $13 million, and $14 million (intro.). Signing bonus isn't Rochester (1), Thornton [open-ended record deal (2)], Mathews, or Wilder (4); it's Davidson. Wilder isn't artistic freedom or escape clause (3); she's chance to produce. $10 million [least] isn't Wilder [produce, so Rochester would be $11 million (1), and accepted offer would be $11 million (3), which isn't possible (1)], Mathews, Davidson [signing bonus], or Thornton

[Davidson [signing bonus] would be $11 million (2)] (4); it's Rochester, so produce [Wilder] is $11 million (1), so accepted offer is $12 million (3). Mathews isn't $13 million [signing bonus [Davidson] would be $14 million [most] (4), but then Thornton couldn't be placed in (2)] or $14 million [most] (4); he's $12 million, so Star Bright's $11 million, and signing bonus is $13 million (4). Thornton's $14 million. Artistic freedom isn't $12 million [accepted offer (above)] (3); it's $10 million. Escape clause is $12 million. Davidson [$13 million, signing bonus] isn't DreamWeaver (2), Lone Star (4), or Odyssey (5); he's Wild Heart. Thornton [$14 million] isn't DreamWeaver (2) or Odyssey (5); she's Lone Star. Mathews [$12 million [accepted offer (above)]] isn't Odyssey (5); he's DreamWeaver. Rochester's Odyssey.

In summary:

DreamWeaver, Mr. Mathews, $12 million, escape clause

Lone Star, Ms. Thornton, $14 million, open-ended record deal

Odyssey, Ms. Rochester, $10 million, artistic freedom

Star Bright, Ms. Wilder, $11 million, chance to produce

Wild Heart, Mr. Davidson, $13 million, signing bonus

LOGIC PROBLEM 261

Hawker Hurricane [*Winged Victory* (4)] isn't figure eight (3), spin [Blake Mason (2), so couldn't be placed in (4)], falling leaf, or roll (5); it's loop, so Hawker Sea Fury is Alex Roth (4). Frances Forester isn't loop [*Winged Victory*], figure eight (3), or falling leaf (5); she's roll, so isn't *The Sky's the Limit*, so is *Operation Eagle*, and figure eight is *The Sky's the Limit* (3). *The Fighting 52nd* [Orson Greco (1)] isn't spin [Blake Mason]; it's falling leaf. *Wild Blue Yonder* is spin. Alex Roth [Hawker Sea Fury] isn't loop [Hawker Hurricane]; he's figure eight. Hannah Lin is loop. Hawker Typhoon isn't Orson Greco (1) or Blake Mason (2); it's Frances Forester. Fairey Swordfish isn't Orson Greco [falling leaf] (2); it's Blake Mason. Supermarine Spitfire is Orson Greco.

In summary:

The Fighting 52nd, Orson Greco, Supermarine Spitfire, falling leaf

Operation Eagle, Frances Forester, Hawker Typhoon, roll

The Sky's the Limit, Alex Roth, Hawker Sea Fury, figure eight

Wild Blue Yonder, Blake Mason, Fairey Swordfish, spin

Winged Victory, Hannah Lin, Hawker Hurricane, loop

LOGIC PROBLEM 262

Sessions are 1-5 (intro.). Audrey [3 sessions (4)] isn't *Modern Kinesiology* [Richard (1)], *Healing Herbs*, *Myotherapy Monthly* (4), or *Chakra Digest* [pulled hamstring (1), so would be Chow [only possible in (3)], but then couldn't be placed in (5)]; she's *Reflexology Today*. 1 session [least] isn't *Chakra*, *Modern* [Richard] (1), or *Myotherapy* (5); it's *Healing*, so isn't Linda (3) or Boyce (5), so is Tanner. *Myotherapy* isn't Boyce (5); it's Linda. *Chakra* is Boyce. 4 sessions [Siabhan (2)] isn't backache (2); it's Linda [only possible in (3)]. *Chakra* isn't 2 sessions (1); it's 5 sessions. Richard [*Modern*] is 2 sessions, so isn't Drexel (5); he's asthma [only possible in (5)], so is Chow [only possible in (3)]. Audrey is Drexel [only unplaced in (5)] and backache [only unplaced in (3)]. Lee [frequent headaches (2)] isn't Boyce [hamstring]; he's Tanner. Boyce is Nissar. Linda is arthritis.

In summary:

Audrey, *Reflexology Today*, Drexel, backache, 3
Boyce, *Chakra Digest*, Nissar, pulled hamstring, 5
Linda, *Myotherapy Monthly*, Siabhan, arthritis, 4
Richard, *Modern Kinesiology*, Chow, asthma, 2
Tanner, *Healing Herbs*, Lee, frequent headaches, 1

LOGIC PROBLEM 263

Yrs. are 2009-2014 (intro.). Master bedroom isn't 2011 or later [2014 last] (1) or 2010 [sculpture would be 2012, and Piper Dolan would be 2014 (1), and study couldn't be 2011 or later [2014 last] (4), so would be 2009, and Wallace Keegan would be 2011 (4), but then Medrie McDaniel couldn't be 2010 [master bedroom] (1), 2009 [1st], 2012 [sculpture] (3), or 2013 [metal cast would be 2012 [sculpture] (3)], so couldn't be placed]; master bedroom's 2009, so sculpture is 2011, and Piper Dolan's 2013 (1). Study isn't 2011 or later [2014 last] (4); it's 2010, so Wallace Keegan's 2012, and watercolor is 2014 (4). 2012 [Wallace Keegan] isn't living room [woodcarving would be 2011 [sculpture] (2)], dining room (4), or front hall [Anton Casper (5)]; it's guest bedroom, so Finola Hirsch's 2009 (6). Medrie McDaniel isn't 2011 [sculpture] (3) or 2010 [metal cast would be 2009 [Finola Hirsch] (3)] (6); she's 2014, so metal cast is 2013 (3). Anton Casper [front hall] isn't 2010 [study]; he's 2011. Ivan Edwards is 2010. Living room isn't 2014 [woodcarving would be 2013 [metal cast] (2)]; it's 2013, so woodcarving's

2012 (2). Dining room's 2014. Photograph isn't 2010 [Anton Casper 2011] (5); it's 2009. Oil painting is 2010.

In summary:

Anton Casper, sculpture, front hall, 2011
Finola Hirsch, photograph, master bedroom, 2009
Ivan Edwards, oil painting, study, 2010
Medrie McDaniel, watercolor, dining room, 2014
Piper Dolan, metal cast, living room, 2013
Wallace Keegan, woodcarving, guest bedroom, 2012

LOGIC PROBLEM 264

Gremlins are 14, 18, 22, 26, and 30 (intro.). WorldCo [recently hired (3)] is Rocco [only possible in (1)]. Alma isn't Ianuzzi & Swift or 14 gremlins [least] (2); she's under copy machine [only possible in (1)]. Ivar isn't Ianuzzi & Swift (2); he's 14 gremlins [only possible in (1)]. Dagmar is Ianuzzi & Swift [recently hired, only unplaced in (1)], so isn't staff lounge, elevator shaft (2), or air-conditioning duct [founding member (3)]; he's supply room. Ivor [14 gremlins [least]] isn't Intellinet or Omicron Industries (4); he's GlobalCorp, and isn't staff lounge or elevator shaft (2), so is air-conditioning duct, so WorldCo is 18 gremlins (3). 30 gremlins [most] isn't Ianuzzi & Swift (2) or Omicron (4); it's Intellinet, so elevator shaft is 26 gremlins (4). Stig isn't Intellinet [30 gremlins [most]] (3); he's Omicron. Alma's Intellinet. Elevator shaft [26 gremlins] isn't Rocco [18 gremlins]; it's Stig. Dagmar's 22 gremlins. Rocco's staff lounge.

In summary:

Alma, Intellinet, 30, under copy machine
Dagmar, Ianuzzi & Swift, 22, supply room
Ivor, GlobalCorp, 14, air-conditioning duct
Rocco, WorldCo, 18, staff lounge
Stig, Omicron Industries, 26, elevator shaft

LOGIC PROBLEM 265

Zed isn't Godmun, Rasmussen, Wachtel, or Cerullo (7); he's Barrie or Rome, so isn't FL (1), OR [couldn't be Rome (2) or Barrie (4), so couldn't be placed (above)], MA, CA (5), or NC [couldn't be Barrie (4) or Rome (6), so couldn't be placed (above)], so is LA. Rome isn't CA, OR (2), or NC (6); that one's FL, LA, or MA, so isn't arrowworm [couldn't be FL, LA, or MA (2), so couldn't be placed (above)], sea snail [couldn't be William or Emily (2), so couldn't be placed in (2)], krill [couldn't be Avi (1), Sterling (3), or Zed [LA] (6), so couldn't be placed in (2)], hydromedusa (4), or barnacle larva [couldn't be FL (1), MA (5), or LA [Zed] (7), so couldn't be placed (above)], so is copepod. Barrie isn't MA (1), OR, NC (4), or CA [couldn't be Darren, Sterling (3), Emily (4), Avi, or William (6), so couldn't be placed]; that one's FL or LA, so isn't arrowworm [couldn't be FL or LA (2), so couldn't be placed (above)], sea snail [couldn't be Emily (4) or William (6), so couldn't be placed in (2)], krill (6), or barnacle larva [couldn't be FL (1) or LA [Zed] (7), so couldn't be placed (above)], so is hydromedusa, so isn't FL (4), so is LA (above). Barnacle larva isn't Rasmussen, Godmun, or Wachtel (7); it's Cerullo. Krill isn't Wachtel (5) or Godmun [couldn't be Avi, William (1), Darren, Sterling (3), or Emily (7), so couldn't be placed]; it's Rasmussen. MA isn't arrowworm (2), barnacle larva, sea snail (5), or krill [Rasmussen] (7); it's copepod [Rome], and isn't Avi (3), so is Sterling [Zed Barrie] (2). FL isn't Cerullo [barnacle] (1), Wachtel, or Godmun (5); it's Rasmussen. NC isn't Godmun (6) or Wachtel (7); it's Cerullo [barnacle], so isn't Avi (1), Darren (3), or Emily (4), so is William, so Emily's sea snail (2), so isn't Rasmussen [krill] or Godmun (7), so she's Wachtel. Darren isn't Godmun (3); he's Rasmussen. Avi's Godmun and arrowworm. Emily isn't OR (4); she's CA. Avi's OR.

In summary:

Avi Godmun, arrowworm, OR
Darren Rasmussen, krill, FL
Emily Wachtel, sea snail, CA
Sterling Rome, copepod, MA
William Cerullo, barnacle larva, NC
Zed Barrie, hydromedusa, LA

LOGIC PROBLEM 266

Yrs. are 1460, 1520, 1580, 1640, and 1760 (intro.). *Mayflower* landing [fed birds or taught Macarena (1)] isn't 1760 [latest] (3); it's light-bulb trees [only possible in (2)], so isn't 1760, 1520, 1580 [Gettysburg Address would be 1760 [latest] (3)] (2), or 1640 [before only 1700] (3), so is 1460 [earliest], so isn't Macarena (4), so is birds. Sistine Chapel isn't 1760 [latest], 1640 [no 1700], or 1520 [Robot Olympics would be 1580 (4), but no 1700] (4); it's 1580, so Olympics is 1640, and Macarena is 1760 (4). Gettysburg isn't 1760 (2) or 1520 [after only 1460] (3); it's 1640, so isn't picked flower or swatted fly (2), so is left wristwatch. Coronation isn't 1760 [Macarena] (4); it's 1520, so isn't sky pink or talking llamas (3), so is giant slugs. *Hamlet* premiere is 1760 [latest], so isn't llamas (3), so is sky pink. Llamas is 1580, and isn't fly (3); it's flower. Fly is 1520.

In summary:

1460, *Mayflower* landing, fed birds, light-bulb trees
1520, coronation, swatted fly, giant slugs

1580, Sistine Chapel, picked flower, talking llamas
1640, Gettysburg Address, left wristwatch, Robot Olympics
1760, *Hamlet* premiere, taught Macarena, sky pink

LOGIC PROBLEM 267

Women are Dr. Estecado, Dr. Garvey, and Dr. Klotz, men are Dr. Russell and Dr. Zelenka, and chromosomes are 2, 5, 11, 14, and 17 (intro.). Chicken dance isn't chromosome 2 [lowest], 5, 14 [no chromosome 8], or 17 [highest] (4); it's chromosome 11, so PGG84 is chromosome 5 (4), and Dr. Garvey isn't chromosome 17 (2), so she's chromosome 14 [only left higher than chromosome 11 [chicken dance]] (4). *Mannix* episodes isn't chromosome 5 [no chromosome 8], 17 [highest], or 14 (5); it's chromosome 2, so Dr. Zelenka is chromosome 5, and isn't chicken dance [chromosome 11], *Mannix* [chromosome 2], fear of pickles [woman (1)], or March Madness (5), so he's Taco Bell, so Dr. Estecado is chromosome 2 (3). BQ1L6 man (2) is Dr. Russell, so isn't chromosome 17 (2); he's chromosome 11. Dr. Klotz is chromosome 17. Chromosome 2 [lowest] isn't M32ST (1) or TUN9 (3); it's HRO7. Chromosome 14 isn't M32ST [chromosome 11 Dr. Russell] (1); it's TUN9. Chromosome 17 is M32ST, so chromosome 14 isn't fear of pickles (1); it's March Madness. Chromosome 17 is fear of pickles.

In summary:

Dr. Estecado, HRO7, 2, *Mannix* episodes
Dr. Garvey, TUN9, 14, March Madness
Dr. Klotz, M32ST, 17, fear of pickles
Dr. Russell, BQ1L6, 11, chicken dance
Dr. Zelenka, PGG84, 5, Taco Bell

LOGIC PROBLEM 268

Conference is 4 days (intro.). Ruegger isn't day 1 [1st], 2, or 4 [last] (4); that one's day 3, so "The Future of Silicon" is day 2, and Kamil is day 1 [1st] (4). Ruegger [day 3 (above)] isn't 1st, 2nd, 6th [last] (above), 3rd [day 4 [last] would be 4th, 5th, and 6th [last] (above), which isn't possible (intro.)], or 5th ["Future" [day 2 (above)] would be 4th, and Kamil [day 1 [1st] (above)] would be 3rd (4), so 1st and 2nd would be day 1 (above), which isn't possible (intro.)]; that one's 4th, so "Future" [day 2 (above)] is 3rd, and Kamil [day 1 [1st] (above)] is 2nd (4), so 1st is day 1, and day 4 [last] is 5th and 6th [last] (above). Bernier [before lunch (1)] isn't day 2, 3 [each has only 1 conference (above)], or 4 [last] (1); that one's day 1 [1st and 2nd (above)], so "Practical Solar Energy" [before lunch (1)] is day 1 (1), so Bernier is 1st, and "Practical" is

2nd [only possible (1, above)]. Pinchbeck [after lunch (3)] isn't day 1 [before lunch (above)], or 2 or 3 [each has only 1 conference (above)] (3); that one's day 4 [5th and 6th [last] (above)], so Cyril is day 4 (3), so is 5th, and Pinchbeck is 6th [last, only possible in (3, above)]. Olympia [before lunch (2)] isn't 6th [after lunch (above)], 1st (3), or 4th [after lunch (3)]; she's 3rd ["Future"], and isn't Devine (2) or Monaco (4), so is Hyatt, so "The History of Solid-State Electronics" is 1st [only left before 3rd] (1). 5th [Cyril] isn't Monaco (3); it's Devine. 2nd is Monaco. "What's New in Oscilloscopes" isn't day 3 [has only 1 conference (above)]; it's day 4 [only left with seminar unplaced (above)], so Zoe is day 4 (2), so Zoe is 6th, and "What's New" is 5th [Cyril, only possible in (2, above)]. "A Hard-Wired World" isn't 6th [last] (4); it's 4th, and isn't Foster (4), so is Lindsey. Foster is 1st. "Superconductors and You" is 6th.

In summary:

1st, "The History of Solid-State Electronics," Foster Bernier

2nd, "Practical Solar Energy," Kamil Monaco

3rd, "The Future of Silicon," Olympia Hyatt

4th, "A Hard-Wired World," Lindsey Ruegger

5th, "What's New in Oscilloscopes," Cyril Devine

6th, "Superconductors and You," Zoe Pinchbeck

LOGIC PROBLEM 269

Female noblemice are Bellamouse, Julirat, and Mouseleine, and male noblemice are R'Atagnan and Ratspierre (intro.). Aramouse humans [female (2)] isn't Bellamouse (2) or Julirat [Aramouse mousetrap (4)]; she's Mouseleine [only female left]. Aramouse Paris sewers isn't R'Atagnan or Bellamouse (4); it's Ratspierre, so Aramouse Cardinal Chatelieu [male (1)] is R'Atagnan [only male unplaced]. Aramouse bad fromage [Porthmouse humans (1)] is Bellamouse. Porthmouse Cardinal Chatelieu isn't Mouseleine, Ratspierre (3), or R'Atagnan [Porthmouse mousetrap (3)]; it's Julirat. Porthmouse bad fromage [Athmouse mousetrap (2)] isn't Mouseleine [Athmouse bad fromage (3)]; it's Ratspierre. Porthmouse Paris sewers is Mouseleine. Athmouse Paris sewers [female (4)] isn't Julirat (4); she's Bellamouse [only female left]. Athmouse Cardinal Chatelieu isn't R'Atagnan [Aramouse Cardinal Chatelieu] (1); it's Julirat. Athmouse humans is R'Atagnan.

In summary (noblemouse, Aramouse, Athmouse, Porthmouse):

Bellamouse, bad fromage, Paris sewers, humans

Julirat, mousetrap, Cardinal Chatelieu, Cardinal Chatelieu

Mouseleine, humans, bad fromage, Paris sewers

R'Atagnan, Cardinal Chatelieu, humans, mousetrap

Ratspierre, Paris sewers, mousetrap, bad fromage

LOGIC PROBLEM 270

Paychecks are $350, $380, $390, $430, $450, $500, and $530, and cash amts. are $20, $60, $80, $110, $120, $140, and $150 (intro.). Make a chart of paychecks versus cash amts., and calculate the deposited amts. for all possible combinations. Prestige Travel [deposited $280 (3)] isn't $150 cash [most] (3); it's $110, so is $390 paycheck [only possible (chart)]. Cliff [deposited $320 (4)] is $380 paycheck and $60 cash [only left for $320 (chart)], so Expert Construction is $20 cash [least] (1), and Darcie paycheck is $350 [least] (2). Evan [deposited $390 (1)] is $530 paycheck and $140 cash [only left for $390 (chart)], so Felix is $150 cash [most] (1). Darcie [$350 paycheck [least, only less than Cliff [$380]]] isn't $110 [paycheck $390], $80 (3), or $20 cash (4); she's $120 cash, so Memories Photography is $150 cash [no $90] (4). $450 paycheck isn't $20 or $80 cash [Prestige $110 cash] (3); it's $150 cash. $20 cash isn't $430 paycheck [Felix $450 paycheck] (4); it's $500 paycheck [less than only Evan [$530 paycheck, $140 cash]], and isn't Gabrielle [less than Blythe (2)] or Adam [less than $80 cash (3)], so is Blythe. $80 cash is $430 paycheck, and isn't Adam (3); it's Gabrielle. Adam is $110 cash. DataWorld isn't Gabrielle, Darcie [$120 cash], or Evan [$140 cash] [Gabrielle $80 cash] (2); it's Cliff. Gabrielle [$430 paycheck, $80 cash] isn't Lacy's (3) or Pro Fitness (5); she's Joe's Auto Body. Evan [$530 paycheck] isn't Lacy's [DataWorld $380 paycheck] (5); he's Pro Fitness. Darcie's Lacy's.

In summary (customer, business, paycheck, cash):

Adam, Prestige Travel, $390, $110

Blythe, Expert Construction, $500, $20

Cliff, DataWorld, $380, $60

Darcie, Lacy's, $350, $120

Evan, Pro Fitness, $530, $140

Felix, Memories Photography, $450, $150

Gabrielle, Joe's Auto Body, $430, $80

LOGIC PROBLEM 271

Real-time strategy are Arcadia Prime and BioControl, and role-playing are Land's End, Necropolis, and Umbra (intro.). Ultima isn't Leah or Land's End [role-playing] (4); it's BioControl [only left in (1)]. Necropolis [role-playing] isn't level design (4) or interface design (6); it's computer AI [only unplaced in (5)], so isn't King's Quest, Super Mario Bros. (3), or Zork (5), so is The Legend of Zelda. Gloria [real-time strategy

(3)] isn't Legend [Necropolis] or Mario Bros. (3); she's BioControl [only left in (1)]. Belinda isn't Mario Bros. [couldn't be Arcadia Prime or Umbra (2), so couldn't be placed in (1)] or Legend [Necropolis] (5); she's Land's [only left in (1)]. Tina [role-playing (4)] isn't Umbra (4); she's Necropolis [only role-playing left]. Phoebe is Mario Bros. [only unplaced in (1)]. Belinda [Land's [role-playing]] isn't Zork (5); she's King's Quest, and isn't level design (4), so is interface design [only unplaced in (5)]. Leah is Zork, so is level design [only unplaced in (5)], and isn't Umbra [role-playing] (4), so is Arcadia Prime. Phoebe is Umbra, so isn't story design (7); she's background art. Gloria is story design.

In summary (woman, game, aspect, influence):
Belinda, Land's End, interface design, King's Quest
Gloria, BioControl, story design, Ultima
Leah, Arcadia Prime, level design, Zork
Phoebe, Umbra, background art, Super Mario Bros.
Tina, Necropolis, computer AI, The Legend of Zelda

LOGIC PROBLEM 272

Each item was purchased in a different quantity of 10 (intro.). Forks isn't 30 or less [20 count least (5)] (2), 60 or more [Petra would be at least 120 count (2), but 100 count most (5)], or 40 count [Petra would be 80 count (2), and Mark and Josie would be 20 [least] and 30 count, in some order [only possible in (2)], but then 1 pack of each item would total 320 [20 + 30 + 40 + 80 + 100 (above) + 50 (4) = 320], which isn't possible (5)]; it's 50 count, so Petra's 100 count (2). Plates isn't 30 count or more [Tyler would be at least 70 count (3), and spoons couldn't be 100 count [most] (1), so would be 80 or 90 count (1), but then 1 pack of each item would total at least 350 [20 [least] + 30 [plates] + 50 [forks] + 70 [Tyler] + 80 [spoons] + 100 [most] = 350], which isn't possible (5)]; it's 20 count [least]. Felicity isn't spoons, napkins (1), cups (3), bowls, or plates [20 count [least]] (4); she's forks [50 count], and bowls isn't 40 count (4), so is 30 count [only possible left less than Felicity] (4). Tyler isn't 40 count or less [plates 20 count] (3) or 70 count or more [spoons couldn't be 100 count [most] (1), so would be 80 or 90 count (1), so 1 pack of each item would total at least 350 [20 [plates] + 30 [bowls] + 50 [forks] + 60 [Tyler] + 80 [spoons] + 100 [Petra] = 350], which isn't possible (5)]; Tyler's 60 count. 6th item is 80 count [340 (5) – 20 [plates] – 30 [bowls] – 50 [forks] – 60 [Tyler] – 100 [Petra] = 80]. Spoons isn't 60 [Tyler] or 100 count [most] (1); it's 80 count, so napkins is 100 count [most] (1). Cups is 60 count. Josie isn't 20 count [plates] (3); she's 30 count, so

Mark's 20 count [only left less than forks [50 count]] (2). Gordon's spoons.
In summary:
Felicity, forks, 50
Gordon, spoons, 80
Josie, bowls, 30
Mark, plates, 20
Petra, napkins, 100
Tyler, cups, 60

LOGIC PROBLEM 273

Guessed Scorpio [romance (1)] and guessed Sagittarius [romance (5)] aren't actual Capricorn (1), Pisces [work (2)], Aries [work (4)], or Virgo [Axel [work (4)] (4)]; they're actual Gemini and Taurus, in some order, so actual Taurus isn't Richard [guessed Cancer (2)], Maurice or Karen [both work (4)], or Dina (5), so is Beth, so is Jade, and Axel's guessed Leo [only possible in (3)], so Zorah is Karen (2). Actual Capricorn [romance (4)] isn't Karen or Maurice [both work (above)] or Dina (4); it's Richard. Actual Pisces isn't Dina or Karen (5); it's Maurice. Actual Aries isn't Dina (4); it's Karen. Actual Gemini is Dina, so isn't guessed Sagittarius (5), so is guessed Scorpio, and actual Taurus [Jade] guessed Sagittarius (above), so Crystal guessed Scorpio [Dina] (1), so Astra is Richard (3). Ebony isn't actual Pisces (2); she's actual Virgo. Miranda's actual Pisces, and didn't guess Aquarius (3); she guessed Libra. Zorah guessed Aquarius.
In summary (caller, psychic, guessed, actual):
Axel, Ebony, Leo, Virgo
Beth, Jade, Sagittarius, Taurus
Dina, Crystal, Scorpio, Gemini
Karen, Zorah, Aquarius, Aries
Maurice, Miranda, Libra, Pisces
Richard, Astra, Cancer, Capricorn

LOGIC PROBLEM 274

Pgs. are 33-38, and eye elements are eyelash curler, mascara, and under-eye cream (intro.). Full-pg. ad (1) isn't pg. 37 (3), 33 [lowest], 34 (5), 38 [Amber (7)], or 35 [Doreen couldn't be pg. 35 [full-pg. ad (above)], 33 [lowest], 34 (2), 36 [Pierre would be pg. 35 [full-pg. ad (above)] (2)], 37 [Pierre would be pg. 36, and bronzer would be pg. 35 [full-pg. ad (above)] (2)], or 38 [only Amber (7)], so couldn't be placed]; it's pg. 36, so Linda is pg. 35, and pink blush is pg. 34 (5). Doreen isn't pg. 36 [full-pg. ad (above)], 38 [only Amber (above)], 33 [lowest], 34 (2), or 37 [Pierre would be pg. 36 [full-pg. ad (above)] (2)]; she's pg. 35, so Pierre is pg. 34, and bronzer is pg. 33

(2), so the 6 makeovers are Linda [pg. 35], pink blush [pg. 34], Doreen [pg. 35], bronzer [pg. 33], pg. 37, and Amber [pg. 38], so Pierre [pg. 34] is pink blush (above). Celeste isn't bronzer or blush (6); she's pg. 37 [only left (above)], so Frédéric is pg. 38 [highest] (6), so is Amber (above). Doreen [pg. 35] isn't bronzer [pg. 33], blush [pg. 34], eyelash curler, mascara, or under-eye cream (2); she's lip pencil, so Kevyn is pg. 33 [lowest, bronzer], and isn't Natalie (4), so is Patrice [only left (above)]. Natalie is pink blush [only unplaced (above)]. Amber [Frédéric] isn't under-eye cream (6) or eyelash curler (7); she's mascara. Celeste isn't under-eye cream (6); she's eyelash curler. Linda is under-eye cream. Rinalde isn't Celeste [pg. 37] or Doreen [lip pencil, but pg. 37 eyelash curler] (3); he's Linda. Lorenzo isn't Doreen [pg. 35] (7); he's Celeste. Jean Claude is Doreen.

In summary:

Amber, 38, Frédéric, mascara

Celeste, 37, Lorenzo, eyelash curler

Doreen, 35, Jean Claude, lip pencil

Linda, 35, Rinalde, under-eye cream

Natalie, 34, Pierre, pink blush

Patrice, 33, Kevyn, bronzer

LOGIC PROBLEM 275

Men are Dave, John, and Sheldon, women are Georgia and Rikki, times left are 10:00 a.m., 10:15 a.m., 10:30 a.m., 12:00 p.m., and 12:15 p.m., times returned are 11:00 a.m., 11:15 a.m., 12:00 p.m., 12:45 p.m., and 1:00 p.m., and messages are 4-8 (intro.). Rikki isn't 8 (1), 5, 4 [least, so Georgia would be 5 messages (1)], or 6 messages [Dave would be 7 messages (4), and Georgia would be 5 messages (1)] (2); she's 7 messages, so Dave's 8 messages (4), and Georgia's 6 messages (1). Dave [8 messages] isn't left 10:00 [1st] (4); he returned 12:00 [only possible in (2)], so Rikki returned 1:00 (1). Dave left [returned 12:00] isn't 12:00, 12:15 (intro.), 10:00, or 10:15 [Georgia would've left 10:00 [1st] (4)] (2); he left 10:30, and Georgia didn't leave 10:00 (2), so left 10:15 [only left before 10:30] (4). Left 12:00 isn't returned 11:00, 11:15, or 12:00 (intro.); it's returned 12:45 or 1:00. Left 12:15 isn't returned 11:00, 11:15, or 12:00 (intro.); it's returned 12:45 or 1:00, so left 12:00 and 12:15 are returned 12:45 and 1:00, in some order (above). Georgia [left 10:15] didn't return 12:45 [left 12:00 or 12:15 (above)] or 11:00 [would've been gone 45 min., so Sheldon would've been gone 15 min. or less (3), but then couldn't have left 10:00 [11:00 1st return], or 12:00 or 12:15 [couldn't have returned

12:45 or 1:00, so couldn't be placed (above)], so couldn't be placed]; Georgia returned 11:15 [gone 60 min.], so Sheldon didn't leave 10:00 [11:00 1st return] (3) or 12:00 [couldn't have returned 12:45 or 1:00 (3), so couldn't be placed (above)], so left 12:15, and didn't return 1:00 [Rikki], so returned 12:45, so left 12:00 returned 1:00 (above). John left 10:00 and returned 11:00, so isn't 5 messages (2); he's 4 messages. Sheldon's 5 messages.

In summary (agent, left, returned, messages):

Dave, 10:30 a.m.-12:00 p.m., 8

Georgia, 10:15 a.m.-11:15 a.m., 6

John, 10:00 a.m.-11:00 a.m., 4

Rikki, 12:00 p.m.-1:00 p.m., 7

Sheldon, 12:15 p.m.-12:45 p.m., 5

LOGIC PROBLEM 276

Sitcom isn't Gould (1), Findlay (2), Warrick (3), or Jarman [couldn't be Donna (1), Michael, Jackie (3), Stephen, or Eric (4), so couldn't be placed]; it's Pressman, so isn't Donna (1), Michael (3), Eric, or Stephen (4), so is Jackie, so isn't political humor (1), ventriloquism, props, or impressions (3), so is songs. Warrick isn't commercial (1), talk show (2), or awards show [couldn't be Donna (1), Michael (3), Stephen, or Eric (4), so couldn't be placed]; it's animated series, so isn't Donna (1), Michael (3), or Eric (4), so is Stephen. Impressions isn't Findlay, Warrick (2), or Jarman (3); it's Gould, so isn't Donna (1) or Michael (3), so is Eric. Awards show isn't Eric Gould or Jarman (4); it's Findlay, so isn't props (2) or ventriloquism (3), so is political humor, so isn't Donna (1), so is Michael. Donna's Jarman, and isn't commercial (1); she's talk show, so isn't props (3), so is ventriloquism. Stephen's props. Eric's commercial.

In summary:

Donna Jarman, ventriloquism, talk show

Eric Gould, impressions, commercial

Jackie Pressman, songs, sitcom

Michael Findlay, political humor, awards show

Stephen Warrick, props, animated series

LOGIC PROBLEM 277

Mos. are Mar., Apr., and May, and glass are snow globe and swizzle stick (intro.). Ceramic frog [MO (2)] isn't Kale Capital of the World (2), Mystery Monster [glass (3)], Haunted Recycling Center [SD (5)], or Fiberglass Dandelion [couldn't be Apr. (1) or Mar. [1st] (2), so would be May, so Kale Capital would be Apr. (2), and couldn't be snow globe, swizzle stick [both glass] (2), or thimble [glass would be May [last, ceramic frog] (3)], so would be googly-eyed rock, but then Lincoln Log Village [same mo. as IA (4)] couldn't be thimble [same mo. as NE (3), so would be 3 items that mo.], snow globe, or swizzle stick (4), so couldn't be placed]; ceramic frog is Lincoln Log Village, so isn't Mar. [1st] (2) or May [last] (4), so is Apr., so Kale Capital is Mar. (2), IA is Apr., and snow globe is May [last] (4). IA [Apr.] isn't Kale Capital [Mar.] or Fiberglass Dandelion (1); it's Mystery Monster. KS isn't Fiberglass Dandelion (1); it's Kale Capital. NE is Fiberglass Dandelion and is Mar. [1st, Mystery Monster Apr.], so KS [Mar.] is thimble (3). Haunted Recycling is May [snow globe], so Mystery Monster is swizzle stick [only glass left] (3). Fiberglass Dandelion is googly-eyed rock.

In summary:
Ceramic frog, Lincoln Log Village, MO, Apr.
Googly-eyed rock, Fiberglass Dandelion, NE, Mar.
Snow globe, Haunted Recycling Center, SD, May
Swizzle stick, Mystery Monster, IA, Apr.
Thimble, Kale Capital of the World, KS, Mar.

LOGIC PROBLEM 278

Days are Mon.-Sat. (intro.). Sat. [last] isn't basement, master bedroom (2), kitchen, living room, or family room (3); it's bathroom, and isn't Beth Norton (2), so is Ken Pfeiffer, and *Making Your Dream a Home* is earlier in the week than master bedroom (4). Ken [Sat. [last], bathroom] isn't *Making* (above), *Your House and You*, *The Unique House* (2), *Room by Room*, or *Room-lifts* (5); he's *From House to Home*, so Vince Dalton is *Room-lifts*, and *Making* is kitchen (1). Master bedroom isn't *Your House*, *Unique* (2), or *Room-lifts* (4); it's *Room by Room*, and isn't Beth (2), so is Tue., and Beth is 2 days before *Room-lifts* (5), so *Making* [kitchen] is Mon. [1st] (above), so Vince [*Room-lifts*] is Wed. (3), so Beth is Mon. [*Making*] (above), so Nat Wilson is earlier than living room [Ken Sat., so only possible in (3)]. *Your House* isn't basement (2) or living room (5); it's family room. *Unique* isn't basement (2); it's living room. *Room-lifts* is basement. Living room isn't Fri. [Nat would be Sat. [last, Ken] (above)]; it's Thu., so Nat is Fri. [only left after living room [Thu.]] (above). *Your House* is Fri. *Room by Room* isn't Cassidy Miles (1); it's Liz Burke. *Unique* is Cassidy.

In summary:
Mon., *Making Your Dream a Home*, Beth Norton, kitchen
Tue., *Room by Room*, Liz Burke, master bedroom
Wed., *Room-lifts*, Vince Dalton, basement

Thu., *The Unique House*, Cassidy Miles, living room
Fri., *Your House and You*, Nat Wilson, family room
Sat., *From House to Home*, Ken Pfeiffer, bathroom

LOGIC PROBLEM 279

Bellagio date isn't odd [couldn't be Serena Chase (1), Alexis Olsavsky, Margaret Whitmore [MGM Grand date would be odd (2, above)], Katerina Cordova [*La Gioconda* date would be odd (2, above)], Justine Whitley [*Carmen* date would be odd (3, above)] (3), or Daniella Dubois (4), so couldn't be placed]; it's even, so Serena date [3 days after Bellagio (1)] is only odd date (above). *Tosca* date [3 days after Caesars Palace (4)] isn't odd [couldn't be Serena [3 days after Bellagio (1)], so couldn't be placed in (3, above)]; it's even, so Caesars date [3 days before *Tosca* (4)] is odd (above), so is Serena (3, above), so isn't *La Traviata* (2), *La Gioconda* [Katerina date would be odd (2, above)], *Carmen* [Justine date would be odd (3, above)] (3), *Tosca* (4), or *Aida* (5), so is *La Bohème*. 1st performance isn't *Aida*, *La Bohème* [Serena] (1), *La Gioconda* (2), *Tosca* (4), or *La Traviata* [couldn't be Mandalay Bay Resort (1), Bally's Las Vegas, Bellagio, Mirage (5), or MGM Grand [8 days before Margaret (2), so couldn't be Alexis, Margaret (2), Daniella, Katerina [8 days before *La Gioconda* (2)] (3), or Justine (4), so couldn't be placed], so couldn't be placed]; it's *Carmen*, so isn't Margaret (2), Justine, Alexis (3), or Katerina (4), so is Daniella, so isn't Mandalay (1), MGM Grand (3), Bellagio (4), or Bally's (5), so is Mirage, and isn't 10th or later [Mandalay would be at least 18th (1), so Bellagio would be at most 9th (4), so would be before earliest performance [10th (above)]], 2nd [Mandalay would be 10th (1), so Bellagio [even (above)] would be 5th (4)], 6th [Mandalay would be 14th (1), so Bellagio [even (above)] would be 7th (4)], or 8th [Mandalay would be 16th (1), so Bellagio would be 8th [Mirage] (4)], so she's 4th, so Mandalay is 12th (1), Justine's 6th (3), and Bellagio is 6th (4), so Serena [Caesars] is 9th (1), and *Tosca* is 12th (4). *La Gioconda* isn't Bellagio [6th] (2) or Bally's (5); it's MGM Grand. *La Traviata* isn't Bellagio [Justine] (4); it's Bally's. *Aida* is Bellagio. Katerina [8 days before *La Gioconda* (2)] isn't *La Gioconda* (2) or *La Traviata* [Bally's, so 8 days after *La Gioconda* (5)]; she's *Tosca* [12th], so *La Gioconda* is 20th (2), so Bally's is 28th (5). Margaret isn't *La Gioconda* (3); she's *La Traviata*. Alexis is *La Gioconda*.

403

In summary:

Alexis Olsavsky, 20th, MGM Grand, *La Gioconda*

Daniella Dubois, 4th, Mirage, *Carmen*

Justine Whitley, 6th, Bellagio, *Aida*

Katerina Cordova, 12th, Mandalay Bay Resort, *Tosca*

Margaret Whitmore, 28th, Bally's Las Vegas, *La Traviata*

Serena Chase, 9th, Caesars Palace, *La Bohème*

LOGIC PROBLEM 280

Shaw [hamburgers, milk (6)] isn't Stan [Frost (4)], Neil [cola (5)], June, or Polly (6); she's Cara. Gray [sandwiches (2)] isn't Neil or Polly (2); she's June. Lemonade isn't Stan or Polly (4); it's June. Neil [cola] isn't fish [wine (3)] or salad (5); he's quiche, so isn't Kerr (1), so is Barrett. Polly's Kerr, and isn't iced tea (1); she's wine. Stan's iced tea and salad.

In summary:

Cara Shaw, hamburgers, milk

June Gray, sandwiches, lemonade

Neil Barrett, quiche, cola

Polly Kerr, fish, wine

Stan Frost, salad bar, iced tea

LOGIC PROBLEM 281

Codes are D3B 4H1, K1W 7C8, L4C 3E6, L8V 4N3, and M9S 4C5, and house nos. are 9, 75, 366, 743, and 851 (intro.). David isn't meteorologist [Hugh (1)], dentist, journalist, or paralegal (3); he's stock-broker. Jerry [no. 743 [2nd highest] (4)] isn't paralegal [no. lower than Holly, so Holly [code not L4C 3E6 (2)] couldn't be 851 [highest, has common nos. with all codes but L4C 3E6 (above)] (2)] or dentist (4); he's journalist. Holly isn't paralegal (2); Kendra is. Holly is dentist. No. for code L8V 4N3 is 851 [only no. higher than no. 743 [journalist]] (5). Holly [dentist] isn't no. 9 [lowest] (2), 366, or 851 (4); she's no. 75. Paralegal is no. 9 [only no. lower than no. 75 [Holly]] (2). Holly [no. 75] isn't L8V 4N3 [no. 851], L4C 3E6, K1W 7C8, or M9S 4C5 (2); it's D3B 4H1. L8V 4N3 code [no. 851] isn't Jerry [no. 743], Kendra [no. 9], or David (3); it's Hugh. David is no. 366. Kendra isn't K1W 7C8 or L4C 3E6 (1); she's M9S 4C5. Jerry isn't L4C 3E6 (4); David is. Jerry's K1W 7C8.

In summary (student, profession, postal code, house no.):

David, stockbroker, L4C 3E6, 366

Holly, dentist, D3B 4H1, 75

Hugh, meteorologist, L8V 4N3, 851

Jerry, journalist, K1W 7C8, 743

Kendra, paralegal, M9S 4C5, 9

LOGIC PROBLEM 282

Madsen [shopped with Toni (5)] isn't Janice (1), Alice Vincent (3), Diana [shopped alone (4)], or Toni (5); she's Karen. Janice isn't lilies (1), peonies (2), irises [Diana (4)], or asters (6); she's carnations. Gallagher [asters (6)] isn't Diana [irises] or Janice [carnations]; she's Toni. Karen Madsen isn't lilies (1); Alice is. Karen's peonies. Diana [shopped alone] isn't Simpson (7); Janice is. Diana's Crandell. Soil isn't Alice [lilies], Janice (1), Karen [peonies, so fertilizer (2)], or Toni [rock (5)]; it's Diana. Janice Simpson isn't pots (7); Alice is. Janice's trowel.

In summary:

Alice Vincent, pots, lilies

Diana Crandell, soil, irises

Janice Simpson, trowel, carnations

Karen Madsen, fertilizer, peonies

Toni Gallagher, rock, asters

LOGIC PROBLEM 283

Packages are 5, 7, 9, 11, and 13, and street nos. are 1250, 1320, 2430, 3140, and 3510 (intro.). No. 3510 [highest, 4 fewer packages than Mr. Orchard (3)] isn't 5 [least, so 3140 (4)] or 7 packages (5); it's 9 packages, so Mr. Orchard will get 13 packages (3)]. Mr. Orchard [13 packages] isn't no. 3140 [5 packages], 3510 (3), or 2430 (6); he's no. 1250 or 1320, so owns Cinema One [only possible in (1)]. Glassworks isn't no. 3140 [5 packages [least]], 1250 (2), 1320 [Mr. Orchard no. 1250 or 1320] (3), or 2430 [Northport Design (6)]; it's no. 3510, so is Ms. Brewster [only possible in (1)]. Playclothes is no. 3140 [only possible in (1)]. Glassworks [no. 3510] is 9 packages, so Ms. Rice is 7, and no. 1250 is 11 (2). Mr. Orchard [Cinema One, 13 packages] isn't no. 1250 [11 packages]; he's no. 1320, and Jacobson's no. 1250 (1). Ms. Rice [7 packages] isn't no. 3140 [5 packages]; Ms. Lyman is. Ms. Rice is no. 2430. Joshua's Restaurant is no. 1250.

In summary (packages, business proprietor, address):

5, Playclothes, Inc., Ms. Lyman, 3140

7, Northport Design, Ms. Rice, 2430

9, Glassworks, Ms. Brewster, 3510

11, Joshua's Restaurant, Mr. Jacobson, 1250

13, Cinema One, Mr. Orchard, 1320

LOGIC PROBLEM 284

Yrs. are 1928, 1929, 1932, 1934, and 1935 (intro.). Maserati is newer than Helen but older than tan car (3), which is older than Nicole, which is older than Aston Martin (4); Helen's 1928 [oldest], Maserati's 1929, tan's 1932, Nicole's 1934, and Aston Martin's

1935 [newest]. 1935 [newest, Aston Martin] isn't Phyllis (2) or Lionel (7); it's Jim. 1928 [oldest, Helen] isn't Bugatti (5) or Alfa Romeo (6); it's Morgan. 1932 car [tan] isn't Bugatti (1); it's Alfa Romeo. Bugatti [Nicole] is 1934, and isn't red (1), green (4), or yellow (5); it's blue. Yellow isn't Maserati (3) or Aston Martin [1935 [newest]] (5); it's Morgan. Aston Martin isn't green (7); it's red. Maserati's green. Lionel isn't Maserati [green] (7); he's Alfa Romeo. Phyllis's Maserati.

In summary:

Helen, Morgan, 1928, yellow

Jim, Aston Martin, 1935, red

Lionel, Alfa Romeo, 1932, tan

Nicole, Bugatti, 1934, blue

Phyllis, Maserati, 1929, green

LOGIC PROBLEM 285

Bridges are 700, 750, 800, 850, and 900 yds. (intro.). 1988 [Hackman or Greig (5)] isn't Tualpa or Florice (1) or Chinapi or Ridalo [Ashley and 1982, in some order (3)]; it's Molne, so isn't Lenoir (5), so is 50 yds. longer than Ashley, and 1984 is Lenoir (2). Molne is longer than Florice (1), which isn't Ashley [Chinapi or Ridalo (above)], so Molne isn't 700 or 750, 900 (1), or 800 yds. (6); it's 850 yds, so Ashley's 800 yds. (above). Tualpa's 900 yds. (1). Ashley [800 yds.] isn't 1982 (3); it's 1990 (6). Volkov isn't 900 (4), 850 [Hackman or Greig (above)], or 750 yds. (7); it's 700 yds. Ridalo's 750 yds. (4), so is 1982, and Ashley [800 yds.] is Chinapi (3). Volkov [700 yds.] is 1986, and isn't Tualpa [900 yds.]; it's Florice. Lenoir's Tualpa [900 yds.], so Hackman's 750 yds. (7). Greig's 850 yds.

In summary:

Chinapi, 1990, 800 yds., Ashley

Florice, 1986, 700 yds., Volkov

Molne, 1988, 850 yds., Greig

Ridalo, 1982, 750 yds., Hackman

Tualpa, 1984, 900 yds., Lenoir

LOGIC PROBLEM 286

Women are Debra, Eliza, and Nina, and men are Joseph, Martin, and Rick (intro.). Each lent 1 book and borrowed 1 book (intro.). Joseph borrowed from Mr. Varney (2), who isn't Rick [lent to Nina (4)]; Martin is Varney. Ms. Foster [lent biography to woman (3)] isn't Debra (3) or Nina [lent to Rick (4)]; she's Eliza, so didn't lend biography to Nina [borrowed from Rick]; she lent to Debra [only woman left]. One who lent science fiction and borrowed mystery (1) isn't Debra [borrowed biography], Eliza

Foster [lent biography], Nina (1), Joseph (2), or Martin [borrowed western (5)]; he's Rick, so Nina lent mystery and borrowed science fiction (4). Eliza didn't borrow romance (7); Joseph did, so Martin Varney lent it (2). Eliza borrowed poetry. Joseph didn't lend western (5); he lent poetry, so is Shaw (2). Debra lent western. Anders isn't Nina nor Rick (4); she's Debra. Rick [borrowed mystery] isn't Kearney (6); Nina is. Rick is Trabert.

In summary (1st name, last name, lent, borrowed):

Debra Anders, western, biography

Eliza Foster, biography, poetry

Joseph Shaw, poetry, romance

Martin Varney, romance, western

Nina Kearney, mystery, science fiction

Rick Trabert, science fiction, mystery

LOGIC PROBLEM 287

Male senders are Brett, Fritz, and Jasper, female senders are Darla and Rebecca, male recipients are Chad and Ellis, female recipients are Karla, Lois, and Meryl, senders live in Atlanta, Billings, Dallas, Salem, and Tampa, and recipients live in Chicago, Fargo, Lansing, Norwalk, and Reno (intro.). Fritz [from Salem (2)] didn't send to Karla (5); he sent to Norwalk [only possible in (1)], so didn't send to Karla, Lois, or Meryl [only women] (4), or Ellis (5), so he sent to Chad. Rebecca sent to Ellis [only man left] (3), so didn't send to Lansing [Lois (2)], Reno (3), or Fargo (4), so she sent to Chicago. Sent from Billings [from man (1)] wasn't to Ellis [from Rebecca], Karla (1), or Meryl (6); it was to Lois. Meryl didn't get from man [the 3 male senders sent to Lois [from Billings], Karla, and Chad [in Norwalk] (1)]; she got from Darla. One from Atlanta [from woman to woman (4)] wasn't from Rebecca [to Ellis, a man]; it was from Darla [only female sender left]. Meryl [received from Atlanta] isn't in Fargo (4); Karla is. Meryl's in Reno. Jasper didn't send to Karla [in Fargo] (4); he sent to Lois. Brett sent to Karla [Fargo], but not from Tampa (4); he sent from Dallas. Rebecca sent from Tampa.

In summary (sender, sent from, recipient, received in):

Brett, Dallas, TX, Karla, Fargo, ND

Darla, Atlanta, GA, Meryl, Reno, NV

Fritz, Salem, MA, Chad, Norwalk, CT

Jasper, Billings, MT, Lois, Lansing, MI

Rebecca, Tampa, FL, Ellis, Chicago, IL

LOGIC PROBLEM 288

Weekdays are Mon.-Fri., women are Betty, Carol, and Sharon, and men are Bill and Jack (intro.). Sharon [2 days before dance (3)] is Mon., Tue., or Wed. (3), but not Mon. [ice skating Wed. (4)] or Wed. (4); she's Tue. Carol's Wed., and dance's Thu. (3). Betty isn't Thu. or Fri. (2); she's Mon. Coworker isn't Mon. (2), Tue. [Sharon] (4), Thu. [Jack couldn't be placed (2)], or Fri. (2); that one's Wed. (2). Jack isn't Fri. (2); he's Thu. (2). Bill's Fri. Jack [dance] isn't neighbor (3); he's boyfriend [only man left]. Bill isn't mother or sister; he's neighbor. Betty [Mon.] isn't sister (5); she's mother. Sharon's sister. Bill isn't garden club or bridge (6); he's PTA. Betty [mother] isn't bridge (1); Sharon is. Betty's garden club.

In summary:

Betty, Mon., mother, garden club

Bill, Fri., neighbor, PTA

Carol, Wed., coworker, ice skating

Jack, Thu., boyfriend, dance

Sharon, Tue., sister, bridge

LOGIC PROBLEM 289

Men are Jacques, Luke, and Nathan, and women are Kathleen and May (intro.). Three won medals (6); 2 were promoted to the next higher rank [only possible to have all ranks represented (intro.)]. Man promoted to green belt [originally orange belt (intro.)] isn't Luke (2) or Jacques [medalist (6)]; he's Nathan. Kathleen [white belt (3)] was promoted (3), so is now yellow belt (intro.). Original blue belt isn't May [higher belt than Luke (4), and blue only higher than Kathleen [white to yellow] and Nathan [green to orange] (intro.)] or Jacques (6); he's Luke. Tsuri Komi Goshi man isn't Luke or Nathan [green belt] (2); he's Jacques, and isn't black belt [highest (intro.)] (5); May is. Jacques's brown belt. Silver medalist isn't Jacques or Luke [blue belt] (6); it's May. Jacques [Tsuri Komi Goshi] isn't bronze medalist (5); Luke is. Jacques's gold medal. Kathleen [white belt [lowest]] isn't De Ashi Hari, Ogoshi (1), or Hiza Guruma (3); she's Osoto Gari. Nathan [orange] is Hiza Guruma, Luke [blue] is De Ashi Hari, and May [black] is Ogoshi (1, intro.).

In summary:

Jacques, Tsuri Komi Goshi, brown belt, gold medal

Kathleen, Osoto Gari, white belt, promoted to yellow

Luke, De Ashi Hari, blue belt, bronze medal

May, Ogoshi, black belt, silver medal

Nathan, Hiza Guruma, orange belt, promoted to green

LOGIC PROBLEM 290

Male ghosts are Charles, Hector, and Joshua, female ghosts are Eliza and Emmeline, and times are 12:00 a.m., 2:00 a.m., 4:00 a.m., 5:00 p.m., and 10:00 p.m. (intro.). Male ghost in wine cellar isn't hum, sing (5), laugh (3), or dance [ballroom (4)]; he's recites. Joshua [5:00 (1)] isn't recites, dances (1), laughs (3), or sings [Hector (6)]; he's hums, and isn't kitchen (2) or library (6), so he's attic. Hector [sings] isn't the male in cellar [recites]; Charles is. Emmeline isn't dances (4); she's laughs. Eliza dances. Hector isn't library [4:00 (6)] (6); Emmeline is. Hector's kitchen, but not 12:00 (2) or 10:00 (6); he's 2:00. Eliza [dances] isn't 10:00 (4); Charles is. Eliza's 12:00.

In summary:

Charles, 10:00 p.m., wine cellar, reciting

Eliza, 12:00 midnight, ballroom, dancing

Emmeline, 4:00 a.m., library, laughing

Hector, 2:00 a.m., kitchen, singing

Joshua, 5:00 p.m., attic, humming

LOGIC PROBLEM 291

Turtle Races on 15th (5) isn't Sam [8th (1)], Lena [Get Fit Aerobic-thon (3)], Tony, or Alex (5); it's Kris. *Fresh Eye* [21st (3)] isn't Kris [15th], Sam [8th], Lena (3), or Tony [*Scribblings* (5)]; it's Alex. Home and Garden Convention isn't Sam (1) or Alex (6); it's Tony. *Home Digest* [Chess Championship (4)] isn't Kris [Turtle Races] or Lena [Aerobic-thon]; it's Sam. Alex's Blueberry Bake-off. Sam [*Home Digest*] is taller than Tony [Home and Garden Convention] (1) but shorter than 27th (4), so Tony isn't 27th; Lena is. Tony's 10th. Kris is older than Tony (2), and Tony [Home and Garden Convention] is older than *Chat Box* reporter (6), so Kris isn't *Chat Box*; Lena is. Kris's *Newsdesk*.

In summary:

Alex, *Fresh Eye*, Blueberry Bake-off, 21st

Kris, *Newsdesk*, Turtle Races, 15th

Lena, *Chat Box*, Get Fit Aerobic-thon, 27th

Sam, *Home Digest*, Chess Championship, 8th

Tony, *Scribblings*, Home and Garden Convention, 10th

LOGIC PROBLEM 292

Plants are geranium and violet (intro.). Plant with Chico (1) isn't geranium [Gummo (3)]; it's violet, so Greta's plant is geranium (1). Harpo isn't child's photo or cat's photo (5); it's dog's photo. Groucho isn't cat's photo (4); it's child's photo. Zeppo is cat's photo. Gummo [geranium] isn't coffee [child's photo (2)], cocoa, Ovaltine (3), or tea (6); it's juice. Chico [violet] isn't Ovaltine (1) or tea (6); it's cocoa. Tea isn't Zeppo (6); it's Harpo. Ovaltine is Zeppo [cat's photo], so isn't Jack (1), Fred (4), or Mildred (6); it's Nancy. Chico [violet] isn't Jack (1) or Mildred (6); it's Fred. Harpo [tea] isn't Mildred (6); it's Jack. Groucho's Mildred.

In summary:
Fred, cocoa, Chico, violet
Mildred, coffee, Groucho, child's photo
Greta, juice, Gummo, geranium
Nancy, Ovaltine, Zeppo, cat's photo
Jack, tea, Harpo, dog's photo

LOGIC PROBLEM 293

Trains are 8:03, 9:15, 10:27, 11:16, and 11:57 (intro.). Rochelle is 10:27 (4), so Michael isn't 8:03 [1st], 11:57 [last] (1), or 11:16 [Bruce would be 10:27 [Rochelle] (1); he's 9:15, so Bruce [Stetson (1)] is 8:03, so fez is 9:15 [only left before 10:27 [Rochelle]] (4). Charles isn't 11:57 [last] (3); he's 11:16, so magician is 11:57 [last] (3). Paula is 11:57 [last], so acrobat [kepi (4)] is 11:16 (4). Beret isn't 11:57 [last, so clown would be 11:16 [acrobat] (2)]; it's 10:27, so clown is 9:15 (2). Tam-o'-shanter is 11:57. 10:27 [beret] isn't juggler (2); it's fire-eater. 8:03 is juggler.

In summary:
Bruce, 8:03, juggler, Stetson
Charles, 11:16, acrobat, kepi
Michael, 9:15, clown, fez
Paula, 11:57, magician, tam-o'-shanter
Rochelle, 10:27, fire-eater, beret

LOGIC PROBLEM 294

Addresses are 203, 303, 403, 503, and 603 (intro.). 603 [highest] isn't west (2), east (3), southwest (4), or southeast (5); it's south, so Grange Dr. is 403 (1). Castle Ln. isn't 203 [lowest], 303 [no 103] (3), or 603 [east would be 503, and Callas 403 (3), so Viking Hill [southwest (4)] couldn't be 503 [east] or 303 [Trebor would be 403 [Callas] (4)], so would be 203, so Trebor would be 303 (4), but then Durward [southeast (5)] couldn't be 203 [southwest], 503 [east], or 603 [south], so couldn't be placed]; it's 503, so east is 403, and Callas 303 (3). Viking [southwest] isn't 603 [south] or 203 [Trebor would be 303 [Callas] (4)]; it's 303, so Trebor's 403 (4). Manor Rd. isn't 203 [lowest] (5); it's 603. Lodge Way is 203. Durward [southeast] isn't 603 [highest] or 503 (5); it's 203. Castle is west. Vaness isn't west (2); Ameling is. Vaness is south.

In summary:
203 Lodge Way, Mr. Durward, southeast
303 Viking Hill, Ms. Callas, southwest
403 Grange Dr., Mr. Trebor, east
503 Castle Ln., Ms. Ameling, west
603 Manor Rd., Ms. Vaness, south

LOGIC PROBLEM 295

Times are 9:30, 9:35, 9:40, 9:45, and 9:50 p.m. (intro.). Chardonnay isn't sago palm [Riesling (2)], dumb cane (3), never-never plant [balloon (3)] (3), or European fan palm (4); it's mauna loa, so Chablis [champagne cork (1)] isn't 5 min. after mauna loa [Chardonnay, so 5 min. before balloon (3)], so is 5 min. before mauna loa (1), so Chablis is 5 min. before Chardonnay (above), which is 5 min. before balloon (3). Balloon [never-never plant] isn't Riesling [sago palm] or zinfandel [Chablis is 5 min. before Chardonnay, which would be 5 min. before zinfandel [balloon] (above), so Riesling would be 5 min. after zinfandel (2), so 4 wines, in consecutive order from 1st to last, would be Chablis, Chardonnay, zinfandel, and Riesling (above), so Gewurztraminer would be either 1st or last, which isn't possible (4)]; it's Gewurztraminer, so Chablis is 5 min. before Chardonnay, which is 5 min. before Gewurztraminer (above), which is 5 min. before European fan palm (4). Chablis isn't European fan palm (above); it's dumb cane. Zinfandel is European fan palm [5 min. after Gewurztraminer (above)], so Riesling is 5 min. after zinfandel (2). Chablis is 5 min. before Chardonnay, which is 5 min. before Gewurztraminer, which is 5 min. before zinfandel, which is 5 min. before Riesling (above); Chablis is 9:30, Chardonnay is 9:35, Gewurztraminer is 9:40, zinfandel is 9:45, and Riesling is 9:50 (above). Paper streamer's 9:35 [only left before 9:40 [Gewurztraminer]] (4). Hat isn't 9:50 [Riesling] (2); it's 9:45. Scarf's 9:50.

In summary:
9:30, Chablis, Champagne cork, dumb cane
9:35, Chardonnay, paper streamer, mauna loa
9:40, Gewurztraminer, balloon, never-never plant
9:45, zinfandel, hat, European fan palm
9:50, Riesling, scarf, sago palm

LOGIC PROBLEM 296

Mos. are Mar.-July, and pos., from lowest to highest, are programmer, computer graphicist, design engineer, systems analyst, and project manager (intro.). Project manager [highest] isn't Technocorp (1), Softworld, Hypermax (2), or Microcom (3); it's Computron. Project manager [Computron] isn't Mar. [1st], Apr. (1), July [last] (2), or June [ENTRANCES would be July

407

[last] (2), which isn't possible (3)]; that one's May, so Technocorp is Apr., APERTURES is Mar. [1st] (1), and ENTRANCES isn't July [last] (3), so is June (2). GATEWAYS isn't May [project manager] (1) or July [last] (2); it's Apr., so Mar. [1st] is systems analyst [1 rank below Computron [project manager]] (2). July [only mo. after ENTRANCES [June]] isn't programmer [lowest] or computer graphicist (3); it's design engineer, so Microcom is computer graphicist, and 1 mo. before PORTALS is programmer (3). Computer graphicist [Microcom] isn't Apr. [Technocorp]; it's June. Programmer's Apr., so PORTALS is May (above). OPENINGS is July. Softworld isn't Mar. (2); it's July. Hypermax is Mar.

In summary:

Mar., Hypermax, systems analyst, APERTURES
Apr., Technocorp, programmer, GATEWAYS
May, Computron, project manager, PORTALS
June, Microcom, computer graphicist, ENTRANCES
July, Softworld, design engineer, OPENINGS

LOGIC PROBLEM 297

Mos. are Apr.-Aug., and days are 3, 5, 8, 9, and 12 (intro.). 3 days [least] isn't May (2), June (3), Aug. [last], or July [Aug. last] (4); it's Apr. [earliest], so isn't Ventnor (1), Kublin [no 7 days] (2), Williams (4), or Amthor (6), so is Durwood, so Ventnor's May (1). 8 days isn't Ventnor [May, and no 4 days] (2), Williams (4), or Amthor [no 4 days] (6); it's Kublin, so May's 12 days (2). Amthor isn't 5 days [no 1 day] (6); it's 9 days, so "Love Your Laptop" is 5 days (6). Williams is 5 days ["Love Your Laptop"], so isn't Aug. [last] (4) or June (6); it's July, so "Stand by Your RAM" is Aug. [only mo. after July] (4). June's 9 days, and Aug.'s 8 days (3). May [12 days [longest]] isn't "Mac and Me" (2) or "Diskotheque" (5); it's "Key to Success." June isn't "Diskotheque" (5); Apr. is. June's "Mac and Me."

In summary:

Amthor, "Mac and Me," June, 9
Durwood, "Diskotheque," Apr., 3
Kublin, "Stand by Your RAM," Aug., 8
Ventnor, "Key to Success," May, 12
Williams, "Love Your Laptop," July, 5

LOGIC PROBLEM 298

Yrs. are 14, 15, 16, 18, and 19 (intro.). Appleseed isn't 18 [Grizzly Bear (1)], 14 [least], 15 [no 13 yrs.], or 19 [no 17 yrs.] (3); that one's 16 yrs., so Frank [*Pontchartrain* (3)] is 14 yrs. (3). Frosty the snowman isn't 14 [least] (2) or 15 yrs. [*Old Ironsides* would be 14 yrs. [*Pontchartrain*] (2)]; that one's 19

yrs. [*De Witt Clinton* (1)], so *Old Ironsides* is 18 yrs. (2). Big Bad Wolf [Tom (4)] isn't 14 yrs. [Frank]; it's 15 yrs. Rip Van Winkle is 14 yrs. *John Bull* isn't 15 yrs. [Big Bad Wolf] (4); it's 16 yrs. *Best Friend* is 15 yrs. Rita isn't 18 [Grizzly Bear] (1) or 16 yrs. [*John Bull*] (4); she's 19 yrs. Gladys isn't 16 yrs. [Appleseed] (3); she's 18 yrs. Marge is 16 yrs.

In summary:

Frank, Rip Van Winkle, *Pontchartrain*, 14
Gladys, Grizzly Bear, *Old Ironsides*, 18
Marge, Appleseed, *John Bull*, 16
Rita, Frosty the Snowman, *De Witt Clinton*, 19
Tom, Big Bad Wolf, *Best Friend*, 15

LOGIC PROBLEM 299

Times are 1:00, 1:30, 2:00, 2:30, and 3:00 p.m. (intro.). Rose [Brooklyn Bridge (4)] isn't Settle [Grand Canyon (1)], Baker [Barry (2)], Markham [Eiffel Tower (2)], or Greenaway (4); she's Halliday. Greenaway [2:00 p.m. (3)] isn't Taj Mahal [Settle would be 1:30 p.m. (3)] (1); that one's Big Ben, and Ted isn't 1:00 p.m. [1st] (5), so he's 1:30 p.m. (5). Barry Baker is Taj Mahal, and he isn't 1:00 [1st] (3) or 2:30 p.m. [Settle would be 2:00 p.m. [Greenaway] (3)]; he's 3:00 p.m., so Settle is 2:30 p.m. (3). Halliday is 1:00 p.m. Markham is 1:30 p.m. Cora isn't 2:30 p.m. (1); she's 2:00 p.m. Gerald is 2:30 p.m.

In summary:

1:00 p.m., Rose Halliday, Brooklyn Bridge
1:30 p.m., Ted Markham, Eiffel Tower
2:00 p.m., Cora Greenaway, Big Ben
2:30 p.m., Gerald Settle, Grand Canyon
3:00 p.m., Barry Baker, Taj Mahal

LOGIC PROBLEM 300

Times are 9:00-9:30, 9:30-10:00, and 10:00-10:30, and memberships, from lowest to highest, are friend, booster, donor, angel, and benefactor (intro.). Ct. Avertovsky 9:30-10:00 [Dr. Griffin 9:00-9:30 (4)] isn't donor [Ct. Avertovsky 10:00-10:30 (2)], friend [donor [Ct. Avertovsky 10:00-10:30 would be Ct. Avertovsky 9:00-9:30 (2)] (intro.), booster [Mrs. Fitzbudget 9:30-10:00 (1)], or angel [Ms. Silique 9:30-10:00 (3)]; it's benefactor. Dr. Griffin 9:30-10:00 isn't friend [donor would be Dr. Griffin 9:00-9:30 [benefactor] (2)]; it's donor. Mr. Poddleway is friend 9:30-10:00, so is also donor 9:00-9:30 (2). Angel 9:00-9:30 [Ms. Silique 9:30-10:00] isn't Ms. Silique (intro.) or Ct. Avertovsky [Dr. Griffin 10:00-10:30 couldn't be donor [Ct. Avertovsky 10:00-10:30] or benefactor [Ct. Avertovsky 9:30-10:00] (intro.), so couldn't be placed (5)]; it's Mrs. Fitzbudget. Angel 10:00-10:30 [Mrs. Fitzbudget

9:00-9:30, Ms. Silique 9:30-10:00] isn't Mrs. Fitzbudget, Ms. Silique (intro.), or Dr. Griffin [Ct. Avertovsky 9:00-9:30 couldn't be donor [Mr. Poddleway 9:00-9:30] or benefactor [Dr. Griffin 9:00-9:30], so couldn't be placed (5)]; it's Mr. Poddleway. Mrs. Fitzbudget 10:00-10:30 isn't booster [Mrs. Fitzbudget 9:30-10:00] (intro.) or friend [Mr. Poddleway 9:30-10:00, but angel is Mrs. Fitzbudget 9:00-9:30] (3); it's benefactor [Dr. Griffin 9:00-9:30], so booster 10:00-10:30 isn't Dr. Griffin (1), so is Ms. Silique. Friend [lowest] is Dr. Griffin 10:00-10:30, so booster is Ct. Avertovsky 9:00-9:30 (5). Friend is Ms. Silique 9:00-9:30.

In summary (membership, 9:00-9:30, 9:30-10:00, 10:00-10:30):

Friend, Ms. Silique, Mr. Poddleway, Dr. Griffin
Booster, Ct. Avertovsky, Mrs. Fitzbudget, Ms. Silique
Donor, Mr. Poddleway, Dr. Griffin, Ct. Avertovsky
Angel, Mrs. Fitzbudget, Ms. Silique, Mr. Poddleway
Benefactor, Dr. Griffin, Ct. Avertovsky, Mrs. Fitzbudget

LOGIC PROBLEM 301

Hrs. are 45, 55, 60, 65, and 75, salaries are $40,000, $42,500, $47,500, $50,000, and $55,000, and increases are 8%, 10%, 12%, 16%, and 18% (intro.). 75 hrs. [most] isn't 10% [no 14%], 16% [no 20%], 18% [highest] (3), or 8% (4); it's 12%, so student loans is 16% (3). Mortgage isn't 8% [$42,500 would be 10% (4), but no $35,000] (2), 12% [no 14%], or 18% [highest] (4); it's 10%, so $42,500 is 12% [75 hrs.] (4), so student loans is $47,500 (3). 10% isn't $40,000 [least] (2) or $55,000 [car payments would be $47,500 [student loans] (2)]; it's $50,000, so car payments is $42,500 (2). Bad investments isn't 8% [lowest] (5); it's 18%. Credit card is 8%, and isn't $40,000 (1); it's $55,000. Bad investments [18%] is $40,000, and isn't 55 [no 70], 65 [no 80] (5), or 60 [16% would be 75 [12%] (5)]; it's 45 hrs., so 16% is 60 hrs. (5). Credit card isn't 65 (1); it's 55. Mortgage is 65 hrs.

In summary (hrs., salary, increase, debt):
45, $40,000, 18%, bad investments
55, $55,000, 8%, credit card
60, $47,500, 16%, student loans
65, $50,000, 10%, mortgage
75, $42,500, 12%, car payments

LOGIC PROBLEM 302

Times are 5:45, 6:00, 6:15, 6:30, and 6:45 (intro.). 5:45 [1st] isn't HMS Pinafore (1), Patience (4), Mikado (5), or Gondoliers (6); it's Iolanthe. 6:00 [no 5:30] isn't Pinafore (1), Patience (4), or Mikado (5); it's Gondoliers, so taupe is 5:45 [only time before 6:00] (6). Lunchbox isn't 5:45 [Iolanthe], 6:30 [no 7:00], 6:45 [last] (5), or 6:15 [Mikado would be 6:45 [last], which isn't possible (5)]; it's 6:00, so Mikado is 6:30, and maroon is 6:45 [only time after 6:30] (5). Pinafore isn't 6:15 [camel would be 5:45 [taupe] (1)]; it's 6:45, so camel is 6:15 (1). Patience is 6:15, so knapsack is 5:45 (4). Sienna isn't 6:30 [no 7:15] (3); it's 6:00, so umbrella is 6:45 (3). Russet is 6:30, and isn't briefcase (2); it's newspaper. Camel's briefcase.

In summary:
Camel, 6:15, briefcase, Patience
Maroon, 6:45, umbrella, HMS Pinafore
Russet, 6:30, newspaper, The Mikado
Sienna, 6:00, lunchbox, The Gondoliers
Taupe, 5:45, knapsack, Iolanthe

LOGIC PROBLEM 303

Cars are A-E, and cabins are 5-9 (intro.). Car A [cabin 6 (1)] isn't cabin 2 higher than car C [no cabin 4]; it's Eloise (3), and car E [1st] is cabin 2 higher than car C (3), so isn't cabin 5 [lowest] (3), 8 [car C would be cabin 6 [car A] (3)], or 7 (4), so it's cabin 9, so car C is cabin 7 (3). Truman isn't car E [cabin 9 [highest]] (4); he's car D [cabin 7 is car C] (4), so he isn't cabin 6 [car A], 7 [car C], 9 [car E], or 5 [Otto would be cabin 6 [Eloise] (4)], so he is cabin 8, so Otto is cabin 9 (4). Car B is cabin 5, so isn't Nancy (1); it's Gregory. Cabin 7 is Nancy. The Darjeeling Limited is cabin 7 (4), so The General isn't cabin 9 [highest], 5 [Gregory] (2), or 6 [The Great Train Robbery would be cabin 7 [The Darjeeling Limited] (2)]; it's cabin 8, so The Great Train Robbery is cabin 9 (2). Car A isn't North by Northwest (1); it's Murder on the Orient Express. Car B is North by Northwest.

In summary (passenger, sleeping car, cabin, film):
Eloise, A, 6, Murder on the Orient Express
Gregory, B, 5, North by Northwest
Nancy, C, 7, The Darjeeling Limited
Otto, E, 9, The Great Train Robbery
Truman, D, 8, The General

LOGIC PROBLEM 304

Rooms are 6, 7, 8, 10, and 11 (intro.). Grad. school isn't 8 [change of scenery (1)], 11 [most] (3), 7 [one with 6 [least] couldn't be climate [VT (2)] (2), job [Tranquility (4), so family would be 7 [grad.] (4)], or family [job [Tranquility] would be 7 [grad.] (4)], so couldn't be placed], or 10 [11 [most] couldn't be climate [VT] (2), job [Tranquility, so family would be

409

10 [grad.] (4)], or family [job [Tranquility] would be 10 [grad.] (4)], so couldn't be placed]; it's 6, so The Nook is 7 (3). 7 [Nook] isn't job [Tranquility] or family [job [Tranquility] couldn't be 6 [grad.] or 8 [scenery], so couldn't be placed (4)]; it's climate [VT], so ME is 6 (2). 8 isn't CO [1st alphabetically] or HI [alphabetically after only CO [Green Fields (2)]] (1); that one's TX. HI isn't 10 (5); it's 11. CO's 10. Tranquility [job] isn't 6 [grad.] or 8 [scenery]; it's 11 [most], so family's 10 (4). Paramount isn't 8 (1); it's 6. Chatsworth House is 7.

In summary:

6, Paramount, ME, graduate school

7, The Nook, VT, climate

8, Chatsworth House, TX, change of scenery

10, Green Fields, CO, family

11, Tranquility, HI, job

LOGIC PROBLEM 305

Valet nos. are 15, 16, 17, 19, and 20, and coat-check nos. are 11, 12, 14, 15, and 16 (intro.). Valet 20 [highest] isn't lineman's pliers [red coat would be valet 19, which isn't possible (2)], locking pliers, slip-joint pliers [no valet 18] (3), or flathead screwdriver (4); it's Phillips screwdriver, so 4th is valet 19 (1). 5th [last] isn't Phillips [valet 15 would be 4th [valet 19] (1)], lineman's [red coat would be 4th [valet 19], which isn't possible (2)], slip-joint [locking would be 4th [valet 19], but no valet 21 (3)], or flat-head [coat 12 would be 4th [valet 19], but no valet 18 (4)]; it's locking, so slip-joint is 4th [valet 19], so locking is valet 17 (3). Flat-head isn't valet 16 [coat 12 would be valet 17 [locking] (4), but no coat 13 (3)]; it's valet 15, so coat 12 is valet 16 (4). Lineman's is valet 16, so red coat is valet 15 or 17 (2), but not valet 17 [5th [last], so lineman's would be 4th [slip joint] (2)]; it's valet 15. Flat-head [valet 15, red coat] is just before or after Phillips (1) and just before or after lineman's (2), so flat-head isn't 1st (above) or 3rd [either Phillips or lineman's would be 4th [slip-joint] (above)]; it's 2nd. Coat 11 [lowest] isn't flat-head [red coat, so slip-joint [valet 19] would be coat 12 [lineman's] (2)], slip-joint (3), or locking [slip-joint would be coat 12 [lineman's] (3)]; it's Phillips, so isn't 3rd (1), so 1st. Lineman's is 3rd. Coat 14 [no coat 13] isn't slip-joint (3) or flat-head [red coat, so slip-joint [valet 19] would be coat 15 (2), so locking would be coat 14 [flat-head] (3)]; it's locking, so slip joint is coat 15 (3). Flat-head is coat 16.

In summary (departure, tool, valet, coat check):

1st, Phillips screwdriver, 20, 11

2nd, flat-head screwdriver, 15, 16

3rd, lineman's pliers, 16, 12

4th, slip-joint pliers, 19, 15

5th, locking pliers, 17, 14

LOGIC PROBLEM 306

Monitors are 13 in., 15 in., 17 in., 19 in., and 21 in., and calendars are *Dilbert* desk, *Dilbert* wall, *Star Trek* desk, *Star Trek* planner, and *X-Files* wall (intro.). Danger Mouse isn't *X-Files* wall [only *X-Files*], *Trek* planner [only planner] (1), *Dilbert* wall [15 in. would be *X-Files* wall [only *X-Files*], which isn't possible (1)], or *Dilbert* desk [15 in. would be *Trek* desk, so Minute would be *Trek* planner [only planner] (1), which isn't possible (3)]; it's *Trek* desk, so "Doorstop" is *Trek* planner, 15 in. is *Dilbert* desk, and Minute is *Dilbert* wall (1), so "Deadbolt" is *X-Files* wall (3). Mickey isn't *Trek* planner [only planner] or *X-Files* wall [only *X-Files*] (2); it's *Dilbert* desk [15 in.], so "Unhinged" is 13 in. [smallest] and *Trek* desk (2). 21 in. [largest] isn't "Deadbolt" (3), "Knock Knock" (4), or "Peephole" (5); it's "Doorstop" [*Trek* planner], so "Knock Knock" is 19 in. (4), and isn't *Dilbert* desk [15 in.], so is *Dilbert* wall. "Peephole" is *Dilbert* desk [15 in.], so Mighty Mouse is 17 in. (5) and is *X-Files* wall [only left with monitor unplaced]. Jerry is *Trek* planner.

In summary:

13 in., Danger Mouse, *Star Trek* desk, "Unhinged"

15 in., Mickey Mouse, *Dilbert* desk, "Peephole"

17 in., Mighty Mouse, *X-Files* wall, "Deadbolt"

19 in., Minute Mouse, *Dilbert* wall, "Knock Knock"

21 in., Jerry Mouse, *Star Trek* planner, "Doorstop"

LOGIC PROBLEM 307

Bacon is 4, 5, 7, 8, and 9, lettuce is 3-7, and tomatoes is 5-9 (intro.). 5 bacon isn't Maureen [no 6 bacon] (3), Jeremiah [no 6 bacon] (4), Larry [no 3 bacon] (5), or Karen (6); it's Ian. 7 bacon isn't 3 [least] (1), 5 [no 6 bacon] (2), 6 [no 6 bacon] (3), or 7 lettuce [no 6 bacon] (4); it's 4, so Jeremiah is 3 lettuce [least] (1). 4 bacon [least] isn't 5 (2), 6 (3), or 7 lettuce (4); it's 3 lettuce [Jeremiah], so 7 lettuce is 5 bacon (4). Jeremiah [4 bacon] isn't 9 [most] (1), 6 [Ian [5 bacon, 7 lettuce] would be 5 tomatoes [only no. less than 6] (4), which isn't possible [no 6 bacon] (2)], 5 [least] (4), or 8 tomatoes [no 6 bacon] (5); he's 7 tomatoes. Ian [5 bacon, 7 lettuce] isn't 5 tomatoes [no 6 bacon] (2); he's 6 tomatoes [only no. lower than Jeremiah [7 tomatoes]] (4). 9 bacon isn't 5 [no 10 bacon] (2) or 8 tomatoes [no 11 bacon] (5); it's 9 tomatoes. 8 bacon isn't 8 tomatoes [no 10 bacon] (5); it's 5 tomatoes, so 5 lettuce is 9 bacon (2). 7 bacon is 8 tomatoes, so

Larry is 9 bacon (5). 8 bacon is 6 lettuce, so Maureen is 7 bacon (3). Karen is 8 bacon.

In summary (friend, bacon, lettuce, tomatoes):
Ian, 5, 7, 6
Jeremiah, 4, 3, 7
Karen, 8, 6, 5
Larry, 9, 5, 9
Maureen, 7, 4, 8

LOGIC PROBLEM 308

Yrs. are 1980, 1981, 1982, 1984, and 1985, prices are $396,000, $396,500, $397,500, $398,000, and $398,500, and nos. of mos. are 2, 4, 6, 9, and 11 (intro.). Ranch isn't $396,500, $397,500 [no $399,000], $398,000 [no $399,500], or $398,500 [highest] (3); it's $396,000, so 2 mos. is $397,500 (3). $396,000 [ranch] isn't 6 [no 8], 11 [longest] (1), or 4 mos. [1985 [last] would be 6 mos. (1)] (2); it's 9 mos., so 1985 is 11 mos. (1) and is $396,500 (3). Ranch is 1984 [$396,500 is 1985 [last]] (3). Victorian is 11 mos. [most, 1984 9 mos.] (5). $398,500 [most] isn't 4 mos. (4); it's 6 mos. $398,000 is 4 mos., so 1981 is $398,500 [most, 6 mos.] (4), so Georgian is 1982 [only left after 6 mos. [1981]] (2). 1982 isn't 4 mos. (4); 1980 is. 1982 is 2 mos. 1981 [6 mos.] isn't Colonial (4); it's Federal. Colonial's 1980.

In summary:
1980, Colonial, $398,000, 4
1981, Federal, $398,500, 6
1982, Georgian, $397,500, 2
1984, ranch, $396,000, 9
1985, Victorian, $396,500, 11

LOGIC PROBLEM 309

User names are Badenov [7 letters], Chewbacca [9 letters], Cyborg [6 letters], Skeletor [8 letters], and SpeedRacer [10 letters], and minutes are 6, 9, 12, 15, and 18 (intro.). SpeedRacer [10 letters [most]] isn't Agent99 (1), Serpico (4), or Kojak (5); that one's Danno or Starsky. If SpeedRacer [10 letters [most], 6 min. [least] (5)] is Starsky, then Gigagab would be Chewbacca [9 letters] and 9 min. (2), and if SpeedRacer is Danno, then Serpico would be Chewbacca [9 letters] and 9 min. (4); Chewbacca is 9 min. (above). SpeedRacer [10 letters [most], 6 min. [least]] isn't Friendly Users (1), Gigagab (2), Speak PC (3), or Cyberchat [Speak PC would be 9 min. [Chewbacca [9 letters]], but no 11 or more letters (3)]; that one's Techtalk. Chewbacca [9 letters, 9 min.] isn't Friendly Users [Agent99 would be 6 min. [least, Speedracer [10 letters [most]]], which isn't possible (1)], Speak PC [Cyberchat would be 6 min.

[Techtalk] (3)], or Cyberchat [Speak PC would be 12 min. (3), but then couldn't be Skeletor [8 letters], Badenov (3), or Cyborg [6 letters [least]] (5), so couldn't be placed]; that one's Gigagab, so Starsky is SpeedRacer [10 letters] (2). Cyberchat isn't Cyborg [6 letters [least]] or Badenov [7 letters] (3); that one's Skeletor [8 letters], so Speak PC is Cyborg [6 letters [least]] (3). Badenov [7 letters] is Friendly Users, so Agent99 is Cyborg [6 letters] (1), so isn't 18 [most] (1) or 12 min. (5); that one's 15 min., so Friendly Users is 18 min. [most] (1). Skeletor [8 letters] is 12 min., so Kojak is Badenov [7 letters, only left with fewer than 8 letters [12 min.]] (5). Serpico is Skeletor [8 letters], and Danno is Chewbacca [9 letters] (4).

In summary:
Badenov, Kojak, Friendly Users, 18
Chewbacca, Danno, Gigagab, 9
Cyborg, Agent99, Speak PC, 15
Skeletor, Serpico, Cyberchat, 12
SpeedRacer, Starsky, Techtalk, 6

LOGIC PROBLEM 310

Dynasties, from earliest to latest, are 17th-21st, and rolls are 2-6 (intro.). Caught in door [6 rolls [most] (1)] isn't shelf paper (1), paper towels [2 rolls (1)], masking tape [stuck to wall (2)], or crepe paper (3); it's gauze, so isn't 21st [latest] (1), 17th (2), 18th [unraveled (3)], or 19th dynasty (4), so is 20th dynasty, so paper towels is 21st dynasty [latest] (1). Couldn't sit isn't 19th or 21st dynasty [2 rolls [least]] (4); it's 17th dynasty. Stuck to wall [masking tape] isn't 21st dynasty [paper towels]; it's 19th dynasty. Spilled punch is 21st dynasty. Crepe paper isn't unraveled (3); it's couldn't sit, so isn't 5 [unraveled would be 6 rolls [most, caught in door] (3)] or 3 rolls [19th dynasty would be 2 rolls [least, 21st dynasty] (4)], so it's 4 rolls, so unraveled is 5 rolls [only left more than crepe] (3), and 19th dynasty is 3 rolls [only left fewer than couldn't sit] (4). Shelf paper is 18th dynasty.

In summary:
17th, 4, crepe paper, couldn't sit
18th, 5, shelf paper, unraveled
19th, 3, masking tape, stuck to wall
20th, 6, gauze, caught in door
21st, 2, paper towels, spilled punch

LOGIC PROBLEM 311

No play began and ended either on same date of mo. or during same mo., runs began Jan. 17, Mar. 20, Apr. 14, June 10, and June 23, and runs ended Jan. 10, Jan. 20, Feb. 23, Mar. 14, and Apr. 17 (intro.). Began June 23 and ended Jan. 20 (4) isn't *Les Terribles* (1), *Mon-*

sieur *Dragonfly*, *North Atlantic* (3), or *Cattle* (4); it's *Man of the Year*. *Atlantic* began June 10 or ended Jan. 10 (3), but not ended Jan. 10 [couldn't have begun Jan. 17, Mar. 20, or June 10 [*Man* began June 23 and ended Jan. 20] (2), so would've begun Apr. 14, but *Terribles* couldn't have begun Jan. 17, June 10, or Mar. 20 (1), so couldn't be placed]; it began June 10. *Atlantic* [began June 10] didn't end Jan. 10 (intro.) or Feb. 23 [*Man* began June 23] (2), so Mar. 14 or Apr. 17, but not ended Apr. 17 [*Terribles* couldn't have begun Jan. 17, Apr. 14, or Mar. 20 (1), so couldn't be placed]; it ended Mar. 14. *Terribles* [*Atlantic* ended Mar. 14] didn't begin Mar. 20 or Apr. 14 (1); it began Jan. 17, and didn't end Apr. 17 or Jan. 10 (intro.), so it ended Feb. 23. *Cattle* didn't end Apr. 17 (3); *Dragonfly* did. *Cattle* ended Jan. 10. *Dragonfly* [ended Apr. 17] didn't begin Apr. 14 (intro.); *Cattle* did. *Dragonfly* began Mar. 20.

In summary (play, date began, date ended):

Cattle, Apr. 14, Jan. 10
Les Terribles, Jan. 17, Feb. 23
Man of the Year, June 23, Jan. 20
Monsieur Dragonfly, Mar. 20, Apr. 17
North Atlantic, June 10, Mar. 14

LOGIC PROBLEM 312

Hawaiian are Maui and Oahu, blue are aqua and indigo, red are rust and scarlet, and yellow is saffron (intro.). Blue 1st (6) isn't indigo (1); it's aqua, so 4th is indigo (6). Mr. Chaney's blue isn't aqua [1st] (2); it's indigo [4th], so Ms. Wolfe's 2nd (2). Hawaiian 1st [aqua] (1) isn't Maui [red (4)]; it's Oahu, so 2nd is Maui (1). Hawaiian scarlet (3) isn't Oahu [aqua]; it's Maui, so Mr. Marcotte's Oahu (3). Jamaica's rust (4). Ms. Fehr isn't 5th [last] (5); she's 3rd. Mr. Vachon's 5th, and isn't saffron (5); he's rust. Ms. Fehr's saffron, and isn't Tahiti (5); she's New Zealand. Mr. Chaney's Tahiti.

In summary:

Jamaica, 5th, Mr. Vachon, rust
Maui, 2nd, Ms. Wolfe, scarlet
New Zealand, 3rd, Ms. Fehr, saffron
Oahu, 1st, Mr. Marcotte, aqua
Tahiti, 4th, Mr. Chaney, indigo

LOGIC PROBLEM 313

Mins. are 15, 20, 30, 35, and 40 (intro.). Pickup truck 't 15 [least], 20 [no 10 min.], 35 [no 25 min.] (1), ` min. [van (4)]; it's 30 min., so preparator's 20 `nservator isn't 30 [no 50 min.], 35 [no 55 `n min. [most] (3); it's 15 min., so rug is 35 `dry bag is 40 min. [only left more than

pickup truck [30 min.]] (1). Posters isn't 15 [least] or 20 min. [sedan would be 15 min. [least] (2)] (2); it's 30 min., so sedan's 20 min., and groceries is 15 min. [least] (2). Tree's 20 min. 15 min. [least] isn't Jeep (3); it's station wagon. 35 min. is Jeep, so designer is 30 min. [only left less than Jeep] (3). Registrar isn't rug (3); it's laundry bag. Tour guide is rug.

In summary:

15, conservator, groceries, station wagon
20, preparator, tree, sedan
30, designer, posters, pickup truck
35, tour guide, rug, Jeep
40, registrar, laundry bag, van

LOGIC PROBLEM 314

Men are Alex, Pete, and Troy, and women are Michaela and Sara (intro.). Each person creates 2 types of puzzle, and each type of puzzle is created by 2 people (intro.). Woman who edits *Original Logic Problems* [creates word seeks (2)] (2) isn't Michaela [edits *Quick & Easy Crosswords* (3)]; she's Sara. Two who create crosswords aren't Michaela [*Crosswords*] (intro.), Troy, or Sara (3); they're Alex and Pete. Two who create logics aren't Sara [*Logic*] (intro.), Alex (1), or Pete (3); they're Michaela and Troy. Alex [crosswords] doesn't create logics or fill-ins (1); he creates crostics or word seeks. Alex [creates crosswords and either crostics or word seeks] doesn't edit *Favorite Fill-In Puzzles* (1); he edits *Puzzler's Choice Crostics* or *All-Star Word Seek Puzzles*, so he either creates crosswords and crostics and edits *Word Seek*, or he creates crosswords and word seeks and edits *Crostics* (above, intro.). Pete doesn't edit *Crostics* [Alex would edit *Word Seek* and create crosswords and crostics (above), and Sara and Troy would create crostics (3), so 3 people would create crostics, which isn't possible (intro.)] or *Word Seek* [Alex would edit *Crostics* and create crosswords and word seeks! (above), and Sara and Troy would create word seeks (3), so 3 people would create word seeks, which isn't possible (intro.)]; he edits *Fill-In*, so Sara and Troy create fill-ins (4). Alex [creates crosswords] doesn't edit *Word Seek* [Pete [edits *Fill-In*] creates crosswords, so at most 3 different types of puzzles could be created by editors of *Word Seek* and *Fill-In*] (4); he edits *Crostics*, so creates word seeks (above). Michaela and Pete [only editors left] create crostics [only left]. Troy edits *Word Seek*.

In summary:

Alex, crosswords & word seeks, *Puzzler's Choice Crostics*

LOGIC PROBLEM 315

Ones who gave scented candles [gave to couple who gave to Dales [gave computer game (1)] (3)] aren't Dales [game], Ashes [gave to couple who gave to ones who gave flowerpot (1)], Edens [gave to couple who gave to ones who gave stationery (2)], Fosters [gave to couple who gave to ones who gave coffee mugs (3)], or Carneys [gave to couple who gave to couple who gave to Ashes (4), so Dales would've given to Ashes (above), who would've given to Carneys, who would've given to ones who gave flowerpot (1), who would've given to Dales, who gave to Ashes (above), which isn't possible [ones who gave flowerpot gave to couple who gave to Fosters (4)]]; they're Brooks. Ones who gave flowerpot [received from couple who received from Ashes (1)] aren't Ashes, Fosters [received from couple who received from ones who gave flowerpot (4), so Ashes would've given flowerpot] (intro.), or Carneys [received from couple who received from Dales (1)]; they're Edens [gave to couple who gave to ones who gave stationery (2)], so Fosters gave stationery (4). Ones who gave picture frame [gave to couple who gave to Brooks (2)] aren't Ashes [gave to couple who gave to Edens [gave flowerpot] (1)]; they're Carneys. Ashes gave coffee mugs. Carneys [gave frame] gave to couple who gave to Brooks [gave candles] (2), who gave to Ashes [gave mugs] (4), who gave to Dales (3), who gave to Edens [gave flowerpot], who gave to Carneys [gave frame] (1), who gave to Fosters [gave stationery], who gave to Brooks (2).

In summary (couple, gift, given to):

Ashes, coffee mugs, Dales

Brooks, scented candles, Ashes

Carneys, picture frame, Fosters

Dales, computer game, Edens

Edens, flowerpot, Carneys

Fosters, stationery, Brooks

LOGIC PROBLEM 316

Rulers, from latest to earliest reign, are Amenhotep I, Thutmose I, Hatshepsut, Akhenaton, and Tutankhamun, lectures are 11, 13, 15, 18, and 21, and pgs. are 3, 4, 5, 7, and 8 (intro.). Mr. Franks isn't 11 [least], 15 [no 17 lectures], 18 [no 20 lectures], or 21 lectures [most] (1); he's 13 lectures, so 5 pgs. is 15 lectures, and Tutankhamun is 11 lectures [least] ( ), so Mr. Ahrens is Akhenaton (2). Akhenaton [Mr. Ahrens] isn't 13 [Mr. Franks], 21 [most] (4), or 15 lectures [5 pgs. [no 6 pgs.]] (5); it's 18 lectures, so Ms. Randal is 21 lectures [most] (4). Mr. Turner isn't 11 lectures [least] (5); he's 15 lectures, so Hatshepsut is 13 lectures [only left less than Mr. Turner] (5). Ms. Phillips is 11 lectures. Mr. Turner [5 pgs.] isn't Amenhotep I [Thutmose I [1 pg. more than Ms. Phillips (3)] would be 1 pg. more than Mr. Ahrens (5)]; he's Thutmose I, so Ms. Phillips is 4 pgs. (3). Ms. Randal's Amenhotep I. Hatshepsut [1 reign earlier than Mr. Turner [Thutmose I]] isn't 3 [least] or 7 pgs. [no 6 pgs.] (5); it's 8 pgs., so Mr. Ahrens is 7 pgs. (5). Ms. Randal is 3 pgs.

In summary (curator, ruler, lectures, pgs.):

Mr. Ahrens, Akhenaton, 18, 7

Mr. Franks, Hatshepsut, 13, 8

Ms. Phillips, Tutankhamun, 11, 4

Ms. Randal, Amenhotep I, 21, 3

Mr. Turner, Thutmose I, 15, 5

LOGIC PROBLEM 317

Women are Belinda, Josie, and Marcia, men are Armando, David, and Scott, gold [bull's-eye (intro.)] is 9 pts., red is 7 pts., blue is 5 pts., black is 3 pts., white is 1 pt., and green [apron (intro.)] is 0 pts. (intro.). Only archer who hit same area more than once (2) hit more than 1 bull's-eye [9 pts. [only possible in (7)]], so is green or red arrows [only possible in (7, above)]. 21 pts. total (2) isn't 3, 9, and 9 or 7, 7, and 7 pts. (2); it's 5 [blue], 7 [red], and 9 [gold] pts. [only other possible to total 21 pts. (above)], so isn't blue arrows (1), so is Belinda [only possible in (4)]. Black arrows [woman (6)] isn't Josie [gold arrows (2)] or Marcia (6); it's Belinda [only woman left, 21 pts. total (above)], so Marcia's 19 pts. total (6). Josie [gold, 8 pts. total (2)] isn't 0, 1, and 7 [red] pts. [couldn't be placed in (4)]; she's 0, 3, and 5 pts. [only other possible to total 8 pts. (above)]. Marcia [19 pts. total (above)] isn't 3, 7 [red], and 9 or 5, 7, [red], and 7 pts [couldn't be blue arrows [man (4)], so couldn't be placed in (4)]; she's 1, 9, and 9 pts. [only other possible to total 19 pts. (above)]. 14 pts. total (5) isn't 5, 7 [red], and 7 pts. [only bull's-eye hit more than once (above)]; it's 0, 5, and 9 pts. [only other possible to total 14 pts. (above)]. 15 pts. total (4) is 3, 5, and 7 pts. [only possible to total 15 pts. using 7 pts. [red]] (4, above). 4 bull's-eyes [9 pts. each] (7) are 21 pts. total [black, 5, 7, and 9 pts.], 14 pts. total [0, 5, and 9 pts.], and 19 pts. total [1, 9, and 9 pts.] (above), so 14 pts. total [0 [green], 5, and 9 pts.] isn't green arrows (1), so is red arrows, and 19 pts. total (above) i een arrows [only possible in (7, above)]. 15 pts. total —above) isn't blue arrows (4); it's white arrows. David isn't red arrows [14 pts. total, so would have 11 and 17 pts. (3), so would have 7 total pts. [8, 11, 14, 15, 17, 19, and 21 (above)]] or white arrows [Scott (5)]; he's blue arrows. Armando's red arrows. Five of the 6 totals are 8, 14, 15, 19, and 21 (above), so David [blue arrows, so 7 pts. [red] (4)] is 11 or 18 pts. [only possible in (3, above)], but not 18 pts. [couldn't be placed with 7 pts. (above)], so is 11 pts. (above), so is 1, 1, and 9 pts., 1, 3, and 7 pts., or 1, 5, and 5 pts. [only possible total 11 pts. (above)], but not 1, 1, and 9 or 1,5, and 5 pts. [only bull's-eye [9 pts.] hit more than once], so is 1, 3, and 7 pts. (above).

In summary:

Armando, red, 0, 5, 9
Belinda, black, 5, 7, 9
David, blue, 1, 3, 7
Josie, gold, 0, 3, 5
Marcia, green, 1, 9, 9
Scott, white, 3, 5, 7

LOGIC PROBLEM 318

Houses, from west to east, are 101, 103, 105, 107, and 109 (intro.). House 101 isn't Dryden, Laing (1), Quon (4), or Nightingale (5); it's McGregor, so isn't "Forward with President Truman—No Retreat" (2), "I Like Ike" (3), "Phooey on Dewey" (5), or "School's Open, Drive Slowly" (6), so is "Think! Prevent Wallacitis." Rear window is west of "School's" (6), which is west of Quon (4), who's west of "Truman" (2), so rear window isn't house 105, 107, 109 (above), or 101 ["Think!"] (6); it's house 103, so "School's" is house 105, Quon is house 107, and "Truman" is house 109 (above). "Ike" isn't house 103 [right rear bumper would be house 101 (3)] (4); it's house 107, so right rear's house 105 (3, illus), Laing's house 103 (4), and trunk's house 101 (1). "Phooey" is house 103. Rear left bumper isn't house 109 (1); it's house 107, so Dryden's house 109 (1). Front bumper's house 109. Nightingale's house 105.

In summary:

101, Mr. McGregor, "Think! Prevent Wallacitis," trunk

103, Ms. Laing, "Phooey on Dewey," rear window

105, Ms. Nightingale, "School's Open, Drive Slowly," right rear bumper

107, Mr. Quon, "I like Ike," left rear bumper

109, Ms. Dryden, "Forward with President Truman—No Retreat," front bumper

LOGIC PROBLEM 319

Times are 2:00, 2:15, 2:30, 2:40, and 2:55 p.m. (intro.). 2:00 [1st] isn't Video Venture (1), Movie Hut (2), Discount Video (3), or Chart Topper (4); it's Rentarama [returned The Mummy's Shroud (2)], so rented isn't Shroud (intro.), The Mummy's Hand (1), The Mummy's Curse (2), or Dawn of the Mummy [no 2:25] (5), so it's Abbott & Costello Meet the Mummy. 2:15 [after only 2:00 [1st, rented Meet]] isn't Video Venture (1), Discount Video (3), or Chart Topper [returned Hand would be 2:00 [1st, returned Shroud] (4)]; it's Movie Hut, so rented isn't Hand (1), Curse (2), or Shroud [returned Dawn would be 2:00 [1st, returned Shroud] (3)], so it's Dawn, so returned Curse is 2:40 (5). Returned Dawn isn't 2:15 [rented Dawn] (intro.) or 2:55 [last] (3); it's 2:30, so rented Shroud is 2:40, and Discount Video is 2:55 [last] (3). Returned Hand isn't 2:55 [last] (4); it's 2:15. Returned Meet is 2:55. Rented Hand isn't 2:30 [Video Venture couldn't be 2:00 [1st, Rentarama] or 2:15 [Movie Hut], so couldn't be placed in (1)]; it's 2:55. Rented Curse is 2:30, so isn't Chart Topper (4); it's Video Venture. 2:40 is Chart Topper.

In summary (time, store, returned, rented):

2:00, Rentarama, The Mummy's Shroud, Abbott & Costello Meet the Mummy

2:15, Movie Hut, The Mummy's Hand, Dawn of the Mummy

2:30, Video Venture, Dawn of the Mummy, The Mummy's Curse

2:40, Chart Topper, The Mummy's Curse, The Mummy's Shroud

2:55, Discount Video, Abbott & Costello Meet the Mummy, The Mummy's Hand